# DIGITAL IMAGE
# PROCESSING AND
# COMPUTER VISION

# DIGITAL IMAGE PROCESSING AND COMPUTER VISION

 *ROBERT J. SCHALKOFF*

*DEPARTMENT OF ELECTRICAL AND*
*COMPUTER ENGINEERING*
*CLEMSON UNIVERSITY*

WILEY

**JOHN WILEY & SONS, INC.**
New York ■ Chichester ■ Brisbane ■ Toronto ■ Singapore

**Library of Congress Cataloging-in-Publication Data**

Schalkoff, Robert J.
    Digital image processing and computer vision / Robert J. Schalkoff.
    Includes bibliographies and index.

    1. Image processing—Digital techniques.    2. Computer vision.
    I.  Title
    TA1632.S29   1989
    621.36'7—de19                                                        89-30954

**Printed in Singapore**

10 9 8 7 6 5 4 3

*to my late father. . .*
*Bernard J. Schalkoff*
*and to my mother. . .*
*Anne A. Schalkoff*

# PREFACE

This book is an introductory text for a course in Digital Image Processing and Computer Vision techniques. Image processing and computer vision applications span many disciplines. Although some of the theoretical topics are familiar to electrical and computer engineers, others are more familiar to computer scientists and applied mathematicians. Considering the extremely broad spectrum of concepts that are (generally) considered a part of image processing and computer vision, the most difficult aspect of writing this text was avoiding *both* superficiality and an *n*-volume text. There is ample material for a two-semester course sequence; instructors may choose some subset of topics for a single semester.

Readers are expected to be familiar with linear algebra, probability and random processes, and a minimal amount of geometry and to have had some exposure to linear systems and filtering concepts. Lack of this background is often a fatal stumbling block to understanding the underlying concepts in image processing and potentially can impede research success.

The book is designed to be largely self-contained. More important, however, the reader is forced to play an active role in the study of this subject. The numerous proofs and properties that are left for reader verification as well as significant problem selections at the end of chapters allow (or force) a "hands on" study approach. Hopefully, students finishing the book will be left with an appreciation for the diversity of the field, and, more important, the ability to participate in it.

The book attempts to make the important distinctions between theory and practice that are often a major factor in the choice and implementation of image processing algorithms. For example, the presentation in Chapter 2 employs the theoretically significant approach to camera calibration (the coordinate transformations) as well as the practical approach (a parameter estimation problem). Both are necessary for study of this topic. A second example of this distinction is found in Chapter 3 under the topic of linearly separable transforms, where matrix notation is used for conceptual purposes, yet the reader is made aware that the summation forms of these transformations are used in actual implementations.

Since this is a teaching text dedicated to those new to the field, an effort has been made to provide the reader with a "soft start." Typically, each new topic is preceded by a reduced complexity example of the concept. For example, the 2-D Discrete Fourier Transform of Chapter 3 is introduced after a closely related review of the 1-D case. In addition, Chapter 2 introduces stereo vision by way of a 1-D "triangulation" example that uses concepts extendable to 2-D. Thus, the reader is "disarmed" by the preliminary, less complex topical introductions.

The book presents the subtopics that are generally considered within the area of image processing and computer vision from the viewpoint of concepts; it does not attempt to be an encyclopedia or bibliographic summary of all related research work ever produced. This emphasis on the conceptual approach explains the organization of the text (i.e., the partitioning of topics). Furthermore, mathematical models for the underlying processes leading to algorithms are stressed. It has often been observed that advances in certain research areas are the direct result of advances in the modeling of the underlying processes. Students contemplating significant research in image processing and computer vision should be cognizant of this fact. Furthermore, they should be able to recognize situations in which assumed underlying models are not valid and therefore the applicability of the algorithm is also suspect. This model-based approach distinguishes this book from others that tend to be illustrated encyclopedic summaries of the plethora of ad hoc image processing and computer vision approaches.

Although the primary objective of the text is to provide a teaching tool, it is quite likely that practicing engineers and scientists will also find the concept-based treatment useful in updating their backgrounds to explore the challenges of this rapidly expanding and emerging field. The author's consulting experience suggests that a number of industries (including defense contractors) could benefit from an introduction to this topic, which explains the "why" (as opposed to the "how") and which indicates the underlying complexity of many image processing and computer vision tasks. The latter are often erroneously considered by newcomers (and some managers) as trivial. Thus, I suspect that practicing engineers and scientists will find the presentation somewhat more practical and perhaps a bit less esoteric than might be found in other texts (particularly those that primarily paraphrase research publications).

Writing a book in this area is risky for several reasons. First, the high-end theory of the discipline is in its infancy and a state of flux. There is little general agreement on the models or processing approaches in general cases. Thus, this area is the most difficult to treat with the potential for the longevity of a book.

Second, although I have tried to cover the subject of image processing and computer vision from a conceptual level, some research topics have been omitted. This in no way reflects an assessment of any particular research; it is more a tribute to the volume of current research in the area and the fact that this book is intended to be a teaching text for beginners.

Third, to provide a useful textbook, it is my opinion that problems or exercises at the end of the chapters are a necessity. These must be sufficiently difficult to challenge and, hopefully, reinforce understanding. A problem solution manual is available. Although these problems provide a test of material comprehension, particularly with respect to the properties and effects of various models and algorithms, they are intended to accompany other instructor-supplied exercises that involve the processing of real imagery. The reasonable cost of personal computers and associated frame grabber and display cards puts an educational laboratory for image processing within the reach of most institutions.

Finally, it is especially difficult to determine what the appropriate level for a text in this area should be. This is due in part to the varying backgrounds (e.g., electrical engineering or computer science) and levels of experience of readers. The text is probably more advanced than several texts now in the area, but it is less sophisticated than most research papers.

Writing this text provided a valuable lesson in humility and led to a much greater appreciation of the efforts of authors of existing texts. This book reflects nearly a decade of my interest in and contribution to this field. Many people—too numerous to mention them all by name—have contributed to this effort. Thanks are due to my thesis advisor, Dr. Gene McVey, who guided me through an initial look at this field over a decade ago. Dr. Jeff Labuz helped me keep a high interest level in the subject matter during periods of collaboration. Several of the reviewers, especially Dr. Aaron Collins, provided valuable feedback that led to a better organized and more accurate manuscript. Numerous students in my classes and those who participated in research projects also contributed significant ideas and suggestions. Special thanks are due to Dr. Xiaoming Wang, who skillfully implemented many of the algorithms herein and thus generated the corresponding image illustrations. The support of the National Science Foundation is gratefully acknowledged. Finally, my wife, Leslie, deserves special recognition for providing manuscript production assistance and accepting the often-frazzled lifestyle that seems to accompany authors.

IT IS IMPOSSIBLE FOR A MAN
WHO TAKES A SURVEY OF
WHAT IS ALREADY KNOWN,
NOT TO SEE WHAT AN IMMENSITY
IN EVERY BRANCH OF SCIENCE
YET REMAINS TO BE DISCOVERED.

THOMAS JEFFERSON
MONTICELLO, JUNE 18, 1799

# ABOUT THE AUTHOR

Robert J. Schalkoff received his Ph.D. degree in Electrical Engineering from the University of Virginia, in 1979. Currently, he is an Associate Professor in the Department of Electrical and Computer Engineering at Clemson University in Clemson, South Carolina. His primary research interests are in image processing and artificial intelligence, with special emphasis on model-based understanding, motion and stereo vision, and associated computer architurectures.

# CONTENTS

# DIGITAL IMAGE PROCESSING AND COMPUTER VISION

# 1

# INTRODUCTION

As the speed, capability, and economic advantages of modern signal processing devices continue to increase, there is simultaneously an increase in efforts aimed at developing sophisticated, real-time automatic systems capable of emulating human abilities. This book concerns one of the most obvious of these, namely vision. Energy from the three-dimensional world we live in is converted into two-dimensional entities called images by either our visual system or an electronic sensor, such as a television camera. How we process these images to form conclusions or take action is a subject of continued, challenging research by people from various disciplines. The answers (algorithms) are far from exact or complete. Thus, lacking this knowledge, we should not be surprised at the difficulty encountered in attempting to develop autonomous systems that, from an input/output point of view, emulate this processing. It appears to be a formidable task to codify and automatically manipulate years of human experience in processing of visual imagery from a three-dimensional world. Often the people who do not appreciate the complexity of this task are those who have never tried to solve even a very simple or reduced version of it. There are other tasks that involve the processing of images by computer where the objective is not to emulate human behavior, but rather to extract or display more (subjectively) useful information from the image. Examples are the enhancement of images degraded by noise or motion, the splicing of low-resolution images to achieve a higher resolution composite, and the processing of radiographic images to reconstruct some three-dimensional object. This book also addresses these tasks.

In pursuing the aforementioned objectives, the book encompasses a plethora of often interdependent "image engineering" tools. They include signal analysis (for enhancement, restoration, and preprocessing), geometry (to extract invariants), linear algebra (to represent the geometry of imaging), estimation theory (for motion or orientation estimation, image compression, and matching), statistical pattern

1

recognition (for object classification), syntactic pattern recognition (for image structural description), and a number of topics often encompassed under the heading of "artificial intelligence." These include knowledge representation and manipulation, constraint satisfaction, and symbolic manipulation. The book deals with all of these with varying levels of sophistication.

## ■ WHAT ARE WE TRYING TO DO AND WHY IS IT SO DIFFICULT?

The discipline of image processing and computer vision is an area which, as it continues to expand (some might claim "explode" is a more accurate descriptor), becomes more difficult to define or describe in a simple phrase. Often applications are used to define the discipline. For example, one might refer to this area as ". . . the science (or art?) of making robots 'see.' " A course in this area consists of two essential topics:

1. The development of models underlying the images or imaged scenes that are relevant to our application;
2. The design and analysis of algorithms and their associated hardware and software requirements which, based on the above models, produce useful and usually application-dependent results.

The above entities apply to both the low-level (e.g., geometric preprocessing) and high-level (e.g., image understanding) aspects of image processing and computer vision.

The computer implementation requirements of computer vision systems are currently overwhelming, particularly when "real-time" system operation is desired. Processing needs are often far in excess of current capabilities; thus, image processing and computer vision research serves as an impetus for the development of radically new processing architectures. This is the topic of Chapter 8.

Major categories of commercial image processing and computer vision markets, in order of dollar value, are "artificial sight," printing/publishing, graphic arts, medical applications, and remote sensing. Indeed, if the U.S. is to survive international trade competition, increasing the productivity of workers through advanced automation may be a necessary prerequisite. Although there exist a plethora of unsolved problems (particularly those with a strong "artificial intelligence" component), many applications are solvable using current technology. The major engineering challenge in these applications is the adaptation of vision technology to the specific problem; it entails:

1. Recognition of the problem as one that is solvable with automated vision;
2. A fundamental understanding of the capabilities and limitations of present image processing and computer vision systems (both available hardware and software); and
3. A background in fundamental algorithmic techniques and their corresponding implementation ramifications.

This book, while emphasizing the third topic, is also intended to contribute to the other two.

There are numerous ways one might study this field. One approach involves a comprehensive study of the *algorithms* that have been developed for image processing and computer vision. Alternately, an exhaustive investigation of the plethora of present and potential *applications* may be used to foster an appreciation of the area. Finally, the numerous and varied image *models* that are either explicitly or (often) implicitly employed to represent the underlying image content at each stage of processing or analysis might be explored. This book uses a mixture of all three. One of the primary objectives, however, is to emphasize the concepts underlying computer processing of image data.

In essence, all modeling is based on a consideration of the details or concepts that describe some entity. The details of the human visual and perceptual processes are both myriad and incompletely understood. Because of this lack of ability to succinctly and mathematically describe these processes, they are often treated superficially in the development of algorithms.

This book may be thought of as two interrelated parts: the low-level, 2-D signal-processing aspects of image processing (e.g., the emulation of low-level or "early" human vision) and the ramifications of higher-order "image understanding" or computer vision. In many applications both must be considered for successful system development. These are shown in Figure 1.1. The former is more familiar to those who have studied "signal processing"; the latter borders on the emerging area of artificial intelligence (AI) and is still in a state of flux. It is not altogether clear which concepts and approaches will become widely accepted and hence "core" to image processing and computer vision and, conversely, which will go down in history as narrow solutions to a specific application. Hence, the concepts presented in the early part of this book are likely to remain reasonably stable, whereas the later chapters will most likely quickly evolve over time.

Image processing and computer vision practitioners tend to concentrate on a particular area of specialization. People refer to their research interests as "texture," "surface mapping," "video tracking," and the like. Nevertheless, there is a

| Processing Objective | Underlying Model | Typical Algorithms |
|---|---|---|
| preprocessing | image formation (physical or assumed) | noise removal contrast enhancement |
| lowest-level feature extraction | low-level image function greyvalue variation (e.g., edges, lines, texture) | edge detection texture detection |
| intermediate-level feature identification | intermediate level features and their relationships (e.g., scene object models) | connectivity pattern matching boundary coding |
| high-level scene interpretation via images | scene models and 3-D world knowledge | model unification |

**FIGURE 1.1**   Example of modeling/processing/data hierarchy

strong need to appreciate the spectrum and hierarchy of processing levels. The development of software to accomplish these different but interrelated operations is becoming increasingly modularized. Analogous to the invoking of "canned" routines to accomplish specific numerical operations (e.g., matrix inversion, roots of polynomials), standardized procedures for image processing subtasks with standardized interfaces are beginning to appear. Examples are edge enhancement, local filtering, and region growing. This allows the creating, debugging, and maintaining of subsets of image processing and computer vision software and, more important, allows the development of new application-oriented systems containing previously proven software modules. This book attempts to modularize these concepts and cite their limitations and interrelationships.

## SAMPLE COMPUTER VISION APPLICATIONS

Computer vision applications abound. Economic forecasts of the future market for vision systems are striking. One forecast ("Insight," 1987) estimates the U.S. vision market alone will experience growth at a compound annual rate of 57% and will reach an annual level of $2.7 billion in 1991.

Throughout the course of this book a number of applications will be explored. As a prelude, we may consider the following illustrative examples. This section should impart to the reader the nontrivial nature of the challenges presented to image processing research.

### ROBOTICS

*Industrial Inspection.* Historically, industry and defense have been two strong forcing functions for the development of automation. The reliability and cost-effectiveness of automation have fostered a sought-after competitive edge in both areas, the former arguably leading to an eventual overall improved standard of living. In a sense, the Industrial Revolution is still with us; it just happens currently to involve the application of "high-tech" concepts, including automated vision. It is worth noting (Birk & Kelley, 1981; Harmon, 1982; "Insight," 1985) that in robotic applications that involve sensory needs, over 75% of these applications require vision. It has been conservatively estimated that vision capable robots will comprise about one-quarter of some 250,000 industrial robots expected to be purchased by U.S. industry over the next 10 years. Currently, the majority of industrial robots are "blind."

Inspection using machine vision, in some applications, has been shown to be more reliable than human visual inspection ("Insight," 1987) and is projected to comprise about two-thirds of the machine vision market by 1991. For example, given the image of a printed circuit board, a computer vision system must determine if the board has been correctly "stuffed." Following automated visual examination of the board, the system might output: "IC 7 is in backwards, IC 3 is missing, etc." In this application, the description and consequent identification of a "chip" and its actual and desired geometric orientation presents a fundamental challenge. In addition, the ability to match pictorial quantities (Chapters 6 and 7) is required. The speed at which this inspection is desired, perhaps quantified in boards/minute, may require dedicated hardware (Chapter 8).

*Surface Measurement or "Mapping".* Quite often, a significant amount of trained machinist time is expended, not in machining 3-D parts, but rather in determining if parts produced are within tolerances. Historically, this requires familiarity with measuring instruments and the ability to read dimensioned mechanical drawings. In addition, a contact-based measurement is usually implied. Computer vision, as shown in Chapter 2, offers a noncontact alternative.

*Manipulator Guidance.* It is fairly common for factory robotic applications to require that the manipulator device identify, move to, grasp, and then move an object in a cluttered workspace (i.e., movement is restricted) using visual guidance. Part of this process involves the determination of the part orientation such that the part may be grasped in an acceptable manner.

*Vehicle Guidance.* The need for autonomous vehicle systems becomes apparent in the need to free human drivers (or pilots) from "hazardous" environments. The term "fire and forget" describes weapons delivery systems that contain a built-in capability to adjust their trajectory on the basis of continuously acquired image information. This type of application involves the modeling of image dynamics and the time-varying aspects of sensor, image, and scene evolution (Chapter 5).

## IMAGE COMPRESSION AND ENHANCEMENT

Historically, the transmission of information has been limited by the information-carrying capacity of transmission media and approaches. Numerous strategies have been developed to minimize the bandwidth required by specific applications without significantly (often a subjective evaluation) changing the characteristics of the transmitted signal. The development of media with large electrical bandwidths, such as optical fibers, has reduced the importance of this effort. The subjectively pleasing appearance of higher-resolution television pictures (1000 lines resolution, for example) creates a demand for systems with the bandwidth capable of delivering this image quality to the viewer. Thus, compression schemes are the subject of continued research.

Image enhancement is another area where results are viewed subjectively. Given imagery degraded by the imaging environment (e.g., atmospheric distortion or insufficient scene illumination) or the transmission medium (e.g., significant electrical noise has now been added to the image data), it is necessary to characterize this distortion and then attempt to process the imagery so that the visual effect of this distortion is minimized. Other applications of algorithms of this type are in the processing of imagery to better enhance the significant image contents, as illustrated by the medical applications below.

## MEDICAL APPLICATIONS

Energy sources that interact with biological mechanisms generate image-like entities. This includes X rays, radio-frequency, magnetic, and ultrasonic energy used by physicians for medical diagnosis. Often, nonideal characteristics of the imaging environments contribute to images that are, subjectively speaking, nonideal. The processing of these images in digital form may improve their subjective appearance

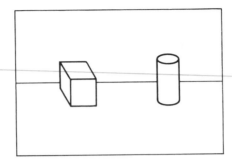

**FIGURE 1.2** Simple image description or understanding example

and consequent utility. For example, we may wish to highlight edge information in a medical X ray so that a physician is aided in his diagnosis.

IMAGE UNDERSTANDING

The development of systems that emulate the visual cognitive ability of high-level biological visual systems is an application of obvious utility. This is arguably the most difficult task facing image processing and computer vision researchers. Many of the previously cited applications inherently require, or could benefit from, this capability. For example, referring to the image in Figure 1.2, the goal is to have an autonomous system process the image data and respond: "You are viewing a table with a cylinder, oriented upward, sitting to the right of a block." The extraction of necessary primitives or features from this image to infer the existence of even these simplistic entities termed "cylinder," "block," and "table" and their spatial relationships is difficult.

## THE DIFFICULTY—TAKING THE HUMAN VISUAL SYSTEM FOR GRANTED

The processing capability of human visual systems is often taken for granted. This is not a negative remark—it merely reflects the fact that much of the cognitive processes are buried in the subconscious. The subtlety and difficulty of describing the exact operation of subconscious functions presents significant difficulty in developing algorithms to emulate human visual behavior.

Figure 1.3 visually illustrates this problem at the lowest level. A sample image of an easily recognized object (a coffee cup) is shown in Figure 1.3a. A plot of the image function—that is, the array of intensities comprising this image—is shown in Figure 1.3b. To human observers this plot conveys little visual information regarding the object contained in the image or the imaged scene. It is fundamental to note, however, that this is what the computer "sees" (i.e., the sensor produces); humans perceive the "objects." Figure 1.3c shows a plot of contours of constant image intensity. Notice that this image "topographic map" represents a form of low-level image preprocessing and, more important, presents information about areas of the image that are similar in intensity. The crude outline of the cup is evident. Finally, Figure 1.3d shows a preprocessed version of the image of Figure 1.3a where edges have been extracted using the techniques of Chapter 4. From the preprocessed version of the image in Figure 1.3d, it is clear that the information content of the image has been retained with a substantial reduction in the amount

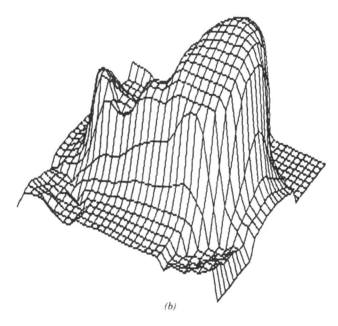

*(b)*

**FIGURE 1.3** "Cup" image (240 × 256 pixels × 6 bits)
(a) Greylevel image display
(b) Image function 3-D plot
(c) Intensity contours in "cup" function
(d) Edge-enhanced "cup"

*(continued)*

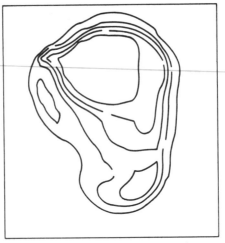

*(c)* Intensity contours in "cup" function.

*(d)*

**FIGURE 1.3** *(continued)*

of raw data. Hopefully, this simple example conveys an appreciation for the complexities involved in developing image understanding systems. Very often an image processing task is regarded as trivial until the algorithm must be coded. Unfortunately, there are no predefined data types (in any current programming language) such as "target, background, house, robot arm, cancerous cell," or the like.

Just as the sensor-computer system does not "see" high-level entities, but rather only takes as input a spatially distributed array of intensities or numbers, a human observer presented with image data displayed in numerical form often has a nearly impossible time trying to infer anything about the image content. Figure 1.3*b* succinctly proves this. Thus, our inherent familiarity with the capabilities of our visual system often is mistaken as understanding of its operations.

Alternately, there also exist situations wherein autonomous vision systems yield results with precision far exceeding the human visual system (HVS) capability. An example is found in stereo vision, where it is possible to develop systems with three-dimensional distance resolutions on the order of thousandths of an inch; humans are only able to approximate distances, and this capability falls off markedly after about 7 m. This lack of precision suggests that a certain level of ambiguity is allowed at certain levels in the HVS. The emulation, quantifying, or coding of this ambiguity is heretofore an exceedingly difficult problem. For example, a few degrees rotation of an image makes little difference in the eventual interpretation by a human observer; but this rotation will cause major changes in the spatial distribution of sensor output data and may yield major errors in the autonomous system processing. An example of this effect in matching using correlation is shown in Chapter 6.

## ■ IMAGE REPRESENTATIONS AND NOMENCLATURE

For future discussion we define the following entities:

image: a 2-D function generated by "viewing" (or, more accurately, sensing) a scene; often called a "picture." It is not necessarily in the (human) visual spectrum. A sensor converts scene radiometric information into images, and it is the (usually) irreversible and nonunique nature of this transformation which presents many of the difficulties in the processing, analysis, and interpretation of imagery.

scene: a collection of 3-D objects with some geometrical arrangement and usually governed by the physical laws of nature. The scene contents include radiometric energy, which becomes the basis for the image of the scene.

The image is represented by the image function

$$f(x,y)$$

$$f(x_1,x_2)$$

$$f(\underline{x}), \quad \text{etc.}$$

where the arguments of the image function—that is, the independent variables (x,y or $x_1$, $x_2$, or $\underline{x}$)—are spatial coordinates related to physical locations in the sensor image plane, and f is the intensity (lumens, volts, etc.) at these locations. The range of the values of f is called the greyscale range. If f takes on at most two values, the image is said to be binary. Each of these quantities has an associated set of units; $x_1$ and $x_2$ are often measured with respect to or in multiples of image plane dimensions (e.g., "pixel units," pels, or simply "pixels"), and f is often expressed in terms of sensor intensity units (e.g., volts, coulombs), which are rarely mentioned. It is the seemingly simplistic relationship posed above that yields much difficulty. Since $x_1$ and $x_2$ are spatial quantities, the concepts of 2-D geometry and shape arise. Conversely, the quantity f is related to the radiometric properties of the scene being imaged. Together, these quantities yield a distributed array of intensities. Unfortunately, however, *a functional form for* f($\underline{x}$) *is almost never known*, although locally (i.e., for limited ranges of $\underline{x}$) a functional form may be approximated. The lack of a more useful, perhaps mathematically tractable, model to relate changes in $\underline{x}$ to those in $f$ (e.g., a closed-form, single-valued, mathematical tractable function) presents much difficulty in algorithm development, since there is little underlying mathematical rigor.

Greyscale images allow more than two intensity values. Binary images are an important class of images that we will consider later, and they usually result from some initial processing of greyscale image data. For illustration, the HVS has a greyscale perception range of about 64 distinct levels (6 bits). In other words, a human observer shown a 6-bit (or larger) greyscale intensity scale chart with intensity bars ranging in intensity from lowest to highest would tend to perceive smooth intensity variations (i.e., the transition from one level to the next would not be perceived as a jump or edge). Given a 4-bit greyscale, however, the observer would perceive jumps ("bars") or discontinuities due to the level changes.

Note that the mathematical formulation above assumes that the intensity function is a scalar quantity (i.e., it spans a one-dimensional range of values ranging from binary to greyscale). If other features, such as color, were extracted by the sensor, we could model $f$ as a vector-valued function.

Practical concerns related to the $f(x)$ representation of an image are:

1. $f$ has a finite range of values;
2. $\underline{x}$ has a finite extent (the image plane or sensor has a limited field of view [FOV] and, due to sampling, a finite resolution) (this is treated in Chapter 8); and
3. Both $f$ and $\underline{x}$ are quantized in practice. The discrete nature of these quantities, while allowing computer processing, introduces other concerns, such as the effect of sampling (Chapter 3).

As shown in Chapter 3, sampling of the image data amounts to multiplication of the image function by an idealized sampling function and results in the production of a discrete array of discrete intensities. Sampling may be inherent in the imaging process if the sensor employs discrete sensing elements, such as found in CCD or CID cameras (described in Chapter 8). Often, as shown in Chapter 3, if sampling is done on a rectangular lattice, it is useful to arrange the intensity samples or pixels in a matrix, referred to as the image function matrix [$f$]. This formulation allows the study of the plethora of image transforms by using linear algebra, considering basis function matrices and the concept of a change of basis function.

It is noteworthy that the continuous or discrete versions of the function $f(x_1, x_2)$ depend on:

1. The viewing geometry—that is, the geometrical relationship of the sensor to the scene; the nature and source(s) of scene illumination; and the characteristics of the sensor (e.g., the focal length or magnification, sensor spectral intensity response, and geometric characteristics).
2. The composition of the scene—that is, object content and geometrical relationships, reflectance/self-illumination properties in the spectra of interest.

Furthermore, the fact that the image function contains spatially distributed arguments ($x_1$ and $x_2$) and an intensity value ($f$) introduces "a tale of two transforms." In the domain of the arguments, due to their two-dimensional nature, we become interested in geometry or, specifically, shape. This suggests a processing hierarchy based solely on geometric considerations as shown below:

relationship of $x_1, x_2$ features $\Rightarrow$ shape

$\Rightarrow$ object description or identification $\Rightarrow$ scene description

Conversely, it might be possible to develop useful algorithms that provide image information solely on the basis of intensity information. For example, we may wish to retain only image points whose intensity value is above a certain threshold; this is described as thresholding in Chapter 3.

Defining the input and output image functions as $f(x)$ and $g(x)$, respectively, we may loosely classify low-level processing efforts using two types of transforms with the following structures:

1. *intensity-based*, $g(\underline{x}) = O\ [f(\underline{x})]$ (i.e., we operate principally on the intensities); and
2. *Geometric-based*, $g(\underline{x}) = \underline{f}(h(\underline{x}))$

Examples of intensity-based transforms are the Fourier and Hadamard transforms and algorithms used for image contrast enhancement; examples of geometric-based transforms are the affine and perspective transforms used for image registration and image geometric manipulation (e.g., rotation).

The physical origin of the array of intensities in the above forms is not prespecified. Therefore, this data representation is common to a number of 2-D processing tasks, including imagery in the visible spectrum, infrared imagery, and imagery produced by synthetic aperture radar. Of course, the underlying characteristics of each of these types of imagery may be radically different and thus lead to significantly different models and processing approaches. Interestingly, however, salient features (such as the edges produced by man-made and natural changes) are often common to both infrared and visible imagery (Gibson, 1978) because of similar radiometric formation properties.

Note that image data may be time varying in nature, as a result of time-varying behavior of scene contents and/or the viewing geometry. The case of time-varying (or so-called dynamic) imagery is modeled by including an additional variable, time ($t$), in the continuous case or, in the discrete case, by indexing the image sequence by a discrete variable (e.g., $kT$). This yields a representation $f(x_1, x_2, t)$. The resulting 4-D spatiotemporal model presents some conceptual limitations due to human inability to readily visualize entities in more than three dimensions.

Image processing (at least at the lowest levels involving input and output images) ultimately involves development of algorithms implemented via time-space hardware realizations through which the above image data structure "flows." Parallel processing decompositions are often necessary for practical implementation and involve partitioning or "slicing" the above data structure for processing. These are treated in Chapter 8.

# ■ RELATIONSHIP OF IMAGE PROCESSING AND COMPUTER VISION TO 2-D SIGNAL PROCESSING, PATTERN RECOGNITION, COMPUTER GRAPHICS, AND ARTIFICIAL INTELLIGENCE

## SIGNAL PROCESSING

Some of the low-level functions achieved by digital image processing are very closely related to signal processing concepts. Examples are the statistical models that underlie image enhancement by histogram equalization. Other concepts, such as the variety of 2-D signal transformations, may be developed from their one-dimensional counterparts. *One must be careful, however, to consider which properties carry over into the 2-D case and the new properties (or lack thereof) that evolve.*

## PATTERN RECOGNITION

To show the relationship between image processing and computer vision and "pattern recognition," we must first determine what is meant by pattern recognition. Classically, a pattern recognition system is used for either pattern classification or pattern description (i.e., syntactic pattern analysis). A simplistic view of a general pattern recognition system is shown in Figure 1.4. If the transducer is an image sensor and the goal (or desired intermediate processing step) of the computer vision system is classification or description, pattern recognition techniques may be employed. For example, features inherent in imagery may be extracted and classified using pattern recognition principles. An example is in the segmentation of images with no a priori knowledge of image characteristics using an unsupervised learning approach. This is shown in Chapter 6.

## COMPUTER GRAPHICS

There is a clear and "inverselike" relationship between image processing and computer vision and computer graphics. This is shown in Figure 1.5. Whereas the objective of image description is to develop an understanding of the scene contents contained in the image, computer graphics is an area where the objective is to take

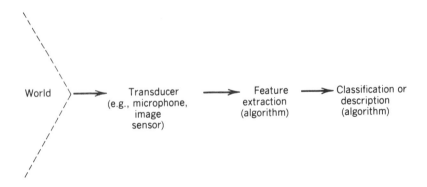

**FIGURE 1.4** Simple pattern recognition system

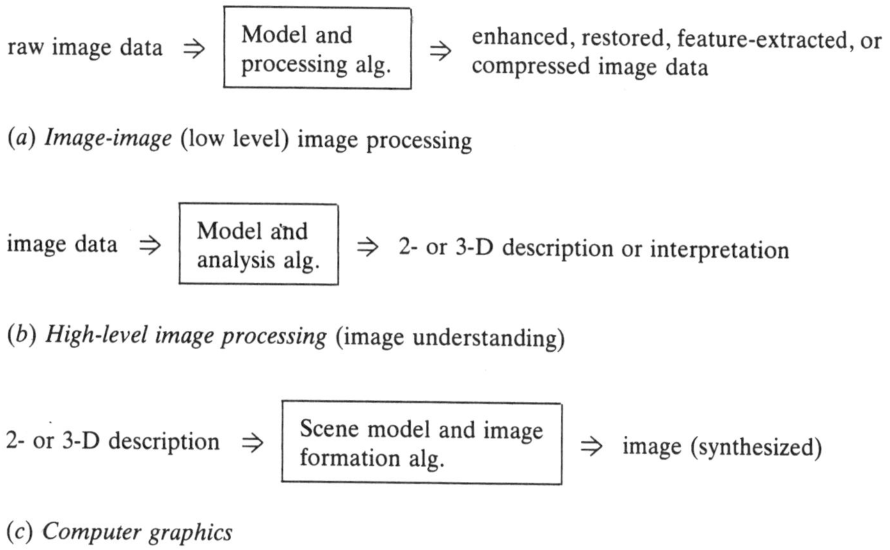

raw image data $\Rightarrow$ | Model and processing alg. | $\Rightarrow$ enhanced, restored, feature-extracted, or compressed image data

(*a*) *Image-image* (low level) image processing

image data $\Rightarrow$ | Model and analysis alg. | $\Rightarrow$ 2- or 3-D description or interpretation

(*b*) *High-level image processing* (image understanding)

2- or 3-D description $\Rightarrow$ | Scene model and image formation alg. | $\Rightarrow$ image (synthesized)

(*c*) *Computer graphics*

**FIGURE 1.5** The image-image processing (low level), image understanding, and computer graphics relationship.

the description of a scene and its contents and generate the appropriate image. Nevertheless, researchers in both these disciplines share a number of common problems, perhaps the most significant of which is the modeling of the description-image relationship.

### *ARTIFICIAL INTELLIGENCE*

The processing necessary for high-level computer vision is considered in Chapter 7. The manipulation of symbolic entities, each with values, properties, and constrained relationships to other symbolic entities is a major component. Computer vision, specifically image understanding, is an area that is often considered to be a subfield of artificial intelligence. This is hardly surprising, because of the objective of emulating high-level human visual capability and the fact that the HVS relies on a significant amount of "natural" intelligence. Thus, concepts fundamental to artificial intelligence, such as inference, resolution, unification, and semantic nets, in modeling and automating the cognitive processes in image understanding suggests that higher-level computer vision objectives are applications of artificial intelligence that happen to involve pictorial features.

## ■ RELATIONSHIP TO THE HUMAN VISUAL SYSTEM

When attempting to develop autonomous systems that emulate or surpass human visual capability, a reasonable starting place is to look at the available, albeit limited, body of knowledge concerning the workings of the human visual system (HVS). When we speak of the HVS in general, we are actually referring to the overall complex biological system that allows human interpretation of electromagnetic radiation in the visible spectrum. This encompasses the physiological operation of the human eye, its conversion process into neural signals (information), and the elusive low-, medium-, and high-level ("thought") processing operations that occur in several distinct areas of the brain.

The eye itself is not unlike man-made cameras. A small opening in the front allows light to enter, which, when passed through a transparent window known as the cornea, is then passed through a flexible lens, where focusing occurs. At the focal point, the light falls on a special structure known as the retina. Several chemical reactions occur, with the results being sensitive to different colors (blue, green, or red). Cells in the retina known as rods and cones convert this chemical energy to electrical impulses for further neural processing. This information is then sent to the back of the brain to a region known as the occipital cortex. Cones in the retina are concentrated in a small central region. The remainder of the retina consists of a mixture of rods and cones. The eye thus possesses nonlinear spatial sampling or resolution characteristics, since resolution is best at the center of the retina. The rods that form the perimeter of the retina are used principally to discern motion. They account for the sensitivity of the eye to peripheral activity and serve as part of a control mechanism for focus of attention.

As noted by Uttal (1975), there exists an anatomical hierarchy of the retina and two areas of the brain, namely the occipital cortex and association cortex. Patterns are discerned in the occipital cortex, and the hierarchical organization and processing of data begins to take place at this point. The occipital cortex is also believed to involve feature encoding, classification, and recognition.

The highest level of feature processing takes place in the association cortex. Operation in this area is thought to be explained by the so-called gestalt theory, which was first suggested as a general principle of perception by the psychologist Charles von Ehrenfels around 1890. This theory was refined by Koffka (1935) in 1935. The gestalt theory proposes that certain intrinsic features are inherent in patterns processed by the retina, which allow association to higher level structures. Note that in the recognition phase this means the human perceptual system does not need to contain a large template of different objects or entities but rather may classify differing objects and entities in libraries to be indexed by features. In Chapter 7 we explore the computer emulation of this capability.

Two other aspects of the human visual system, as they pertain to computer imaging, are noteworthy. The first is that the eyes are mounted inside a socket (the so-called orbit) and are allowed to rotate and thereby control their field of view. This yields an efficient, closed-loop control system whereby human vision attention may be guided by early processing. Furthermore, the obvious fact that humans are equipped with two eyes separated only by a horizontal distance suggests that the HVS is inherently equipped for stereo vision and the consequent estimation of depth.

The mechanics of radiometric energy conversion in biological image sensors (i.e., eyes) is fairly well understood. For example, prolific research findings concerning the low-level visual processes of the frog (motion is an important cue), the spider (edges and shape are important), and the human retina are available. Readers interested in the study of psychological and neurophysical aspects of animal vision will find a comprehensive and detailed summary in Levine (1985).

# ■ OVERVIEW OF THIS BOOK

The book is roughly divided into three topical areas:

1. Early vision (preprocessing) concerns and algorithms;
2. High-level visual processing and understanding; and
3. Image processing and computer vision hardware.

Many image processing and computer vision concepts are interrelated. For example, passive stereo vision relies on geometric modeling concepts, feature extraction, matching, solution of the correspondence problem, 3-D object modeling, and perhaps scene interpretation. It is necessary, however, to partition the study of these concepts in order to avoid a simultaneous explosion of new and interrelated concepts. In this book the partitioning is into concept-related groups as opposed to common application areas. Thus, geometric concerns are addressed in Chapter 2, greylevel processing is addressed in Chapters 3 and 4 (including reconstruction), and image motion modeling and estimation in Chapter 5. Chapters 6 and 7 provide an introduction to higher-level aspects of image processing, including pattern recognition, description, constraint satisfaction, and understanding. Practical concerns, including sensor operation and algorithm implementation via dedicated hardware, are addressed in Chapter 8. To some extent, the later chapters build on the earlier ones.

A summary of the interrelationships among basic image processing concepts, applications, and current research efforts is presented in Figure 1.6 (Kanade & Reddy, 1983).

# ■ SOURCES OF ADDITIONAL REFERENCE MATERIAL

No one book may hope to give absolute coverage to a field as diverse as image processing and computer vision. Readers may wish to consult additional documentation contained in the references cited in each chapter. Furthermore, the following readings are recommended.

# ■ RECOMMENDED READINGS

## *Texts*

Ballard, D. H., and Brown, C. M. *Computer vision*. Englewood Cliffs, NJ: Prentice-Hall, 1982.

Chellappa, R., and Sawchuck, A. A. (Eds.). *Digital image processing and analysis*, Vols. 1 and 2. New York: IEEE Computer Society Press, 1985. (This is a collection of selected research papers over the past 20 years.)

Duda, R. O., and Hart, P. E. *Pattern classification and scene analysis*. New York: Wiley, 1973.

Duff, M. J. B., and Levialdi, S. *Languages and architectures for image processing*. New York: Academic Press, 1981.

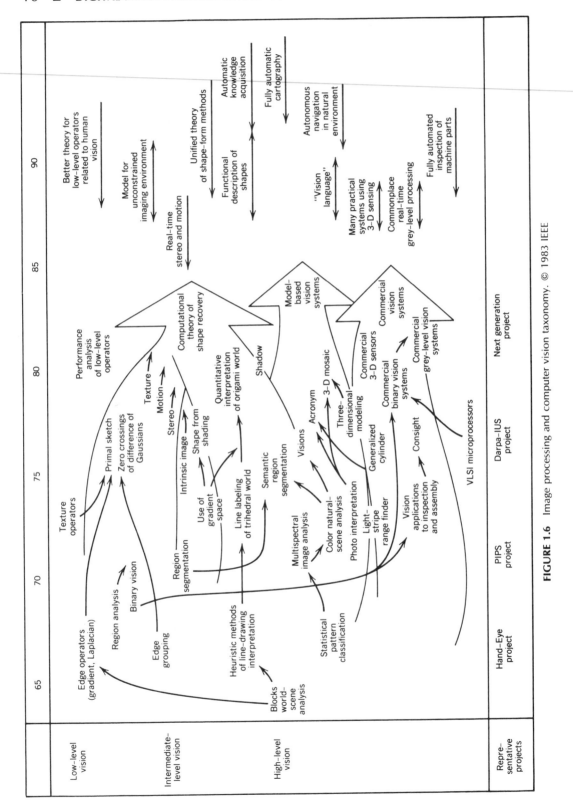

**FIGURE 1.6** Image processing and computer vision taxonomy. © 1983 IEEE

Gonzalez, R. C., and Wintz, P. *Digital image processing* (2nd ed.). Reading, MA: Addison-Wesley, 1987.

Hall, E. L. *Computer image processing and recognition.* New York: Academic Press, 1979.

Levine, M. D. *Vision in man and machine.* New York: McGraw-Hill, 1985.

Nevatia, R. *Machine perception.* Englewood Cliffs, NJ: Prentice-Hall, 1982.

Pavlidis, T. *Algorithms for graphics and image processing.* Computer Science Press, 1982.

Pratt, W. K. *Digital image processing.* New York: Wiley, 1978.

Rosenfeld, A., and Kak, A. C. *Digital picture processing.* New York: Academic Press, 1976.

### Periodicals

*Computer Vision, Graphics and Image Processing.* New York: Academic Press.

*IEEE Transactions on Pattern Analysis and Machine Intelligence.* New York: IEEE.

*Image and Vision Computing.* London: Butterworths.

*Pattern Recognition.* Elmsford, NY: Pergamon.

Proceedings of the Computer Vision and Image Processing Conference (formerly Pattern Recognition and Image Processing), IEEE Computer Society, New York.

Proceedings of the International Conference on Pattern Recognition, International Association for Pattern Recognition (IAPR), IEEE Computer Society, New York.

Selected issues of *Proceedings of the Society of Photo-Optical and Instrumentation Engineers*, as well as *Optical Engineering*.

Special issues of IEEE *Computer*. New York: IEEE.

## ■ REFERENCES

Birk, J. R., and Kelley, R. B. An overview of the basic research needed to advance the state of knowledge in robotics. *IEEE Trans. on Systems, Man and Cybernetics*, 1981, Vol. SMC-11, No. 8, 574–579.

Cornsweet, T. N. *Visual perception.* New York: Academic Press, 1970.

Gibson, H. L. *Photography by infrared.* New York: Wiley, 1978.

Harmon, L. D. Automated tactile sensing. *Robotics Research*, 1982, *1*(2), 3–32.

Insight. *Image and Vision Computing*, 1985, *3*(3), p. 143.

Insight. *Image and Vision Computing*, 1987, *5*(4), p. 302.

Kanade, T., and Reddy, R. "Computer vision—The challenge of imperfect inputs. *IEEE Spectrum*, 1983, *20*(11), p. 90.

Koffka, K. *Principles of gestalt psychology.* London: Routledge & Kegan, 1935.

Levine, M. D. *Vision in man and machine.* New York: McGraw-Hill, 1985.

Uttal, W. R. *An autocorrelation theory of form detection.* Hillsdale, NJ: Lawrence Erlbaum Associates, 1975.

Wurtz, R., Goldberg, M., and Robinson, D. Brain mechanisms in visual attention. *Scientific American*, June 1982, Vol. 246, No. 6, 124–135.

# 2

# A GEOMETRICAL MODEL FOR IMAGING AND SOME APPLICATIONS

## ■ THE PERSPECTIVE-PROJECTIVE TRANSFORM (WORLD POINTS TO IMAGE POINTS AND TRYING TO GET BACK)

An obvious starting point for the processing and analysis of imagery is a look at *the physical processes of image formation.* This chapter develops the geometric aspects of the image formation process. Through a careful modeling of the imaging process, object point locations are converted into image plane locations. Three of the most significant outcomes are (a) the perspective-projective transform; (b) the need for correspondence information in inferring 3-D world point locations from multiple images; and (c) the need for known (or estimatable) camera orientation parameters.

Although inferences as to the exact nature of the 3-D world that generated the image(s) may not be directly recovered from the image, a knowledge of how the 3-D scene is projected onto the image plane gives insight into:

1. Finding clues about 3-D structure in the scene under observation, which may prove useful in scene interpretation;

2. Developing stereo or multiple camera systems for measurement and range determination;

3. Identifying and correcting image geometric distortions (due either to the camera optics and/or different viewing geometry);

4. Forming camera control (e.g., pan/tilt mounts and zoom signals); and

5. Understanding and estimating 3-D motion (Chapter 5).

Initially, in order to make a somewhat tedious derivation easier, no distinction is made between continuous or discrete spatial indices. Later, we show that the discrete nature of the pixel indices leads to a number of fundamental concerns. We start with the problem of relating 3-D object points to 2-D image plane locations; we will quickly see that other 2-D to 2-D and 3-D to 3-D transformations are related to this initial goal. In addition, we develop a new linear representation for several inherently nonlinear relationships, which leads to the concepts of homogeneous and superhomogeneous coordinate representations.

## SCENE-IMAGE GEOMETRIC MODELS (3-D TO 2-D)

The objective, as shown in Figure 2.1*a*, is to develop a mathematically tractable relationship between 3-D object point *locations* (not intensities), measured with respect to a user-selected world or global coordinate system, and image point locations, measured with respect to a coordinate system in the image plane.

The approach in this chapter proceeds in order of difficulty and sophistication as follows:

1. Develop a pinhole camera model with both object and image points measured with respect to a coordinate system centered in the image plane.

2. Explore the properties of this model.

3. Revise this model to allow measurement of object points with respect to an arbitrary global coordinate system.

4. Explore the ramificatons and utility of the revised model. This includes, as shown in Figure 2.*1b*:

   i. Perspective distortion and other geometrically significant properties of the imaging process, for example, the concepts of lines in 3-D remaining lines in 2-D and parallel lines in space becoming intersecting lines in the image;

   ii. The stereo vision equations; in this case the image points corresponding to a single object point in two (or more) spatially distributed cameras with known orientations are used, via a triangulation procedure, to determine the absolute location of the object point. Thus, noncontact measurement possibilities, using either a pair of passive cameras, or an active camera (projector or structured light) with a passive camera, result from this model;

   iii. 3-D constraints for the motion of rigid bodies observed in a time-varying image sequence (Chapter 5);

   iv. Techniques for camera calibration/recalibration; and

   v. A model and algorithm for the determination of camera mount control signals as a function of image plane point perturbations.

The general form of the geometric image formation model we seek is

$$\underline{x}_i = \underline{g}(\underline{x}_o,.)$$  (2-1)

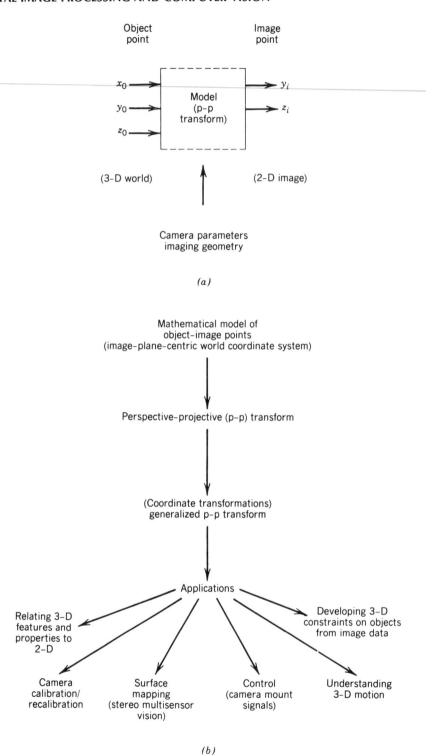

**FIGURE 2.1** Perspective-projective transform
(a) Modelling goal (perspective-projective transform)
(b) Hierarchy of our study of the perspective-projective (pp) transform

where $g$ is the generally noninvertible geometric transformation that relates object points, $\underline{x}_o$, in the 3-D scene to image points, $\underline{x}_i$, in the image plane. $g$ is a function of the imaging geometry, lens model, and coordinate system choices.

The model is derived by considering the pinhole camera model shown in Figure 2.2. Using coordinate transformations, object points measured with respect to a global coordinate system are related to image points measured in an image plane-centric coordinate system. Examples of this derivation may be found in Duda (1973) and Hall (1979).

Several entities in Figure 2.2 are noteworthy. The point located at a distance $f$ in front of the image plane is known as the *center of projection*. Since the image plane is located behind the center of projection, this pinhole sensor model is often referred to as the back-projection version. The $x$-axis is often referred to as the central projection or optical axis and yields an indication of sensor viewing direction. Knowledge of image plane finite extent may also be used to calculate the camera field of view (Chapter 8). Finally, if the inversion caused by this particular geometrical arrangement is inconvenient, an equivalent model without this inversion may be obtained by placing the image plane at a distance $f$ along the optical axis in front of the center of projection, retaining an image plane-centric coordinate system and thus deriving the equations for the *front-projection model*. This is left to the problems.

Initially, assume that the coordinate systems for both object and image points are coincident and centered in the image plane, as shown in Figure 2.2. This figure represents an approximation to the case of a simple lens placed in front of the image plane. Thus, the inversion of images one would expect is shown both graph-

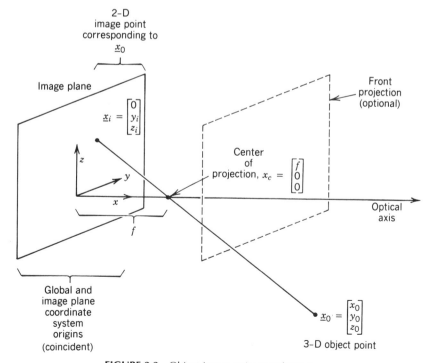

**FIGURE 2.2** Object-image point transformation

ically and analytically. Figure 2.2 shows that the imaging model constrains any imaged point to correspond to an object point located anywhere on the 3-D line segment containing $x_i$, $x_c$, and $x_o$. These three colinear points are related by

$$k(x_i - x_c) = (x_c - x_o) \tag{2-2}$$

Expanding this equation yields (the reader is advised to verify this)

$$k\left\{\begin{bmatrix} 0 \\ y_i \\ z_i \end{bmatrix} - \begin{bmatrix} f \\ 0 \\ 0 \end{bmatrix}\right\} = \begin{bmatrix} f \\ 0 \\ 0 \end{bmatrix} - \begin{bmatrix} x_o \\ y_o \\ z_o \end{bmatrix} \tag{2-3}$$

Therefore,

$$k = (x_o - f)/f = x_o/f - 1 \tag{2-3b}$$

so

$$y_i = -y_o/k = fy_o/(f - x_o)$$

and $\hspace{8cm}$ (2-4)

$$z_i = -z_o/k = fz_o/(f - x_o)$$

The consequences of this elementary model are numerous. Salient results are listed below.

1. It is nonlinear in the object point parameters $(x_o, y_o, z_o)$.
2. It is nonlinear in the camera parameters $(f)$. (The concepts of nonlinearity on the parameters versus nonlinearity in the input/output sense are described in Eykhoff [1974].)
3. It restricts the object point (or "world" or "global") coordinate system to be centered in the image plane.
4. The relationships in Eq. (2-4) are often approximated. Since in many applications $x_o \gg f$, we reduce these equations under what is often referred to as the far-field or large magnification ratio assumption to

$$y_i = -fy_o/x_o = y_o[1/(x_o/f)](-1)$$

and $\hspace{8cm}$ (2-5)

$$z_i = -fz_o/x_o = z_o[1/(x_o/f)](-1)$$

The quantity $x_o/f$ is called the *magnification ratio* and is generally $\gg 1$. Thus, with the approximation cited, Eq. 2-5 indicates that *object points are converted into image points through division by the magnification ratio and a sign inversion.*

*The measuring of world or object points with respect to an image plane-centric system is both cumbersome and unrealistic.* A model that allows the measurement of points with respect to a user-chosen world or global coordinate system is desired. Fortunately, a series of 3-D coordinate system conversions (transformation), using the previous model will lead to this. The measurement of image points with respect to an image plane-centric system is, however, both convenient and desirable. Furthermore, the inherently nonlinear nature of these equations makes their analysis difficult. Therefore, we will temporarily digress to introduce a convenient representation approach that aids further modeling.

## HOMOGENEOUS COORDINATES

The concept of homogeneous coordinates is a technique commonly used in the development of computer graphics (Roberts, 1965). A comprehensive introduction is presented in Riesenfeld (1981). Our concern is with the basic approach.

The homogeneous coordinates for the physical object point $(x_o, y_o, z_o)^T$ in 3-D space are represented by the $4 \times 1$ vector $(kx_o, ky_o, kz_o, k)$, where $k$ is a nonzero and arbitrary constant. An immediate consequence of this representation is that there is no unique representation of a physical point in homogeneous coordinates. To convert a point represented as an $n \times 1$ vector from a homogeneous coordinate representation to physical coordinates of dimension $n - 1$, it is necessary to divide all components by the $n$th element and delete the $n$th component, thus forming a new $(n - 1) \times 1$ vector. An image point is represented in homogeneous coordinates by augmenting the $2 \times 1$ physical vector dimension by one (the scale factor) and multiplying the physical image point coordinates by this nonzero factor. The two examples below show this representational conversion using image and object points where the ^ is used to denote vectors $x_i$ and $x_o$ in homogeneous coordinates, as shown below.

image points

$$\underline{x}_i = \begin{bmatrix} y_i \\ z_i \end{bmatrix} \Rightarrow \hat{\underline{x}}_i = \begin{bmatrix} wy_i \\ wz_i \\ w \end{bmatrix} \tag{2-6a}$$

object points

$$\underline{x}_o = \begin{bmatrix} x_o \\ y_o \\ z_o \end{bmatrix} \Rightarrow \hat{\underline{x}}_o = \begin{bmatrix} wx_o \\ wy_o \\ wz_o \\ w \end{bmatrix} \tag{2-6b}$$

where $w \neq 0$.

This augmentation of the vector space dimension by one allows the preceding nonlinear relationship to be written as a

$$\hat{x}_i = P_1 \hat{x}_o \tag{2-7a}$$

where the matrix $P_1$ is written as

$$P_1 = \begin{bmatrix} f & 0 & 0 & 0 \\ 0 & f & 0 & 0 \\ 0 & 0 & f & 0 \\ -1 & 0 & 0 & f \end{bmatrix} \tag{2-7b}$$

Notice that the representation for $P_1$ is not unique. This is a direct result of the use of homogeneous coordinates. $P_i$ may be multiplied by any nonzero scalar and the relationship in Eq. 2-7 still holds. For example, an alternative to $P_1$ is $P_2$:

$$P_2 = \begin{bmatrix} 1 & 0 & 0 & 0 \\ 0 & 1 & 0 & 0 \\ 0 & 0 & 1 & 0 \\ -1/f & 0 & 0 & 1 \end{bmatrix} \tag{2-8}$$

ORTHOGRAPHIC PROJECTION

As $|f| \to$ infinity in the above model, the matrix $P_2$ in Eq. 2.8 approaches the $4 \times 4$ identity matrix $I$. This yields the so-called *orthographic projection*, where object points are projected orthogonally onto the image plane. Perspective distortion does not exist in this case. Each image point is simply a scaled version of its corresponding object point. In cases where the *variation* of object point-image plane distance $(x_o)$ is negligible (i.e., $x_o$ may be regarded as fixed) for all points on an object or surface under consideration, the algebraically and geometrically simpler orthographic projection model may be used. For example, when the object dimensions in the $x_o$ direction are much smaller than the object-image distance $(x_o)$, this model may be used.

To verify the correctness of the approach, choose an object point in homogeneous coordinates as $\hat{\underline{x}}_o = (x_o, y_o, z_o, 1)^T$, form the product indicated by Eq. 2-7, and convert the resulting image point to physical coordinates. This yields

$$\hat{\underline{x}}_i = \begin{bmatrix} w_i\ x_i \\ w_i\ y_i \\ w_i\ z_i \\ w_i \end{bmatrix} = \begin{bmatrix} f\ x_o \\ f\ y_o \\ f\ z_o \\ f - x_o \end{bmatrix} \tag{2-9}$$

Therefore, in physical coordinates

$$\underline{x}_i = \begin{bmatrix} x_i \\ y_i \\ z_i \end{bmatrix} = \begin{bmatrix} f\ x_o/(f - x_o) \\ f\ y_o/(f - x_o) \\ f\ z_o/(f - x_o) \end{bmatrix} \tag{2-10}$$

This result, while achieving the representation of Eq. 2-4 for $y_i$ and $z_i$, does not yield $x_i = 0$. Thus, although it is a useful mathematical representation, the homogeneous coordinate model must be interpreted with this in mind. To force $x_i = 0$, an obvious solution is to simply eliminate the first row of the $P_1$ matrix, thus reducing the dimension to $3 \times 4$. However, we first look at the consequences of Eq. 2-7a. Of particular interest is the invertibility of this transformation. The reader may calculate the inverse of $P_1$ (the form in Eq. 2-7b or 2-8 is invertible). Therefore, object points may be determined from $\hat{\underline{x}}_i$ as

$$\hat{\underline{x}}_o = P_1^{-1}\hat{\underline{x}}_i \tag{2-11}$$

The above result presumes the first component of $\hat{\underline{x}}_i$—that is, $x_i$—is known. Therefore, the transformation is only invertible given this component. We achieve a more realistic model by assuming no knowledge of $x_i$ and deleting the first row of the $P_1$ matrix, yielding the noninvertible relationship

$$\hat{\underline{x}}_i = P\hat{\underline{x}}_o \tag{2-12}$$

where $\hat{\underline{x}}_i$ is a $3 \times 1$ vector ($x_i$ has been deleted) and the new $P$ is of dimension $3 \times 4$ and written as

$$P = \begin{bmatrix} 0 & f & 0 & 0 \\ 0 & 0 & f & 0 \\ -1 & 0 & 0 & f \end{bmatrix} \tag{2-13}$$

This is the desired relationship. Next, we seek to determine, even if the relationship is not invertible, what information relative to the 3-D object point locations we may infer from the image points and $P$.

Rewriting the equations in Eq. 2-4 in physical coordinates and some algebraic manipulation yields:

$$\frac{y_o}{y_i} = \frac{z_o}{z_i} = \frac{x_o - f}{-f} \tag{2-14}$$

Fixing the image plane coordinates $y_i$ and $z_i$, this is easily seen to be the equation of a line in 3-D in ratio form (see Appendix 1). This line passes through the point $(f\ 0\ 0)^T$, as expected. Therefore, while the object-image point transformation is not invertible, choice of a specific image point constrains corresponding object points to lie along a ray in 3-D space. This ray is precisely the one shown in Figure 2.2.

### RAMIFICATIONS OF THE p-p MODEL

By using the previously developed perspective-projective transform Eq. 2-12, it is relatively easy to prove (see the problems) that lines in the 3-D world map into lines in the image plane. The case of a point in the image plane resulting from the 3-D line passing through the center of projection is considered the degenerate case. An alternate and simple proof of this property proceeds as follows.

Recall from elementary geometry the following two facts:

1. Any line and any point not on the line determine a unique plane.
2. The intersection of two (nonparallel) planes determines a unique line.

Let $XY$ be a line in 3-D space and $F$ be the point that is the center of projection. A unique plane, denoted $XYF$, is determined by this line and point. (Notice here that we do not allow the line to include $F$, thus avoiding the degenerate case.) The intersection of plane $XYF$ and the image plane thus determine a unique line. This line is the image of the 3-D line in the image plane, since any point on this 3-D line that passes through $F$ must lie in $XYZ$ and the image plane.

This property of the perspective-projective (p-p) transform is both intuitively appealing and extremely useful, since man-made objects are generally composed of a number of intersecting surfaces whose intersections and edges appear as lines in 3-D space. The fact that these lines carry over into the image plane suggests an obvious and powerful starting point for extraction and manipulation of image features to infer scene information. Note that this conclusion applies regardless of the object point coordinate system chosen. The astute reader will note that an exception to this occurs when the line formed is coincident with the optical axis.

Parallel lines in 3-D do not, in general, map into nonintersecting lines in the image plane. The latter result is often used as an example of "perspective distortion" in pictorial information. A good example is an image of a scene containing (parallel) railroad tracks, which appear in the image to intersect at some point in the scene. In addition, the distance between any two points in the image plane does not reveal, in general, anything about their distance in the 3-D scene. Although this postulate may seem discomforting, the reader should note that humans frequently are able to judge distances from images by using a significant amount of structural and relational information in the image and comparing objects in the image with known (or inferred) spatial relationships. This postulate, although easily proved using the above equations, is conceptually obvious, since every image point may

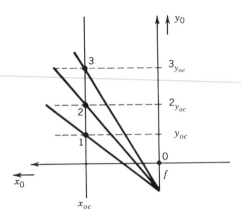

$$x_i = \frac{fx_o}{y_o + f} \approx \frac{x_o}{y_o} \quad \begin{bmatrix} f = 1.0 \\ y_o \gg f \end{bmatrix}$$

| Point | $x_o$ | $y_o$ | $x_i$ | $\Delta y$ (obj. space) | $\Delta x_i$ (mm) |
|-------|-------|-------|-------|------------------------|-------------------|
| ① | $x_{oc}$ | $y_{oc}$ | $x_{ic} = \dfrac{x_{oc}}{y_{oc}}$ | — | — |
| ② | $x_{oc}$ | $2y_{oc}$ | $\dfrac{1}{2} x_{ic}$ | $y_{oc}$ | $\dfrac{1}{2} x_{ic}$ |
| ③ | $x_{oc}$ | $3y_{oc}$ | $\dfrac{1}{3} x_{ic}$ | $y_{oc}$ | $\dfrac{1}{6} x_{ic}$ |

Const.

**FIGURE 2.3**   Foreshortening due to p-p distortion

be back-projected into a 3-D ray; thus, any line in 3-D that connects a point on either of these rays will appear as the same line in the image.

The effect of the perspective transform in distorting perceived 3-D scene distances is both calculable and useful (e.g., in architectural design). Figure 2.3 shows graphically why equally spaced (in the $x_o$ direction) object points would not yield equally spaced image points.

## MEASUREMENT OF OBJECT POINTS WITH RESPECT TO AN ARBITRARY COORDINATE SYSTEM

As mentioned, the choice of a global coordinate system in the preceding is neither reasonable nor practical. We now proceed to derive a more useful model that allows the measurement of object points with respect to a user-selected coordinate system. What we will need to know, however, is the relationship between the selected coordinate system and the previously chosen image plane centric system. This procedure involves, in general, a tedious set of coordinate transformations. This relationship is specified as a series of coordinate transformations, involving translations and rotations.

The case of relating the relative coordinate system orientations by a simple translation, as shown in Figure 2.4, is considered first. Recall from Eq. 2-12 that we have the relationship

$$\hat{\underline{x}}_i = P \, \hat{\underline{x}}_o \tag{2-15}$$

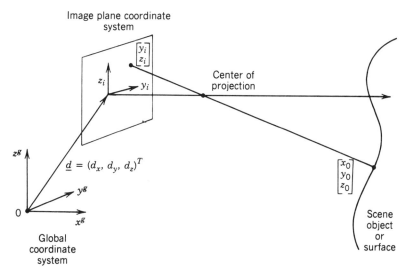

**FIGURE 2.4** Global coordinate system offset from image plane

where both $\underline{\hat{x}}_i$ and $\underline{\hat{x}}_o$ are represented in homogeneous coordinates *and measured with respect to the image plane-centered coordinate system.* It is desired to represent object points in the global system shown in Figure 2.4. Points measured with respect to this system are denoted with the superscript $g$.

Since we already have the model for the perspective distortion Eq. 2-12 or Eq. 2-15, an efficient approach is to convert object points measured with respect to the arbitrarily chosen (global) coordinate system into object points measured with respect to the image plane centric system and then apply Eq. 2-15. For the case of translation shown in Figure 2.4, a simple conversion for arbitrary 3-D physical vectors $\underline{x}$ and $\underline{x}^g$ is

$$\underline{x} = \underline{x}^g - \begin{bmatrix} d_x \\ d_y \\ d_z \end{bmatrix} \tag{2-16a}$$

Converting $\underline{x}$ and $\underline{x}^g$ into homogeneous representations yields

$$\underline{\hat{x}} = \begin{bmatrix} 1 & 0 & 0 & -d_x \\ 0 & 1 & 0 & -d_y \\ 0 & 0 & 1 & -d_z \\ 0 & 0 & 0 & 1 \end{bmatrix} \underline{\hat{x}}^g \tag{2-16b}$$

where the $4 \times 4$ matrix in the above equation is referred to as a translation matrix, $T$. Thus,

$$\underline{\hat{x}} = T \underline{\hat{x}}^g \tag{2-16c}$$

This transformation may be applied to any object point. The model for the p-p transform, therefore, becomes

$$\underline{\hat{x}}_i = P T \underline{\hat{x}}_o^g \tag{2-17}$$

Similarly, when the coordinate systems are related by a rotation, the transformation relating measured object points in both systems is

$$\underline{\hat{x}} = R\underline{\hat{x}}^g \tag{2-18}$$

where $R$ is the matrix that accomplishes the specific 3-D rotation. Specific matrix forms for rotation about the coordinate axes are shown in Foley and Van Dam (1983). Examples of these matrices and their application are found in detail in the section on Applications: Camera Control Concepts later in this chapter.

In general, a model wherein the global and image plane-centric coordinates are related by an often complex series of successive rotations and transformations results. Note that *there is no unique path or order that these rotations must take; however, the composite result must be the same regardless of the order in which the mapping was accomplished.* This does not mean the same matrices may simply be interchanged in order; if the path is different, the transformation matrices' parameters may also be different. A succession of these transformations may be of the form:

$$\underline{\hat{x}} = T1 \ R1 \ T2 \ R2 \ R3 \ \underline{\hat{x}}^g \tag{2-19}$$

where, in this example, the transformation is first a rotation ($R3$), followed by another rotation ($R2$), a translation ($T2$), a rotation ($R1$), and finally a translation ($T1$). The consequences and visual effects of each of these transformations from the point of view of computer graphics are shown in Foley and Van Dam (1983).

Defining the composite of the above transformation as $R^{i-g}$ where

$$R^{i-g} = T1 \ R1 \ T2 \ R2 \ R3 \tag{2-20}$$

the desired relationship between the object points measured with respect to the chosen global coordinate system and the image points measured with respect to the image plane centric system is

$$\underline{\hat{x}}_i = P R^{i-g} \ \underline{\hat{x}}_o^g \tag{2-21}$$

The resulting 3 × 4 matrix $PR^{i-g}$ is thus the "new" p-p transformation matrix.

Although it is theoretically possible to convert knowledge of relative coordinate system orientations into the new p-p transform parameters, the above series of transformations is often quite cumbersome to calculate. Rarely are the exact values of the angular rotations and translations required by Eq. 2-20 and Eq. 2-21 known. It is important to note, however, that *Eq. 2-21 yields the* form *or parametric structure of the resulting equations.* In the relationship of Eq. 2-21, the parameters in $P$ and $R^{i-g}$ may be left as variables. The general relationship between object points measured with respect to any user-selected world coordinate system and the image plane points is denoted, in homogeneous coordinates, by a 3 × 4 matrix denoted $A$; that is,

$$\underline{\hat{x}}_i = A \ \underline{\hat{x}}_o^g \tag{2-22}$$

where $A$ has the form:

$$A = \begin{bmatrix} a_{11} & a_{12} & a_{13} & a_{14} \\ a_{21} & a_{22} & a_{23} & a_{24} \\ a_{31} & a_{32} & a_{33} & a_{34} \end{bmatrix} \tag{2-23}$$

Recall that $A$ is not unique, due to our use of homogeneous coordinates. The $A$ matrix has 12 entities, which are nonlinear functions of the 7 parameters (3 rotation angles, 3 translations, and $f$) that determine the sensor system geometry.

## CAMERA CALIBRATION

Expressing the vectors shown in Eq. 2-22 and Eq. 2-23 in terms of their components in homogeneous coordinates yields

$$
\begin{bmatrix} w_i y_i \\ w_i z_i \\ w_i \end{bmatrix} = \begin{bmatrix} a_{11} & a_{12} & a_{13} & a_{14} \\ a_{21} & a_{22} & a_{23} & a_{24} \\ a_{31} & a_{32} & a_{33} & a_{34} \end{bmatrix} \begin{bmatrix} x_o^g \\ y_o^g \\ z_o^g \\ 1 \end{bmatrix} \tag{2-24}
$$

where $y_i$ and $z_i$ are the physical image plane pixel or point locations. The form of Eq. 2-24 enables estimation of the $a_{ij}$ parameters in a process referred to as *camera calibration* (Sobel, 1974). The process of camera calibration is a necessary prelude to the achievement of a stereo vision system.

Equation 2-24, expressed in physical coordinates, has the form:

$$
\underline{x}_i = \underline{h}(\underline{x}_o, \underline{a}) \tag{2-25}
$$

where $\underline{a}$ is a vector containing the $a_{ij}$ parameters. A set of corresponding physical object and image point pairs yields estimation equations for the $a_{ij}$ parameters. The nonuniqueness of the parameters in Eq. 2-24 requires some normalization to remove this ambiguity. It is common to set element $a_{34} = 1.0$. Of course, other normalizations are also possible and equally valid.

Rewriting Eq. 2-24 in physical coordinates, we get

$$
y_i = \frac{a_{11} x_o + a_{12} y_o + a_{13} z_o + a_{14}}{a_{31} x_o + a_{32} y_o + a_{33} z_o + a_{34}}
$$

and $\tag{2-26}$

$$
z_i = \frac{a_{21} x_o + a_{22} y_o + a_{23} z_o + a_{24}}{a_{31} x_o + a_{32} y_o + a_{33} z_o + a_{34}}
$$

Setting $a_{34} = 1.0$, after some algebraic manipulation, each corresponding object/image point pair yields two equations that are linear in the $a_{ij}$ parameters and may be written in matrix notation as

$$
\begin{bmatrix} x_o & y_o & z_o & 1 & 0 & 0 & 0 & 0 & -(y_i x_o) & -(y_i y_o) & -(y_i z_o) \\ 0 & 0 & 0 & 0 & x_o & y_o & z_o & 1 & -(z_i x_o) & -(z_i y_o) & -(z_i z_o) \end{bmatrix} \begin{matrix} a_{11} \\ a_{12} \\ a_{13} \\ a_{14} \\ a_{21} \\ a_{22} = \\ a_{23} \\ a_{24} \\ a_{31} \\ a_{32} \\ a_{33} \end{matrix}
$$

$$
\begin{bmatrix} y_i \\ z_i \end{bmatrix} \tag{2-27}
$$

The $A$ matrix has been converted by row concatenation to a vector of parameters to be estimated. A single point pair yields 2 equations and 11 unknowns. Given $n$ such point pairs, we may formulate the above equation as

$$
Q \, \underline{a} = \underline{d} \tag{2-28}
$$

where $Q$ is a $2n \times 11$ matrix whose rows are of the form in Eq. 2-27, $\underline{a}$ is the vector of unknown calibration parameters in Eq. 2-27, and the entries in $\underline{d}$ are of the form shown in Eq. 2-27. Consequently, we seek $n$ points such that the matrix $Q$ has full column rank, and therefore least squares estimation approaches may be applied to Eq. 2-28 to estimate $\underline{a}$. Since the two equations in Eq. 2-27 must be linearly independent (the reader should be aware why), this suggests that we might select the minimum number of points that yield full column rank in Eq. 2-28 as $n = 6$. The requirement on the geometric location or distribution of these points (explored in the problems) is that they be noncoplanar (Hall, et al., 1982).

In practice, we choose $n \gg 6$ and solve Eq. 2-28 using $Q$-$R$ decomposition. A summary of the theoretical and practical aspects of least squares estimation is found in Appendix 2. In the case where numerical sensitivity is insignificant, we may formulate the least squares solution in terms of the pseudoinverse of $Q$ denoted $Q^+$ as

$$\underline{a}^e = Q^+ \underline{d} \qquad (2\text{-}29)$$

where

$$Q^+ = (Q^T Q)^{-1} Q^T \qquad (2\text{-}30)$$

Thus, estimation of $\underline{a}^e$ yields a calibrated imaging system, which is a prerequisite for stereo vision.

## ■ STEREO (MULTIPLE CAMERA) VISION

A knowledge of the $3 \times 4$ $A$ matrix, obtained either from the appropriate coordinate transformations or a calibration procedure, still only permits the determination of image points from object points. Recall that the inverse of this relationship, given a particular image point and the $A$ matrix, only quantifies the ray along which object points corresponding to this image point must lie. Suppose our problem is to determine the 3-D location (measured with respect to a global coordinate system) of a set of object points, perhaps to determine if the dimensions of a particular machine part are within tolerance. Alternately, we may be interested in determining the distance, $x_o$, to an object—that is, we may be implementing depth perception. One approach, given the constraint of Eq. 2-24, would be to use more than one (usually two) calibrated cameras. Given the image points corresponding to a particular object point, the object point may be determined by finding the intersection of the two object point rays. This triangulation concept is the basis for the elementary approaches to stereo vision. More sophisticated approaches, such as determining the orientation of a 3-D surface, are covered later in this chapter.

Several other entities warrant investigation:

1. The allowed or preferred orientations of the cameras;
2. The consequences of the need for corresponding image points (this raises the "correspondence problem"); and
3. The use of an "active" camera, which, given an image pattern, projects rays. This is the basis of structured light approaches.

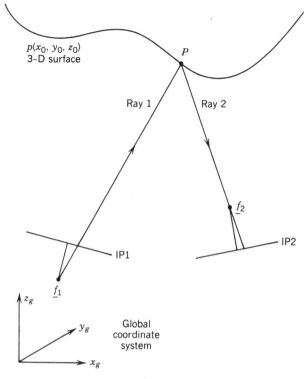

**FIGURE 2.5** Surface mapping geometry

A general diagram of the stereo vision problem is shown in Figure 2.5. An object or surface is viewed in both cameras, shown as IP1 and IP2, respectively. It is assumed that the scene portion contained in the field of view of both cameras contains object points measured with respect to the global coordinate system shown. Note:

1. Sensor IP1 is shown (for illustration purposes only) as a front projection model. This may be due to the nature of the camera lensing or, more important, because this camera is not simply a passive sensor but an *active camera* or projector.

2. The sensors are shown with intersecting optical axes. This is common; in fact, it is desirable that these axes converge near to the object points being determined, so that viewing does not take place from oblique angles. This type of arrangement is referred to as *convergent* stereo vision and emulates the positioning of the eyes in the HVS. In *nonconvergent* stereo vision, the optical axes are nonintersecting—that is, the cameras are "staring" at the object more or less independently of each other. Either case occurs in practice and is solvable with the same approach.

3. One of the most significant concerns that arises is referred to as the *correspondence* problem. The location of the image point corresponding to the object point being measured must be known exactly in one image plane and (as shown subsequently) constrained in the other image plane. Often the exact correspondence between points in both images is determined and then

used to solve for $\underline{x}_o$, using least squares to minimize 3-D location errors. *This image point correspondence data is perhaps the most difficult information to autonomously extract* and generally involves a great deal of ancillary processing. It also explains the popularity of active stereo approaches, in which this correspondence information may be obtained by using special projected light patterns (e.g., grids, lines, and concentric circles) or even time modulated projected rays or patterns (Altschuler, et al., 1981). In the passive case, it is assumed that the scene being imaged contains sufficient structure, which is reflected in the image plane as a set of features such as edges, common regions, or unique shapes. It is through the preprocessing of these features (with the techniques described in Chapters 4–7) that this correspondence is estimated.

4. The stereo vision approach is not restricted to the determination of object point locations but may be extended to include surface parameters or orientation as well as integration with the problem of object motion detection and estimation.

### SIMPLIFIED PRELIMINARY APPROACH

A reduced dimension example is presented prior to delving into the stereo vision problem in general. The "scene," as shown in Figure 2.6, consists of a 2-D plane, indexed by the global coordinates $(x_o, y_o)$. The origin of the global coordinate system is chosen in this example to be the origin of the IP1 image plane. Image points are measured in IP1 and IP2, respectively, with coordinate systems centered in these image planes. The rays emanating from a specific image point in each image plane that intersect at object point $(x_o, y_o)^T$ are shown in Figure 2.6. Thus, the lack of invertibility of the p-p transform is circumvented in this case by the use

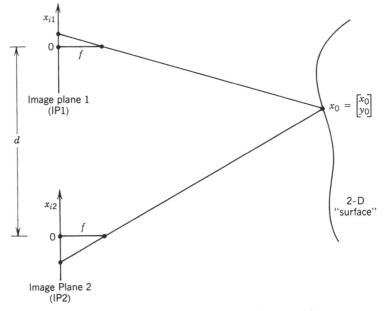

**FIGURE 2.6** Reduced dimension stereo vision example

of two sensors, each containing an object point ray that may be thought of as being "back projected" from an image point.

Triangulation is inherent in stereo vision, as shown clearly in the reduced dimension example of Figure 2.6. A choice of alternate sensor orientations would tend to make solving this example with simple trigonometry tedious, if not impossible. Instead, the p-p model and (global) coordinate transformations will be used to determine the unique object point location.

The reduced dimension p-p transform that relates object points measured with respect to the IP1 system may be formulated in terms of a reduced dimension $2 \times 3$ $P$ matrix. This relation is, in homogeneous coordinates,

$$\begin{bmatrix} wx_i \\ w \end{bmatrix} = \begin{bmatrix} 1 & 0 & 0 \\ 0 & -1/f & 1 \end{bmatrix} \begin{bmatrix} x_o \\ y_o \\ 1 \end{bmatrix} \qquad (2\text{-}31a)$$

which yields, in physical coordinates in the "1-D" image plane location,

$$x_i = \frac{f \ x_o}{-y_o + f} \qquad (2\text{-}31b)$$

*Our difficulty comes in the measurement of object points in IP2.* The origin of the IP2 coordinate system is at $(-d, 0)^T$ with respect to the IP1 system. Therefore, object points measured with respect to the IP2 coordinate system, denoted $x_o^{IP2}$, may be related to object points measured with respect to the IP1 system, denoted $x_o^{IP1}$ or simply $x_o$, by the coordinate conversion equation analogous to Eq. 2-16a:

$$\underline{x}_o^{IP2} = \underline{x}_o + \begin{bmatrix} d \\ 0 \end{bmatrix} \qquad (2\text{-}32)$$

or, in homogeneous coordinates, by analogy with Eq. 2-16b

$$\hat{\underline{x}}_o^{IP2} = \begin{bmatrix} 1 & 0 & d \\ 0 & 1 & 0 \\ 0 & 0 & 1 \end{bmatrix} \hat{\underline{x}}_o^{IP1} \qquad (2\text{-}33)$$

Denote this translation matrix $T^{1-2}$. Therefore, image points, denoted $x_{2i}$, in IP2 may be related to object points measured with respect to the global system as

$$\hat{\underline{x}}_{2i} = p \ T^{1-2} \ \hat{\underline{x}}_o^{IP1} \qquad (2\text{-}34)$$

In physical coordinates the reader should verify that Eq. 2-34 becomes

$$x_{2i} = \frac{f(x_o + d)}{-y_o + f} \qquad (2\text{-}35)$$

Object points in both Eq. 2-35 and Eq. 2-31(b) are now measured with respect to a common coordinate system. Rearranging Eq. 2-35 and Eq. 2-31(b) in terms of $x_o$ and setting these quantities equal yields

$$\frac{x_{2i}(f - y_o)}{f} - d = \frac{x_i(f - y_o)}{f} \qquad (2\text{-}36)$$

We may therefore solve object point distance for $y_o$ as

$$y_o = \frac{-d f + (x_{2i} - x_i) f}{x_{2i} - x_i} \qquad (2\text{-}37)$$

Note that the depth parameter, $y_o$, is solely determined by the quantities $(x_{2i} - x_i)$, $d$, and $f$. The reader should determine the significance of the quantity $(x_{2i} - x_i)$ becoming zero. Once $y_o$ is determined, $x_o$ may now be found using either Eq. 2-31 or Eq. 2-35.

### THE 3-D CASE AND RAMIFICATIONS

We now consider the full dimension (3-D) stereo vision case. It is important to reiterate that the most difficult problem in the development of a stereo vision algorithm is in the determination of the necessary image plane point correspondences. At this point we assume this correspondence has been determined and therefore turn our attention to the geometric and algebraic consequences of the solution.

The general arrangement shown in Figure 2.5 may be described using two or more calibrated sensors, the parameters of each quantified in the form of Eq. 2-22. These parameters are indexed by $k$, where $k = 1,2$, and available as two $3 \times 4$ calibration matrices $A_k$ where

$$A_k = [a_{kij}] \tag{2-38}$$

Therefore, the sensor equations may be written in homogeneous coordinates as:

$$\hat{\underline{x}}_{ik} = A_k \, \hat{\underline{x}}_o \qquad k = 1, 2 \tag{2-39}$$

Since each matrix equation in Eq. 2-39 represents two equations in physical coordinates, we have, using two sensors, the case of four equations and three unknowns $(x_o, y_o, z_o)$. Given two image points (one in each image plane) corresponding to the same object point, expand each of the four linear equations in Eq. 2-39 in physical coordinates. Regrouping terms as coefficients of $x_o$, $y_o$, and $z_o$, a set of four equations in three unknowns is written compactly in matrix notation as (the reader is encouraged to verify this)

$$P \underline{x}_o = \underline{F} \tag{2-40}$$

where the $4 \times 3$ matrix $P$ is

$$P = \begin{bmatrix} a_{111} - a_{131} x_{i1} & a_{112} - a_{132} x_{i1} & a_{113} - a_{133} x_{i1} \\ a_{121} - a_{131} y_{i1} & a_{122} - a_{132} y_{i1} & a_{123} - a_{133} y_{i1} \\ a_{211} - a_{231} x_{i2} & a_{212} - a_{232} x_{i2} & a_{213} - a_{233} x_{i2} \\ a_{221} - a_{231} y_{i2} & a_{222} - a_{232} y_{i2} & a_{223} - a_{233} y_{i2} \end{bmatrix} \tag{2-41}$$

and in physical coordinates the $3 \times 1$ object point that corresponds to image points $\underline{x}_{i1}$ and $\underline{x}_{i2}$ is

$$\underline{x}_o = \begin{bmatrix} x_o \\ y_o \\ z_o \end{bmatrix} \tag{2-42}$$

and the $4 \times 1$ vector $\underline{F}$ is

$$\underline{F} = \begin{bmatrix} a_{134} \, x_{i1} - a_{114} \\ a_{134} \, y_{i1} - a_{124} \\ a_{234} \, x_{i2} - a_{214} \\ a_{234} \, y_{i2} - a_{224} \end{bmatrix} \tag{2-43a}$$

Equation 2-40 may be directly solved for a least squares estimate of $\underline{x}_o$, denoted $\underline{x}_o^e$, by forming the pseudoinverse of $P$, denoted $P^+$, yielding the object point estimate:

$$\underline{x}_o^e = P^+ \underline{F} \qquad (2\text{-}43b)$$

Alternately, the use of the $Q-R$ decomposition approach or the elimination of one equation and a simple matrix inversion approach may be employed.

One interesting observation from Equations 2-40 through 2-43a is that, although we have assumed the knowledge of corresponding image point locations, not all of this information is required to estimate $\underline{x}_o$. We may be able to determine $\underline{x}_o$ using only three of these four equations, assuming that the remaining three equations are linearly independent (see the problems).

There are several other ways to view the stereo vision model. The relationship given in Eq. 2-40, using Eq. 2-41 through Eq. 2-43a in homogeneous coordinates, is

$$[-P|\underline{F}] \, \hat{\underline{x}}_o = 0 \qquad (2\text{-}44)$$

Defining the $4 \times 4$ matrix $C$ as

$$C = [-P|\underline{F}] \qquad (2\text{-}45)$$

Equation 2-44 specifies that, since $C\hat{\underline{x}}_o = 0$, every column of $C^T$ (i.e., the rows of $C$) is orthogonal to $\hat{\underline{x}}_o$. This is the basis for developing *constraints on corresponding image point locations* in a stereo vision system. The elements in $C$ are functions of $a_{kij}$ (the calibration parameters for the two sensor systems), and the corresponding image plane points $(x_{i1}, y_{i1}, x_{i2}, y_{i2})$. The algebraic significance of Eq. 2-44 and Eq. 2-45 is that the columns of $C$ must not span $R^4$. This forces the determinant of $C$ to be zero; that is,

$$|C| = 0 \qquad (2\text{-}46)$$

Expanding this determinant by rows or columns (the reader is advised to verify this) and simplifying the result yields the important result that $x_{i1}$, $y_{i1}$, $x_{i2}$, and $y_{i2}$ are constrained by the single equation

$$x_{i1} \, x_{i2} \, m_1 + x_{i1} \, y_{i1} \, m_2 + x_{i1} \, y_{i2} \, m_3 + x_{i2} \, y_{i1} \, m_4$$
$$+ \, x_{i1} \, m_5 + x_{i2} \, m_6 + y_{i1} \, m_7 + y_{i2} \, m_8 + m_9 = 0 \qquad (2\text{-}47)$$

Equation 2-47 is referred to as a bilinear relationship in the variables $x_i$ and $y_i$. The $m_i$ coefficients in the above equation are, from the determinant expansion, functions of the $a_{kij}$ sensor calibration parameters. This relationship has the geometric *significance that, given a point in one image plane (i.e., $[x_{i1}, y_{i1}]$), the set of corresponding image points in the second image plane are constrained to lie along a line.* This is seen easily by fixing the values of $x_{i1}$ and $x_{i2}$ in Eq. 2-47; the resulting equation in terms of unknowns ($x_{i2}$ and $y_{i2}$) describes a line in 2-D. The exact location of a corresponding image point on this line in the image plane is determined by the choice of object point. Thus, given a point in IP1, the search for the corresponding point in IP2 is restricted to a line in that plane. This is a significant savings in search complexity, considering that the alternative is to search all the points in the other image plane (Hwang & Hall, 1982).

The preceding mathematical results may be explained in a more intuitive fashion graphically. Referring to Figure 2.7, we may develop the constraint by noting that a plane is determined by the three points consisting of the two sensor centers of

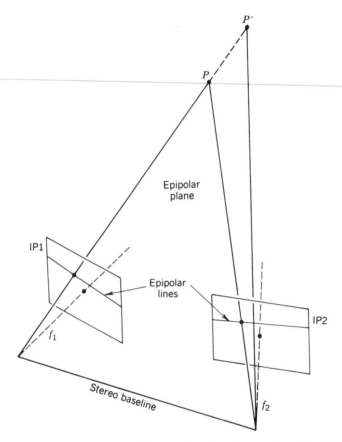

**FIGURE 2.7** Geometric view of the overdetermined nature of equation (2-47).

projection and any other point. Choosing this other point to be in the image plane of either sensor clearly indicates the line segment, which is then formed as the intersection of the second image plane and this plane. Notice that this constraint does not exist if the two centers of projection are coincident. In fact, in this situation stereo vision is computationally impossible. The significance of this is that it constrains the possible geometry of the multiple sensors used in stereo vision. Further examples are explored in the problems.

### STEREO VISION USE OF AN ACTIVE CAMERA (PROJECTOR)— STRUCTURED LIGHT

Alternative stereo vision systems wherein one camera, termed the active camera or projector, is used in conjunction with one or more passive cameras, or sensors are possible. By controlling projected pixel intensities in the active image plane, uncertainty in determining image point correspondences may be reduced. A system that illuminates one point at a time in the active plane may be used to illuminate a small region (ideally an object "point") in 3-D, which in turn is imaged by the passive sensor. Under reasonable assumptions, this point (or region) is easily discerned in the passive image plane.

Most people are familiar with the concept of structured light from experience. For example, automobile headlights projected into a darkened room through venetian blinds are observed to illuminate objects in the room with a series of bending, distorted, and discontinuous lines, as the planes of light emanating from the blinds "fall" on the walls, ceiling, and furniture in the room. The shape or surface-dependent modification of the projected light is evident.

Figure 2.8 shows the results obtained by projecting two patterns onto two different surfaces. These were obtained by using the Surface Mapping Simulator (SMS), the theory of which is described in Labuz and Schalkoff (1985). In Figure 2.8a, the passive image resulting from projecting a rectangular grid of dots onto a 3-D sphere is shown (active image plane points that do not intersect the sphere are not shown; they would intersect another 3-D surface elsewhere in the scene). The distortion of the observed pattern due to the curved surface of the sphere is evident. Given that a rectangular pattern of dots was projected, from the resulting passive image most humans would perceive that the surface under observation is a sphere.

Figure 2.8b shows the effect of projecting a set of concentric circles onto a plane with an oblique orientation with respect to both the active and passive cameras. The passive image allows inferences as to the orientation of this plane. Note also that the use of concentric circles aids in the correspondence problem; the center of this set is a unique point in the passive image. For a more comprehensive look at the use of projected patterns, see Altschuler (1981) and Topa and Schalkoff (1986).

The use of active cameras in these structured light approaches is not without practical difficulties obscured by the simplistic geometrical model. First, there are obvious situations where active stereo vision or structured light is impractical. In satellite imagery, for example, the power requirements would be unrealistic (at least for nonmilitary systems). In an industrial application where lighting and object reflectance properties (see section in this chapter on radiometric image formation, p. 65) may be more carefully controlled, this approach may yield useful results. Second, a scheme that is based on *projecting rays* (or lines or patterns, as described below) assumes that a narrow area of the scene is illuminated (i.e., that the projected radiation does not reflect off scene surfaces and cause the illumination of multiple image regions) and that the imaged point (or small region) in the passive plane may be determined based on intensity information. The latter approach becomes more difficult if the scene contains sources of light other than the projector (e.g., the intensity of ambient light may be greater than that of the projector). Even with these restrictions, structured light enjoys considerable attention in automated visual inspection systems (Frobin & Hierholzer, 1983; Potsmesil, 1979; Sato, Kitagawa, & Fujita, 1982).

The use of active cameras still requires the knowledge of camera calibration procedures. This may be obtained in precisely the same manner for passive sensors—that is, a known object (often a carefully graduated "calibration cube") may be used to determine a set of object-image point pairs.

One of the immediate results using structured light that may be derived from the preceding model is the strategy employed by line-projectors or "slit"-based techniques. Consider the case of an active camera that consists of a projection device coupled with an optical mask that allows the projection of light through a single slit. The projector is modeled as an active camera that projects a set of rays

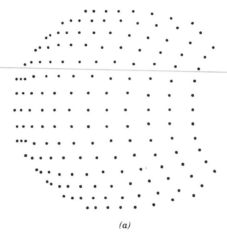

(a)

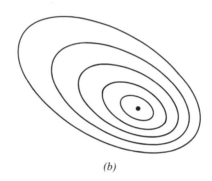

(b)

**FIGURE 2.8**
(a)   3-D sphere with projected dots
(b)   Projection of concentric circles onto plane

emanating from a line in the image plane. A "wedge" in object space is generated. The specific image plane location that generated any given illuminated object point in the scene is not known; we know only that this image point lies on a line in the active image plane. Suppose an image point in the passive plane is observed which corresponds to an object point illuminated by this projector. To determine whether this information alone is sufficient to enable the location of the object point, the following quantities are used:

1. The calibration parameters of both cameras—that is, two sets of equations with known $a_{kij}$ parameters, in the form of Eq. 2-39;
2. A linear constraint between the image points in the active image plane (assumed to be the $k = 1$ camera system)—that is, in homogeneous coordinates an equation of the form:

$$[a \ b \ c]^T \ \hat{\underline{x}}_{i1} = 0 \qquad (2\text{-}50)$$

3. An illuminated image point in the passive plane $(x_{i2}, y_{i2})$.

From the above information it is apparent that, in physical coordinates, the passive image plane contributes two linear equations from Eq. 2-39 and the active image plane contributes one linear constraint from the combination of Eq. 2-39 and Eq. 2-50. Since there are three unknowns $(x_o, y_o, z_o)^T$, if this set of equations is linearly independent the solution may be found by matrix inversion. It is left to the reader to derive the resulting estimation equations.

## ■ IMAGE PLANE-IMAGE PLANE (GEOMETRIC) TRANSFORMATIONS

### IMAGE-IMAGE GEOMETRIC MODELS (2-D TO 2-D)

Up to this point, geometric imaging concerns involving transformations of object points into image points and the ramifications of the inverse of this relationship have been emphasized. Consider now the related modeling problem of relating changes in the 3-D scene or in the imaging geometry to changes in the image plane coordinates. The form of this model is shown in Figure 2.9. In physical coordinates, the 2-D image plane point locations are indexed by

$$x_i = \begin{bmatrix} y_i \\ z_i \end{bmatrix} = \begin{bmatrix} x_1 \\ x_2 \end{bmatrix} \quad \text{and} \quad x_i' = \begin{bmatrix} y_i' \\ z_i' \end{bmatrix} = \begin{bmatrix} x_1' \\ x_2' \end{bmatrix} \qquad (2\text{-}51)$$

where the ' denotes corresponding image points after the change.

The development of this model relies on the 3-D coordinate transformations developed in sections A and B. Looking ahead, this model is geometrically based and is used in a broad spectrum of applications. It is typically expressed in the form

$$f'(\underline{x}_i) = f(\underline{x}_i') = f[g(\underline{x}_i, \underline{a})] \qquad (2\text{-}52a)$$

where $f'$ is the geometrically perturbed or "distorted" image, formed by a coordinate transformation in the plane (sometimes referred to as a "planar transform") of the form

$$\underline{x}_i' = \underline{g}(\underline{x}_i, \underline{a}) \qquad (2\text{-}52b)$$

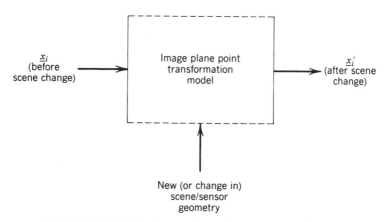

FIGURE 2.9  Model for image plane to image plane transformation

The expression $g(\underline{x}_i, \underline{a})$ is approximated as a function of a set of parameters, denoted by $\underline{a}$. An example is the affine transform (Appendix 1). Under other suitable geometric assumptions, the exact transform for modeling $g$ is the nonlinear perspective transform, where the image points are related in physical coordinates by

$$
\begin{bmatrix} y'_i \\ z'_i \end{bmatrix} = \begin{bmatrix} \dfrac{a_1 y_i + a_2 z_i + a_3}{c_1 y_i + c_2 z_t + c_3} \\ \dfrac{b_1 y_i + b_2 z_i + b_3}{c_1 y_i + c_2 z_i + c_3} \end{bmatrix} \tag{2-53}
$$

The parameters $a_i$, $b_i$, and $c_i$ are, in general, nonlinear functions of the camera orientation and parameters (e.g., $f$), the magnification ratio, and the parameters of the particular transformations (e.g., translations and rotations) considered. Note that the affine transform described in Appendix 1 is a degenerate case (or approximation) of the perspective transform where coefficients $c_i = c_2 = 0$ and $c_3 = 1$.

*The geometric transformation-based model in Eq. 2-52a models changes in intensity only through mapping of coordinate intensities.* There is no attempt to model the intensity changes due to different sensor or scene radiometric characteristics (e.g., spectral response). This is not a significant limitation, since (as we show in Chapter 4) the images may also be processed using a greylevel transformation to adjust for this effect.

Most important, the non-1:1 mapping of geometric transformations on discrete (sampled) data points introduces additional complexity in actually carrying out the transformation in Eq. 2-52a.

## MODEL DERIVATION

A physical basis for derivation of the model involves forming the original image from 3-D to 2-D transformation of object points into image points and then deriving the series of rotations and translations in 3-D space that correspond to the scene or viewing geometry change. Following determination of the new 3-D to 2-D point mappings, the original (unperturbed) image plane coordinates are related to those of the perturbed image. This is shown in Hall (1979). The functional form of the resulting coordinate transformation is that of the perspective transform. Shortcomings of models obtained in this manner are the inability to represent frame to frame occlusion effects as well as radiometric changes in 3-D space that change the image plane intensities. Models for the latter are considered in the section on radiometric image formation.

The model we develop has two major application areas:

Application 1: *Modeling the image plane-image plane transformations due to a change in viewing conditions.* This includes changes in sensor parameters ($f$ in our model) as well as viewing geometry (i.e., sensor geometric orientation). This allows the case, for example, of relating images of a stationary scene obtained by a moving sensor.

Application 2: *Modeling the movement or "motion" of 3-D object points and relating their positions in the image plane (using the p-p transform) before and after the motion* (as a function of the object point motion parameters). This approach is extended in Chapter 5 for the estimation of the 3-D motion of rigid objects.

The model development procedure is easily described by the following three steps:

1. Compute, using the p-p transform, the mapping of object points in the image plane;
2. Compute the same, for the corresponding object point location that results from the change; and
3. Relate the results from these two computations.

Figure 2.4 shows the coordinate system orientation, where the image plane coordinates are indexed by $(y_i, z_i)^T$ and the scene depth is measured with global coordinate $x_o$. Assume, for simplicity, that the relationship of the origin of the global coordinate system and the image plane coordinate system orientation is a simple translational offset by a vector of parameters $(d_x, d_y, d_z)^T$; that is, the origin of the image plane-centric system is at $(d_x, d_y, d_z)^T$ in the global coordinate system. There are, in this model, no other translations or rotations needed to bring the coordinate systems into alignment.

Initially assuming that $d_x = d_y = d_z = 0$, the p-p transform in homogeneous coordinates for the coincident image and global coordinate systems becomes

$$\begin{bmatrix} wy_i \\ wz_i \\ w \end{bmatrix} = \begin{bmatrix} 0 & 1 & 0 & 0 \\ 0 & 0 & 1 & 0 \\ -1/f & 0 & 0 & 1 \end{bmatrix} \begin{bmatrix} x_o \\ y_o \\ z_o \\ 1 \end{bmatrix} \qquad (2\text{-}54)$$

We first consider a simplified case of Application 1, namely a change in the camera focal length, $f$. This may occur, for example, in automatic inspection, where the sensor is autonomously adjusted to control field of view and the size of the part under observation. A change in focal length of the camera from $f$ to $f'$ yields new image points (denoted with a $'$), which correspond to the original (unchanged) object points as

$$\begin{bmatrix} w'y_i' \\ w'z_i' \\ w' \end{bmatrix} = \begin{bmatrix} 0 & 1 & 0 & 0 \\ 0 & 0 & 1 & 0 \\ -1/f' & 0 & 0 & 1 \end{bmatrix} \begin{bmatrix} x_o \\ y_o \\ z_o \\ 1 \end{bmatrix} \qquad (2\text{-}55)$$

Observe from Eq. 2-54 and Eq. 2-55 that the only change in $P$ is in the homogeneous coordinate scaling factor, $w$. Intuitively, this might have been expected. An approximate relationship may be obtained by equating terms for $x_o$ in Eq. 2-54 and Eq. 2-55 yielding

$$f(w - 1) = f'(w' - 1) \qquad (2\text{-}56)$$

For large magnification ratios and reasonably small focal length changes, $|w| \gg 1$ and $|w'| \gg 1$, and therefore Eq. 2-56 may be approximated as

$$f w = f' w' \qquad (2\text{-}57)$$

More significantly, the relationship of image plane points before and after the focal length change is, with this approximation, written in homogeneous coordinates as

$$\begin{bmatrix} w'y'_i \\ w'z'_i \\ w' \end{bmatrix} = \begin{bmatrix} 1 & 0 & 0 \\ 0 & 1 & 0 \\ 0 & 0 & f/f' \end{bmatrix} \begin{bmatrix} w & y_i \\ w & z_i \\ w & \end{bmatrix} \tag{2-58}$$

Although this result is useful in itself, we relate this effect (a scaling) with a similar effect that would be produced by the translation of an object point. Given the location of an object point (i.e., $[x_o, y_o z_o]^T$), which then moves in the $+x$, $+y$, and $+z$ directions along a vector $(d_x, d_y, d_z)^T$ to a new location $(x_o + d_x, y_o + d_y, z_o + d_z)^T$, we seek to, as in the previous case, relate image plane coordinate changes. This is done with homogeneous coordinates. The object point perturbation may be written as

$$\hat{\underline{x}}'_o = T \hat{\underline{x}}_o \tag{2-59}$$

where $T$ is a $4 \times 4$ translation matrix of the form

$$T = \begin{bmatrix} 1 & 0 & 0 & d_x \\ 0 & 1 & 0 & d_y \\ 0 & 0 & 1 & d_z \\ 0 & 0 & 0 & 1 \end{bmatrix} \tag{2-60}$$

Computing image points $\underline{x}_i$ and $\underline{x}_i'$ corresponding to this perturbation yields a relationship between image points that is nonlinear even in homogeneous coordinates (the reader should verify this). This is accomplished by expanding

$$\hat{\underline{x}}_i = P \hat{\underline{x}}_o \tag{2-61a}$$

and

$$\hat{\underline{x}}'_i = PT \hat{\underline{x}}_o \tag{2-61b}$$

in physical coordinates and eliminating object point terms. Therefore, we introduce the concept of *superhomogeneous coordinates* for image plane points, which, as in the case of the homogeneous representation, results in an increase in dimensionality but allows a linear representation. The relationship in Eq. 2-61 may be written as

$$\begin{bmatrix} w' & y'_i \\ w' & z'_i \\ w' & \\ 1 & \end{bmatrix} = \begin{bmatrix} 1 & 0 & 0 & d_y \\ 0 & 1 & 0 & d_z \\ 0 & 0 & 1 & -d_x/f \\ 0 & 0 & 0 & 1 \end{bmatrix} \begin{bmatrix} w & y_i \\ w & z_i \\ w & \\ 1 & \end{bmatrix} \tag{2-62a}$$

or, in superhomogeneous coordinates, (denoted with a $\hat{}$ )

$$\hat{\underline{x}}'_i = \overline{T} \hat{\underline{x}}_i \tag{2-62b}$$

where $\overline{T}$ is a translation matrix relating *image plane coordinates* in superhomogeneous coordinates and shown in Eq. 2-62a.

NOTICE

1. The equation for $w'$ involves the addition of the quantity $(-d_x/f)$. This is the part of the model that requires superhomogeneous coordinates.
2. The case of $d_y = d_z = 0$ (i.e., relative motion of the coordinate systems along the optical axis) yields results similar to the change of focal length case

of Eq. 2-58. Both changes accomplish a scale change. This is intuitively obvious, since a translation of a point away from the image plane yields scaling effects similar to a change of $f$.

3. The relationship in Eq. 2-62$a$ implicitly involves the object point distance from the image plane through the magnification ratio in $w$.

As an alternative to the translation of object points, consider the case of translation of the global coordinate system. For example, if the origin of the global system were translated by the vector $(-d_x, -d_y, -d_z)^T$, object points measured in the newly centered coordinate system would be given by Eq. 2-59 and Eq. 2-60. This is the *symmetry argument*: Instead of computing the coordinate transformations and subsequent image plane point perturbations due to a movement or motion of the camera, we instead recognize that the same effect could have been achieved by perturbing object points with the *inverse* relationship.

A rotation of either an object point or the image plane is handled similarly with the notable exception that rotations about points other than the origin of the image plane must be treated with special care. These rotations are significant since they correspond to the effects of camera mount angular control (pan and tilt) signals.

The symmetry argument and the models it produces must be examined carefully. First, the (unmodified) model applies to *all* object points in the scene, thus precluding application of the model to cases of independently moving points or objects. Second, only object points are considered, not arbitrary objects or surfaces. In the case of the latter, it is easy to envision cases where the object point correspondence assumed in Eq. 2-61 does not hold. For example, a change of camera orientation may cause part of the scene to occlude other parts. Nonetheless, the use of this principle allows the solution of an otherwise formidable problem.

The use of homogeneous and superhomogeneous coordinates, although handy for succinct mathematical description, is even more significant when considering composite transformations. For example, in developing a methodology to adjust the camera focal length ($f$) for objects that are moving away from the camera, an objective could be to minimize the image plane changes. Estimating $d_x$ in Eq. 2-62, a combination of Eq. 2-62 and Eq. 2-58 yields the basis for a control strategy.

# ■ APPLICATIONS

## CAMERA CONTROL MODELING AND ALGORITHM DEVELOPMENT

The modeling of this section is extended to the case of camera pan and tilt motion. This example is useful for several reasons:

1. It occurs frequently in practice, since many cameras are mounted on mounts or platforms that do not translate but rather pan (i.e., rotate about the $z$-axis in Figure 2.4) and tilt (i.e., rotate about the $y$-axis in Figure 2.4) on the basis of applied control signals. It is necessary to know the arrangement of particular mount gimbals, since it is possible for the panning platform to contain the tilting platform or vice versa. The mathematical significance of this information is reflected in the order in which we arrange the pan and tilt transformation matrices.

2. It provides us with a comprehensive example of the actual computation of the matrices used in the model and the explicit relation of the image plane coordinates before and after.

3. It allows development of reasonable engineering approximations that significantly reduce the complexity of the equations and provide intuitively satisfying results.

4. It provides the framework for an example in camera control.

This example is derived from Dzialo and Schalkoff (1986). More comprehensive experimental results may be found in this reference. Note that the image plane coordinates are chosen according to Figure 2.4 and are $(y_i, z_i)$, not $(x_i, y_i)$. Also, components of vectors shown in homogeneous and superhomogeneous coordinates are understood to be multiplied by the respective scaling factors; that is, it is no longer necessary to write component $y_i'$ in Eq. 2-63 as $w_i' y_i'$. This simplifies the notation considerably.

Our initial objective is to determine the image plane point perturbation effects of panning and tilting the image plane shown in Figure 2.10a. Complex transformations result since the panning and tilting of the image plane are about the global coordinate system axes. If the rotations were about the image plane-centric system,

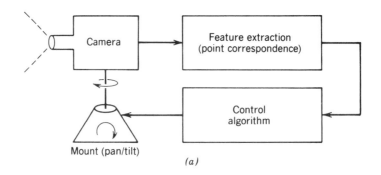

*(a)*

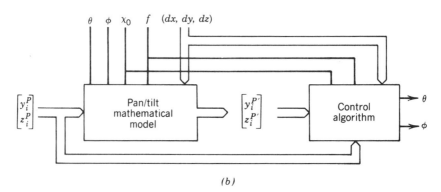

*(b)*

**FIGURE 2.10** System description and salient model
(a) Physical system
(b) Closed-loop mathematical model

the derivation would be considerably simpler. The overall approach is

1. Compute the original (unperturbed) image plane point locations as a function of object point locations (the p-p transform).
2. Translate the image plane coordinate system to the global coordinate system origin (about which the pan and tilt rotations occur). Note that both coordinate systems were chosen to be simply related by a translation, whereas in practice other transformations may be involved.
3. Perform the rotations that correspond to the pan and tilt operations.
4. Transform the results of step 3 back to the original image plane location. This transform is the inverse of that used in step 2.
5. Compute the new image plane locations as a function of the object point locations.
6. Relate the image plane coordinates in step 5 to those in step 1.

Recall that regardless of the object/sensor movement, the general form of the image-plane to image-plane geometric model is

$$
\begin{bmatrix} y_i' \\ z_i' \\ w_i' \\ 1 \end{bmatrix} = \begin{bmatrix} a_{11} a_{12} a_{13} a_{14} \\ a_{21} a_{22} a_{23} a_{24} \\ a_{31} a_{32} a_{33} a_{34} \\ 0 \;\; 0 \;\; 0 \;\; 1 \end{bmatrix} \begin{bmatrix} y_i \\ z_i \\ w_i \\ 1 \end{bmatrix}
\tag{2-63}
$$

where the $a_{ij}$ parameters in Eq. 2-63 are functions of the sensor geometry and object/sensor motion.

The system consists of a camera mounted on a controlled pan/tilt camera mount, an image processing system to extract the required signals from the camera (this is the subject of Chapters 3–7), and a computer controller interface to pan or tilt the mount. This closed-loop system is shown in Figure 2.10. The model needed relates the original image point (physical) coordinates, denoted $(y_i^P, z_i^P)$ and the physical coordinates after the pan/tilt movement, denoted $(y_i^{P'}, z_i^{P'})$. This transformation is dependent on the focal length of the camera $(f)$, the mount pan $(\phi)$ and tilt $(\theta)$ angles, the offset between the global origin and the image plane origin $(d_x, d_y, d_z)$, the original object $(x_o, y_o, z_o)$ and image $(y_i, z_i)$ coordinates, and the object $(x_o', y_o', z_o')$ and image $(y_i', z_i')$ coordinates after the pan/tilt movement.

First, the transformation for the mount pan (rotation about the $z$-axis) is determined. Using the symmetry argument, the effect of a pan by the camera through angle $-\phi$ is equivalent to rotating the object by $\phi$. Rotation of the object coordinates requires a transformation from a camera coordinate system to the global (or mount) system, the rotation transformation, and finally an inverse transformation back to camera-centric coordinates. This is shown below in homogeneous (object) coordinates:

$$
\begin{bmatrix} x_o' \\ y_o' \\ z_o' \\ 1 \end{bmatrix} = \begin{bmatrix} 1 & 0 & 0 & -d_x \\ 0 & 1 & 0 & -d_y \\ 0 & 0 & 1 & -d_z \\ 0 & 0 & 0 & 1 \end{bmatrix} \begin{bmatrix} \cos\phi & -\sin\phi & 0 & 0 \\ \sin\phi & \cos\phi & 0 & 0 \\ 0 & 0 & 1 & 0 \\ 0 & 0 & 0 & 1 \end{bmatrix} \begin{bmatrix} 1 & 0 & 0 & d_x \\ 0 & 1 & 0 & d_y \\ 0 & 0 & 1 & d_z \\ 0 & 0 & 0 & 1 \end{bmatrix} \begin{bmatrix} x_o \\ y_o \\ z_o \\ 1 \end{bmatrix}
$$

$$
= \begin{bmatrix} \cos\phi & -\sin\phi & 0 & (d_x\cos\phi & -d_y\sin\phi & -d_x) \\ \sin\phi & \cos\phi & 0 & (d_x\sin\phi & +d_y\cos\phi & -d_y) \\ 0 & 0 & 1 & 0 \\ 0 & 0 & 0 & 1 \end{bmatrix} \begin{bmatrix} x_o \\ y_o \\ z_o \\ 1 \end{bmatrix}
\tag{2-64}
$$

The p-p transform converts these perturbed object points into perturbed image points via

$$\begin{bmatrix} y_i' \\ z_i' \\ w_i' \end{bmatrix} = \begin{bmatrix} 0 & 1 & 0 & 0 \\ 0 & 0 & 1 & 0 \\ -1/f & 0 & 0 & 1 \end{bmatrix} \begin{bmatrix} x_o' \\ y_o' \\ z_o' \\ 1 \end{bmatrix}$$

(2-65)

This yields

$$y_i' = (x_o + d_x)\sin\phi + (y_o + d_y)\cos\phi - d_y$$

$$z_i' = z_o$$

(2-66)

$$w_i' = -[(x_o + d_x)\cos\phi - (y_o + d_y)\sin\phi - d_x + f]/f$$

Originally, $y_i = y_o$, $z_i = z_o$, and $x_o = f(1 - w_i)$. Combining these equations yields

$$y_i' = (f - fw_i + d_x)\sin\phi + (y_i + d_y)\cos\phi - d_y$$

$$z_i' = z_i$$

(2-67)

$$w_i' = w_i\cos\phi + [y_i\sin\phi - (f + d_x)\cos\phi + d_y\sin\phi + d_x + f]/f$$

Thus, the relationship in superhomogeneous coordinates is

$$\begin{bmatrix} y_i' \\ z_i' \\ w_i' \\ 1 \end{bmatrix} = \begin{bmatrix} \cos\phi & 0 & -f\sin\phi & A \\ 0 & 1 & 0 & 0 \\ \sin\phi/f & 0 & \cos\phi & B \\ 0 & 0 & 0 & 1 \end{bmatrix} \begin{bmatrix} y_i \\ z_i \\ w_i \\ 1 \end{bmatrix}$$

(2-68)

$$A = (f + d_x)\sin\phi + d_y\cos\phi - d_y$$

$$B = [-(f + d_x)\cos\phi + d_y\sin\phi + d_x + f]/f$$

The transformation for the camera mount tilt is derived in an analogous manner. "Tilting" the mount corresponds to a rotation of angle $-\theta$ about the y-axis. Using the symmetry argument, this is the same as rotating the object points by $\theta$. The overall transformation is shown below

$$\begin{bmatrix} x_o' \\ y_o' \\ z_o' \\ 1 \end{bmatrix} = \begin{bmatrix} 1 & 0 & 0 & -d_x \\ 0 & 1 & 0 & -d_y \\ 0 & 0 & 1 & -d_z \\ 0 & 0 & 0 & 1 \end{bmatrix} \begin{bmatrix} \cos\theta & 0 & \sin\theta & 0 \\ 0 & 1 & 0 & 0 \\ -\sin\theta & 0 & \cos\theta & 0 \\ 0 & 0 & 0 & 1 \end{bmatrix} \begin{bmatrix} 1 & 0 & 0 & d_x \\ 0 & 1 & 0 & d_y \\ 0 & 0 & 1 & d_z \\ 0 & 0 & 0 & 1 \end{bmatrix} \begin{bmatrix} x_o \\ y_o \\ z_o \\ 1 \end{bmatrix}$$

$$= \begin{bmatrix} \cos\theta & 0 & \sin\theta & (d_x\cos\theta + d_z\sin\theta - d_x) \\ 0 & 1 & 0 & 0 \\ -\sin\theta & 0 & \cos\theta & (-d_x\sin\theta + d_z\cos\theta - d_z) \\ 0 & 0 & 0 & 1 \end{bmatrix} \begin{bmatrix} x_o \\ y_o \\ z_o \\ 1 \end{bmatrix}$$

(2-69)

Using the p-p transformation to find these object points in the image plane yields

$$y_i' = y_o$$

$$z_i' = -(x_o + d_x)\sin\theta + (z_o + d_z)\cos\theta - d_z$$

$$w_i' = -[(x_o + d_x)\cos\theta + (z_o + d_z)\sin\theta - d_x - f]/f$$

Recall, originally, $y_i = y_o$, $z_i = z_o$, and $x_o = f(1 - w_i)$. The new image points may be related to these by

$$y_i' = y_i$$

$$z_i' = (fw_i - f - d_x)\sin\theta + (z_i + d_z)\cos\theta - d_z$$

$$w_i' = w_i\cos\theta - [(z_i + d_z)\sin\theta + (f + d_x)\cos\theta - d_x - f]/f$$

Thus, we represent this relationship in superhomogeneous coordinates as

$$\begin{bmatrix} y_i' \\ z_i' \\ w_i' \\ 1 \end{bmatrix} = \begin{bmatrix} 1 & 0 & 0 & 0 \\ 0 & \cos\theta & f\sin\theta & C \\ 0 & -\sin\theta/f & \cos\theta & D \\ 0 & 0 & 0 & 1 \end{bmatrix} \begin{bmatrix} y_i \\ z_i \\ w_i \\ 1 \end{bmatrix} \tag{2-70}$$

$$C = -(f + d_x)\sin\theta + d_z\cos\theta - d_z$$

$$D = [-(f + d_x)\cos\theta - d_z\sin\theta + d_x + f]/f$$

Since the transformations are linear in superhomogeneous coordinates, the image plane transformation of a pan/tilt camera mount can be determined by multiplying the corresponding matrices. Assuming the mount pan then tilts (i.e., it is a "pan over tilt" configuration), the image coordinates are first multiplied by the panning matrix Eq. 2-68 and then by the tilt matrix Eq. 2-70 as follows:

$$\begin{bmatrix} y_i' \\ z_i' \\ w_i' \\ 1 \end{bmatrix} = \begin{bmatrix} 1 & 0 & 0 & 0 \\ 0 & \cos\theta & f\sin\theta & C \\ 0 & -\sin\theta/f & \cos\theta & D \\ 0 & 0 & 0 & 1 \end{bmatrix} \begin{bmatrix} \cos\phi & 0 & -f\sin\phi & A \\ 0 & 1 & 0 & 0 \\ \sin\phi/f & 0 & \cos\phi & B \\ 0 & 0 & 0 & 1 \end{bmatrix} \begin{bmatrix} y_i \\ z_i \\ w_i \\ 1 \end{bmatrix}$$

$$= \begin{bmatrix} \cos\phi & 0 & -f\sin\phi & A \\ \sin\theta\sin\phi & \cos\theta & f\sin\theta\cos\phi & E \\ \cos\theta\sin\phi/f & -\sin\theta/f & \cos\theta\cos\phi & F \\ 0 & 0 & 0 & 1 \end{bmatrix} \begin{bmatrix} y_i \\ z_i \\ w_i \\ 1 \end{bmatrix} \tag{2-71}$$

$$E = -(f + d_x)\cos\phi\sin\theta + d_y\sin\phi\sin\theta + d_z\cos\theta - d_z$$

$$F = [-(f + d_x)\cos\phi\cos\theta + d_y\sin\phi\cos\theta - d_z\sin\theta + d_x + f]/f$$

To obtain the physical coordinates of the new image points, each component is divided by $w_i'$, yielding

$$y_i^{P'} = (y_i\cos\phi - w_i f\sin\phi + A)/G$$

$$z_i^{P'} = (y_i\sin\theta\sin\phi + z_i\cos\theta + fw_i\sin\theta\cos\phi + E)/G \tag{2-72}$$

$$G = (y_i\cos\theta\sin\phi - z_i\sin\theta + fw_i\cos\theta\cos\phi + fF)/f$$

Expressing $y_i$ and $z_i$ in physical coordinates yields

$$y_i^{P'} = (y_i^P\cos\phi - f\sin\phi + A/w_i)/H$$

$$z_i^{P'} = (y_i^P\sin\theta\sin\phi + z_i^P\cos\theta + f\sin\theta\cos\phi + E/w_i)/H \tag{2-73}$$

$$H = [y_i^P\cos\theta\sin\phi - z_i^P\sin\theta + f\cos\theta\cos\phi + (fF/w_i)]/f$$

The resulting transformation may be written as a linear relationship in superhomogeneous coordinates but is nonlinear in physical coordinates. We note this transformation is dependent on the focal length of the camera ($f$), the distance from the object to the camera ($x_o$), the offset between the platform origin and the lens center origin ($d_x$, $d_y$, $d_z$), the pan angle ($\phi$), and the tilt angle ($\theta$).

In order to use this model for camera control, the original image point physical coordinates ($y_i^p$, $z_i^p$) and the transformed physical coordinates ($y_i^{p'}$, $z_i^{p'}$) can be measured directly. The focal length and the object distance can be estimated, as described in Dzialo and Schalkoff (1986). The offset vector ($d_x$, $d_y$, $d_z$)$^T$ would be needed in order to form a control algorithm to estimate the pan ($\phi$) and tilt ($\theta$) angles. These offsets, as might be expected, are not easily obtained since it is impractical to measure inside the camera case. However, an important result is that their effect is minimized in systems with large magnification ratios—that is, large $x_o/f$. For example, if the object distance, $x_o$, is 300 feet (100 meters) and the focal length, $f$, is 100 millimeters, then the magnification ratio $x_o/f = 1000$. Since $w_i = -(x_o/f) + 1$, $w_i$ is approximated by $-x_o/f$, and therefore $1/w_i$ becomes insignificant in the above equations. This is the key to development of practical control strategies.

Using this "large magnification ratio" assumption, the relationship between physical coordinates is

$$y_i^{p'} = (y_i^p \cos\phi - f\sin\phi + A')/H'$$

$$z_i^{p'} = (y_i^p\sin\theta\sin\phi + z_i^p\cos\theta + f\sin\theta\cos\phi + E')/H' \qquad (2\text{-}74)$$

$$A' = -[(f + d_x)\sin\phi + d_y(\cos\phi - 1)]\, f/x_o$$

$$E' = -[-(f + d_x)\cos\phi\sin\theta + d_y\sin\phi\sin\theta + d_z(\cos\theta - 1)]\, f/x_o$$

$$H' = (y_i^p\cos\theta\sin\phi - z_i^p\sin\theta + f\cos\theta\cos\phi + fF')/f$$

$$F' = -[-(f + d_x)\cos\theta\cos\phi + d_y\sin\phi\cos\theta - d_z\sin\theta + d_x + f]/x_o$$

The physical image plane coordinate relationship in Eq. 2-74 may be simplified by using small angle approximations and neglecting second-order effects. (The problems consider a trigonometric interpretation of this.) This yields

$$y_i^{p'} = y_i^p - f\tan\phi$$

$$z_i^{p'} = y_i^p\tan\theta\tan\phi + z_i^p + f\tan\theta \qquad (2\text{-}75)$$

Equation 2-75 is used to estimate the respective mount pan and tilt control angles necessary to recenter object points in the camera field of view as

$$\phi = \arctan[-(y_i^{p'} - y_i^p)/f]$$

$$\theta = \arctan[(z_i^{p'} - z_i^p)/(y_i^p\tan\phi + f)] \qquad (2\text{-}76)$$

In order to see the effects that the offsets ($d_x$, $d_y$, $d_z$,)$^T$, location of $y_i^p$ and $z_i^p$, and magnification ratio have on the physical coordinate perturbations, plots of the exact and approximated relationships are shown. A summary of the cases is shown in Table 2-1. Figure 2.11 shows the effect that different offsets have when the magnification ratio is small. Equation 2-68 was plotted without an offset (case 1) and with an offset of five times the focal length (case 2). Figure 2.12 shows the

■ **TABLE 2-1**
Table of cases plotted in Figures 2.11, 2.12, and 2.13 ($f = 0.1$)

| | $x_o$ | magnification ratio | offset $d_x = d_y = d_z$ | $y_i^P, z_i^P$ |
|---|---|---|---|---|
| Case 1 | 0.2 | 2 | 0 | 0,0 |
| Case 2 | 0.2 | 2 | $5f$ | 0,0 |
| Case 3 | 1.0 | 10 | $5f$ | 0,0 |
| Case 4 | 10 | 100 | $5f$ | 0,0 |
| Case 5 | 10 | 100 | $5f$ | $0.5f$,0 |

image perturbation versus the pan angle with different magnification ratios. As the magnification ratio increases (i.e., $x\phi/f = 100$), the relationship in Figure 2.12 approaches that of $y = -f\tan\phi$, which was derived in Eq. 2-76 under the large magnification ratio assumption. Figure 2.13 demonstrates the effect of the object not being centered in the image plane. In case 5, $y_i^p$ is located one-half the focal length away from the origin; in case 4, $y_i^p$ is centered at the origin. Thus, the image

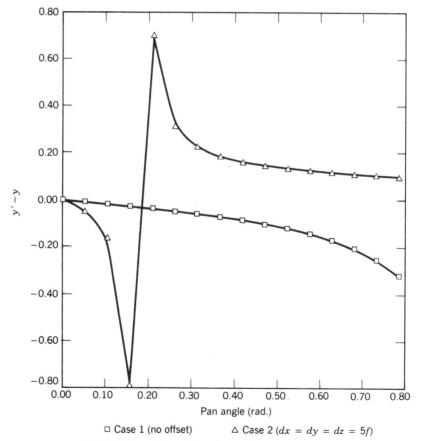

**FIGURE 2.11** Offset effects for small magnification ratio

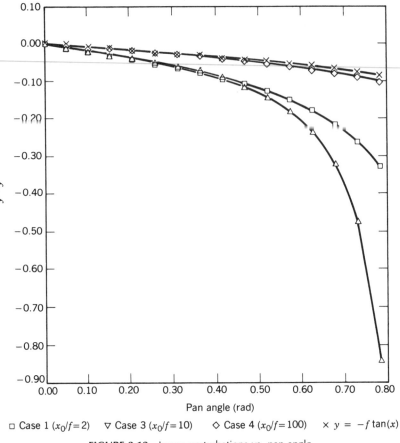

**FIGURE 2.12** Image perturbations vs. pan angle

plane perturbation effects of significantly noncentered object motion cannot be modeled as simple transformations (i.e., approximated by $-f\tan\phi$). Note that this result may be derived from the perspective-projective model and occurs even in large magnification ratio environments.

## GEOMETRIC CORRECTION AND REGISTRATION

Other applications exist wherein geometric image changes are of fundamental interest. Two such cases are introduced here. A new image geometric distortion model is introduced which does not rely on a knowledge of camera parameters or a priori known geometric transformation parameters (e.g., rotation angles $\theta$ and $\phi$).

Perspective correction of imagery is a significant problem. Given two images of the same scene, perhaps taken by sensors with different or time-varying orientations, it is desirable to correct one of the images to the viewpoint of the other. This is particularly important in applications involving multiple sensors that are geometrically distributed, such as those that might be found in industrial and tactical applications. The integration of this often redundant and noisy sensor information

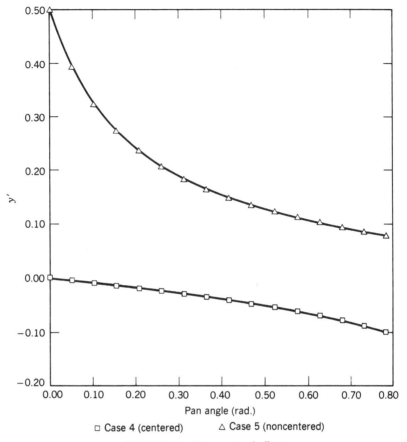

**FIGURE 2.13**  Non-centered effects

("sensor fusion") to achieve higher-level conclusions is important. Correction is a necessary prerequisite in applications where greylevel change detection (perhaps leading to higher-level conclusions regarding possible underlying scene changes) is the processing goal. A *polynomial warp model* is developed and employed to compensate for the geometrical changes resulting from change of viewing angles, such as might occur in satellite imagery with different satellite-earth relative orientations. The origin of the polynomial warp model is somewhat different in that a "rubber sheet" distortion of the image plane is assumed. This may simulate the "pincushion" and "barrel" distortion resulting from vidicon sensor tube curvature and nonideal geometrical optics. This correction is often crucial in the use of nonmetric cameras (Karara, 1980) for close range photogrammetry. "Pincushion" and "barrel" distortion are illustrated in Figure 2.14. Models of additional flexibility (and modeling capability) for nonideal sensor characteristics including specific functional forms and parameters for lens distortion may be found in Karara (1980).

## CONTROL POINTS AND PARAMETER ESTIMATION

To achieve geometric distortion correction, two entities are required:

**1.** A mathematical model that describes the distortion; and

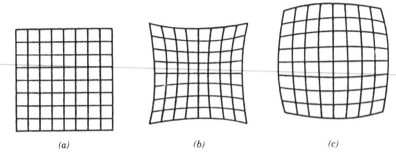

(a)                     (b)                   (c)

**FIGURE 2.14**  Example of geometric distortion
(a)  Original grid
(b)  Pincushion distortion
(c)  Barrel distortion

2. A set of corresponding image points of the form $(x, w)$ where the $2 \times 1$ vector $x$ represents location of the undistorted image plane point and $w$ represents the vector location of the distorted (or actually imaged) point. These points are frequently termed "control" points.

The correction process starts by assuming two images are given (although a set larger than two is theoretically possible). These may be images taken by sensors with different geometric orientations and in different spectral ranges. For example, a visible image and an infrared (or IR) (Gibson, 1978) image, or a visible image and an image produced by an imaging radar (Wong, 1977) may be given. These images are represented by functions $f_1(x)$ and $f_2(w)$, where image 1 is recorded in the $(x_1, x_2)$ coordinate system and image $f_2$ is recorded using the $(w_1, w_2)$ coordinate system. A relationship between the coordinate systems is used to relate these two image functions. Note that we do not attempt to relate the intensities in the two images; often this is impossible. Consequences of the usually discrete nature of the pixel indices in spatially sampled imagery are temporarily ignored. The independent spatial variables used in the two coordinate systems are related by

$$x_1 = g_1(w_1, w_2)$$

and                                                             (2-77)

$$x_2 = g_2(w_1, w_2)$$

A simple example of this relationship and control points are shown in Figure 2.15.

In previous sections, the perspective and affine transforms were used as realizations of the geometric distortion function. Here, the $g_i$ functions are approximated by $N^{\text{th}}$ order 2-D polynomials, yielding the so-called *polynomial warp model*. Notice no assumptions regarding the viewing geometry or the underlying nature of the geometric distortion are necessary. The degree of the 2-D polynomial is often selected by empirical methods or, as shown in the following discussion, on the basis of available control point limitations.

The polynomial warp relationship is

$$x_1 = \sum_{i=0}^{N} \sum_{J=0}^{N} k_{ij}^1 \, w_1^i \, w_2^j \tag{2-78a}$$

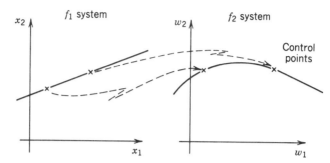

**FIGURE 2.15** Image registration geometric distortion model and control points

and

$$x_2 = \sum_{i=0}^{N} \sum_{j=0}^{N} k_{ij}^2 \, w_1^i \, w_2^j \tag{2-78b}$$

Given a set of $m$ corresponding control points in the $x$- and $w$-based coordinate systems of the form:

$$(x_i, w_i) \qquad i = 1,2,3 \ldots m$$

that is, point pairs of the form

$$(x_{1i}, x_{2i}, w_{1i}, w_{2i})$$

the relationship in Eq. 2-78 is expanded. This allows estimation of the polynomial coefficients—that is, the $k_{ij}^1$ and $k_{ij}^2$ variables that are used to fit the control point set to the 2-D polynomial of order $N$. It is left for the reader to derive these estimation equations and the corresponding constraints on control points for a least squares solution formulation for the general case of a polynomial of order $N$. A simple derivation for the case $N = 2$ (a so-called 2nd order warp) is shown below. For $N = 2$, for the $k^{\text{th}}$ control point, Eqs. 2-77 and 2-78 become

$$
\begin{aligned}
x_{1k} = \; & k_{00}^1 + k_{10}^1 \, w_{1k} + k_{01}^1 \, w_{2k} \\
& + k_{11}^1 \, w_{1k} \, w_{2k} + k_{20}^1 \, (w_{1k})^2 \\
& + k_{02}^1 \, (w_{2k})^2 + k_{21}^1 \, (w_{1k})^2 \, w_{2k} \\
& + k_{12}^1 \, w_{1k} \, (w_{2k})^2 + k_{22}^1 \, (w_{1k})^2 \, (w_{2k})^2
\end{aligned} \tag{2-79a}
$$

$$
\begin{aligned}
x_{2k} = \; & k_{00}^2 + k_{10}^2 \, w_{1k} + k_{01}^2 \, w_{2k} \\
& + k_{11}^2 \, w_{1k} \, w_{2k} + k_{20}^2 \, (w_{1k})^2 \\
& + k_{02}^2 \, (w_{2k})^2 + k_{21}^2 \, (w_{1k})^2 \, w_{2k} \\
& + k_{12}^2 \, w_{1k} \, (w_{2k})^2 + k_{22}^2 \, (w_{1k})^2 \, (w_{2k})^2
\end{aligned} \tag{2-79b}
$$

Equation 2-79 indicates that for the case of $N = 2$, 18 coefficients of the 2-D polynomial need to be estimated, and each control point yields two estimation equations. Therefore, at least nine points (which yield a set of linearly independent equations) are necessary. The reader may show that, in general, the number of required coefficients in a 2-D polynomial of order $N$ is $2(N + 1)^2$. This indicates, for example, that for $N = 3$ the number of required control points is 16. This dependence usually restricts the approach to low-order polynomials. In addition, for a given distortion, the choice of $N$ is often made by trial and error. Although the "flexibility" of the distortion representation increases as $N$ is increased, estimation errors also become more pronounced. Thus, a trade-off is usually necessary.

Three useful properties of Eq. 2-79 are noteworthy:

1. The estimation equations are linear in the $k_{ij}$.
2. Since the polynomial coefficients ($k_{ij}^1$ or $k_{ij}^2$) only appear in one of the two equations, the estimation process for these coefficients is separable. Thus, the coefficient matrices will be of dimension $m \times (N + 1)^2$.
3. The $k_{ij}$ coefficients in Eq. 2-79 are the respective powers of $w_1$ and $w_2$, which are identical in Eqs. 2-79a and 2-79b. These terms are the entries in the coefficient matrix, and, therefore, the coefficient matrix needs to be formed only once.

## IMPLEMENTATION OF THE CORRECTION ALGORITHM (INCLUDING INTERPOLATION)

Once the estimation of the geometric transform model coefficients is complete, the real computational effort in geometric distortion correction begins. Neglecting effects like occlusion and missing (or hidden) image information in the two images (which rarely occur in satellite imagery, but might be a concern in other applications), one of the images is corrected to the control points (i.e., the coordinate system) of the other. The overall process is as follows:

1. Determine a set of suitable (and reliable) control points, from which the transform parameters are determined.
2. Apply the actual correction to the image data using this transform (by finding all corresponding pixel locations in the two images, as described below).
3. Remap intensity data (i.e., interpolate), if necessary.

We begin our example by correcting image $f_1$ to the coordinate system of $f_2$. From Eq. 2-77, a view of the necessary correction is "the greylevel at point ($x_1$, $x_2$) in the $f_1$ coordinate system appears at location ($w_1$, $w_2$) in the $f_2$ coordinate system. Alternately, the greylevel that *should appear* at location ($w_1$, $w_2$) in the $f_2$ coordinate system actually appears at ($x_1$, $x_2$), given that $f_1$ is the distorted image and $f_2$ is the 'reference' image."

This relationship is shown in Figure 2.16. Picking a point $P_2$, as shown in the figure, Eq. 2-77 is used to find the location at which this point actually appears, denoted $P_1$ in the $f_1$ coordinate system. Thus, for all corrected image points of interest in $f_1$ (i.e., all [$w_1$, $w_2$]), we determine the corresponding ($x_1$, $x_2$) locations and then map the intensities found at ($x_1$, $x_2$) to ($w_1$, $w_2$) and thus achieve geometric correction. Note from Figure 2.16 that the resultant effect is the "bending" of features using Eq. 2-77.

It is paramount to observe that both $f_1$ and $f_2$ are typically sampled images. The mapping of arbitrary geometric transforms will, in general, complicate the correction process, since if ($w_1$, $w_2$) is a point on the sampling grid, ($x_1$, $x_2$) may not be (and vice versa). This necessitates some form of pixel intensity assignment. In Figure 2.16, point $P_1$ falls in between sampling grid locations. Therefore, some way to determine the intensity at $P_1$ from the grid locations surrounding $P_1$ is

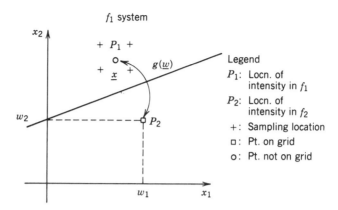

**FIGURE 2.16**  Geometric correction of $f_1$ to the $f_2$ geometry

necessary. An obvious approach would be determine the point closest to $P_1$ and map this intensity to $P_2$. However, this approach introduces a distortion or inaccuracy into the correction process. An alternate strategy is to interpolate the intensity at $P_1$ from each of its nearest grid neighbors.

*Interpolation.* Successful application of geometric transformations requires, in general, strategies to assign pixel intensities to these points that are not on the sampling grid. Therefore, the practical achievement of geometric transformations involves computations to map pixel indices as well as computations to achieve interpolation.

Formulations for image reconstruction are examined in Chapter 3. We make use of that result here. A suitably bandlimited nonsampled or continuous image may be reconstructed from its sampled version, denoted $f^*(m, n)$, using a reconstruction function, $g$, as follows:

$$f(x_1, x_2) = \sum_m \sum_n f^*(n, m)\, g(x_1 - nX_s, x_2 - mY_s) \qquad (2\text{-}80)$$

where $X_s$ and $Y_s$ are the $x_1$ and $x_2$ spatial sampling intervals.

For bandlimited images, optimal interpolation may be accomplished in this case by choosing $g$ to be a sinc function. In view of the computational cost of this processing (note that Eq. 2-80 requires a weighted sum over all the image samples, not just in the neighborhood), a more practical, albeit suboptimal, set of interpolation functions is desired.

**1.** Nearest Neighbor Interpolation

An obvious and computationally advantageous interpolation strategy is to simply assign $P$ the intensity of its "nearest neighbor." A distance metric to define "nearest" in the image plane must be chosen; a likely candidate is the familiar Euclidean measure of distance. In a number of applications this strategy yields acceptable results; however, in others it leads to significant image distortion.

The nearest neighbor interpolation strategy may be formulated and analyzed in terms of Eq. 2-80. Simply stated, given a point $(x_1', x_2')$, which may or may not be on the sampling grid, $g()$ becomes unity in Eq. 2-80 for the sampled image plane location closest in distance to $(x_1', x_2')$. This choice of interpolation function corresponds to

$$g(x_1' - nX_s, x_2' - mY_s) =$$

$$\begin{cases} 1 \text{ for } (n, m) \text{ s.t. } [(x_1' - nX_s)^2 + (x_2' - mY_s)^2] \text{ is min.} \\ 0 \text{ otherwise} \end{cases}$$

$$(2\text{-}81)$$

The discontinuous pulse or step-like nature of $g(x_1' - nX_s, x_2' - mY_s)$ in Eq. 2-81 introduces high-frequency characteristics into the interpolation process. This formulation also allows handling of the case wherein there is no unique value of $(m, n)$ that satisfies Eq. 2-81, such as the case of $P$ being equidistant from all four neighbors. In this instance a priority or decision scheme must also be embedded in $g(\ )$.

### 2. Bilinear Interpolation

A somewhat more suitable and commonly employed interpolation function is bilinear interpolation. Given the four nearest neighbors to the point $(x_1', x_2')$, as shown in Figure 2.17, bilinear interpolation assigns an intensity to $(x_1', x_2')$ via the following relation:

$$\begin{aligned} f(x_1', x_2') &= (1 - a)(1 - b)\, f(x_1, x_2) \\ &\quad + a\,(1 - b)\, f(x_1 + 1, x_2) \\ &\quad + (1 - a)\, b\, f(x_1, x_2 + 1) \\ &\quad + a\, b\, f(x_1 + 1, x_2 + 1) \end{aligned}$$

$$(2\text{-}82)$$

where $a$ and $b$ are the respective $x_1$ and $x_2$ distances (expressed as fractions of $X_s$ and $Y_s$) of the point $(x_1', x_2')$ from the grid point $(x_1, x_2)$. The reader is encouraged

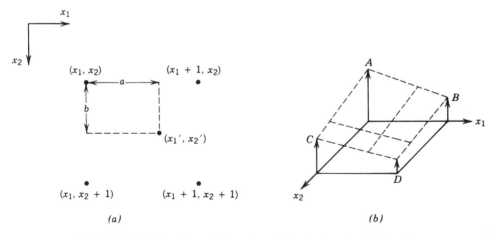

**FIGURE 2.17** Bilinear interpolation: determining the intensity of $(x_1', x_2')$
(a) Image plane view
(b) Graphical description

to verify the suitability of this mapping by examining its effect on specific $(x_1', x_2')$ locations, for example, $a = b = 1$, $a = \frac{1}{2}$, $b = \frac{1}{2}$, etc.

It is useful to note from Eq. 2-82, in contrast with our notion of 1-D linear interpolation (where the range of intensities between two points is approximated by a line), that the mapping in Eq. 2-82 does not correspond to approximation of the intensities inside the four pixel region by a plane. In general (this is left to the problems), the interpolated intensity surface resulting from Eq. 2-82, as shown in Figure 2.17, is nonplanar.

### 3. Other Interpolation Approaches

An ideal interpolation function for bandlimited imagery is the sinc function. Complexity is the reason the sinc function is seldom used directly. Instead it is either approximated by computationally simpler forms (such as 2-D low-pass filters) or replaced by the approaches shown above. Another appropriate, but suboptimal, interpolation function is given by the Gaussian function (Pratt, 1972).

One of the desirable properties of an interpolation function is computational efficiency. Additionally, interpolation functions that are separable are desirable. For example, the sinc function may be written as the product of two functions of the form $\sin(x_i)/(x_i)$, where each function depends only on $x_1$ or $x_2$. ·

Comparison of interpolation functions is difficult analytically and usually highly dependent on the image characteristics, thus yielding a trade-off between image precision and computational expense. Figure 2.18 compares the visual effects of interpolation on a particularly difficult image, namely one with significant and regular high frequency characteristics.

Several closing remarks regarding geometric correction are in order:

1. In the correction process (here involving correcting $f_1$ to $f_2$), only intensities in $f_1$ are involved; $f_2$ was only necessary for the control point determination. We do not map intensities from $f_2$ into $f_1$; rather, we remap the intensities in $f_1$.

2. It is possible, even in the case of correcting $f_1$ to the $f_2$ geometry using the bilinear interpolation cited above, to have points $(w_1, w_2)$ in the resulting corrected image with no corresponding intensities. This is due to the fact that Eq. 2-79 does not constrain the corresponding $(x_1, x_2)$ locations to lie within the image extent (i.e., the range of values for $x_1$ and $x_2$). Typically with large geometric distortions, the effect of incomplete "off the image plane" pixel information yields regions of no intensity assignment in the corrected image.

3. A similar formulation is possible using the inverse of Eq. 2-77; that is, the coordinate system relationship may be alternately formulated as

$$w_1 = h_1(x_1, x_2)$$

and

$$w_2 = h_2(x_1, x_2)$$

(2-83)

where the function $h$ relates the $(x_1, x_2)$ coordinates to the $(w_1, w_2)$ system. This is left for the reader to explore.

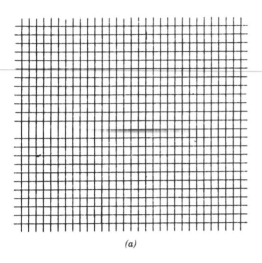

*(a)*

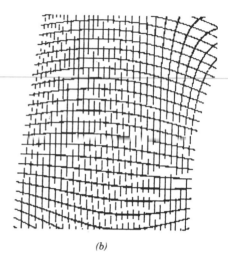

*(b)*

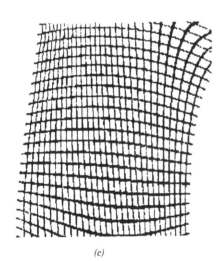

*(c)*

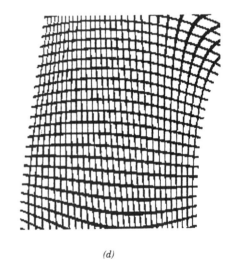

*(d)*

**FIGURE 2.18**  Interpolation function examples

(a)  Original binary grid image
(b)  Binary image with Nene interpolation
(c)  Binary image with AVG4 interpolation (threshold at level 25)
(d)  Binary image with Med4 interpolation
(e)  Binary image with Bili interpolation (threshold at level 10)
(f)  Description of interpolation functions used

## GEOMETRIC CORRECTION/SENSOR FUSION EXAMPLE—MULTIPLE SENSOR CHANGE DETECTION

A simple example of the application and practical limitations of geometric correction techniques for sensor fusion is shown in Figure 2-19. Parts (*a*) through (*g*) of the figure illustrate geometric correction, and (*e*) through (*g*) show correction combined with the difference operator to indicate geometrically corrected sensor

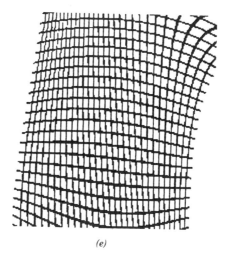

*(e)*

*Intensity assignments for interpolated pixel intensity:*

NENE: nearest neighbor
AVG4: average value of 4-NNR's
MED4: rank 2 (second highest intensity of 4-NNR's)
BILI: bilinear

*(f)*

**FIGURE 2.18** *(continued)*

differences. The example culminating in part (*g*) illustrates the case where the second tank may only appear in one of the sensors; it is either missing or an artifact in the other. In the case where significant 3-D scene radiometric variations have occurred during the imaging period, or sensor parameter variations (e.g., AGC) have affected one of the images, it is necessary to also apply an intensity transformation in the correction process (e.g., histogram equalization or a lookup table). This intensity model effect is treated in Chapter 4.

## *IMAGE MOSAICING*

Image mosaicing is another application based on the geometric model and involves techniques to "splice" or geometrically register an ensemble of low resolution digitized images to form a high resolution composite or "mosaic." A number of theoretical and practical ramifications arise. The high-resolution composite image should have the correct perspective and a minimum of algorithm-induced artifacts. Historically, the most significant application for image mosaicing is due to satellite imaging of the earth. Large mosaics are commonly used as substitutes for maps produced by hand by visually splicing smaller images together. In the terminology of Wolf (1974), these are known as "uncontrolled" mosaics. Another emerging application area for mosaic-formation technology (Schalkoff, 1986) is imagery where it is necessary to splice high-resolution imagery over a wide field of view (e.g., flight simulators) and systems wherein sensor zooming or magnification over large

**FIGURE 2.19** Example of geometric correction for multisensor fusion
(a) Two tanks observed from sensor orientation "A"
(b) Same tanks observed from sensor orientation "B"
(c) Image (b) corrected to "A" viewing geometry (note "rubber sheet" effect)
(d) Image (c)—image (a) (note errors)
(e) One tank from orientation "B"
(f) Image (e) corrected to "A" viewing geometry
(g) Image (f)—image (a) (note large sensor disparities)

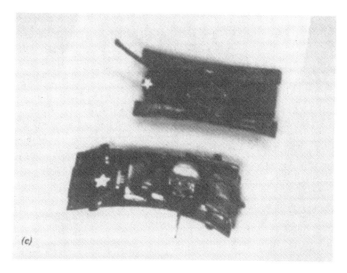

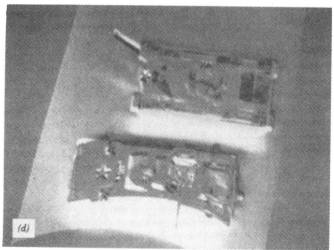

**FIGURE 2.19** *(continued)*

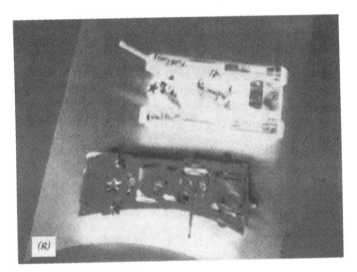

FIGURE 2.19   *(continued)*

ratios may be encountered (e.g., imaging missile control simulators). The basic objective is to acquire and process an ensemble of spatially related images from a low-resolution camera with a narrow field of view (FOV) and then form a higher-resolution, larger FOV composite ("mosaic"). This creates an image that is formed like a patchwork quilt. Salient concerns are

1. The required number of control points;
2. The amount of necessary image overlap;
3. The total number of images necessary to achieve a specified high-resolution mosaic; and
4. The time, computational, and storage requirements necessary to acquire and make discrete these images.

The fundamental problem is shown in Figure 2-20(a) and (b). For simplicity, only two overlapping images are shown. Since it is known that they share common pixel areas, the task is to determine their spatial relationship such that the "new" or correctly registered pixel area (i.e., the extension of image 1) reflects the correct geometric relationship among pixels in the two images and with respect to other images in the mosaic.

In the context of the previous geometric correction discussion, the objective is to correct $f_2$ to the $f_1$ coordinate system.

In the registration process, the "corners" of $f_1$ and $f_2$ are matched using a geometric transform and suitable control points.

$$\underline{x}_i' = g(\underline{x}_i) \tag{2-84}$$

If we assume that image points in the $f_2$ system (denoted by primes) are related to the $f_1$ system by $\underline{g}$, control points are used to estimate $\underline{g}$ parametrically. We then step the registration algorithm to the points of interest in the $f_1$-centric coordinate system, use Eq. 2-84 to calculate the corresponding location in the $f_2$-centric system, and form

$$f_1(\underline{x}) = f_2(\underline{x}') \tag{2-85}$$

for "extended" (i.e., beyond the extent of $f_1$) $x$. Interpolation is necessary, as described in the previous section.

There is no unique way to cover ("tesselate") a 2-D area (the composite or mosaic) with smaller 2-D images. Given the following definitions:

$t$:   the desired resolution (in lines) of the composite image

$w$:   the resolution (in lines) of the low-resolution camera

$x$:   the linear ($x_1$ or $x_2$ dimension) overlap used (a fraction in the interval [0, 1])

$n$:   the number of levels in composite image (i.e., $n = 0$ is center image, $n = 1$ is center image, and two images overlapping center image in both dimensions). This is shown in Figure 2-20(c).

$I_{2D}$: the total number of images required for the mosaic.

It is then possible to relate the above variables to get an idea of the computational complexity involved. Assuming the overlap occurs sequentially in each dimension, it may be shown (c.f. the problems) that

$$n = INT_m[(t - w)/(2w(1 - x))] \tag{2-86}$$

where $INT_m$ is the smallest integer larger than the bracketed quantity.

Assume the images simultaneously overlap in both the horizontal and vertical dimensions by 50%. In this case $x = 0.5$, (25% area overlap) and the number of required images is given by

$$I_{2D}(25\% \text{ area overlap}) = 1 + 2n(n + 1) \tag{2-87}$$

For example, with $x = 0.5$, $t = 1400$, $w = 200$, Eq. 2-87 yields $I_{2D}(25\% \text{ A}) = 85$. Other sample data (with $n$ rounded to the nearest, not higher integer) are shown in Table 2-2. Notice the number of required images is significant, even for relatively small mosaics. Acquisition of an image ensemble with the 25% area

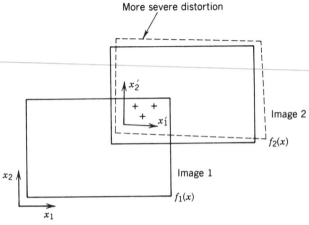

$$x_i' = g^{-1}(x_i)$$
$$f_1(x_i) = f_2(x_i')$$

(a)

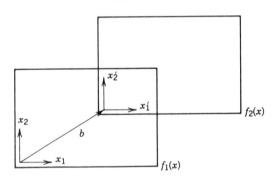

$$f_2(x) = f_1(x + b)$$
$$f_2(x - b) = f_1(x)$$

(b)

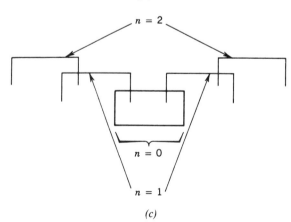

(c)

**FIGURE 2.20**
(a)  General mosaic geometric registration model(s) and control points in "overlap" region
(b)  Simple registration example (translation only)
(c)  Composite image level concept (one dimension only)

■ TABLE 2-2
Example of ensemble required

| $w$ | $n$ | $I_{2D}$ (25% A) |
|------|------|------|
| 100 | 14 | 421 |
| 200 | 6 | 85 |
| 360 | 3 | 25 |
| 480 | 2 | 13 |
| 512 | 2 | 13 |
| 800 | 1 | 5 |
| 1000 | 1 | 5 |

overlap described above may be achieved through subjective human judgment and hand adjustment of the pan/tilt camera mount control or an automated approach (Schalkoff, 1986).

# ■ RADIOMETRIC IMAGE FORMATION (MODELING GEOMETRIC CONCERNS)

## RADIOMETRIC MODEL ORIGIN

The conversion of light from a scene by a sensor (usually a television camera) is a transfer of 3-D radiometric information to 2-D pixel intensity data. A conceptually simplistic but useful model is derived below under reasonable assumptions. The result is shown first. The surface reflectivity function, $r(\underline{x})$, which relates resultant image function intensity, $f(\underline{x})$, to incident surface illumination, $e(\underline{x})$, and surface reflectivity is

$$f(\underline{x}) = e(\underline{x}) \, r(\underline{x}) \tag{2-88}$$

with the constraints

$$0 \le f(\underline{x}) \le f_{\max}$$

$$0 \le r(\underline{x}) \le 1$$

and

$$0 \le e(\underline{x}) \le \infty$$

Notice the nonlinear (multiplicative) nature of Eq. 2-88. Furthermore, note all functions are 2-D, not 3-D. The reflectivity function, $r(\underline{x})$, is dependent on the surface texture and finish, *angles of incidence and reflection* (the scene and viewing geometry), and is also a function of the wavelength of the incident illumination. Assuming Lambertian surfaces (the surface is assumed an ideal diffuser of light) and a large magnification ratio, we remove the angular dependence from the above model and show image formation as a nonlinear (multiplicative) process in 2-D.

The physics of image formation involve radiometric analysis techniques that are beyond the scope of this discussion. A simple model that leads to Eq. 2-88 (useful in the visual spectrum) assures that no self-illuminating bodies are present in the scene—that is, sensor or image plane intensities are *only* due to reflection. This

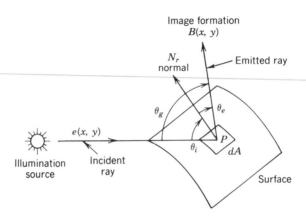

**FIGURE 2.21**  Radiometric image formation

excludes images of scenes containing isolated illumination sources such as auto-mobile headlights, fires, and the like. This model is usually not applicable to infrared imagery, since the source of sensor energy in the infrared case is usually the thermal energy of bodies in the scene.

Given a particular image, acquired with a particular viewing geometry, it is desirable to determine the effects of (and perhaps changes in): (a) illumination source strength and orientation; (b) surface orientation (slope) and reflectivity; and (c) sensor orientation viewing angle. The basis for the model is shown in Figure 2-21. It is assumed the viewer is very far from objects relative to their size. The resultant 3-D scene therefore occupies a small visual angle, as if viewed by a telephoto lens. This corresponds to two sets assumed orthographic projection; that is, surface to source and surface to image distances are assumed large and ap-proximately constant.

The light incident on any point $P$ of a 3-D scene is a function of the composition and orientation of light sources relative to $P$. This allows light being reflected toward $P$ or occluded from $P$ by other entities in the scene. The light reflected from $P$ in a direction along the emitted ray depends on the relative orientations of the incident and emitted rays and surface characteristics. In Figure 2.21 it is assumed the sensor-surface distances and the illumination source-surface are suf-ficiently large. Therefore, surface depth variations are insignificant, and surface points are indexed by $(x_1, x_2)$ coordinates. (Notice that this does not eliminate the need to represent relative orientations, specified by the angles $\theta_i$, $\theta_e$, and $\theta_g$.)

The following nomenclature and definitions are shown in Figure 2.21:

$P(\underline{x})$: point in scene at fixed sensor-surface distance

$\theta_i$:  incidence angle; angle between incident illumination ray and surface nor-mal

$\theta_e$:  emittance angle; angle between ray to viewer and surface normal

$\theta_g$:  phase angle; angle between incident and emitted rays.

$e(\underline{x})$:  Spectral irradiance incident on the surface at $P(x)$ due to a point source oriented at angle $\theta_i$ relative to the surface normal, $N_s$. (units: flux/area or W/m²).

$B(\underline{x})$: Resulting surface luminance oriented in direction of viewer at angle $\theta_e$

with respect to surface normal (units are W/m²). (Note $B(\underline{x}) \neq f(\underline{x})$ (yet).)

Assuming the sensor conversion of reflected radiometric surface energy into image plane intensities introduces only a scale factor; image intensities are therefore proportional to $B(\underline{x})$. We assume this scale factor is 1.0.; therefore, $B(\underline{x}) = f(\underline{x})$. In practice, this conversion is highly nonlinear.

In addition, *the intensity of the imaged scene irradiance is not significantly dependent on the surface-sensor distance.* $B(\underline{x})$ is specified per steradian (solid angle) and per surface area. Thus, the surface illumination area "spreads out" in a conical fashion from $P(\underline{x})$ toward the sensor. The sensor, however, integrates incident illumination over a solid angle, which is a function of the focal length and sensor optics. Thus, the offsetting effects of projected and imaged solid angles tend to minimize distance-induced intensity variations.

The final quantity to be derived in the radiometric model is that of the surface reflectivity function $r(\underline{x})$. This function relates emitted source flux "captured" by an infinitesimal surface element $dA$ and that seen by the viewer (or sensor) as a function of incidence and emittance angles and surface shape and composition. From Figure 2.21, an infinitesimal surface element $dA$ captures an amount of flux given by the projection $e(\underline{x}) \cos(\theta_i) \, dA$. Similarly, the amount of surface illumination seen by the viewer, comprising the image, is given by $B(\underline{x}) \cos(\theta_e) \, dA$. A simple model for the surface reflectivity function, $r(\underline{x})$, relates these two quantities by the ratio:

$$r(\underline{x}) = \frac{B(\underline{x}) \cos\theta_e}{e(\underline{x}) \cos\theta_i} \tag{2-89}$$

and provides a quantitative measure of the surface reflectivity. In practice, $r(\underline{x})$ is dependent on the surface texture, finish, and temperature and is also a function of the wavelength of incident illumination. The reflected intensity that is imaged therefore depends on the angles $\theta_i$ and $\theta_e$, which are measured with respect to the surface normal. Special examples of this angular dependence are

1. Specular reflection, where the reflected intensity is zero except where the incident ray, the reflected ray, and the surface normal are coplanar and $\theta_i = \theta_e$. This is characteristic of highly polished surfaces (such as metals).
2. Lambertian surfaces, where the surface is assumed an ideal diffuser of light (i.e., the emitted radiation does not depend on viewing angle). In this case $B(\underline{x}) = e(\underline{x}) \cos\theta_i \, r(\underline{x})$. Note that for Lambertian surfaces and constant illumination and viewing orientations, $\theta_i$ remains fixed and the relationship of Eq. 2-88 results. In general, surfaces have a reflectivity function which is a combination of 1. and 2.

The Lambertian model shows image formation as a nonlinear (multiplicative) process. Several applications of this model are:

1. In determining surface orientation (Babu, Lee, & Rosenfeld, 1985; Horn, 1977) from image intensities. Given (or assuming) information regarding $r(\underline{x})$, $e(\underline{x})$, and $\theta_i$, the image intensity function is used to infer surface normal orientation (or to constrain the above quantities).

2. In homomorphic filtering (Chapter 4) for contrast enhancement, where it is assumed that $r(\underline{x})$ has significant high frequency characteristics, and $e(\underline{x})$ usually has only low frequency characteristics. To develop an enhancement or filtering strategy for this case, a logarithmic transformation on $B(\underline{x})$ $(=f(\underline{x}))$ is used to convert the multiplicative model to one linear in two new functions, namely $\ln(r(\underline{x}))$ and $\ln(e(\underline{x}))$. In this manner, the image contrast and dynamic range due to illumination may be enhanced separately from that due to scene reflectivity.

3. In developing a paradigm for structural modeling (Tenenbaum, Fischler, & Barrow, 1981) (Chapter 7). Through a consideration of the physics of image formation, image intensity data may be used to develop constraints on extracted data such that sets of intrinsic images may be developed.

4. In considering image motion (Neumann, 1980) (Chapter 5).

## ■ SUMMARY

One of the most significant concerns that emerges in the above geometric modeling, algorithm development, and applications discussion is the effects of sampling—that is, the fact that the image is most often modeled and processed as a discrete process or array. This causes a number of difficulties. First, due to the discrete nature of the spatial indices, geometric transformations are not one-to-one transformations. This property may necessitate a significant amount of additional computations in order to correctly or approximately assign intensities to the transformed pixel locations. Second, the discrete nature of imagery causes some difficulty in the definition and precise location of "edges." Third, in imagery that is not band-limited, the sampling process yields a loss of some image information. In Chapter 3 we consider the modeling of sampling effects through the Fourier transform.

## ■ REFERENCES

Altschuler, B. A., et al. Laser electro-optic system for rapid three-dimensional (3-D) topographic mapping of surfaces. *Optical Engineering*, 1981, 20,(6), 953–961.

Babu, M. D., Lee, C. H., and Rosenfeld, A. Determining plane orientation from specular reflectance. *Pattern Recognition*, 1985, 18(1), 53–62.

Barnard, S. T., and Fischler, M. A. Computational stereo. *Computing Surveys*, 1982, 14(4), 553–572.

Duda, R. O., and Hart, P. E. *Pattern classification and scene analysis*. New York: Wiley, 1973.

Dzialo, K. A., and Schalkoff, R. J. Control considerations in tracking moving objects using time-varying perspective-projected imagery. *IEEE Trans. Industrial Electronics*, August 1986m Vol. IE-33 No. 3, pp. 247–253.

Eykhoff, P. *System identification*. New York: Wiley, 1974.

Foley, J. D., and Van Dam, A., *Fundamentals of interactive computer graphics*. Reading, MA: Addison-Wesley, 1983.

Frobin, W., and Hierholzer, E. Automatic measurement of body surfaces using raster-stereography, Part I. *Photogrammetric Engineering and Remote Sensing*, 1983, 49(3), 377–384.

Gibson, H. L. *Photography by infrared*. New York: Wiley, 1978.

Hall, E. L., *Computer image processing and recognition*. New York: Academic Press, 1979.

Hall, E. L., et al. Measuring curved surfaces for robot vision. *IEEE Computer*, Dec. 1982, Vol. 15, pp. 42–54.

Horn, B. K., Understanding image intensity. *Artificial Intelligence*, 1977, 8, 201–231.

Hwang, J. J., and Hall, E. L. Matching of featured objects using relational tables from stereo images. *Computer Graphics and Image Processing*, 1982, 20, 22–42.

Karara, H. M. Non-metric cameras. In Atkinson, K. B. (Ed.), *Developments in close-range photogrammetry*. London: Applied Science Publishers, 1980.

Labuz, J., and Schalkoff, R. J. Three-dimensional surface mapping simulator: Theory, capabilities and operation. *Image and Vision Computing*, 1985, 3(1), 36–39.

Milgram, D. L. Computer methods for creating photomosaics. *IEEE Trans. Computers*, Nov. 1975, Vol. C-24, No. 11, 1113–1119.

Neumann, B. Exploiting image formation knowledge for motion analysis. *IEEE Trans. Pattern Analysis and Machine Intelligence*, Nov. 1980, Vol. PAMI-2, No. 6, pp. 550–554.

Potsmesil, M. Generation of 3-D surface descriptions from images of pattern illuminated objects. *Proceedings of the IEEE Conference on Pattern Recognition and Image Processing*, Chicago, IL, (Aug. 1979), pp. 553–559.

Pratt, W. *Digital image processing*. New York: Wiley, 1972.

Riesenfeld, R. Homogeneous coordinates and projective planes in computer graphics. *IEEE Computer Graphics and Applications*, 1981, Vol. 1, pp. 50–55.

Roberts, L. G. "Homogeneous Matrix Representation and Manipulation of N-Dimensional Constructs", MS-1405, Lincoln Laboratory, MIT, 1965.

Sato, Y., Kitagawa, H., and Fujita, H. Shape measurement of curved objects using multiple slit-ray projections. *IEEE Trans. PAMI*, 1982, 4(6), 641–649.

Schalkoff, R. J. Development of high-resolution digital image mosaics from low-resolution sensors using image processing techniques. *Proceedings of the 18th Southeastern Symposium on System Theory*, Knoxville, TN, April 1986, pp. 42–46.

Sobel, I. On calibrating computer controlled cameras for perceiving 3-D scenes. *Artificial Intelligence*, 1974, (5), 185–198.

Tenenbaum, J. M., Fischler, M. A., and Barrow, H. G. Scene modelling: A structural basis for image description (pp. 371–390). In Rosenfeld, A. (Ed.), *Image modelling*. New York: Academic Press, 1981.

Topa, L., and Schalkoff, R. J. An analytical approach to the determination of planar surface orientation using active—passive image pairs. *Computer Vision, Graphics, and Image Processing*, 1986, 35, 404–418.

Wolf, P. R., *Elements of photogrammetry*. New York: McGraw-Hill, 1974.

Wong, R. Sensor transformations, *IEEE Trans. on Systems, Man, and Cybernetics*, Dec. 1977, Vol. SMC-7, No. 12.

# ■ PROBLEMS

1. Show, by using the general equations for camera calibration (Eq. 2-27) why the $n > 6$ points used must be noncoplanar. In other words, what happens to the $2n \times 11$ matrix and the $A_{ij}$ estimates if the points used are coplanar? Additionally, can you give some physical or intuitive reason for this? (Hint: Consider a simple 1-D case.)

2. Referring to Table 1 (attached), determine the calibration parameters for the active and passive cameras using these nine data points: 1, 3, 4, 5, 6, 8, 9, 10, 11. Set $A_{134} = A_{234} = 1.0$.

■ **TABLE 1**
**Calibration experiment**

| Point # | Active camera coordinates | | Passive camera coordinates | | Object-centered coordinate location (global) (inches) | | |
|---------|---------|-----------|---------|-----------|---------|---------|---------|
| | $X_A$ | $Y_A$ (pixels) | $X_I$ | $Y_I$ (pixels) | $X_O$ | $Y_O$ | $Z_O$ |
| Origin 1 | 48 | 48 | 174 | 217 | 0 | 0 | 0 |
| 2* | 36 | 36 | 247 | 278 | | | |
| 3 | 36 | 48 | 223 | 283 | 1.72 | 1.95 | 0 |
| 4 | 48 | 36 | 217 | 223 | 0 | .05 | 0.24 |
| 5 | 36 | 24 | 280 | 275 | 0.64 | 3.04 | 0 |
| 6 | 24 | 24 | 339 | 356 | 2.76 | 5.88 | 0 |
| 7* | 48 | 24 | 257 | 232 | | | |
| 8 | 113 | 36 | 239 | 89 | 0 | 1.22 | 4.00 |
| 9 | 36 | 92 | 119 | 294 | 3.57 | 0.26 | 0 |
| 10 | 92 | 92 | 136 | 172 | 3.38 | 0 | 3.44 |
| 11 | 92 | 36 | 233 | 137 | 0 | 1.16 | 2.84 |

3. Using the calibration results of Problem 2 and the image plane data for points 2 and 7, find the object point locations for these points.

4. Prove that the general perspective-projective transform maps a 3-D line in object space into a 2-D line in the image plane. (Use the p-p equations; the geometrical argument is on page 25.)

5. (a) Show that any image plane-image plane transformation that results from any movement of the camera may be represented in superhomogeneous coordinates.

   (b) Show that the above transformation, in physical image plane coordinates, may be represented using the perspective-transform (Eq. 2-53).

6. (a) Discuss situations, with respect to camera geometry and object point motion, where the image plane-image plane perturbations in Problem 5 may be approximated by

   (i) The affine transform (Appendix 1); and

   (ii) A polynomial warp transform.

   (b) Under what circumstances are the affine, perspective, and polynomial warp transforms equal?

7. (a) Given arbitrary rotation and translation matrices $R$ and $T$, respectively, show that

$$RT \neq TR$$

   (i.e., they do not commute).

   (b) Given that $R$ in 7(a) represents a rotation about a *single* coordinate axis (e.g., the $y$-axis), and $T$ represents an arbitrary translation, show that *although they do not commute*, we can find two sets of matrix parameters (delx, dely, delz)$T_i$ and $\theta_i$ such that

$$R_1 T_1 = T_2 R_2$$

8. (Apply least-square techniques to the problem of *image geometric correction*, given "grid points".) A problem frequently encountered in Landsat imagery analysis is the determination of parameters to enable the geometric correction of an image (or set of images). Given a reference image and a set of labeled "grid" or "control" points in each, we may be trying to "realign" images of the same terrain or ground data that were taken with different satellite viewing geometries. For simplicity, assume that the control or grid points may be related by an affine transform—that is, we are given a set of corresponding points in two images where

$$\underline{x}'_i = A \, \underline{x}_i + \underline{b} \qquad\qquad i = k, 2, \ldots m$$

where $\underline{x}'_i$ is the corresponding location of the control point in 2nd image and $\underline{x}_i$ is the location of the control point in 1st image.

(a) Using the above equation for $m$ points, formulate the problem as an overdetermined set of linear equations. What constraint does this put on $m$ for a solution?

(b) Formulate the least-squares solution to (a). To test your results, estimate the $A$ and $\underline{b}$ parameters using the attached data (Table 2). To see if your results are reasonable, you might want to plot the corresponding points.

(c) Once the $A$ and $\underline{b}$ parameters have been determined, discuss (in detail) the process of actually correcting each point in image 2 to the image 1 viewing geometry. What are the problems?

(d) (Prelude to "clustering" in pattern recognition) Suppose in the data given, we know *one* point is in error—that is, it does not represent the control

■ TABLE 2
Points for least squares geometric correction problem

| | |
|---|---|
| $\underline{X}_1 = \begin{bmatrix} 0 \\ 0 \end{bmatrix}$ | $\underline{X}'_1 = \begin{bmatrix} .25 \\ 0 \end{bmatrix}$ |
| $\underline{X}_2 = \begin{bmatrix} 1 \\ 1 \end{bmatrix}$ | $\underline{X}'_2 = \begin{bmatrix} 1.4084 \\ .8112 \end{bmatrix}$ |
| $\underline{X}_3 = \begin{bmatrix} 1 \\ 0 \end{bmatrix}$ | $\underline{X}'_3 = \begin{bmatrix} 1.2348 \\ -.1736 \end{bmatrix}$ |
| $\underline{X}_4 = \begin{bmatrix} 0 \\ 1 \end{bmatrix}$ | $\underline{X}'_4 = \begin{bmatrix} .4236 \\ .9848 \end{bmatrix}$ |
| $\underline{X}_5 = \begin{bmatrix} 1 \\ 2 \end{bmatrix}$ | $\underline{X}'_5 = \begin{bmatrix} 1.582 \\ 1.796 \end{bmatrix}$ |
| $\underline{X}_6 = \begin{bmatrix} 2 \\ 1 \end{bmatrix}$ | $\underline{X}'_6 = \begin{bmatrix} 2.3932 \\ .6376 \end{bmatrix}$ |
| $\underline{X}_7 = \begin{bmatrix} -1 \\ 2 \end{bmatrix}$ | $\underline{X}'_7 = \begin{bmatrix} -.3876 \\ 2.1432 \end{bmatrix}$ |

point correspondence. Suggest one or more ways to detect and eliminate this bad data.

9. A test engineer wanted to acquire a set of images with horizontal and/or vertical overlap of ±1/2 image dimension between successive images as shown below.

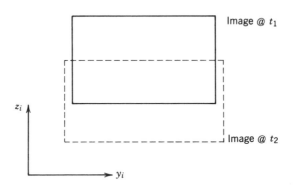

For this problem, let's assume we work with overlap in the $z_i$ dimension only, i.e., we are only using pan *or* tilt gimbal controls (not both). Assume that the relationship between the image plane-centered coordinate system and the gimbal axis-centered coordinate system is a simple 3-D translation (i.e., $d_x$, $d_y$ and $d_z$ offsets).

Furthermore, it is desired to automate the process of image acquisition, i.e., a (perhaps variable) computer-generated *gimbal axis* tilt angle increment, $\Delta\Theta_T$, is sent to the mount following acquisition of each image in the overlapping sequence.

Given the following information:

$$x_o \text{ (approx. constant)} = 300'$$

$$f = 100 \text{ mm}$$

$$|d_x|, |d_y|, |d_z| < 6''$$

$$\text{image plane FOV} = 2°$$

will a constant increment of $\Delta\Theta_T \approx \pm 1°$ yield a reasonable solution?

*NOTE:* To solve this problem you must
   i. Compute, in superhomogeneous coordinates, the transformation corresponding to a camera mount tilt
   ii. Convert the relationship from (i) to physical coordinates and selectively employ the above data and some reasoning.

10. (a) Given the two binary images (below), choose appropriate control points and correct image 2 to the image 1 coordinate system using:
   (i) An affine transform;
   (ii) A perspective transform; and
   (iii) A 2-D polynomial warp of 2nd order ($N = 2$).

   In all three cases be sure to show the estimated transform parameters.

(b) Comment on:
   (i) The relationship among the three sets of parameters; and
   (ii) Your opinion as to the one that most adequately models the geometric distortion between the two images.

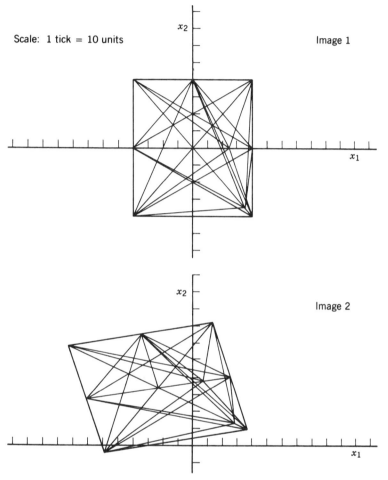

11. Due to the expense involved, it has been suggested that a stereo vision system could be implemented with a single (passive) camera that is used to acquire the two images, the second of which is acquired after the camera orientation has been changed. A hypothetical entrepreneur suggests that, in order to achieve commercial success, the image plane (camera) movement be restricted to a rotation of the image plane about the optical axis by $\Theta$ degrees.

   (i) State, using as much quantitative analysis as possible, whether the idea will work. Is it possible to map object points in this manner?
   (ii) Describe, again with analytical detail, any shortcomings of the above scheme, particularly with respect to accuracy and possible 3-D points that it may not be able to map.

12. Structured light-based stereo vision approaches help to minimize the correspondence problem. One additional modification that has been suggested is

to use "self-calibrating" or "self-corresponding" patterns. These patterns would display characteristics in the passive image plane such that point correspondences could readily be determined. For example, the projection of concentric circles has been proposed. In this case, the center of the circular array is readily distinguishable.

Discuss the design, characteristics, and applications of "self-corresponding" active camera patterns. Specifically, propose or consider:

(i) The types of patterns that would be useful. (Hint: A simple grid pattern contains no unique line intersections.)

(ii) The amount of and type of processing necessary in the passive image. For example, would the particular characteristics of your projected pattern be easily lost in a noisy passive image, or would the point correspondence be impossible to determine if the distortion of the pattern by the scene objects were significant?)

(iii) The extraction, from the passive image, of image information due to illumination *not* due to the active camera.

13. Often (e.g., in solving the correspondence problem) we seek to recognize 3-D invariants—that is, entities that will be preserved due to the imaging process. Given four points on a line in 3-D,

$$\underline{x}_{o_i} = (x_{o_i}, y_{o_i}, z_{o_i})^T \text{ for } i = 1, 2, 3, 4, \text{ use the p-p equations}$$

(and a model for a 3-D line) to show that, in physical image plane coordinates, the corresponding image points

$$\underline{x}_{i_j} = (x_{i_j}, y_{i_j}) \, j = 1, 2, 3, 4$$

satisfy the *cross-ratio* in the 3-D and 2-D $x$ and $y$ coordinates; that is,

$$\frac{(x_{i3} - x_{i1})(x_{i4} - x_{i2})}{(x_{i3} - x_{i2})(x_{i4} - x_{i1})} = \frac{(x_{o3} - x_{o1})(x_{o4} - x_{o2})}{(x_{o3} - x_{o2})(x_{o4} - x_{o1})}$$

(A similar relationship for the $y_i$ and $y_o$ coordinates may be obtained.) Suggest a possible use for this relationship.

14. In a stereo vision system, two image planes correspond to $(x_i^1, y_i^1)$ and $(x_i^2, y_i^2)$ are arranged as follows:

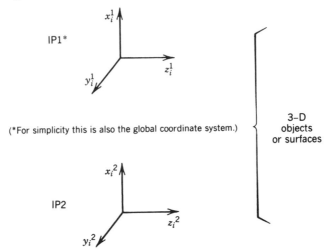

IP1*

(*For simplicity this is also the global coordinate system.)

3–D objects or surfaces

IP2

where the origin of IP2 is located at $\begin{bmatrix} -20 \\ 0 \\ 0 \end{bmatrix}$ w.r.t. IP1

(the global coordinate system).

IP1 is *back projected* with $f = 1$

IP2 is *front projected* with $f = 1$

(a) Show with the above orientation between the systems that image points in IP2 are mapped into points in IP1 by a point- or $Z_o$-dependent perspective transform (write out the equations).

(b) When $Z_o \gg f$, show what this perspective transform reduces to, and try to see if this makes intuitive sense.

(c) Show that this point- or $Z_o$-dependence reduces to parametric dependence if we have a parametric object or surface model of the form:

$$a\, x_o + b\, y_o + C\, Z_o + d = 0$$

What is the minimum number of corresponding points in IP1 and IP2 needed to estimate these surface parameters?

(d) Using $x_o + Z_o - 200 = 0$ as the surface equation, if circles $(x_i^2)^2 + (y_i^2)^2 = r^2$ are *projected* in IP2, what will be *imaged* in IP1? (Specifically characterize these shapes.)

15. (a) Using both analytical justification as well as graphical examples, show why the bilinear interpolation technique (Eq. 2-82) does not necessarily fit a plane to the interpolated intensity region.

(b) What are the conditions on the local image intensities such that the bilinear interpolation technique results in fitting a plane to the image intensities?

16. Using Eqs. 2-41, 2-42, and 2-43, assume the second sensor is an active device (a slit projector) that projects a line with known parameters of the form:

$$a_1\, x_{i2} + a_2\, y_{i2} = a_3$$

Derive an estimation approach and corresponding equations for object point determination in this case.

17. (Image Mosaicing) Derive the equation for image ensemble size as a function of overlap (Eq. 2.2-13).

18. (a) Referring to Figure 2.2, derive the image model for *front projection*—that is, the situation where the image plane is located a distance $f$ *in front of* the center of projection.

(b) Determine the $P$ matrix corresponding to the object-image point relationship in (a), expressed in homogeneous coordinates.

(c) How is the matrix in (b) related to the corresponding matrix for the back-projected model? Does this make intuitive sense?

19. The solution for object point locations in stereo vision systems relies on Eqs. 2-41, 2-42, and 2-43. Notice we are given four equations for three unknowns; therefore, not all of the point correspondence information is required. Discuss, using these equations and the bilinear constraint Eq. 2-47, the variety of possibilities concerning corresponding point constraints.

20. The derivation for the image plane-image plane geometric transformation was given under the large magnification ratio assumption in Eqs. 2-54 thru 2-58. Extend this derivation by considering the near-field case (i.e., do not use the large magnification ratio assumption). Specifically:

    (a) How do the derivations differ (i.e., describe the effects of this transformation for objects close to the center of projection, both analytically and graphically)?

    (b) Is the extended model representable in homogeneous coordinates?

21. Referring to Eq. 2-75, verify that these approximations are intuitively reasonable by sketching, to scale, the geometrical solution to the camera movement problem for the cases of (i) $\phi \neq 0$ and $\theta = 0$, and (ii) $\phi = 0$, $\theta \neq 0$. That is, in each case, choose and fix an object point, draw a 1-D image plane (in the $y$ or $z$ direction, respectively), rotate this plane, and show the image point change.

22. Consider an alternative interpretation of stereo vision using 2-D and 3-D *line features*. It was previously verified that the p-p transformation back-projects a line in the image plane into a plane in 3-D (see the text or problem 4). Assume that we are given two sensors, suitably arranged, and that the parameters of a line (segment) (corresponding to a 3-D scene feature) have been extracted in each.

    (a) Show (quantitatively) that the *intersection* of the two 3-D planes that result from the back projection of these lines is a line in 3-D.

    (b) Does knowledge of the sensor geometries and the 2-D line parameters enable unambiguous determination of the 3-D line parameters? (Justify your answer analytically.)

# 3

# IMAGE GREY-LEVEL MODELING AND EARLY PROCESSING FUNDAMENTALS, PART I

## ■ TRANSFORMS & SAMPLING

## ■ INTRODUCTION

In this chapter and Chapter 4, models and processing algorithms that rely significantly on image grey-value or intensity variation are considered. This is in contrast to the geometric concerns of Chapter 2. The algorithms developed in this chapter are seldom used alone to achieve a system goal (such as object inspection), but rather are often the initial preprocessing of a grey-level image. Chapters 5, 6, and 7 build on the concepts presented here.

### DETERMINISTIC AND STOCHASTIC TRANSFORMS

We begin our exploration of grey-level dependent image models and corresponding processing algorithms by considering four subdivisions of image grey-value models considered here and in Chapter 4:

1. Stochastic (probabilistic) models that have no geometric dependence. An example is the use of image intensity histograms for enhancement purposes (histogram equalization).

2. Deterministic models that rely on local (i.e., in the immediate pixel neighborhood) grey-value variations. An example is edge enhancement algorithms.

3. Stochastic models that rely on local grey-value dependence. An example is the use of co-occurence matrices.

4. Deterministic models that rely on global image properties, both geometric and intensity based. An example is the use of a new set of basis functions to represent the entire image. This introduces image transforms and is our first objective.

This chapter explores the plethora of deterministic 2-D transforms that have both intensity and geometric dependence. We first study the concept of a *basis function matrix* for the representation of discretized image data. The use of a separable linear transform, implemented as pre- and postmultiplication of the image function by transform matrices, is used to facilitate a change of basis functions. Examples of this type of transform are the Discrete Fourier Transform and the Hadamard Transform. Implicit in the use of such transformation is the assumption that the underlying image possesses some characteristics that may be related to the transformed image basis functions. In other words, the image intensity array has some properties that are more clearly discernible or extractable in the transformed representation. If the image has a significant contribution due only to a few basis functions, the resulting transform matrix will be sparse, which leads to a strategy for compression or encoding of image data. Furthermore, the transform approach may be of use in the development of algorithms for image classification and feature extraction (Chapter 6).

The 1-D Fourier transform is reviewed first, and the discrete version of this 1-D transform is represented in matrix vector notation. Properties of the complex matrix used to achieve this transform are explored. This makes sense, since the 2-D Discrete Fourier Transform (DFT) may be expressed using this matrix and calculated using the 1-D DFT.

The 2-D DFT then follows. It is shown that the structure and visualization of this transform is related to a larger class of linear separable transformations. Studying transforms as basis function changes allows insight into the transform properties and utility. Following the development of the 2-D DFT, a broader class of transforms is considered and several representative transforms and their basis functions and properties are studied.

### GLOBAL VERSUS LOCAL IMAGE MODELING AND PROCESSING APPROACHES

The fundamental concept of global versus local model applicability enters into the selection of image models and subsequent design of processing algorithms. Therefore, it is important to understand the representational limitations of a specific model. For example, many global approaches employing global information representations (e.g., moments, Fourier transforms) must assume that there is a single object that is completely visible in the image.

Applying a moment-based modeling approach, for example, to an image consisting of a group of overlapping parts most likely produces a set of features (i.e., transform coefficients) that have relatively little in common with individual part features. Clearly, there is regionally varying or local information that needs to be modeled and extracted first, followed by a globally based model and corresponding algorithm to interpret and determine the significance of the local model information. A more "intelligent" algorithm would then be used to infer a more global assessment of the image(s) content; for example, a set of object production rules may be used to determine if known objects or parts thereof are present (Chapter 6).

## ■ BASIC LINEAR SYSTEM AND DISCRETE TRANSFORM CONCEPTS

### *IMAGE BASIS FUNCTIONS*

Let us postpone temporarily our concern for the quantitative and qualitative effects of sampling a continuous 2-D function, $f(\underline{x})$, and assume that a matrix of image intensities, $f(x_1, x_2)$, is available. We are interested in developing a methodology that allows straightforward analysis and visualization of the plethora of available 2-D transforms. Our effort is concentrated on linear separable transforms, which are written in the form

$$[F] = U^T [f] V \tag{3-1}$$

where $[f]$ is an N × N image function matrix, and $U$ and $V$ are matrices that effect the appropriate transform (at this point we assume they are real matrices). An image function matrix may be written in terms of "basis function matrices" as

$$
[f] = 
\begin{bmatrix}
f_{11} f_{12} & \cdots & f_{1N} \\
f_{21} & & \\
& \cdot & \\
& \cdot & \\
& \cdot & \\
f_{N1} f_{N2} & \cdots & f_{NN}
\end{bmatrix}
$$

$$
= f_{11}
\begin{bmatrix}
1 & 0 & \cdots & 0 \\
0 & & & \cdot \\
\cdot & & & \cdot \\
\cdot & & & \cdot \\
\cdot & & & \cdot \\
0 & 0 & \cdots & 0
\end{bmatrix}
$$

$$
+ f_{12}
\begin{bmatrix}
0 & 1 & \cdots & 0 \\
0 & & & \cdot \\
\cdot & & & \cdot \\
\cdot & & & \cdot \\
\cdot & & & \cdot \\
0 & 0 & \cdots & 0
\end{bmatrix}
\tag{3-2}
$$

$$
+ \cdots +
$$

$$
f_{NN}
\begin{bmatrix}
0 & 0 & \cdots & 0 \\
0 & & & \cdot \\
\cdot & & & \cdot \\
\cdot & & & \cdot \\
\cdot & & & \cdot \\
0 & 0 & \cdots & 1
\end{bmatrix}
$$

or, by defining the set of $N^2$ NXN matrices on the right side of Eq. 3-2 as $E_{mn}$,

$$[f] = \sum_{m=1}^{N} \sum_{n=1}^{N} f_{mn} E_{mn} \tag{3-3}$$

Hereafter, these matrices are referred to as *basis function matrices*.

Referring to Eq. 3-1, observe that the associativity property of matrix multiplication allows us to write the $k$, $l^{\text{th}}$ element of $F$ as

$$F_{kl} = \sum_{m=1}^{N} \sum_{n=1}^{N} u_{mk} f_{mn} v_{nl}$$
$$= \sum_{m} \sum_{n} f_{mn} (u_{mk} v_{nl}) \tag{3-4}$$

Thus, Eq. 3-4 indicates that $F_{kl}$ is formed by summing the projection of $[f]$ onto a matrix formed as the outer product of the $k^{th}$ column of $U$ and the $l^{th}$ column of $V$. Writing $U$ and $V$ as

$$U = [\underline{u}_1, \underline{u}_2 \cdot \cdot \underline{u}_N]$$

and $\tag{3-5}$

$$V = [\underline{v}_1, \underline{v}_2 \cdot \cdot \underline{v}_N]$$

we form the $(k, l)^{\text{th}}$ element of $[F]$, $F_{kl}$, in Eq. 3-1 by writing Eq. 3-4 as

$$F_{kl} = \sum_{\substack{\text{all} \\ \text{elements} \\ \text{in product}}} [f] \otimes u_k v_l^T \tag{3-6}$$

where the $\otimes$ operator denotes a product of two matrices formed by a point-by-point multiplication of corresponding elements. An alternate view of Eq. 3-6 is that $F_{kl}$ is formed by correlating $[f]$ with $\underline{u}_k$, $\underline{v}_l^T$. Denoting the outer product operation of $\underline{u}_k$ and $\underline{v}_k$ in Eq. 3-6 as $> \underline{u}_k, \underline{v}_l <$, we see that the result is a matrix whose rank is exactly 1. More important, the entire separable linear transform in Eq. 3-1 is achieved by projecting the image function matrix, $[f]$, onto the $N^2$ basis functions of the transform as indicated by Eq. 3-6. Thus, Eq. 3-2 or Eq. 3-3 may be viewed as a "transform" whose $i$, $j^{\text{th}}$ element is formed by projecting $[f]$ onto the basis function $E_{ij}$, where

$$E_{ij} = > \underline{e}_i, \underline{e}_j < \tag{3-7}$$

and $\underline{e}_i$ is a vector whose elements are zero except for the $i^{\text{th}}$ element, which equals 1. The reader is encouraged to show that this results in "transform" matrices

$$U^T = I$$

and

$$V = I$$

where $I$ is an NXN identity matrix.

The inverse of Eq. 3-1 is now considered. For practical reasons as well as ease of presentation, it is assumed that $U$ and $V$ are orthogonal matrices (i.e., they are composed of orthonormal column vectors); therefore $[f]$ may be recovered by computing the inverse transform as

$$[f] = [U] [F] [V]^T \tag{3-8}$$

Decomposing the transformed function $[F]$, as in Eq. 3-2, yields

$$[F] = \begin{bmatrix} F_{11} & 0 & \cdots & 0 \\ 0 & & & \\ \vdots & & & \\ 0 & 0 & \cdots & 0 \end{bmatrix} + \begin{bmatrix} 0 & F_{12} & 0 & \cdots & 0 \\ 0 & & & & \\ \vdots & & & & \\ 0 & 0 & & \cdots & 0 \end{bmatrix}$$

$$+ \cdots +$$

$$\begin{bmatrix} 0 & 0 & \cdots & 0 \\ 0 & & & \\ \vdots & & & \\ 0 & 0 & \cdots & F_{NN} \end{bmatrix}$$

(3-9)

Equation 3-8 may be expanded as

$$[f] = [\underline{u}_1\ \underline{u}_2 \cdots \underline{u}_N]\ [F]\ [\underline{v}_1\ \underline{v}_2 \cdots \underline{v}_N]^T$$

(3-10)

It is left for the reader to show that Eq. 3-10 and the decomposition of $[F]$ in Eq. 3-9 yield

$$[f] = \sum_{k=1}^{N} \sum_{l=1}^{N} F_{kl}\ \underline{u}_k \underline{v}_l^T$$

(3-11)

Thus, whereas $F_{kl}$ represents the projection of the image function matrix onto the transform basis function $> \underline{u}_k, \underline{v}_l <$, Eq. 3-11 indicates that the image function is recovered by summing the transform basis functions weighted by the corresponding projection. This is shown in Figure 3.1. This result, although intuitively appealing, also suggests applications, since:

1. In the process of identifying certain image features, it may be appropriate to choose these features as basis functions, compute the transform, and thereby determine the content of each of these features in the image.
2. Images (or ensembles of images) that may be represented or approximated

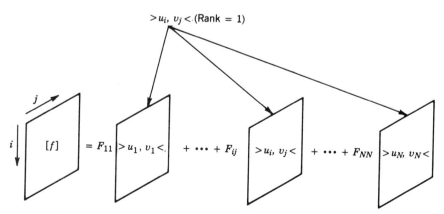

**FIGURE 3.1** Expansion of |f| onto set of rank-1 basis function matrices

by the weighted sum of a small number of the basis functions of a particular transform may be efficiently stored and/or transmitted in transformed form.

## DISCRETE TRANSFORMS

### BACKGROUND

*1-D Fourier Transform (Discrete) Review.* In the study of new concepts, it is useful to begin with a review of something already known and then extend this known information to the new concept. We take this approach here. Specifically, we confine our attention to the case of discrete transforms.

We define a transform of a 1-D function whose argument is an integer ranging from 0 to $N - 1$. Such functions may be $N$ samples of a continuous function, but this is not necessary. The Discrete Fourier Transform (DFT) of this 1-D function is defined as

$$F(u) = \sum_{k=0}^{N-1} f(k)\exp[-j\frac{2\pi}{N}uk] \quad 0 \le u \le N-1 \tag{3-12}$$

The universe of this transform, the Discrete Inverse Fourier Transform (DIFT) is given by

$$f(k) = \frac{1}{N}\sum_{u=0}^{N-1} F(u)\exp[j\frac{2\pi}{N}uk] \tag{3-13}$$

Matrix-vector representations facilitate analysis of this transform. Defining a complex variable $z$ as

$$z = \exp[-j\frac{2\pi}{N}] \tag{3-14}$$

and an NXN complex matrix $Z$ as

$$Z = \begin{bmatrix} 1 & 1 & 1 & \cdots & 1 \\ 1 & z & z^2 & \cdots & z^{N-1} \\ 1 & z^2 & & & \\ \vdots & \vdots & & & \\ & & & & z^{(N-1)^2} \\ 1 & z^{N-1} & & & \end{bmatrix} \tag{3-15}$$

(i.e., $Z$ is a matrix whose $u,k^{th}$ element $Z_{uk} = z^{uk}$), we index row and column elements in $Z$ from 0 to $N-1$ to write the $1-D$ DFT as

$$\underline{F} = Z\underline{f} \tag{3-16}$$

Where $F$ is an NX1 column vector of transform values, i.e.,

$$\underline{F} = \begin{bmatrix} F(0) \\ F(1) \\ \cdot \\ \cdot \\ \cdot \\ \cdot \\ F(N-1) \end{bmatrix} \tag{3-17}$$

and $\underline{f}$ is a NX1 column vector of function values, i.e.,

$$\underline{f} = \begin{bmatrix} f(0) \\ f(1) \\ \cdot \\ \cdot \\ \cdot \\ f(N-1) \end{bmatrix} \tag{3-18}$$

The relationship in Eq. 3-16 is important because it represents a *change* of *basis vectors* for our representation of $\underline{f}$, achieved in this case as a change of coordinates. The original basis function set was the columns of the NXN identity matrix, $I$, whereas in the transform the new basis vectors for the representation are the columns of $Z$. It is also important to note (we often force this to occur) that $N$ is not only even, but also a power of 2. This is useful in "fast" transform implementations mentioned subsequently.

We digress temporarily to study a few concepts related to complex matrices and some properties of $Z$.

A complex matrix, $F$, with complex conjugate matrix $F^*$ may be said to be

**1.** Hermitian, if

$$(F^*)^T = F \tag{3-19}$$

and

**2.** Unitary, if

$$F^{-1} = (F^*)^T \tag{3-20}$$

In dealing with real matrices, Case 2 corresponds to the case of an orthogonal matrix. Finally, recall that if $\underline{x}$ and $\underline{y}$ are complex vectors, their inner product, denoted $< x, y >$ is given by

$$< \underline{x}, \underline{y} > = [\underline{x}^*]^T \underline{y} \tag{3-21}$$

and if $< \underline{x}, \underline{y} > = 0$, the vectors are said to be orthogonal.

Referring to the definition of the complex variable $Z$, we note

$$z^N = 1$$
$$z^{N/2} = -1$$
$$z^{N/4} = -j \tag{3-22}$$

and

$$z^{3N/4} = j$$

With this, notice the $Z$ matrix has the following properties:

**1.** $Z = Z^T$
**2.** the columns (or rows) of $Z$ are orthogonal
**3.** the inner product of a column (or row) with itself $= N$.

This yields the important result

$$[Z^*]^T Z = N I \tag{3-23}$$

or, equivalently,

$$Z^{-1} = \frac{1}{N} [Z^*]^T \tag{3-24}$$

Thus, $Z$ is an "almost unitary" matrix.

On the basis of the above, we may form the DIFT in vector-matrix notation as

$$\underline{f} = Z^{-1} \underline{F} \tag{3-25}$$

$$= \frac{1}{N} [Z^*]^T \underline{F}$$

which simplified to

$$\underline{f} = \frac{1}{N} Z^* \underline{F} \tag{3-26}$$

The significance of this result is that the original functions may be recovered from the transformed version (*without the need for matrix inversion*). This is a property which is especially useful in computation of 2-D transforms, where the transform matrices may be quite large and therefore the computation of general inverses is impractical.

*Elementary 2-D Functions.* We begin our study with the concept of a point source, mathematically characterized as a 2-D delta function. The utility of this function is identical to its 1-D counterpart, namely it yields a technique to characterize 2-D systems via impulse response or point-spread functions. It also has significant utility in our modeling of the reconstruction process (Chapter 4).

Defining a 2-D function, rect$(x, y)$, as follows:

$$\text{rect}(x, y) = \begin{cases} 1 & |x| \le \frac{1}{2} \text{ and } |y| \le \frac{1}{2} \\ 0 & \text{elsewhere} \end{cases} \tag{3-27}$$

allows us to define the 2-D delta function through a limiting process. Letting

$$\delta_n(x, y) = n^2 \, \text{rect}(nx, ny) \quad n > 0 \tag{3-28}$$

we observe that:

1. $\delta_n$ is non-zero only inside a $1/n \times 1/n$ square in the image plane, and
2. $\iint_{-\infty}^{\infty} \delta_n(x, y) \, dxdy = 1.0 \quad \forall n$      (3-29)

Taking the limit as $n \to \infty$ yields the (2-D) Dirac delta function:

$$\delta(x, y) = \begin{cases} \infty & \text{at } (0,0) \\ 0 & \text{elsewhere} \end{cases} \tag{3-30}$$

Note that $\delta(x, y)$ also retains the 2nd property cited above, namely

$$\int_{-\infty}^{\infty} \delta(x, y) \, dxdy = 1.0 \tag{3-31}$$

Several additional properties of $\delta(x,y)$ are noteworthy:

1. The *sifting* property, which may be derived from:

$$\lim_{n\to\infty} \left\{ \iint_{-\infty}^{\infty} g(x,y)\delta_n(x,y)dxdy \right\} = g(0,0) \qquad (3\text{-}32)$$

Note the integrated quantity above represents the average value of $g(x,y)$ over a $1/n \times 1/n$ window centered at $(0,0)$.

The reader is encouraged to verify that the above expression may be generalized to:

$$\iint_{-\infty}^{\infty} g(x,y)\delta(x-\alpha, y-\beta)dxdy = g(\alpha,\beta) \qquad (3\text{-}33)$$

2. An extremely useful property (which actually comprises a transform pair) is

$$\iint_{-\infty}^{\infty} \exp[j2\pi(ux+vy)]dudv = \delta(x,y) \qquad (3\text{-}34a)$$

and

$$\iint_{-\infty}^{\infty} \delta(x,y)\exp[-j2\pi(ux+vy)]dxdy = 1.0 \qquad (3\text{-}34b)$$

This relationship may be shown by either invoking the sifting property, or using the rect function, computing the transformation indicated by Eq. 3-34$b$, and applying a limiting process.

One of the most frequently encountered and useful transform pairs is based upon the rect function. If

$$f(x,y) = \text{rect}(x,y) \qquad (3\text{-}35a)$$

then it is straightforward to show (this is left to the reader) that

$$F_{\text{rect}}(u,v) = \iint_{-\infty}^{\infty} \text{rect}(x,y) \exp[-j2\pi(ux+vy)]dxdy$$

$$= \frac{\text{Sin}\pi u}{\pi u} \cdot \frac{\text{Sin}\pi v}{\pi v} \qquad (3\text{-}35b)$$

$$\stackrel{\triangle}{=} \text{sinc}(u,v)$$

*Linear Operations and Convolution.* The linearity concept for 2-D functions and their operations may be defined by considering two image functions $f_1(\underline{x})$ and $f_2(\underline{x})$. An operator, $\mathcal{O}$, is said to be linear if

$$\mathcal{O}\{\alpha f_1(\underline{x}) + \beta f_2(\underline{x})\} = \alpha \mathcal{O}\{f_1(\underline{x})\} + \beta \mathcal{O}\{f_2(\underline{x})\} \qquad (3\text{-}36)$$

where $\alpha$ and $\beta$ are arbitrary scalars.

Two additional remarks are:

1. The concept of linearity should be distinguished from other independent concepts such as time or space-varying; and

**2.** Alternately, a linear operator is one for which superposition (indicated above) holds.

By representing an image function using the sifting property of the $\delta$ function, we arrive at:

$$f_1(x,y) = \int\int_{-\infty}^{\infty} f_1(\xi,\eta)\delta(x-\xi, y-\eta)d\xi d\eta \tag{3-37}$$

Suppose an output image function, $f_2(\underline{x})$ is obtained by a linear operator on $f_1(\underline{x})$, i.e.,

$$f_2(x,y) = \mathcal{O}\{f_1(x,y)\} \tag{3-38}$$

The concepts of a linear operator and the above decomposition of $f_1$ allows us to expand (3-38) as:

$$f_2(x,y) = \int\int_{-\infty}^{\infty} f_1(\xi,\eta)\,\mathcal{O}\{\delta(x-\xi, y-\eta)\}d\xi d\eta \tag{3-39}$$

where the second term in the above integral is defined as the *impulse response function* or *point-spread function* of the linear system, i.e.,

$$\mathcal{O}\{\delta(x-\xi, y-\eta\} \triangleq h(x,y,\xi,\eta) \tag{3-40}$$

is the response of the system, at $(x,y)$, to a 2-D point source applied at $(\xi,\eta)$. If the system is *space (or shift) invariant*, then

$$h(x,y,\xi,\eta) = h(x-\xi, y-\eta) \tag{3-41}$$

that is, the response is only a function of the (vector) *difference* between the point of application and response, not the absolute locations.

Applying the result of Eq. 3-41 to Eq. 3-39 yields

$$f_2(x,y) = \int\int_{-\infty}^{\infty} f_1(\xi,\eta)h(x-\xi, y-\eta)d\xi d\eta \tag{3-42}$$

which is referred to as the *convolution integral* for a linear, space invariant 2-D system.

# ■ CONVOLUTION, CORRELATION AND RELATED OPERATIONS

We digress to explore some of the ramifications as well as alternate and associated formulations of the convolution operation expressed in Eq. 3-42. The formulation of Eq. 3-42 spawns two associated and similar operations—namely, *correlation* and *matched filtering*. In many papers and texts on the subject, convolution and correlation are loosely interpreted as identical, which is not the case unless additional conditions are met. However, convolution and correlation may be formulated in terms of one another.

2-D and higher dimensional convolution is merely an extension of the 1-D formulation. First, notice that the convolution integral of Eq. 3-42 is formulated with the input image function, $f_1$, and the system impulse response function, $h$, expressed in terms of the $(\varepsilon, \eta)$ coordinate system. Without loss of generality, assume that the coordinate system origin is chosen such that both functions are centered about $(0, 0)$. Note also that typically (or practically) the system impulse response, $h$, is only nonzero over a finite region in the $(\varepsilon, \eta)$ plane, denoted $R$, and therefore the infinite limits in Eq. 3-42 are only of theoretical significance. As a practical matter, the amount of computation required to form the output image, $f_2$, is related to the nonzero extent of $h$, which is typically small relative to the extent of the input image, $f_1$. A convenient interpretation of the convolution operation of Eq. 3-42 leads to a graphical interpretation as follows:

1. Rotate $h(\varepsilon, \eta)$ about the origin by 180° in the $(\varepsilon, \eta)$ plane. This is a reflection of $h$ about both the $\varepsilon$ and $\eta$ axes. This forms $h(-\varepsilon, -\eta)$.
2. Translate the rotated or reflected $h$ by an amount $(x, y)$ with respect to $f_1(\varepsilon, \eta)$ in the $(\varepsilon, \eta)$ plane. This forms $h(x - \varepsilon, y - \eta)$. For example, the value of $h(0, 0)$ is now at location $(x, y)$. This makes intuitive sense, since one contribution to $f_2$ at $(x, y)$ should be due to the response to an impulse at this point in the input image. This is determined by $h(0,0)$.
3. Integrate $f_1(\varepsilon, \eta) \, h(x - \varepsilon, y - \eta)$ over the region in which both functions are nonzero.

This is shown graphically in Figure 3.2a.

Through a change of variables, the convolution expression of Eq. 3-42 may be reformulated as

$$f_2(x, y) = \iint_{-\infty}^{\infty} f_1(x - \varepsilon, y - \eta) \, h(\varepsilon, \eta) \, d\varepsilon \, d\eta \qquad (3\text{-}42b)$$

The associated operation of *correlation* of an image function, $f_1$, and another function, $h$, may be expressed as

$$f_2(x, y) = \iint_{-\infty}^{\infty} f_1(\varepsilon, \eta) \, h(\varepsilon + x, \eta + y) \, d\varepsilon \, d\eta \qquad (3\text{-}42c)$$

Again through a change of variables, the correlation of Eq. 3-42c may be written as

$$f_2(x, y) = \iint_{-\infty}^{\infty} f_1(\varepsilon - x, \eta - y) \, h(\varepsilon, \eta) \, d\varepsilon \, d\eta \qquad (3\text{-}42d)$$

Note that *the operations of convolution and correlation differ only in the 180° rotation (or reflection) of $h(\varepsilon, \eta)$.* If $h(\varepsilon, \eta)$ is symmetric with respect to the $\varepsilon$ and $\eta$ axes, these operations yield the same result. Due to symmetry $h(\varepsilon, \eta)$, many formulations used for enhancement and restoration often refer to these operations as either correlation or convolution. A graphical view of correlation is shown in Figure 3.2b.

Finally, as a prelude to matching operations in Chapter 6, we remark that the operations of convolution in Eq. 3-42 and correlation in Eq. 3-42c may be viewed alternately as the equivalent processes of *matched filtering* and *template matching*, respectively. Both operations are used to find regions in the image function, $f_1(\varepsilon, \eta)$, which closely match a function termed the *template*. In the case of matched filtering, $h(\varepsilon, \eta)$ is chosen to be a 180°-rotated version of the template, whereas in correlation we use the value of the template for $h(\varepsilon, \eta)$.

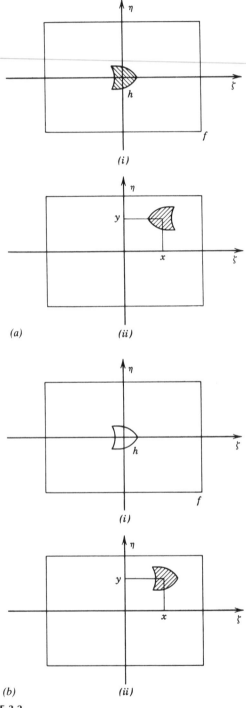

**FIGURE 3.2**

(a)  Graphical view of convolution from (3-42)
    (i)   Functions f and h (nonzero regions of support shown)
    (ii)  The convolution result (integral of product in shaded region)
(b)  Graphical view of correlation from (3-42c)
    (i)   Image of f and template h
    (ii)  Correlation of f and h at location x

# ■ DISCRETE VERSIONS OF CONVOLUTION AND CORRELATION

The discrete version of convolution and correlation follow from the analog formulations. The discrete convolution of functions $f_1$ and $h$, to produce $f_2$, may be written as

$$f_2(m, n) = \sum_{i=0}^{M-1} \sum_{j=0}^{N-1} f_1(i, j) \, h(m - i, n - j) \qquad (3\text{-}42e)$$

where the limits on the summation are due to the assumed rectangular region of support (or an $M \times N$ "window") of $h$. In contrast with Eq. 3-42e, "periodic" convolution of the functions $f$ and $h$ is defined as

$$f_2(m, n) = \sum_{i=0}^{M-1} \sum_{j=0}^{N-1} f_1(i, j) \, h([m - i], [n - j]) \qquad (3\text{-}42f)$$

where $h$ is assumed periodic with

$$[m - i] = (m - i) \bmod M$$

and

$$[n - i] = (n - i) \bmod N$$

Note, without proof, that the second definition of discrete convolution is necessary to yield the multiplicative property of the corresponding discrete signal spectra in the frequency domain (i.e., the DFTs of $f_1$ and $h$). Recall that due to sampling, $f_1$ is also assumed periodic. This assumption poses a small dilemma, since neither function, practically speaking, is periodic. To overcome this dilemma, and therefore be able to use the frequency domain analysis tools, we assume that $f_1$ and $h$ are defined over larger sampling lattices whose corresponding extents are much greater than the regions of support of $f_1$ and $h$. *This is accomplished in practice by forming the larger arrays by padding* f *and* h *in two dimensions with zeros to achieve the larger extent.*

Similarly, the discrete correlation of $f_1$ and $h$ may be written by analogy with Eq. 3-42c as

$$f_2(m, n) = \sum_{i=0}^{M-1} \sum_{j=0}^{N-1} f_1(i, j) \, h(m + i, n + j) \qquad (3\text{-}42g)$$

The graphical interpretations for these operations using discrete functions are analogous to their continuous counterparts.

RELATION BETWEEN CONVOLUTION AND THE FOURIER TRANSFORM

It is a well known 1-D result that convolution of two waveforms in the spatial domain corresponds to the equivalent operation of multiplication of their respective Fourier transforms in the Fourier (or frequency) domain. This result carries over directly into 2-D in both the continuous and discrete formulations, with the proviso that in the latter periodic convolution is used. This result is significant since it facilitates study of the frequency domain behavior of many of the discrete spatial or "window" functions used for smoothing, sharpening, and other enhancement and restoration functions. Furthermore, efficient implementation of many spatial domain computations may be achieved in the frequency domain. This partially explains the utility of fast, parallel, and optical implementation of the Fourier transform.

## THE 2-D DISCRETE FOURIER TRANSFORM

This transform was alluded to in Eq. 3-34 and Eq. 3-35. In addition, we have seen how to write its 1-D counterpart in matrix notation. Consider a 2-D image function matrix $[f]$, written as the $N \times N$ matrix:

$$[f] = \begin{bmatrix} f(0,0) & f(0,1) & \cdots & f(0,N-1) \\ f(1,0) & & & \\ \vdots & & & \\ \vdots & & & \\ f(N-1,0) & & \cdots & f(N-1,N-1) \end{bmatrix} \tag{3-43}$$

The 2-D Discrete Fourier Transform (DFT) and Discrete Inverse Fourier Transform (DIFT) definitions, respectively, may initially be written using summation notation

(DFT)

$$F(k, l) = \frac{1}{N} \sum_{m=0}^{N-1} \sum_{n=0}^{N-1} f(m, n) \exp\left[\frac{-2\pi j(km + ln)}{N}\right] \tag{3-44}$$

and

(DIFT)

$$f(m, n) = \frac{1}{N} \sum_{k=0}^{N-1} \sum_{l=0}^{N-1} F(k, l) \exp\left[\frac{2\pi j(km + ln)}{N}\right] \tag{3-45}$$

Three notes regarding this transform pair are in order:

1. Note that the scale factor $(1/N^2)$ in Eqs. 3-44 and 3-45 has been distributed equally between the DFT and the DIFT. This is a matter of convenience; it is equally valid to formulate these transforms distributing the scale factor differently.
2. Continuous versions of these transforms are considered later.
3. The DIFT of Eq. 3-45 may be implemented using the structure of the forward transform Eq. 3-44, by replacing coefficients $F(k, l)$ with their conjugates and conjugating the result; that is, an alternate formulation in the form of Eq. 3-44 is

$$f(m, n) = \left[\frac{1}{N} \sum_{k=0}^{N-1} \sum_{l=0}^{N-1} F^*(k, l) \exp\left[-\frac{2\pi j(km + ln)}{N}\right]\right]^* \tag{3-45b}$$

An examination of the exponential term in Eqs. 3-44 and 3-45 indicates

$$\exp\left[\frac{-2\pi j(km + ln)}{N}\right] = \exp\left[\frac{-2\pi jkm}{N}\right] \exp\left[\frac{-2\pi jln}{N}\right] \tag{3-46}$$

Each of the factors on the right hand side of Eq. 3-46 is a complex number of magnitude 1.0, and may be written as

$$W_{km} = \exp\left[\frac{-j2\pi km}{N}\right] \tag{3-47}$$

The phase of $W_{km}$ changes, for fixed $N$, as $k$ and $m$ vary. The modulo-$2\pi$ characteristic of exponential functions in Eq. 3-47 constrains $W_{km}$, for all discrete values of $k$ and $m$, to assume at most $N$ distinct values, often referred to as the "$N$ roots of unity," since these values are the solutions, $X$, to

$$X = \overline{Z}^{1/N} \tag{3-48}$$

where

$$\overline{Z} = \exp[-j2\pi n] \tag{3-49}$$

Note $\overline{Z}$ equals 1.0 for any value of $n$.

In a manner similar to that of Eq. 3-15, we define an NXN complex matrix, $W$, whose rows and columns are indexed from 0 to $N - 1$ and whose $k,m^{th}$ element is $W_{km}$. Thus,

$$W = [W_{km}] \tag{3-50}$$

Since we developed the 1-D DFT in Section 2(a)–(i) using the same matrix, we recall that

1. $W$ is symmetric; and
2. $W^{-1} = [1/N]\, W^*$

One extremely important property of $W$ is that it may be decomposed into the product of $2n$ sparse matrices, where $n = \log_2 N$. This explains why we want $N$ to be a power of 2. This decomposition is the basis of the "fast Fourier transform" or FFT [Tretter, (1976)].

Using the definitions in Eqs. 3-46, 3-47, and 3-50, we may now write the 2-D DFT of Eq. 3-44 in matrix form. Expanding Eq. 3-44 using the definition of Eq. 3-47 yields

$$F(k, l) = \frac{1}{N}\sum_{m=0}^{N-1}\left[\sum_{n=0}^{N-1} f(m, n)W_{ln}\right] W_{km} \tag{3-51}$$

Notice the inner sum in Eq. 3-51 is a function of the indices $m$ and $l$ and may be written as $H(m, l)$. Alternately, this partial product may be written in matrix form as

$$H = [f]\, W \tag{3-52}$$

where

$$H = [H(m,l)] \tag{3-53}$$

Thus, Eq. 3-51 becomes

$$F(k,l) = \frac{1}{N}\sum_{m=0}^{N-1} H(m, l)W_{km} \tag{3-54}$$

We may write the sum indicated in Eq. 3-54 as a matrix product, yielding

$$[F] = \frac{1}{N} W [f] W \qquad (3\text{-}55)$$

where $[F]$ is a matrix whose $k,l^{\text{th}}$ entry is $F(k,l)$; that is,

$$[F] = \begin{bmatrix} F(0,0) & F(0,1) & \cdots & F(0,N-1) \\ F(1,0) & F(1,1) & & \\ \vdots & & & \\ F(n-1,0) & F(N-1,1) & \cdots & F(N-1,N-1) \end{bmatrix} \qquad (3\text{-}56)$$

1. Due to the "almost orthogonal" property of $W$, the inverse of Eq. 3-55 is easily shown to be

$$[f] = \frac{1}{N} W^*[F]W^* \qquad (3\text{-}57)$$

   Thus, the 2-D DIFT has a structure analogous to the 1-D inverse (i.e., Eq. 3-26).

2. The 2-D DFT and IDFT may be computed using the 1-D DFT and, more important, "fast" implementations. This is seen by examining Eqs. 3-55 and 3-16. Writing Eq. 3-55 as

$$[F] = \left[ \frac{1}{N} W [f] \right] W \qquad (3\text{-}58)$$

   indicates that the first operation is a 1-D DFT on each of the $N$ columns of $[f]$. Following this (since $W = W^T$), a 1-D DFT is then performed on the rows of the previous transform.

   This result is not unique; we might choose to partition Eq. 3-58 alternately and, for example, compute a 1-D DFT in the rows of $[f]$, followed by a 1-D DFT on the columns of this intermediate result. We should also not place too much significance on the choice of where to place the $1/N$ factor in Eq. 3-55. For example, an alternate formulation is obtained by defining a new (unitary) version of $W$, denoted $\overline{W}$, as

$$\overline{W} = \frac{W}{\sqrt{N}} \qquad (3\text{-}59)$$

   Thus,

$$[\overline{W}]^{-1} = \sqrt{N}\, W^{-1} = \frac{W^*}{\sqrt{N}} = \overline{W}^* \qquad (3\text{-}60)$$

3. Most importantly, the DFT operation indicated by Eq. 3-55, *represents a change of basis function matrices*. For example, using Eqs. 3-55 and 3-7, the basis function of the $(0,0)^{\text{th}}$ element of $[F]$ corresponds to the outer product

of the first column and first row of $W$ and is

$$E_{11} = \left(\frac{1}{N}\right) > \underline{W}_1, \underline{W}_1 < = \frac{1}{N} \begin{bmatrix} 1 & 1 & \cdots & 1 \\ 1 & 1 & & \\ & & \cdot & \\ & & \cdot & \\ & & \cdot & \\ 1 & 1 & \cdots & 1 \end{bmatrix} \quad (3\text{-}61)$$

Thus, using Eq. 3-6 we see that $F(0,0)$ is obtained by projecting the image function onto the basis function in Eq. 3-61, thereby determining the "DC value." Similar analysis for other transform elements may be carried out within the framework of Eqs. 3-6 and 3-11; however, the complex property of the $W$ matrix makes modification of the basis function analysis necessary (see the problems at the end of this chapter).

The 2-D Fourier transform (in particular its discrete version) possesses a number of useful properties that are exploited in the development of image processing algorithms. Those effects due to affine perturbations of $f(\underline{x})$, including shifting, scaling, and rotations, are derived in Appendix 3. Two important properties of the DFT are explored here. The first, which is easily shown, is that the 2-D DFT displays conjugate symmetry about the origin; that is, from Eq. 3-44 it may be shown

$$F^*(-u, -v) = F(u, v) \quad (3\text{-}62)$$

The second property is significant for several reasons and concerns the effect of a shift (or translation) in the image function. From Eq. 3-44 it may be shown that the following transform properties hold

$$\left[ f(k - k_o, l - l_o) \right] \Leftrightarrow \left[ F(u, v)\exp\frac{-j2\pi(uk_o + vl_o)}{N} \right] \quad (3\text{-}63)$$

and

$$\left[ \exp\left[\frac{j2\pi(u_ok + v_ol)}{N}\right] f(k,l) \right] \Leftrightarrow \left[ F(u - u_o, v - v_o) \right] \quad (3\text{-}64)$$

Recalling that the origin of our coordinate system in the sampled image is $(0,0)$, which corresponds to the upper left hand element of $[F]$, Eq. 3-64 may be used to derive a more suitable viewing arrangement. Forming a new image function matrix by shifting the phase of each element in $[f]$ by the phase modulation function (with $u_o = v_o = N/2$ in Eq. 3-64)

$$p\left[k,l,\frac{N}{2},\frac{N}{2}\right] = \exp\left[\frac{j2\pi\left[\frac{N}{2}k + \frac{N}{2}l\right]}{N}\right] \quad (3\text{-}65)$$

yields, from Eq. 3-64, a new transform function, which is $F(u - N/2, v - N/2)$. This corresponds to a shift of the origin from $(0,0)$ to the approximate center (note $N$ is even; there is no exact center) of the image function matrix, $(N/2, N/2)$. This preprocessing of the image function allows viewing of the Fourier transform in a "centered" reference frame; this aids in comparing digital results with optically achieved Fourier transforms (see Goodman, (1968) for an initial reference), which are inherently "centered-zero."

Note that (fortunately) little effort is involved in preprocessing the image function matrix with the quantity in Eq. 3-65. The reader is left to verify that this quantity reduces as follows

$$p\left[k,l,\frac{N}{2},\frac{N}{2}\right] = (-1)^{k+l} \tag{3-66}$$

Thus, the conversion of the image function that would yield a "noncentered zero" Fourier transform is easily achieved by multiplying each element by this quantity. Equivalently, this corresponds to point-by-point multiplication of $[f]$ by a "checkerboard" pattern of $-1$ and $1$.

Although typically the magnitude of the Fourier transform is calculated and displayed, due to the complex nature of the transform, the phase is equally important. This is described in Oppenheim and Lim (1981).

The final important property of the 2-D Fourier transform is analogous to its 1-D counterpart—namely, that convolution in the spatial domain corresponds to multiplication in the Fourier domain, and vice versa. These effects are useful for the study of linear filtering (Chapter 4) and correlation of the image function with a template (Chapter 6).

FOURIER TRANSFORM EXAMPLES

Several examples of Fourier transform are presented here. All transforms are "centered-zero." Figure 3.3a shows a 128 × 128 pixel binary "image" consisting of an array of eight rectangles. Notice the frequency content of this image:

1. Will not be bandlimited due to the superposition of a number of rect functions, which themselves are not bandlimited; and
2. Is greater in the horizontal direction due to the presence of four blocks/image in this direction, as opposed to two blocks/image in the vertical.

The magnitude of the Fourier transform corresponding to this image is shown in Fig. 3.3b. Since the image consists of the superposition of a series of rect functions, the sinc form of the transform (from Eq. 3-35) follows. Notice the visual effect of the 2-D sinc function. In addition, the effect of remark 2 above is verified by the higher-frequency characteristics observed in the $u$ direction.

Figure 3.3c consists of a 128 × 128 pixel image consisting of four 16-pixel-wide bars or stripes. To illustrate the concept of reconstruction with basis functions (and filtering, which is the subject of Chapter 4), the Fourier transform of this image was computed (not shown). The image was then reconstructed using only the low-frequency values of the Fourier transform—that is, values of $u$ and $v$ in the range [0 . . 8]. This corresponds to a low-pass filtering of the image in the Fourier domain. More significantly, for conceptual purposes this is equivalent to generation of $[f]$ using only 64 (of $128^2$) basis functions of the Fourier transform (corresponding to low frequencies). The expected visual results are shown in Fig. 3.3d, where the inverse-transformed image is noticeably blurred, due to the loss of the contribution because of high-frequency basis functions.

Applications for the Fourier transform include the following:

1. To facilitate an analysis of 2-D (spatial) and 3-D (spatiotemporal) sampling;
2. To enable the reconstruction of images from projections (Chapter 4);
3. To recognize/segment images based on spatial frequency content or texture (Chapter 6);
4. To implement and analyze linear filtering, including high-pass (edge enhancement), and low-pass (noise removal and smoothing) filters (Chapter 4); and
5. To facilitate object recognition and motion analysis (Chapter 5).

OTHER 2-D TRANSFORMS

*Rationale.* The DFT has many useful properties and applications in image processing; however, it has one significant computational drawback: Complex operations are required in both the DFT and the DIFT. Considering the number of samples in $[f]$ and elements in $W$ when $N = 512$ (a medium resolution image), it is useful to seek similar linearly separable transforms, implemented via pre- and post-multiplication of $[f]$ by transform matrices. We therefore seek a transform of the form

$$[F] = P[f]Q \qquad (3\text{-}67)$$

with the following characteristics:

1. It has some useful properties (e.g., the transformed version of an image function displays information that was not immediately apparent by examining $[f]$);
2. It may be implemented via real (as opposed to complex), or perhaps even integer, arithmetic operations. This means $P$ and $Q$ are real matrices in Eq. 3-67; and
3. The inverse of this transform

   i) exists ($P$ and $Q$ are invertible); that is, in general $[f]$ is recovered via

   $$[f] = P^{-1}[F]Q^{-1} \qquad (3\text{-}68)$$

   and

   ii) Eq. 3-68 is easy (computationally) to form. This requires $P^{-1}$ and $Q^{-1}$ to be easily formed, usually without matrix inversion.

It should be noted that the matrix forms of the linearly separable transforms under consideration are principally a conceptual tool that allows the study of the transforms from the viewpoint of basis functions. For example, the DFT may be written either in the matrix form of Eq. 3-67 (i.e., Eq. 3-55) or in summation notation as in Eq. 3-44. It is relatively impractical to form $W$ (or generally $P$ and $Q$) in the actual computer implementation, since these are often very large ($N = 512$, for example) matrices. Therefore, the transform algorithms, when reduced to software, are likely to be in summation form.

Although there exist a multitude of transforms that satisfy the above criteria,

**FIGURE 3.3**

(a) Image of eight rectangles

(b) Fourier transform of Figure B.3(a) (magnitude)

(c) "Bar" image (for Fourier transform) 16 pixel wide bars; 128 × 128 pixel image

(d) (Low pass filtering) inverse Fourier transform of image of Figure B.3(c). (Note: only elements u, v ∈ [0,8] used for reconstruction)

each with its own properties and utility, we concentrate our efforts on a particular transform, hereafter referred to as the Walsh-Hadamard transform. We begin by (recursively) defining the matrix that underlies this particular transform.

*The Walsh-Hadamard Transform.* The Hadamard transform may be developed

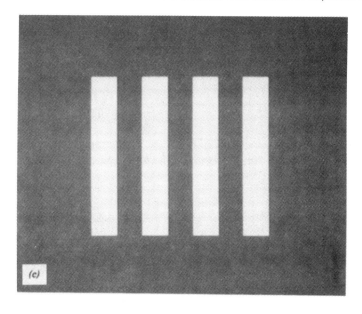

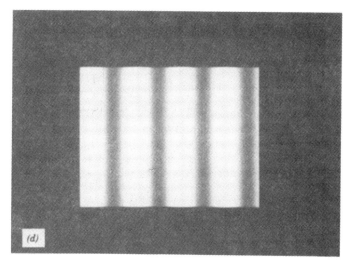

FIGURE 3.3 *(continued)*

in the matrix form of Eq. 3-67 through the NXN Hadamard matrix, $H$, as

$$[F_H] = H[f]H \tag{3-69}$$

Note, in relation to Eq. 3-67, that $P = Q = H$ in this case. In this formulation, the transform matrix may be defined recursively, starting with $N = 2$.

A Hadamard matrix is a matrix whose columns are orthogonal and comprised of elements whose value is either $-1$ or $+1$. For $N = 2$

$$H_2 = \begin{bmatrix} 1 & 1 \\ 1 & -1 \end{bmatrix} \tag{3-70}$$

Equivalently, we may define $H_2$ as a matrix whose $(i, j)^{th}$ element, $h_2(i, j)$

where $i,j \; \varepsilon [0, 1]$

is given by

$$h_2(i, j) = (-1)^{ij} \tag{3-71}$$

Given a Hadamard matrix of order $N$, Hadamard matrices of higher order may be generated by the simple recursive formulation

$$H_{2N} = \begin{bmatrix} H_N & H_N \\ \hline H_N & -H_N \end{bmatrix}$$

It is left to the reader to verify that Hadamard matrices of order $N > 2$ are symmetric and have orthogonal columns, using Eqs. 3-70 and 3-72.

Due to the orthogonality of the columns of $H_N$, it is easily shown that

$$H_N H_N = NI \tag{3-73}$$

Thus, we often normalize $H_N$ to achieve orthonormal columns in the transform matrix, $H$; that is,

$$H = \left[ \frac{1}{\sqrt{N}} \right] H_N \tag{3-73}$$

Let us examine an unnormalized Hadamard transform matrix of order $N = 8$. Applying Eq. 3-72 recursively (twice), starting with $N = 2$, yields

$$H_4 = \begin{bmatrix} 1 & 1 & 1 & 1 \\ 1 & -1 & 1 & -1 \\ 1 & 1 & -1 & -1 \\ 1 & -1 & -1 & 1 \end{bmatrix} \tag{3-74}$$

and

$$H_8 = \begin{bmatrix} 1 & 1 & 1 & 1 & 1 & 1 & 1 & 1 \\ 1 & -1 & 1 & -1 & 1 & -1 & 1 & -1 \\ 1 & 1 & -1 & -1 & 1 & 1 & -1 & -1 \\ 1 & -1 & -1 & 1 & 1 & -1 & -1 & 1 \\ 1 & 1 & 1 & 1 & -1 & -1 & -1 & -1 \\ 1 & -1 & 1 & -1 & -1 & 1 & -1 & 1 \\ 1 & 1 & -1 & -1 & -1 & -1 & 1 & 1 \\ 1 & -1 & -1 & 1 & -1 & 1 & 1 & -1 \end{bmatrix} \tag{3-75}$$

⓪ ⑦ ③ ④ ① ⑥ ② ⑤

Notice from Eq. 3-75 that the major characteristic or property of each column of $H_8$ is the number and spatial arrangement of sign transitions. This is shown via the circled entries under the columns of Eq. 3-75. (A transition is defined as a 1 to

$-1$ or $-1$ to 1 change.) Writing Eq. 3-75 as

$$H_8 = [\underline{h}_0 \underline{h}_1 \cdots \underline{h}_7] \tag{3-76}$$

we see that $\underline{h}_0$ has no sign transitions, $\underline{h}_4$ has one, $\underline{h}_6$ has two, $\underline{h}_2$ has three, $\underline{h}_3$ has four, $\underline{h}_7$ has five, $\underline{h}_5$ has six, and $\underline{h}_1$ has seven.

Although we could analyze this transform with the columns ordered as in Eq. 3-75, a more useful conceptual formulation results if we arrange the columns *in order of increasing sequency*, yielding an unnormalized Walsh transform matrix of order 8, by reordering the columns of Eq. 3-75 as

$$W_8 = \begin{bmatrix} 1 & 1 & 1 & 1 & 1 & 1 & 1 & 1 \\ 1 & 1 & 1 & 1 & -1 & -1 & -1 & -1 \\ 1 & 1 & -1 & -1 & -1 & -1 & 1 & 1 \\ 1 & 1 & -1 & -1 & 1 & 1 & -1 & -1 \\ 1 & -1 & -1 & 1 & 1 & -1 & -1 & 1 \\ 1 & -1 & -1 & 1 & -1 & 1 & 1 & -1 \\ 1 & -1 & 1 & -1 & -1 & 1 & -1 & 1 \\ 1 & -1 & 1 & -1 & 1 & -1 & 1 & -1 \end{bmatrix} \tag{3-76}$$

Notice this matrix may easily be normalized to achieve orthonormal columns using a process equivalent to Eq. 3-73. The Walsh transform results by using a normalized and sequence-ordered Hadamard transform matrix, denoted $W$, as:

$$[F] = W[f]W \tag{3-77a}$$

The properties of $W$ previously cited yield

$$[f] = W[F]W \tag{3-77b}$$

Using the previously developed conceptual framework of Eqs. 3-1 and 3-11—that is, viewing a real separable linear transform as a change of basis functions—it is straightforward to analyze Eq. 3-77. We note several points:

1. The basis functions corresponding to Eq. 3-77 are formed as the outer product of the columns of $W$; that is, the $i,j^{\text{th}}$ basis function in the normalized transform, denoted $E_{ij}$, is given by

$$E_{ij} = \underline{w}_i \underline{w}_j^T \tag{3-78}$$

where $\underline{w}_i$ and $\underline{w}_j$ are the $i^{\text{th}}$ and $j^{\text{th}}$ columns of the normalized $W$ matrix, respectively. For example, in the above $n = 8$ example,

$$E_{00} = \frac{1}{N} \begin{bmatrix} 1 & 1 & 1 & 1 & 1 & 1 & 1 & 1 \\ 1 & 1 & 1 & 1 & 1 & 1 & 1 & 1 \\ 1 & 1 & 1 & 1 & 1 & 1 & 1 & 1 \\ 1 & 1 & 1 & 1 & 1 & 1 & 1 & 1 \\ 1 & 1 & 1 & 1 & 1 & 1 & 1 & 1 \\ 1 & 1 & 1 & 1 & 1 & 1 & 1 & 1 \\ 1 & 1 & 1 & 1 & 1 & 1 & 1 & 1 \\ 1 & 1 & 1 & 1 & 1 & 1 & 1 & 1 \end{bmatrix} \tag{3-79}$$

This basis function matrix is analogous to its Fourier counterpart in the sense that it extracts "DC" information from the image.

Looking at

$$E_{10} = \frac{1}{N} \begin{bmatrix} 1 & 1 & 1 & 1 & 1 & 1 & 1 & 1 \\ 1 & 1 & 1 & 1 & 1 & 1 & 1 & 1 \\ 1 & 1 & 1 & 1 & 1 & 1 & 1 & 1 \\ 1 & 1 & 1 & 1 & 1 & 1 & 1 & 1 \\ -1 & -1 & -1 & -1 & -1 & -1 & -1 & -1 \\ -1 & -1 & -1 & -1 & -1 & -1 & -1 & -1 \\ -1 & -1 & -1 & -1 & -1 & -1 & -1 & -1 \\ -1 & -1 & -1 & -1 & -1 & -1 & -1 & -1 \end{bmatrix} \qquad (3.80a)$$

and

$$E_{01} = \frac{1}{N} \begin{bmatrix} 1 & 1 & 1 & 1 & -1 & -1 & -1 & -1 \\ 1 & 1 & 1 & 1 & -1 & -1 & -1 & -1 \\ 1 & 1 & 1 & 1 & -1 & -1 & -1 & -1 \\ 1 & 1 & 1 & 1 & -1 & -1 & -1 & -1 \\ 1 & 1 & 1 & 1 & -1 & -1 & -1 & -1 \\ 1 & 1 & 1 & 1 & -1 & -1 & -1 & -1 \\ 1 & 1 & 1 & 1 & -1 & -1 & -1 & -1 \\ 1 & 1 & 1 & 1 & -1 & -1 & -1 & -1 \end{bmatrix} \qquad (3\text{-}80b)$$

we see that these basis functions extract the projection (or contribution) of the image onto low-sequency binary functions with variation in the vertical and horizontal directions, respectively.

2. By analogy with the 2-D Fourier transform, where the columns of the transform matrix in Eq. 3-55 consist of samples of sinusoidal waveforms of increasing *frequency*, we note that the columns of $W$ in Eq. 3-77 correspond to samples of a rectangular waveform of increasing *sequency*.

Figure 3.4 illustrates the Hadamard transform of a real 128 × 128 pixel image. Notice the image content is principally contained in the low-sequency components. Figure 3.5 shows a visual display of the basis functions for $N = 8$.

A simple example is used to further reinforce the change-of-basis function concept. Suppose we consider the Hadamard (or Walsh in this case) transform, when $N = 2$, of the following 2 × 2 "image" function

$$[f] = \begin{bmatrix} 1 & -1 \\ -1 & 1 \end{bmatrix} \qquad (3\text{-}81a)$$

In this case, the normalized transform matrix is

$$H_2 = \frac{1}{\sqrt{2}} \begin{bmatrix} 1 & 1 \\ 1 & -1 \end{bmatrix} \qquad (3\text{-}81b)$$

and the transform is given by Eq. 3-69 where

$$[F] = \begin{bmatrix} F(0,0) & F(0,1) \\ F(1,0) & F(1,1) \end{bmatrix} \qquad (3\text{-}81c)$$

First, we calculate the basis function corresponding to transform element $F(1,1)$.

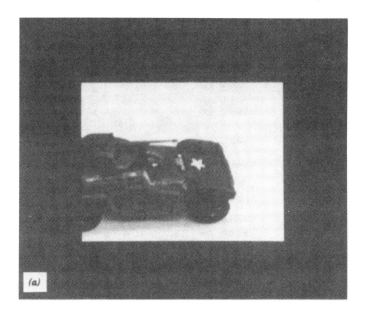

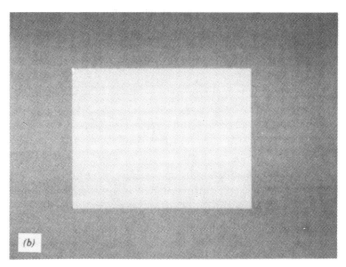

**FIGURE 3.4**
(a)  128 × 128 × 6 bit "tank" image
(b)  Hadamard transform of (a)

From Eq. 3-11 this is

$$E_{11} = \frac{1}{\sqrt{2}} \begin{bmatrix} 1 \\ -1 \end{bmatrix} \begin{bmatrix} 1 & -1 \end{bmatrix} = \frac{1}{2} \begin{bmatrix} 1 & -1 \\ -1 & 1 \end{bmatrix} \qquad (3\text{-}81d)$$

Thus, we notice $[f] = 2 E_{11}$. Computing the transform of $[f]$ confirms this, since applying Eq. 3-69 yields

$$[F] = \frac{1}{2} \begin{bmatrix} 1 & 1 \\ 1 & -1 \end{bmatrix} \begin{bmatrix} 1 & -1 \\ -1 & 1 \end{bmatrix} \begin{bmatrix} 1 & 1 \\ 1 & -1 \end{bmatrix} = \begin{bmatrix} 0 & 0 \\ 0 & 2 \end{bmatrix} \qquad (3\text{-}81e)$$

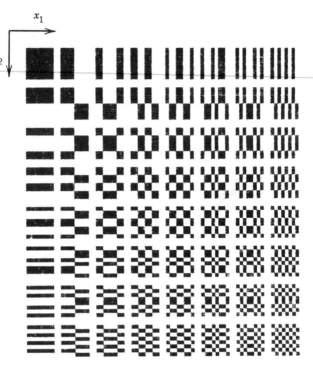

**FIGURE 3.5** Hadamard basis functions (N = 8)

In computing the inverse from Eq. 3-77b, we also note that the function should be recovered from the inverse transform as $[f] = 2\,E_{11}$. The reader is left to verify that this is the case.

3. Although the formulations in Eqs. 3-69 and 3-77 are useful for conceptual purposes, as noted previously it is impractical to implement the Walsh-Hadamard transform by forming $H$ or $W$ and then computing Eq. 3-69 or Eq. 3-77, respectively.

   As an alternative, Eqs. 3-71 and 3-72 may be used to derive a formulation for the Hadamard transform that involves summation notation as

$$F_H(u,\ v) = \frac{1}{N} \sum_{j=0}^{N-1} \sum_{k=0}^{N-1} f(j,\ k)(-1)^{p(j,k,u,v)} \qquad (3\text{-}82a)$$

and

$$p(j,k,u,v) = \sum_{i=0}^{N-1} (u_i j_i + v_i k_i) \qquad (3\text{-}82b)$$

where the $u_i$, $v_i$, $j_i$, and $k_i$ in Eq. 3-82b correspond to the bits in the binary representation of each of these quantities. Here $p$-bit binary numbers are assumed represented in the form

$$u_{p-1}\, u_{p-2}\, \cdots\, u_1 u_0 \qquad (3\text{-}82c)$$

where $u_0$ is the LSB. In addition, a similar formulation for the Walsh transform is available [Pratt (1972)].

4. "Fast" versions of the Walsh-Hadamard transforms exist [Pratt, et. al (1969)].

Viewing transformations such as those above via a change of basis function matrices allows the multitude of linear separable transforms to be treated similarly. For illustration, we cite two additional popular transforms of this form. The first is the Haar transform, where, in terms of Eq. 3-67,

$$P = Q = H_a$$

$H_a$ is a binary matrix consisting of the elements $-1$, $0$, and $1$. The formation of $H_a$ is more complex than that of the Walsh-Hadamard matrix.

*The Slant Transform.* The slant transform is another transform realization of the form of Eq. 3-67. The slant transform matrices $P$ and $Q$ are chosen to be orthonormal and the basis function matrices have 2-D ramp-like characteristics. These matrices are defined recursively [Ahmed and Rao (1975)] starting with the $N = 2$ matrix, which is identical to the normalized Hadamard transform matrix; that is,

$$S_2 = H_2 = \frac{1}{\sqrt{2}} \begin{bmatrix} 1 & 1 \\ 1 & -1 \end{bmatrix} \tag{3-83}$$

Matrices of higher order are defined via the recursive equation

$$S_N = \frac{1}{\sqrt{2}} \begin{bmatrix} \begin{array}{cc|cc} 1 & 0 & & \\ a_N & b_N & [0] & \\ \hline [0] & & I_{(N/2)-2} & \\ 0 & 1 & & \\ \hline & & [0] & \\ -b_N & a_N & & \\ \hline [0] & & I_{(N/2)-2} & \end{array} \middle| \begin{array}{cc|cc} 1 & 0 & & \\ -a_N & b_N & [0] & \\ \hline 0 & & I_{(N/2)-2} & \\ 0 & -1 & & \\ \hline & & [0] & \\ b_N & a_N & & \\ \hline [0] & & -I_{(N/2)-2} & \end{array} \end{bmatrix} \begin{bmatrix} S_{N/2} & [0] \\ \hline [0] & S_{N/2} \end{bmatrix} \tag{3-84}$$

where $S_{N/2}$ denotes the slant transform of order $N/2$, $I_N$ represents an $N \times N$ identity matrix, and the scalars $a_N$ and $b_N$ in Eq. 3-84 are determined for $N \geq 2$ by

$$a_{2N} = \left[ \frac{3N^2}{4N^2 - 1} \right]^{1/2} \tag{3-85a}$$

$$b_{2N} = \left[ \frac{N^2 - 1}{4N^2 - 1} \right]^{1/2} \tag{3-85b}$$

For illustration, we will look at the basis function matrices for the slant transform in the case $N = 8$. To calculate $S_8$, we first calculate $S_4$, using Eqs. 3-83, 3-84, and

3-85 as

$$S_4 = \frac{1}{\sqrt{2}} \begin{bmatrix} 1 & 0 & 1 & 0 \\ a_4 & b_4 & -a_4 & b_4 \\ \hline 0 & 1 & 0 & -1 \\ -b_4 & a_4 & b_4 & a_4 \end{bmatrix} \begin{bmatrix} & & 0 & 0 \\ S_2 & & 0 & 0 \\ \hline 0 & 0 & & \\ 0 & 0 & & S_2 \end{bmatrix}$$

(3-86)

$$= \frac{1}{\sqrt{4}} \begin{bmatrix} 1 & 1 & 1 & 1 \\ \frac{3}{\sqrt{5}} & \frac{1}{\sqrt{5}} & \frac{-1}{\sqrt{5}} & \frac{-3}{\sqrt{5}} \\ 1 & -1 & -1 & 1 \\ \frac{1}{\sqrt{5}} & \frac{-3}{\sqrt{5}} & \frac{3}{\sqrt{5}} & \frac{-1}{\sqrt{5}} \end{bmatrix}$$

The reader is encouraged to verify the orthogonality property of $S_4$. In a similar fashion, these equations may now be used to generate $S_8$. It is left to the reader to verify

$$S_8 = \frac{1}{\sqrt{8}} \begin{bmatrix} 1 & 1 & 1 & 1 & 1 & 1 & 1 & 1 \\ \frac{7}{\sqrt{21}} & \frac{5}{\sqrt{21}} & \frac{3}{\sqrt{21}} & \frac{1}{\sqrt{21}} & \frac{-1}{\sqrt{21}} & \frac{-3}{\sqrt{21}} & \frac{-5}{\sqrt{21}} & \frac{-7}{\sqrt{21}} \\ 1 & -1 & -1 & 1 & 1 & -1 & -1 & 1 \\ \frac{1}{\sqrt{5}} & \frac{-3}{\sqrt{5}} & \frac{3}{\sqrt{5}} & \frac{-1}{\sqrt{5}} & \frac{1}{\sqrt{5}} & \frac{-3}{\sqrt{5}} & \frac{3}{\sqrt{5}} & \frac{-1}{\sqrt{5}} \\ \frac{3}{\sqrt{5}} & \frac{1}{\sqrt{5}} & \frac{-1}{\sqrt{5}} & \frac{-3}{\sqrt{5}} & \frac{-3}{\sqrt{5}} & \frac{-1}{\sqrt{5}} & \frac{1}{\sqrt{5}} & \frac{3}{\sqrt{5}} \\ \frac{7}{\sqrt{105}} & \frac{-1}{\sqrt{105}} & \frac{-9}{\sqrt{105}} & \frac{-17}{\sqrt{105}} & \frac{17}{\sqrt{105}} & \frac{9}{\sqrt{105}} & \frac{1}{\sqrt{105}} & \frac{-7}{\sqrt{105}} \\ 1 & -1 & -1 & 1 & -1 & 1 & 1 & -1 \\ \frac{1}{\sqrt{5}} & \frac{-3}{\sqrt{5}} & \frac{3}{\sqrt{5}} & \frac{-1}{\sqrt{5}} & \frac{-1}{\sqrt{5}} & \frac{3}{\sqrt{5}} & \frac{-3}{\sqrt{5}} & \frac{1}{\sqrt{5}} \end{bmatrix}$$

(3-87)

The slant transform may be implemented with this matrix via the separable transform

$$F_s = S[f]S^T \qquad (3-88)$$

Note that Eq. 3-88 is similar in form to our previous formulation of Eq. 3-1 for a change of basis function matrix, with the relation $U = V = S^T$. Thus, in examining basis function matrices for the slant transform, we examine the *columns of* $S^T$ (or, equivalently, the *rows of S*) to get the basis functions, denoted $E_{ij}^s$ from Eq. 3-11 as

$$E_{ij}^s = \,> \underline{s}_i, \underline{s}_j <$$ 

(3-89)

where

$$S_N = \begin{bmatrix} \underline{s}_1^T \\ \underline{s}_2^T \\ \cdot \\ \cdot \\ \cdot \\ \underline{s}_N^T \end{bmatrix}$$

(3-90)

For example, computing $E_{11}^s$ yields

$$E_{11}^s = \frac{1}{8} \begin{bmatrix} 1 & 1 & 1 & 1 & 1 & 1 & 1 & 1 \\ 1 & 1 & 1 & 1 & 1 & 1 & 1 & 1 \\ 1 & 1 & 1 & 1 & 1 & 1 & 1 & 1 \\ 1 & 1 & 1 & 1 & 1 & 1 & 1 & 1 \\ 1 & 1 & 1 & 1 & 1 & 1 & 1 & 1 \\ 1 & 1 & 1 & 1 & 1 & 1 & 1 & 1 \\ 1 & 1 & 1 & 1 & 1 & 1 & 1 & 1 \\ 1 & 1 & 1 & 1 & 1 & 1 & 1 & 1 \end{bmatrix}$$

(3-91)

which is seen to be equivalent to the "DC" basis function of the Fourier or Hadamard transforms. More interestingly, however, is an examination of $E_{12}^s$, given by (the matrix in Eq. 3-87 has been converted to decimal values)

$$E_{12}^s = \frac{1}{8} \begin{bmatrix} 1.53 & 1.09 & 0.655 & 0.218 & -0.218 & -0.655 & -1.09 & -1.53 \\ 1.53 & 1.09 & 0.655 & 0.218 & -0.218 & -0.655 & -1.09 & -1.53 \\ 1.53 & 1.09 & 0.655 & 0.218 & -0.218 & -0.655 & -1.09 & -1.53 \\ 1.53 & 1.09 & 0.655 & 0.218 & -0.218 & -0.655 & -1.09 & -1.53 \\ 1.53 & 1.09 & 0.655 & 0.218 & -0.218 & -0.655 & -1.09 & -1.53 \\ 1.53 & 1.09 & 0.655 & 0.218 & -0.218 & -0.655 & -1.09 & -1.53 \\ 1.53 & 1.09 & 0.655 & 0.218 & -0.218 & -0.655 & -1.09 & -1.53 \\ 1.53 & 1.09 & 0.655 & 0.218 & -0.218 & -0.655 & -1.09 & -1.53 \end{bmatrix}$$

(3-91)

Note that this function represents a 3-D "wedge," which varies in the horizontal direction with a constant slope. Figure (3-6) shows plots of selected $E_{ij}$ for the $N = 8$ case. Figure 3-7 yields a grey-level display of the $8 \times 8$ slant transform basis functions.

The slant transform matrix coefficient $s_{12}$ corresponds to $E_{12}^s$, which, from Eq. 3-6, represents the projection of $[f]$ onto this function. Thus, this coefficient yields an indication of the overall linear variation of the image function in the horizontal direction. Similar remarks may be made for $E_{21}^s$, which is simply the transpose of $E_{12}^s$, and indicates "rampness" of the overall image function in the vertical direction.

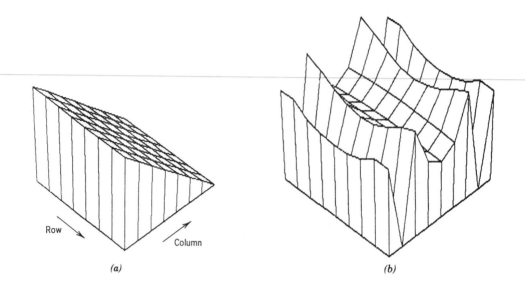

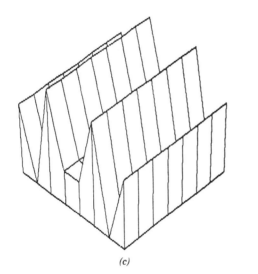

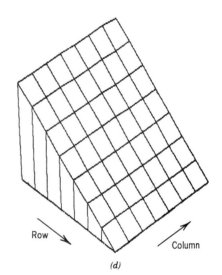

**FIGURE 3.6** Selected slant transform basis functions ($N = 8$)

(a) $E_{12}$
(b) $E_{18}$
(c) $E_{81}$
(d) $E_{21}$
(e) $E_{22}$
(f) $E_{13}$
(g) $E_{31}$
(h) $E_{88}$

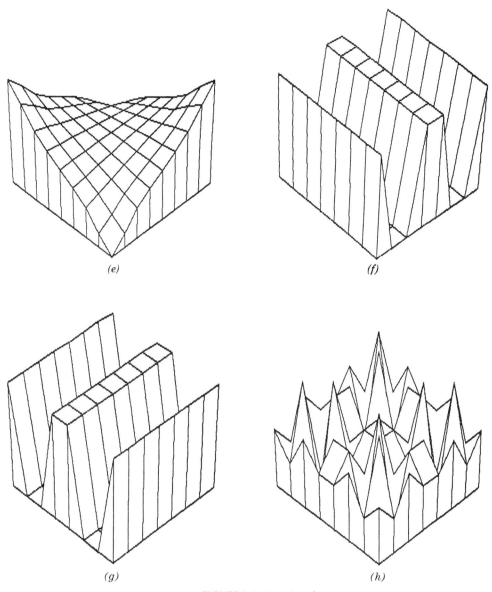

**FIGURE 3.6** *(continued)*

# ■ SAMPLING

Since we are dealing with discrete (perhaps sampled both spatially and temporally) image data, the consequences of the discrete nature of the data are of interest. Some extensions of 1-D sampling theory are of use; however, many of the 2-D (and higher dimensional) computational consequences of sampling are unique.

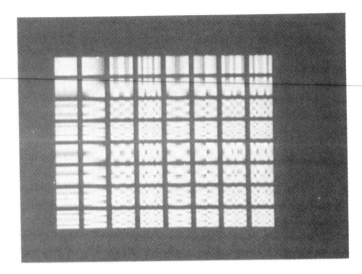

**FIGURE 3.7**  Basis functions for 8 × 8 slant transform (visual display)

Starting from the sampling viewpoint allows the introduction of new concepts, such as:

1. The geometric arrangement of the sampling lattice;
2. The use of multidimensional interpolation functions; and
3. The visual effects of aliasing in space and time.

### SAMPLING FROM THE TRANSFORM VIEWPOINT

#### 1-D SAMPLING THEORY REVIEW

A brief refresher of 1-D time sampling of functions is presented. This widely used approach is usually credited to Whittaker (1915) or Shannon (1949).

We consider the consequences of representing a continuous 1-D function, $f(t)$, in terms of its samples—that is, a new function $f^*(t)$ or $f(kT)$ where $T$ is the (time) sampling interval or period, and $k = 0,1,2. \ldots$ Although the index, $t$, usually denotes time, the presentation is equally valid for 1-D spatial functions—that is, $f(x)$, where $x$ is a spatial argument. In many cases, the validity of the sampled representation depends on whether it is possible to reconstruct $f(t)$ or $f(x)$ from its sampled version. Although this approach assumes reconstruction of the continuous signal as the goal, a number of other ramifications arise. Notice above we have assumed equally spaced samples. This is not necessary. In fact, in the 2-D case we will relax this requirement and only assume samples with some periodicity.

A family of (usually orthogonal) functions, $g( \ )$, is chosen to serve as "interpolation" functions. They are used along with the function samples to recover values of the continuous function not on the sampling grid. One form for the reconstructed signal, $f_r(t)$, is postulated as

$$f_r(t) = \sum_{k=-\infty}^{k=\infty} f(kT)g(t - kT) \tag{3-92}$$

We then seek to determine the conditions on $f$, $g$, and $T$ such that Eq. 3-92 holds for any $t$ of interest.

It is convenient to recast the right hand side quantity in Eq. 3-92 using the "sifting" property of the 1-D Dirac delta function, $\delta$; that is,

$$f(kT)g(t - kT) = \int_{-\infty}^{\infty} f(\tau)g(t - \tau)\delta(\tau - kT)\delta\tau \tag{3-93}$$

Alternately, Eq. 3-93 suggests $f(kT)$ is obtained by modulation with a series of Dirac delta functions $\delta(t - kT)$—that is, a "comb"-like function. Substitution of Eq. 3-93 into Eq. 3-92 and interchanging the order of the summation and integration operations yields

$$f_r(t) = \int_{-\infty}^{\infty} f(\tau)g(t - \tau) \left\{ \sum_{k=-\infty}^{\infty} \delta(\tau - kT) \right\} d\tau \tag{3-94}$$

The bracketed quantity in Eq. 3-94 is periodic and therefore has a Fourier series representation given by

$$\sum_{k=-\infty}^{\infty} \delta(\tau - kT) = \sum_{n=-\infty}^{\infty} a_n \exp\left[ \frac{j2\pi n\tau}{T} \right] \tag{3-95}$$

The coefficients $a_n$ are given by

$$a_n = \frac{1}{T} \int_{-T/2}^{T/2} \left[ \sum_{k=-\infty}^{\infty} \delta(t - kT) \right] \exp\left[ -\frac{j2\pi nt}{T} \right] dt \tag{3-96}$$

The reader may easily verify that Eq. 3-96 reduces to

$$a_n = \frac{1}{T} \forall n \tag{3-97}$$

Substitution of Eq. 3-97 into Eq. 3-94 yields

$$f_r(t) = \sum_{n=-\infty}^{\infty} \int_{-\infty}^{\infty} \left[ f(\tau)\exp\left[ j\frac{2\pi n\tau}{T} \right] \right] \left[ \frac{g(t - \tau)}{T} \right] d\tau \tag{3-98}$$

which is a *convolution* of the functions

$$f(\tau)\exp\left[ j\frac{2\pi n\tau}{T} \right]$$

and

$$\frac{g(\tau)}{T}$$

Therefore, the convolution and shifting properties of the Fourier transform enable this result to be written in the Fourier domain as

$$F_r(\omega) = \frac{1}{T} G(\omega) \cdot \sum_{n=-\infty}^{\infty} F\left[ \omega - \frac{2\pi n}{T} \right] \tag{3-99}$$

where $F_r(\omega)$ represents the Fourier transform of $f_r(t)$, $F(\omega)$ represents the transform of $f(t)$, and $G(\omega)$ corresponds to the Fourier transform of the interpolation function, $g(t)$.

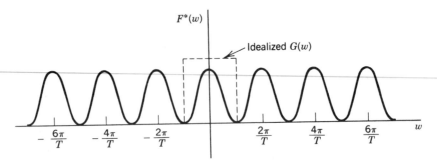

**FIGURE 3.8**  F ∗ (w) for case of no aliasing (bandlimited signal; ideal sampling)

Eqs. 3-99 and 3-92 are a 1-D Fourier transform pair and illustrate several well-known ramifications of sampling:

1. The Fourier transform, $F^*(\omega)$, of the sampled signal, $f(kT)$, is given by

$$F^*(\omega) = \frac{1}{T} \sum_{n=-\infty}^{\infty} F\left[\omega - \frac{2\pi n}{T}\right] \qquad (3\text{-}100)$$

   That is, $F^*(\omega)$ consists of an infinite number of replications of the unsampled signal spectrum, $F(\omega)$, each centered around multiples of $2\pi/T$ in the $\omega$ domain (this is shown in Figure 3.8);

2. The summation in Eq. 3-100 implies that unless $F(\omega)$ is bandlimited such that

$$F(\omega) = 0 \quad \text{for} \quad |\omega| > \frac{\pi}{T} \qquad (3\text{-}101a)$$

   $F^*(\omega)$ will be a corruption of $F(\omega)$ with the higher frequency copies of $F(\omega)$ affecting the original copy centered at $\omega = 0$;

3. If the conditions in number 2 above hold, $F(\omega)$ may be recovered by forming

$$G(\omega) = \begin{cases} T & |\omega| \leq \dfrac{\pi}{T} \\ 0 & |\omega| > \dfrac{\pi}{T} \end{cases} \qquad (3\text{-}101b)$$

   That is, in the time (or space) domain an ideal reconstruction or interpolation function is given by the inverse transform of Eq. 3-101b and is of the form sinc $(\pi t/T)$.

4. Due to the fact that the interpolation function in number 3 above does not become zero for some $t > t'$, the reconstruction process is often
   i) computationally expensive (all samples of $f(t)$ are needed); and
   ii) approximated with other more computationally tractable interpolation functions (which may depend on the characteristics of $(F(\omega))$.

5. Eq. 3-101a determines, for any $F(\omega)$, what the sampling interval must be to allow reconstruction. Given that $F(\omega)$ is zero for all values of $\omega \geq \omega_c$, this result simplifies to

$$\omega_c < \frac{\pi}{T} \qquad (3\text{-}101c)$$

or, defining $f_s = 1/T$ and

$$f_c = \frac{\omega_c}{2\pi},$$

we get

$$(3\text{-}101d)$$

$$f_s > 2 f_c$$

which is often simply stated as "sample the signal at a rate at least twice as great as the highest frequency in the signal."

### N-D CONTINUOUS FOURIER TRANSFORMS

An analysis of frequency-domain sampling effects in higher dimensions parallels the previous treatment. The notable new concept that arises, however, is that of *shape*. For example, in the 2-D case we now consider the 2-D Fourier transform to be bandlimited if it is nonzero in a *region* of $(u, v)$ space with an arbitrary *shape*. Thus, concerns about the *geometry* of the sampling lattice arise (e.g., it may be rectangular, circular, square, or hexagonal). We begin with a straightforward 2-D extension of the previous case, assuming a rectangular grid of samples.

First, however, we digress briefly to discuss the continuous version of the N-D Fourier transform. For an $N$-dimensional function $f(\underline{x})$, where $\underline{x}$ is an $N \times 1$ vector of arguments (e.g., $N = 3$ would allow the case of a time varying 2-D spatial function where $\underline{x} = (x,y,t)^T$, the N-D Fourier transform of this quantity may be expressed as

$$F(\underline{u}) = \int_X f(\underline{x}) \exp\left[-j2\pi \underline{u}^T \underline{x}\right] d\underline{x} \qquad (3\text{-}102a)$$

where the integral above denotes an $N$-dimensional integration over the region of support of $f(\underline{x})$, that is, $X$. The $N$-dimensional Fourier domain is correspondingly indexed by the $N$ variables, which are components of the $N$-dimensional vector $\underline{u}$ (e.g., $N = 3$ yields the frequency domain arguments $\underline{u} = (u,v,w)^T$ where $u$, $v$, and $w$ are the transform arguments corresponding to $x$, $y$, and $t$, respectively). The inverse of this relationship is, not surprisingly,

$$f(\underline{x}) = \int_U F(\underline{u}) \exp[j2\pi \underline{u}^T \underline{x}] d\underline{u} \qquad (3\text{-}102b)$$

In the case of functions of two spatial arguments—that is, $f(x, y)$—these equations simplify for the familiar transform pair

$$F(u,v) = \int_{-\infty}^{\infty} \int_{\infty}^{\infty} f(x,y) \exp[-j2\pi(ux + vy)] dx dy \qquad (3\text{-}103a)$$

and

$$f(x,y) = \int_{-\infty}^{\infty} \int_{\infty}^{\infty} F(u,v) \exp[+j2\pi(ux + vy)] du dv \qquad (3\text{-}103b)$$

Appendix 3 provides an analysis of the effects on the 2-D Fourier transform of affine transformations of $f(x,y)$. As indicated by (A.3-14), these effects are:

1. A translation (via a vector $\underline{b}$) of $f(\underline{x})$ results in a linear change of phase in $F(\underline{u})$;

**2.** A rotation of $f(x,y)$ rotates $F(u,v)$ accordingly; and

**3.** A dilation or magnification of $f(x,y)$ produces a corresponding "spreading" or "contraction" of $F(u,v)$, as would be expected.

The results in Appendix 3 may be used to generate other conceptually useful results.

2-D (AND HIGHER DIMENSION) SAMPLING AND RAMIFICATIONS

As in the previous sampling derivation, we postulate reconstructability of the continuous 2-D function $f(x,y)$, based on an interpolation function $g(x,y)$ and a sampled version of $f(x,y)$ with $x$ and $y$ spatial sampling intervals $X$ and $Y$, respectively, as

$$f_r(x,y) = \sum_{m=-\infty}^{\infty} \sum_{n=-\infty}^{\infty} f[mX, nY]g[x - mX, y - mY] \qquad (3\text{-}104)$$

where $f_r(x,y)$ is the reconstructed signal.

It is left for the reader to show, in a manner analogous to the derivation in Eq. 3-92 through Eq. 3-99, that the spatial convolution in Eq. 3-104 corresponds to a frequency domain multiplication of the form

$$F_R(u,v) = \frac{1}{XY} \sum_{m=-\infty}^{\infty} \sum_{n=-\infty}^{\infty} G(u,v)F\left[u - \frac{m}{X}, v - \frac{n}{Y}\right] \qquad (3\text{-}105)$$

Thus, the replication or copying of $F(u,v)$ in $(u,v)$ space due to sampling results in copies centered around multiples of $1/X$ and $1/Y$. As shown in Figure 3.9, if $F(u,v)$ is nonzero inside a *region*, $R$, in the $u,v$ plane with a certain shape, then it is possible to find spatial sampling increments $X$ and $Y$ such that the replicated versions of $F(u,v)$ in Eq. 3-105 are nonoverlapping. It is especially important to

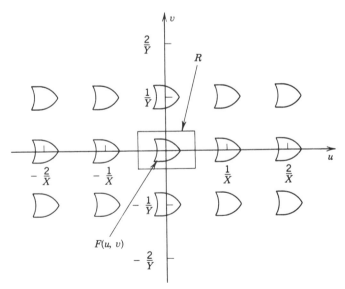

**FIGURE 3.9** 2-D sampling from the frequency (u,v) viewpoint (nonzero regions of the sampled signal spectrum are shown)

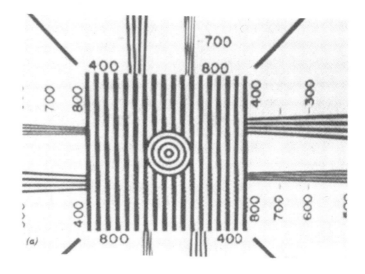

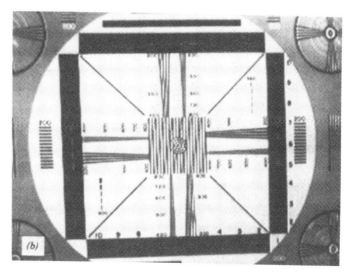

**FIGURE 3.10** Aliasing example
(a) Image with minimal aliasing
(b) Significant aliasing

notice that this overlapping occurs in two dimensions; that is, we are concerned about overlap resulting from the spectrum replication in *either* $u$ or $v$ (or both). This complicates our analysis, in contrast to the 1-D case, since the *shape* of the domain of non-zero $F(u,v)$ must be considered.

Conversely, if $F(u,v)$ is not bandlimited, or $X$ and $Y$ are chosen such that overlapping copies of $F(u,v)$ result in the 2-D sampled signal spectrum, this overlapping causes frequencies from the replicas to effect values of $F(u,v)$ inside $R$. Since these frequencies are two-dimensional, the effects of aliasing in imagery may be visualized in the image as a distortion of spatial frequencies. These effects are shown in the images of Figure 3.10. Finally, notice from Eq. 3-105 that the interpolation function $G(u,v)$ may be specified in the frequency domain as

$$G(u,v) = \begin{cases} XY & \text{for } (u,v) \, \varepsilon \, R \\ 0 & \text{elsewhere} \end{cases} \tag{3-106}$$

The previous derivation allows the spatial sampling *increments* to be unequal. Thus, for a given *shape* of $F(u,v)$, it is possible to choose $X$ and $Y$ such that the sampled signal spectrum shown in Figure 3.9 is "packed" as tightly as possible. A practical application for this type of nonsquare (i.e., rectangular) sampling lattice is in generating the minimum number of samples of a signal with a priori known unequal $x$ and $y$ variations. For example, given a signal

$$f(x,y) = \frac{\sin(x)}{(x)} \cdot \frac{\sin(3y)}{(3y)} \tag{3-107}$$

(the reader is left to verify that this signal has a rectangular region of support in the $(u,v)$ plane), this signal may be sampled with sampling increments related by $X = 3Y$, due to the fact that the $y$-direction variation is three times that in the $x$-direction.

The preceding analysis may be generalized [Peterson and Middleton (1962)] to consider the effects of nonorthogonal spatial sampling lattices. For example, whereas the previous derivations define sampling intervals to be integer multiples of orthogonal vectors in the $x$ and $y$ dimension (of length $X$ and $Y$), a more general approach in $N$-dimensions is to form a *sampling lattice* from a set of basis vectors for the $N$-dimensional space

$$\{\underline{v}_1, \underline{v}_2, \ldots, \underline{v}_N\} \tag{3-108}$$

An $N$-dimensional spatial *sampling lattice*, denoted $v_{[l]}$, is then generated via a linear combination of multiples of these vectors as:

$$\underline{v}_{[l]} = l_1\underline{v}_1 + l_2\underline{v}_2 + \cdots + l_N\underline{v}_N \tag{3-109}$$

where the $l_i$ are integers.

The Fourier transform of a continuous (unsampled) $N$-dimensional function was defined in Eq. 3-102a in vector notation as

$$F(\underline{u}) = \int_X f(\underline{x})\exp[-j2\pi\underline{u}^T\underline{x}]dx \tag{3-110}$$

where $\underline{x}$ and $\underline{u}$ are $N \times 1$ vectors of arguments in the original and transformed spaces, respectively. In the multidimensional case, the $N$-dimensional Fourier transform of $F(\underline{u})$ is then replicated, due to sampling, in $(u_1, u_2, \ldots, u_N)$ space, along a set of *reciprocal basis vectors*, $\underline{u}_k$, defined via

$$\langle \underline{v}_j, \underline{u}_k \rangle = \delta_{jk} \qquad j,k = 1, 2, \ldots, N \tag{3-111}$$

where $\delta_{jk}$ is the Kroneker delta function. For example, in the 2-D case in which the sampling lattice in the $\underline{x} = (x,y)^T$ domain is given by

$$\underline{v}_1 = \begin{bmatrix} 1 \\ 0 \end{bmatrix} \tag{3-112a}$$

and

$$\underline{v}_2 = \begin{bmatrix} 1 \\ 1 \end{bmatrix} \tag{3-112b}$$

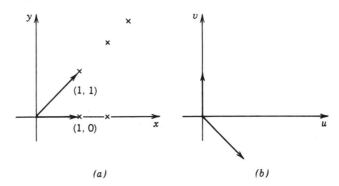

**FIGURE 3.11** Reciprocal basis vectors example for 2-D case
(a)   Spatial sampling lattice
(b)   Frequency domain array

it is easily shown that the reciprocal basis functions that generate the Fourier domain
spectrum are:

$$\underline{u}_1 = \begin{bmatrix} 1 \\ -1 \end{bmatrix}$$

and                                                                                                        (3-112c)

$$\underline{u}_2 = \begin{bmatrix} 0 \\ 1 \end{bmatrix}$$

This is shown in Figure 3.11.

Recall that the spatial "narrowing" of a 1-D signal results in a "spreading" in
the 1-D Fourier domain. Similarly, the "narrowing" (i.e., a decrease in the angle
between $\underline{v}_1$ and $\underline{v}_2$) of the 2-D spatial sampling lattice results in a "spreading" (i.e.,
a consequent increase in the angle between $\underline{u}_1$ and $\underline{u}_2$) in the frequency domain.

SAMPLING FROM THE SPATIAL DOMAIN VIEWPOINT

The 2-D image effects due to sampling may be studied from several alternative
viewpoints:

1.  Aliasing only affects image regions where the existence of spatial frequencies
    sufficiently high (relative to the sampling rate) allow it to exist. In many
    practical applications, these regions are small, contain insignificant features,
    and are often overlooked by humans viewing the sampled imagery.
2.  The modifications to the spectrum of a sampled image may be studied via
    shape distortion. Typical effects are shown in Figure 3.12. Part (a) shows
    the shape distortion and high (spatial) frequency artifacts introduced in the
    sampled version of alphanumeric quantities. (It might be remarked that this
    effect is often ignored by the HVS.) Part (b) shows the severe loss of infor-
    mation and shape distortion incurred in sampling with a coarse lattice. Finally,
    Part (c) shows the possible shape misinterpretations (or ambiguities) possible
    in undersampling a binary pattern.
3.  In non-bandlimited imagery (e.g., an image containing a 2-D step function),
    spatial sampling of the image introduces an uncertainty in the spatial location
    of the continuous domain edge.

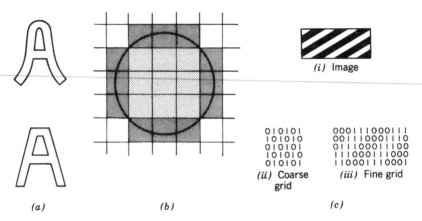

(a)   (b)   (c)

**FIGURE 3.12**   Spatial domain sampling effects
(a)   Boundary discretization
(b)   Shape distortion
(c)   Ambiguity due to resolution
   (i)   Image
   (ii)   Coarse grid
   (iii)   Ambiguity due to resolution

4. Undersampling or skipping spatial samples (either pixels or lines) is a simple approach to image compression. The frequency domain model for sampling allows the quantitative analysis of this strategy. Prefiltering the images to be compressed may minimize aliasing effects.

5. The ideal interpolation or reconstruction function in Eq. 3-102 is seldom used. Instead, it is usually approximated with a local spatial filter with low-pass characteristics and implemented in the spatial domain (Chapter 4). This approach mimics the low-pass filter of the HVS (with cutoff frequency of about $f_c = 40$ cycles/image), which often explains why undersampled imagery appears more discernible when held some distance from the eyes.

6. The selection of a spatial sampling lattice shape or arrangement may be guided by concerns other than aliasing. For example, consider the measurement of concentric circular objects, with a circular sampling grid consisting of samples taken at spatial locations:

$$x = k \cos (n\Delta\theta)$$

$$(3\text{-}113)$$

$$y = k \sin (n\Delta\theta)$$

where

$$k = 0, 1, 2, \ldots, k_{max}$$

and

$$n = 0, 1, 2, \ldots, \left[\frac{2\pi}{\Delta\theta} - 1\right]$$

For a predetermined camera geometry, this spatial sampling grid reflects the shape of the imaged object. For practical (hardware) reasons, sampling lattices other than rectangular are seldom employed.

7. Perhaps the most significant effect of sampling is not in the aliasing effects, but rather in the need for interpolation and the loss of feature metric properties, which arise in implementing geometric transforms [Rosenfeld and Johnson (1970)].

For example, a major problem with rotations of sampled 2-D image data with angles other than multiples of 90° is that such rotations are not, in general, one-to-one transformations of points on the (spatial) sampling lattice. Furthermore, in order to preserve length, it is not generally possible to preserve the number of points, and vice versa. This is shown by a simple example using the following binary "image" function.

Given a 5 × 5 image function:

$$
\begin{matrix}
0 & 0 & 1 & 0 & 0 \\
0 & 0 & 1 & 0 & 0 \\
0 & 0 & 1 & 0 & 0 \\
0 & 0 & 1 & 0 & 0 \\
0 & 0 & 1 & 0 & 0
\end{matrix}
$$

a counterclockwise rotation of this function produces (assuming the image function is zero outside of the 5 × 5 grid):

$$
\begin{matrix}
1 & 0 & 0 & 0 & 0 \\
0 & 1 & 0 & 0 & 0 \\
0 & 0 & 1 & 0 & 0 \\
0 & 0 & 0 & 1 & 0 \\
0 & 0 & 0 & 0 & 1
\end{matrix}
$$

Notice, for a fixed sampling grid dimension, the rotated image contains the rotated feature (a line), but the length of this feature is the $\sqrt{2}$ times its length in the unrotated image. Clearly, this effect would not occur if the object in the scene that generated the original image were rotated $-45°$ with respect to the $x$-$y$ image plane, and the second (sampled) image acquired.

## TEMPORAL SAMPLING EFFECTS

We extend the analysis of the previous section further to sampling imagery spatially and *temporally*, thus yielding a 3-D sampling case. For example, consider the reduced dimension case of a 1-D time varying "image" that is sampled in 2 dimensions, spatially and temporally. (Whereas the case of a 2-D time-varying image function is conceptually no more difficult, it presents visualization difficulties due to the 4-D display required for the function of three independent variables.)

Suppose the 1-D "image" is a moving cosine function that results in a 2-D function of $x$ and $t$ as

$$f(x,t) = f(x - \bar{v}t,0) \qquad (3\text{-}114a)$$

where

$$f(x,0) = \cos x \qquad (3\text{-}114b)$$

For simplicity, the (constant) "velocity" of the moving wave is $\bar{v} = \pi/2$ pixel units/second. Figure 3.13 shows a sketch of $f(x,t)$ in continuous time and space. Note

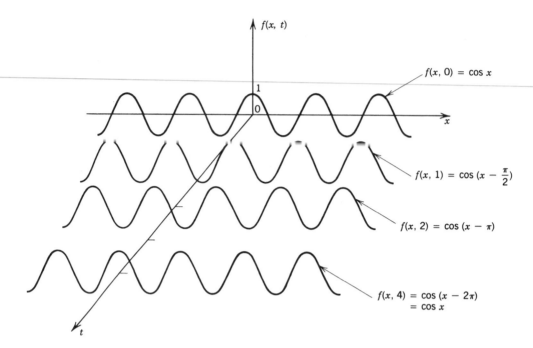

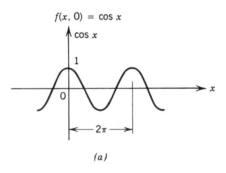

(a)

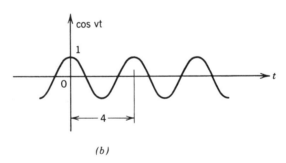

(b)

**FIGURE 3.13**

(a)  f(x,t) from (3-114a)

(b)  Slices along x and t axes

(c)  Example of motion

(d)  Spectrum of sampled f(x,t) (no aliasing)

(e)  Sampled signal spectrum (aliasing due to temporal under-sampling)

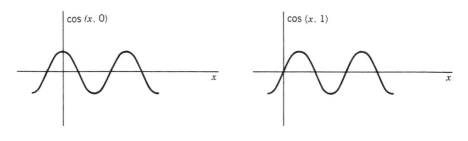

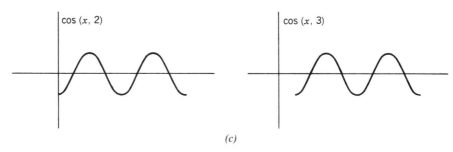

(c)

**FIGURE 3.13** *(continued)*

*(continued on next page)*

that the formulation of Eq. 3-114 yields a 1-D image moving to the right—that is, in the $+x$ direction.

We now determine the minimum spatial and temporal sampling intervals necessary to avoid aliasing. In this simple example, since the spatial frequency of the 1-D image does not change with time, we may determine a time-invariant spatial sampling rate that satisfies the Nyquist criteria. As shown in Figure 3.13$a$, the maximum spatial sampling interval, denoted $\Delta X$, must satisfy

$$\Delta x < \frac{1}{2\left[\frac{1}{2\pi}\right]} = \pi \tag{3-115a}$$

Similarly, $f(x,t)$ may also be considered a periodic function in the time domain, as shown in parts (b) and (c), by viewing the signal for $x = 0$. In this case,

$$f(0,t) = \cos(-\overline{v}t) \tag{3-115b}$$

and the time period of the signal is determined from

$$\overline{v}t = 2\pi \tag{3-115c}$$

or

$$t = 4 \text{ secs.} \tag{3-115d}$$

Thus, the maximum temporal sampling interval, denoted $\Delta t$, is

$$\Delta t < 2 \text{ secs.} \tag{3-115e}$$

Referring to the result of problem 1, the Fourier transform of $\cos(x - \pi/2t)$ is

$$\frac{1}{2}\left[\delta\left[u - \frac{1}{2\pi}, v + \frac{1}{4}\right] + \delta\left[u + \frac{1}{2\pi}, v - \frac{1}{4}\right]\right],$$

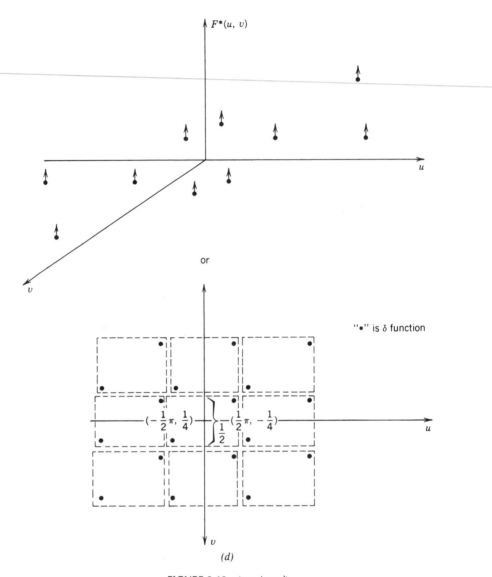

**FIGURE 3.13** *(continued)*

Figure 3-13*d* shows the spectrum of the sampled signal with $\Delta x$ and $\Delta t$ chosen such that replication of the spectrum of $F(u,v)$ does not occur. The central dotted rectangular region in Figure 3-13*e* indicates the spectrum of the unsampled time-space signal, whereas the replicated dotted rectangular regions show the effect of spatiotemporal sampling. Note that the center of each of these regions is separated from the replicas by a distance that is equal to $1/\Delta t$; no aliasing (overlapping) occurs. Note that we could define at least one ideal interpolation function for this case, which would "extract" (in the $(u,v)$ domain) the frequency domain contents of the central (dotted) rectangular region denoted $R$. For simplicity, assume that this function is

$$G(u,v) \begin{cases} 1.0 \ \forall \ u,v \ \varepsilon \ R \\ 0 \quad \text{elsewhere} \end{cases} \tag{3-115f}$$

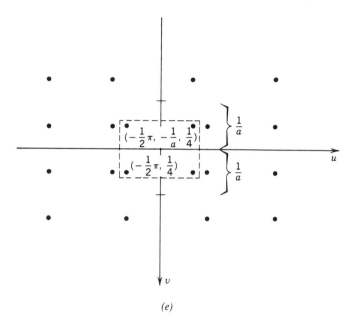

*(e)*

**FIGURE 3.13** *(continued)*

Now consider temporal undersampling of this signal, or cases for which $\Delta t = a \geq 2$. From Figure 3-13$e$, it is seen that the central dotted region in the Fourier domain now contains overlapped versions of $F(u,v)$ copies in the $v$ (corresponding to time) direction. The center-to-center spacing of these rectangles in the $v$ direction is now $1/a$. This overlapping will affect the spatial content of the reconstructed signal even though the Nyquist rate was satisfied in the spatial direction (i.e., $\Delta x < \pi$). Specifically, the reconstructed signal may contain:

    (a) a wave moving in the $+x$ direction;
    (b) a wave moving in the $-x$ direction;
    (c) a stationary wave; and
    (d) all of the above.

The spectrum reconstructed using the interpolation function $G(u,v)$ of Eq. 3-115$f$ will consist of *four*, not two, impulses, and is of the form

$$F_R(u,v) = \frac{1}{2}\left[\delta\left[u - \frac{1}{2\pi}, v + \frac{1}{4}\right] + \delta\left[u + \frac{1}{2\pi}, v - \frac{1}{4}\right]\right]$$
$$+ \frac{1}{2}\left[\delta\left[u + \frac{1}{2\pi}, v + \frac{1}{a} - \frac{1}{4}\right] + \delta\left[u - \frac{1}{2\pi}, v - \frac{1}{a} + \frac{1}{4}\right]\right] \tag{3-115g}$$

with an inverse transform of

$$f_R(x,t) = \cos\left[x - \frac{\pi}{2}t\right] + \cos\left[x + 2\pi\left[\frac{1}{a} - \frac{1}{4}\right]t\right] \tag{3-115h}$$

For example, if $\Delta t = a = 2$

$$f_R(x,t) = \cos\left[x - \frac{\pi}{2}t\right] + \cos\left[x + \frac{\pi}{2}t\right] = 2\cos x \cos\frac{\pi}{2}t \qquad (3\text{-}115i)$$

indicating that the 1-D image function will be observed as consisting of *two waves*, moving (translating) with the same velocity $(\pi/2)$, but in *opposite directions*. Thus, the result is a stationary wave. Similarly, if

$$2 < \Delta t < 4 \qquad (3\text{-}115j)$$

then

$$\frac{1}{a} - \frac{1}{4} > 0 \qquad (3\text{-}115k)$$

and the second component of $f_R(x,t)$ in Eq. 3-115h is a cosine wave moving in the $-x$ direction with a velocity of $2\pi(1/a - 1/4)$.

When $a = 4$, the second term in $f_R(x,t)$ is a stationary cosine wave. When $a > 4$,

$$\frac{1}{a} - \frac{1}{4} < 0 \qquad (3\text{-}115l)$$

and the second term in $f_R(x,t)$ is a cosine wave moving in the positive direction with velocity $2\pi(1/4 - 1/a)$.

The previous example only considered the effects of two copies of $F(u,v)$ (specifically, the two nearest copies of $F(u,v)$) in corrupting the reconstructed signal. In fact, for larger values of $\Delta t$ we need to consider the effects of other copies of $F(u,v)$ corrupting the central dotted region. (The reader is encouraged to verify this.)

The results, of this reduced-dimension example are summarized in the table below.

| Case | | Reconstructed $f(x,t)$ contents |
|---|---|---|
| 1. | $\Delta t < 2$ | moving cosine wave in $+x$ direction with speed $\pi/2$ [i.e., $\cos[x - \pi/2\ t]$] |
| 2. | $\Delta t = 2$ | $\cos[x - \pi/2\ t] + \cos[x + \pi/2\ t]$, a stationary wave |
| 3. | $4 > \Delta t > 2$ | $\cos[x - \pi/2\ t] + \cos[x + 2\pi\ [1/a - 1/4]\ t]$ |
| 4. | $\Delta t = 4$ | $\cos[x - \pi/2\ t] + \cos(x)$ |

In case 3, the existence of a component that moves in the opposite direction as that expected helps to explain, by analogy, the situation that commonly occurs in temporally undersampled film or television imagery. Often, the corruption of spatial and temporal frequencies yields television or movie image sequences containing automobile wheels that appear to move in the correct direction (as the vehicle begins moving); then become stationary (at some velocity and camera geometry); and then appear to rotate backwards (not all viewers catch this). Note also, the *local* effect of this aliasing; that is, there is no global image corruption due to this temporal undersampling. The only significant difference between the previous 1-D example and the 2-D situation is that in time-varying television and filmed imagery the temporal sampling rate is fixed and the frequency content of the imagery varies, whereas in the previous example the situation is reversed.

## ■ REFERENCES

Andrews, H. C., and Hunt, B. R. *Digital image restoration*, Prentice-Hall, N.Y., 1977.

Tretter, S. *Introduction to discrete-time signal processing*. New York: John Wiley, 1976.

Goodman, J. W. *Introduction to Fourier optics*. New York: McGraw-Hill, 1968.

Cornsweet, T. N. *Visual perception*. New York: Academic Press, 1970.

Pratt, W. K. *Digital image processing*. New York: John Wiley, 1972.

Pratt, W. K., Andrews, H. C., and Kane, J. Hadamard transform image coding. *IEEE Proceedings*, 1969, *57*(1), 58–68.

Ahmed, N., and Rao, K. R. *Orthogonal transforms in digital signal processing*. New York: Springer-Verlag, 1975.

Whittaker, E. T. On the functions which are represented by the expansions of the interpolation theory. *Pros. Royal Society of Edinburgh*, 1915, *35*, 181–194.

Shannon, C. E. Communication in the presence of noise. *Pros. IRE*, 1949, *37*(1), 10–21.

Oppenheim, A. V., and Lim, J. S. The importance of phase in signals. *IEEE Proceedings*, 1981, *69*(5), 529–541.

Peterson, D. P., and Middleton, D. Sampling and reconstruction of wave-number-limited functions in *N*-dimensional Euclidean spaces. *Information and Control*, 1962, *5*, 279–323.

Rosenfeld, A., and Johnson, E. G. Geometrical operations on digital pictures. In Lipkin and Rosenfeld (eds.), *Picture Processing and Psychopictorics*. New York: Academic Press, 1970.

## ■ PROBLEMS

1. (i) Show that the Fourier transform of $\cos 2\pi(\alpha x + \beta y)$ is $\frac{1}{2}[\delta(u - \alpha, v - \beta) + \delta(u + \alpha, v + \beta)]$.

   (ii) Suppose that this image function is sampled spatially with sampling intervals X and Y in the $x$ and $y$ directions, respectively. Show the resulting Fourier transform of the sampled image as a function of $\alpha$, $\beta$, and X and Y. (Show cases of aliasing and no aliasing.)

   (iii) Assume the above signal is sampled using a nonrectangular sampling grid with basis vectors (refer to Eq. 3-108) of the form

   $$\underline{v}_1 = \begin{bmatrix} 1 \\ 0 \end{bmatrix} \qquad v_2 = \frac{1}{\sqrt{2}} \begin{bmatrix} 1 \\ 1 \end{bmatrix}$$

   • Show the Fourier domain reciprocal basis vectors and regions of signal replication.
   • Repeat (ii) for this case.

2. (Application of Hadamard transform to bar code identification.) Suppose we digitized a video-sensed black-and-white bar code to obtain an $8 \times 8$ image function matrix $[f]$. We are interested in determining if the Hadamard transform of this bar code yields easy-to-interpret information concerning the contents and orientation of the bar code.

   (i) Show the Hadamard transform matrix for $N = 8$.

(ii) Given two sampled-image function matrices, i.e.,

$$[f_1] = \begin{matrix} 1 & 1 & 1 & 1 & 1 & 1 & 1 & 1 \\ 0 & 0 & 0 & \cdot & \cdot & \cdot & \cdot & 0 \\ 1 & 1 & 1 & \cdot & \cdot & \cdot & \cdot & 1 \\ 0 & 0 & 0 & \cdot & \cdot & \cdot & \cdot & 0 \\ 1 & 1 & 1 & \cdot & \cdot & \cdot & \cdot & 1 \\ 0 & 0 & 0 & \cdot & \cdot & \cdot & \cdot & 0 \\ 1 & 1 & 1 & \cdot & \cdot & \cdot & \cdot & 1 \\ 0 & 0 & 0 & 0 & 0 & 0 & 0 & 0 \end{matrix}$$

and

$$[f_2] = \begin{matrix} 1 & 0 & 1 & 0 & 1 & 0 & 1 & 0 \\ 1 & 0 & 1 & \cdot & \cdot & \cdot & 1 & 0 \\ 1 & 0 & 1 & \cdot & \cdot & \cdot & 1 & 0 \\ 1 & 0 & 1 & \cdot & \cdot & \cdot & 1 & 0 \\ 1 & 0 & 1 & \cdot & \cdot & \cdot & 1 & 0 \\ 1 & 0 & 1 & \cdot & \cdot & \cdot & 1 & 0 \\ 1 & 0 & 1 & \cdot & \cdot & \cdot & 1 & 0 \\ 1 & 0 & 1 & 0 & 1 & 0 & 1 & 0 \end{matrix}$$

Compute the Hadamard transform of each. Do they make intuitive sense? Consider the Hadamard transform basis function matrices from (i). Does this suggest a technique based on the Hadamard transform for the recognition of bar codes?

(iii) Extend the results of (ii) in cases where

(a) The "image" is not strictly horizontal or vertical, i.e., it is slanted, e.g.,

(b) The code is shifted either horizontally or vertically.

3. Given the orthogonal properties of the matrices $U$ and $V$ in Eq. 3-1, use Eq. 3-9 to show the result of Eq. 3-11.

4. Derive in detail Eq. 3-33.

5. Prove the following two relations:

(i)
$$\iint_{-\infty}^{\infty} \exp\left[-j2(ux + vy)\right] \delta(x,y) \, dx dy = 1.0$$

and

(ii)
$$\iint_{-\infty}^{\infty} \exp[j2\pi(ux + vy)] \, du dv = \delta(x,y)$$

6. In Chapter 7, we will be concerned with the *moment transform*. The discrete version of this transform is given by a matrix of elements

$$m(p,q) = \sum_x \sum_y x^p y^q f(x,y)$$

(a) Find the matrix representation for the moment transform in the form

$$M = [D^T] [f] [C]$$

where $p, q \; \varepsilon \; [0, N - 1]$. Test your results on the following two $4 \times 4$ "images"

(i) $[f] = \begin{bmatrix} 1 & 1 & 1 & 1 \\ 1 & 1 & 1 & 1 \\ 1 & 1 & 1 & 1 \\ 1 & 1 & 1 & 1 \end{bmatrix}$ (ii) $[f] = \begin{bmatrix} 1 & 0 & 0 & 0 \\ 0 & 1 & 0 & 0 \\ 0 & 0 & 1 & 0 \\ 0 & 0 & 0 & 1 \end{bmatrix}$

(b) Notice that these resulting transform matrices are considerably different from a Fourier or Hadamard transform; in particular, "DC" images such as (i) return nonzero values for coefficients other than $m_{00}$. Comment on why.

(c) Discuss the invertibility of this transform from theoretical and practical points of view.

7. Given $H_2$, verify that Hadamard matrices for $N \geq 4$ retain the symmetry and orthogonality properties.

8. Show that the preprocessing necessary to achieve a "centered zero" DFT may be accomplished by a preprocessing step consisting of multiplying each image value by $(-1)^{i+j}$.

9. It is straightforward (see Appendix 2) to verify the Fourier transform phase effects that result from a shifting or translation of the image function. The discrete version of this property follows from Eq. 3-44—that is, the 2-D DFT definition

$$F(k,l) = \frac{1}{N} \sum_{m=0}^{N-1} \sum_{n=0}^{N-1} f(m,n) \exp\left[\frac{-2\pi j(km + ln)}{N}\right]$$

(i) Derive this property for translations of $f(m,n)$ that are *integer multiples* of the sampling lattice.

(ii) Does the property resulting from (i) depend on a bandlimited image function?

(iii) Rederive (i) by assuming that $f(m,n)$ is a sampled version of a continuous image function $f(x,y)$. That is, compute the Fourier transform of the sampled signal from $F(u,v)$ (the unsampled transform) and then show the effect of a shift of $f(x,y)$. In this case, consider this shift to be in multiples of the spatial sampling increments.

(iv) How do the results of (iii) change when this shift is *not* in multiples of the spatial sampling increments?

10. (This problem is related to problem 9). We have seen (Appendix 3) how a shift or translation in the image function, $f(x,y)$, introduces a phase change in the 2-D Fourier transform. Describe, as quantitatively as possible, how this phase information could be applied to the task of determining this shift—that is, *translational motion estimation*. (This will be addressed in depth in Chapter 5.) Specifically:

(i) Assume only $F(u,v)$ at times $t_2$ (after the shift) and $t_1$ (prior to the shift) is available.

(ii) Consider the impact of "new information" that "enters" the image because of the shift. Does the model account for this?

**11.** Prove the separability property of the 2-D Fourier transform, i.e., if

$$f(x, y) = f_x(x) f_y(y)$$

$$F(u, v) = \mathcal{F}\{f_x(x)\}\mathcal{F}\{f_y(y)\}$$

**12.** Given the OTF of a defocused lens shown below,

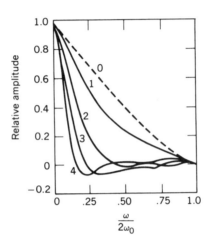

Suggest a method based upon Fourier methods for automatically focusing a camera.

**13.** (i) Prove the spatial differentiation properties of the 2-D Fourier transform, i.e.,

$$\mathcal{F}\left\{\frac{\partial f(x, y)}{\partial x}\right\} = j2\pi u\, F(u, v)$$

$$\mathcal{F}\left\{\frac{\partial f(x, y)}{\partial y}\right\} = j2\pi v\, F(u, v)$$

where

$$\mathcal{F}\{f(x, y)\} = F(u, v).$$

(ii) Based on (i), show that the Fourier transform of the Laplacian of an image function is equal to

$$\mathcal{F}\left\{\frac{\partial^2 f(x, y)}{\partial x^2} + \frac{\partial^2 f(x, y)}{\partial y^2}\right\} = -(2\pi)^2\,(u^2 + v^2)F(u, v)$$

(iii) Using the results of (i), can we realistically expect to implement differentiators for images with wide bandwidth: (What is the frequency response of a differentiator?)

**14.** (This problem is related to problem 15.) Show the basis function matrices (in "phasor" representation[1]) for the 8×8 Fourier transform corresponding to elements $F_{11}, F_{12}, F_{21}, F_{77}$. Recall that the DFT indices are from $(0,0)$ and the basis function indices are from $(1,1)$. Give some indication of what large values of each of the above elements (one at a time) would indicate about $[f]$.

15. Under the assumption of a linearly separable transform, based on real, orthonormal matrices $U$ and $V$, we have shown that the basis function matrices corresponding to the transform

$$[F] = U^T [f] V$$

are formed as $> \underline{u}_i, \underline{v}_j <$. This was determined by considering the inverse transformation of the above transform with the cited properties of $U$ and $V$, i.e.,

$$[f] = U [F] V^T$$

Notice the Fourier transform, because of the complex nature of $W$, does not fit this case.

(a) From the point of view of reconstructing $[F]$ as a sum of rank-1 matrices, each weighted by the corresponding coefficient of $[F]$, what are the basis function matrices for the Fourier transform?

(b) From the point of view of the forward transform, what are the rank-1 matrices onto which $[f]$ is projected to generate $F_{ij}$?

(c) How are the rank-1 matrices in (a) and (b) related?

16. Prove that $f(x,y)$ may be recovered from $F(u,v)$, where $F(u,v)$ is given by Eq. 3-103$a$, by the inverse transform in Eq. 3-103$b$. Hints:

(i) Integrate the right-hand side of Eq. 3-103$a$ using 3-103$b$.

(ii) Use the sifting property of the Dirac delta function.

17. Shape and position analysis via 2-D Fourier transforms. One might be curious whether it is possible to discriminate among square, rectangular, and circular objects on the basis of their corresponding Fourier transforms. In fact, we may be interested in discriminating among these classes of objects *independently* of their 2-D *position*; that is, we allow them to translate in the camera FOV.

(i) Show that if we allow translation and "throw away" phase information, we may observe the three classes of objects anywhere in the camera FOV.

(ii) Compute the 2-D Fourier transform of a square and a rectangle. How do they differ?

(iii) Compute the 2-D Fourier transform of a circle of radius $R$. (Hint: the results of problem 18 and properties of Bessel functions may be useful here.) How does it differ from the transforms in (ii)?

18. Show that if $f(x,y)$ is a circularly symmetric function—that is, $f(x,y) = f(\sqrt{x^2 + y^2})$—then its frequency spectrum is also circularly symmetric and is given by

$$F(u,v) = F(p) = 2\pi \int_o^\infty rf(r)J_0(2\pi rp)dr \qquad \text{(P-1)}$$

---

[1]This means the elements of the basis function matrix, which are comprised of complex variables with magnitude = 1.0, may be written as a unit length vector whose angle represents the angle associated with the particular element.

while the inverse relationship is given by

$$f(r) = 2\pi \int_o^\infty pF(p)J_0\,(2\pi rp)dp$$

where

$$r = \sqrt{x^2 + y^2}, \quad \theta = \tan^{-1}(y/x), \quad p = \sqrt{u^2 + v^2}, \quad \phi = \tan^{-1}(v/u)$$

and

$$J_0\,(x) = (1/2\pi) \int_o^{2\pi} \exp\left[-jx \cos(\theta - \phi)\right] d\theta$$

where $J_0\,(x)$ is the zero-order Bessel function of the first kind. The transformation in Eq. P-1 is also called the Hankel transform of zero order.

19. With respect to the image function given by Eq. 3-107,

$$f(x,y) = \frac{\sin(x)}{x} \cdot \frac{\sin(3y)}{3y}$$

   (a) Show that the Fourier transform of $f(x,y)$ has a rectangular region of support in the $(u,v)$ plane;
   (b) Determine the maximum (nonaliased) spatial sampling intervals, denoted $X_m$ and $Y_m$; and
   (c) Show the spectrum of the sampled signal for the cases of
      (i) $X = Y = X_m$
      (ii) $X = Y = Y_m$
      (iii) $X = X_m; Y = Y_m$

20. (a) Derive the alternate form of convolution (Eq. 3-42$b$).
   (b) Show a graphical interpretation of this form of convolution (analogous to that of Figure 3.2). Assume $h\,(\varepsilon,\eta)$ is nonzero over $R$.

21. (a) Explore the frequency-domain characteristics of:
      (i) the nearest-neighbor interpolation approach; and
      (ii) the bilinear interpolation approach.
   (b) Determine, quantitatively, how the bilinear interpolation approach differs from idealized (e.g., 2-D sinc function) interpolation. Show examples in both the spatial and frequency domains.

22. Consider the matrix representation for the DFT of a nonsquare matrix, i.e., $[f]$ is $M \times N$.
      (i) Using the definition of the 2-D DFT (Eq. 3-44), show a matrix representation.
      (ii) From (i), how is the inverse transform formed?
      (iii) Is this result extendable to other transforms, such as the slant or Hadamard approaches?

23. The so-called Fast Fourier Transform (FFT) is an efficient method of computing the DFT. In the 1-D case, the FFT is derived by employing the cyclic characteristics of the exp function and factoring the matrix $Z$ in Eq. 3-16 into

a set of sparse matrices, thus reducing the required number of multiplications. There are several ways to do this [Tretter,1976].

(i) Show, for the 1-D DFT of an $N \times 1$ vector, that the number of complex multiplications and additions required to implement Eq. 3-16 (or Eq. 3-12) is proportional to $N^2$.

(ii) The FFT decomposition reduces the computational expense in (i) to $N\log_2 N$. For $N \in [64, 1024]$ compute the computational savings, expressed as the ratio of the direct DFT computation expense divided by the FFT computation expense.

(iii) Repeat (ii) for the case of a 2-D image.

# 4

# IMAGE GREY-LEVEL MODELING AND PROCESSING FUNDAMENTALS, PART II

## ■ ENHANCEMENT, RESTORATION, AND CONVERSION

## ■ INTRODUCTION

In this chapter, the model-based approach to image processing and computer vision is continued. A number of low level algorithmic approaches for the enhancement or restoration of images are developed, the majority of which are related to image "edge" information. *It is difficult to underestimate the utility of reliable edge extraction*, particularly as a precursor to higher-order image processing operations. In addition, several additional model-based approaches are used for image conversion. This includes halftone renditions of images and the reconstruction of image data from projections.

# ■ OPERATORS AND MODELS FOR ENHANCEMENT AND RESTORATION

### DISCRETE LINEAR OPERATORS

We begin our analysis with the formulation and analysis of several simple operators. Local linear operators are considered first. These operators form the output pixel intensity at $(x,y)$ from a weighted summation of input pixel intensities in the *neighborhood* of $(x,y)$. This is accomplished via a window kernel which is convolved with the image intensities in the local region. Figure 4.1 illustrates this operation. The corresponding frequency domain ramifications of this type of grey-level operator are significant.

SPATIAL SMOOTHING OPERATORS (FILTERS)

Spatial smoothing filters are typically used for noise removal and the reduction of effects due to undersampling. (Thus, they serve as simplified interpolation functions.) The simplest example of a smoothing filter is one that employs spatial neighborhood averaging and may be formulated as a linear operation on the input image of the form $g(x,y) = 0\,[f(x,y)]$, which may be quantified mathematically as

$$g(x,y) = \frac{1}{M} \sum_{S} f(m,n) \tag{4-1}$$

where $S$ is an $M$-pixel neighborhood of points surrounding (and perhaps including) the point $(x,y)$. Often, $S$ is a rectangular neighborhood of $(x,y)$—for example, an $n \times n$ square. The smoothing operator of Eq. 4-1 for the case of this $n \times n$ "window" is formulated

$$g(x,y) = \sum_{i=-n/2}^{n/2} \sum_{j=-n/2}^{n/2} h_{sm}(i,j)\, f(x+i,\, y+j) \tag{4-2}$$

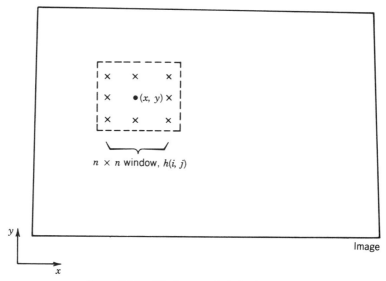

FIGURE 4.1   Filtering as a "window" operator

where $h_{sm}(i,j)$ is the smoothing function, whose nonzero values in region $S$ are given by

$$h_{sm}(i,j) = \frac{1}{n^2} \qquad (4\text{-}3)$$

Often we may use a change of variables to rewrite Eq. 4-2 in a more useful form. Note that Eq. 4-2 is in convolution (or correlation) form.

In the case of $n = 3$, the output image function is then the correlation of the $3 \times 3$ window function

| | | |
|-----|-----|-----|
| 1/9 | 1/9 | 1/9 |
| 1/9 | 1/9 | 1/9 |
| 1/9 | 1/9 | 1/9 |

with the image function $f(x,y)$ for all $(x,y)$ locations (neglecting "edge" effects in the image plane).

Note that $n$ is often chosen to be odd in order for the window center to be on the sampling grid. It is often convenient to shift the origin of the window using

$$\begin{aligned} k &= i + n/2 \\ l &= i + n/2 \end{aligned} \qquad (4\text{-}4)$$

From Chapter 3, the Fourier transform of this window function is

$$H_{sm}(u,v) = \frac{1}{N} \sum_{k=0}^{n-1} \sum_{l=0}^{n-1} h_{sm}(k,l) \exp[-j2\pi(uk + vl)/N] \qquad (4\text{-}5)$$

where the scaling term $(1/N^2)$ has been distributed between the forward and inverse transforms. Using Eq. 4-3, Eq. 4-4 reduces to

$$H_{sm}(u,v) = 1/N \sum_{k=0}^{n-1} \sum_{l=0}^{n-1} (1/n^2) \exp[-j2\pi uk/N] \exp[-j2\pi vl/N] \qquad (4\text{-}6)$$

Equation 4-6 represents a separable transform. Hereafter, we ignore the $(1/N)$ scaling term and illustrate the properties of this transform by computing the first term; that is,

$$H_1(u) = 1/n \sum_{k=0}^{n-1} \exp[-j2\pi uk/N] \qquad (4\text{-}7)$$

Defining the quantity

$$z = \exp[j2\pi u/N] \qquad (4\text{-}8)$$

Eq. 4-7 may be rewritten (scaled by $1/n$) as

$$H_1(u) = \sum_{k=0}^{n-1} z^{-k} \qquad (4\text{-}9)$$

This type of summation occurs frequently in the derivation of Z-transforms, and may be rewritten as

$$H_1(u) = \sum_{k=0}^{\infty} z^{-k} - \sum_{k=n}^{\infty} z^{-k} \qquad (4\text{-}10)$$

which reduces to

$$H_1(u) = 1/(1 - z^{-1}) - z^{-n}/(1 - z^{-1}) \qquad (4\text{-}11)$$

Equation 4-11 may be viewed as the difference of the $z$-transforms of two unit step functions, one occurring at $k = 0$ and the other (a negative step) at $k = n$.

Recalling the definition of $z$ in Eq. 4-8, Eq. 4-11 becomes

$$H_1(u) = \frac{1 - z^{-n}}{1 - z^{-1}} = z^{-(n-1)/2} \frac{z^{n/2} - z^{-n/2}}{z^{1/2} - z^{-1/2}} \qquad (4\text{-}12)$$

or

$$H_1(u) = \exp[-j\pi u(n - 1)/N] \sin(\pi u n/N)/\sin(\pi u/N) \qquad (4\text{-}13)$$

for $n \geq 1$. Note the effect of the shift due to Eq. 4-4 is a phase term in (4-13).

A similar derivation may be made for $H_2(v)$. Notice from Eq. 4-13 that this separable frequency response function has low-pass characteristics, as shown by the magnitude plot in Figure 4.2. This figure shows the effect of varying the window size from $3 \times 3$ to $9 \times 9$. Note the corresponding narrowing of the filter frequency response, as expected. This plot is analogous to the (phase shifted) sinc function that would have been obtained in the continuous case.

An example of an image processed with this smoothing filter for the case $n = 3$ is shown in Figure 4.3. Note the somewhat blurred appearance of the output image. This blurring is an undesirable side effect of the filter.

### Temporal Smoothing Operators (Filters)

Whereas the previous discussion concerned spatial smoothing, this approach may be extended to time-varying imagery. Assume a noise effect model of the form

$$f_i'(\underline{x}) = f_i(\underline{x}) + m_i(\underline{x}) \qquad (4\text{-}14)$$

where $f_i'(\underline{x})$ represents a noise-corrupted image and $m_i(\underline{x})$ is the noise process at spatial location $\underline{x}$. Assuming a zero-mean, time-uncorrelated noise process, Eq. 4-14 suggests that a suitable smoothing operation on an ensemble of images $M$ (whose time-changes are due *only* to the noise process), of the form

$$g(\underline{x}) = \frac{1}{M} \sum_{\text{ensemble}} f_i'(\underline{x}) \qquad (4\text{-}15)$$

is desirable. This averaging operation therefore reduces the noise effects in $g(x)$ by reducing the variance of the (averaged) noise process. It does not involve any spatial domain operations (i.e., all the summation takes place at fixed $(x,y)$ locations in each of the $M$ ensemble images). This operation is often considered an automatic image acquisition preprocessing operation (e.g., 30 frames, each taken $\frac{1}{30}$ of a second apart are often averaged by image processing systems in hardware).

### Spatial Sharpening Operators (Filters)

Another window-based operator is the sharpening operator or high-pass filter. Primary applications of this filter are *high frequency emphasis* or *edge enhancement*. One edge enhancement technique, known as *unsharp masking*, produces the en-

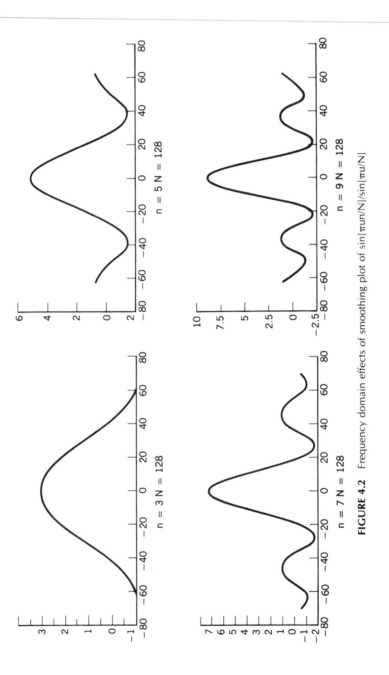

**FIGURE 4.2** Frequency domain effects of smoothing plot of $\sin(\pi un/N)/\sin(\pi u/N)$

**FIGURE 4.3** Smoothed images
(a) Original
(b) Smoothed using 3 × 3 window (note loss of edge sharpness)

hanced image $g(x,y)$ from the input image $f(x,y)$ via

$$g(x,y) = f(x,y) - f_{sm}(x,y) \qquad (4\text{-}16)$$

where $f_{sm}(x,y)$ is a smoothed version of $f(x,y)$.

One approach is to form $f_{sm}(x,y)$ as a local average of the eight neighboring pixels surrounding, but not including, $(x,y)$ as

$$f_{sm}(x,y) = \frac{1}{8} \sum_{i=-1}^{i=1} \sum_{j=-1}^{j=1} f(x+i, y+j) \quad \text{for} \quad i \neq 0 \text{ and } j \neq 0. \qquad (4\text{-}17)$$

Therefore, the resulting 3 × 3 window function or mask that implements Eq. 4-16 is shown below:

$$
\begin{array}{ccc}
-1/8 & -1/8 & -1/8 \\
-1/8 & 1 & -1/8 \\
-1/8 & -1/8 & -1/8
\end{array}
$$

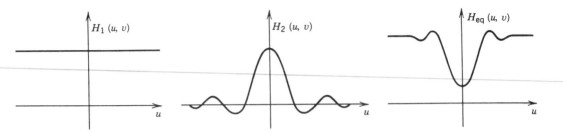

**FIGURE 4.4** Frequency domain characteristics of unsharp masking. Computation of Heq (u,v) (circularly symmetric functions assumed; only u-axis projections shown)

The frequency response characteristics of the unsharp masking operator may be determined in several ways. A direct calculation of the window function DFT is left to the reader. An alternative (and somewhat easier) approach employs the linearity property of the Fourier transform. For example, Eq. 4-16 indicates a corresponding frequency domain interpretation of unsharp masking as forming the output image Fourier transform from

$$G(u,v) = F(u,v) - F_{sm}(u,v) \qquad (4\text{-}18)$$

where each term corresponds to the spatial domain terms in Eq. 4-16. This equation may be rewritten as

$$G(u,v) = [H_1(u,v) - H_2(u,v)] \, F(u,v) = H_{eq}(u,v)F(u,v) \qquad (4\text{-}19)$$

where $H_1(u,v)$ and $H_2(u,v)$ are the frequency domain operators that produce $F(u,v)$ and $F_{sm}(u,v)$ in Eq. 4-18. Because the first term in Eq. 4-18, $F(u,v)$, is recognized as the (unaltered) Fourier transform of $f(x,y)$, the "filter" $H_1(u,v)$ that produces this first term in Eq. 4-19 has unity frequency response and, therefore, corresponds to an impulse function in the spatial domain. The second term is recognized as a smoothing filter from the previous section, with the Fourier domain characteristic shown in Figure 4.4. Therefore, the resultant filter, $H_{eq}(u,v)$ is determined by superposition and is shown in Figure 4.4. This filter possesses high-pass characteristics, as expected. Figure 4.5 shows an image that has been enhanced using a 3 × 3 unsharp masking window. This figure also illustrates one of the undesirable side effects of the unsharp masking filter, namely the forming of additional "edges" in the output image from input image edges. This filter "ringing" may be explained simply on the basis of a 1-D example, as shown in Figure 4.6.

### NONLINEAR OPERATORS

The theory of 2-D linear filters is well understood. However, properties of this class of filters are often inferior to a wider class of filters which, although defying detailed theoretical analysis, often yield superior results for a given image degradation model or application. For example, the smoothing operator reduces image noise but blurs edges. This is an undesirable side effect and spawns a search for alternative smoothing approaches (Justusson & Huang, 1981; Narendra 1980). Similarly, the sharpening operator sharpens edge information but also introduces sensitivity to (high frequency) noise and "ringing." We look to a set of nonlinear filters that accomplish the same objectives as the linear class but do not possess

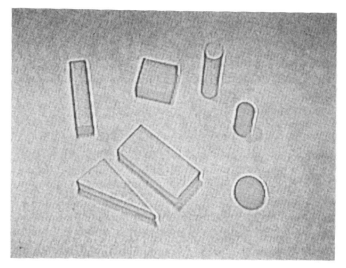

**FIGURE 4.5** High frequency enhanced image using unsharp masking operator

these negative attributes. Since the field of nonlinear filtering is not comprehensively developed, a less rigorous analysis is used.

## RANK (AND MEDIAN) FILTERS

Historically, median filtering is a stochastic model-based approach (Hodgson, et al., 1985; Pratt, 1978; Tukey, 1977) for one-dimensional filtering. Median filters are a subset of the class of *rank* filters where the output image intensity at spatial

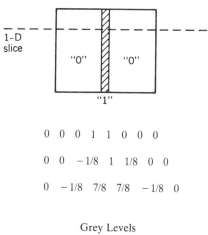

$$0 \quad 0 \quad 0 \quad 1 \quad 1 \quad 0 \quad 0 \quad 0$$

$$0 \quad 0 \quad -1/8 \quad 1 \quad 1/8 \quad 0 \quad 0$$

$$0 \quad -1/8 \quad 7/8 \quad 7/8 \quad -1/8 \quad 0$$

| Grey Levels |
| --- |
| $-1$ Darkest |
| $0$ "Grey" |
| $1$ Brightest |

**FIGURE 4.6** Filter "ringing" in unsharp masking (1-D example)
(a)   Input image (2 pixel wide stripe)
(b)   1-D input image intensity slice
(c)   Corresponding slice through filter
(d)   Output image intensities

location $\underline{x} = (x,y)^T$ is chosen on the basis of the relative rank or intensity of pixels in the neighborhood of $\underline{x}$. Given a set of $N$ pixel intensities obtained over a local image region, $S$, denoted simply as $f_i$, $i = 1,2, \ldots N$, an ordering of these values in increasing value, i.e.,

$$R(\underline{x}) = \{f_1, f_2, \ldots f_N\}$$

where

$$f_i \leq f_{i+1} \tag{4-20}$$

may be used to derive the rank filter operation. The output image intensity, $g(\underline{x})$, is

$$g(\underline{x}) = \text{Rank}_j \ R(\underline{x}) \tag{4-21}$$

where $\text{Rank}_j$ is the intensity of the output intensity at position, or rank, $j$ in $R(\underline{x})$. For example, choosing $j = 1$ yields the *min* filter, where the first element of $R(\underline{x})$ is chosen; that is,

$$\begin{aligned} g(\underline{x}) &= \text{min} \ R(\underline{x}) \\ &= \text{min } \{f(\underline{x}) \mid \underline{x} \in S\} \end{aligned} \tag{4-22}$$

where $S$ is the chosen neighborhood of $\underline{x}$. Alternately, the *max* filter is derived from choosing $j = N$ and yields

$$\begin{aligned} g(\underline{x}) &= \text{max} \ R(\underline{x}) \\ &= \text{max } \{f(\underline{x}) \mid \underline{x} \in S\} \end{aligned} \tag{4-23}$$

The most popular rank filter is derived for the case of $N$ odd, and is based on choosing the filter output to be $f_m$ where $m$ is the median intensity; that is, for $N$ intensity samples the position

$$m = (N + 1)/2 \tag{4-24}$$

is the median. Thus, $f_m$ is the pixel intensity in the ordered sample set that is greater than $(N - 1)/2$ of the samples. We denote the median operator on a sequence of samples as

$$\text{med} \ (R(\underline{x})) = \text{Rank}_{\frac{N+1}{2}} (R(\underline{x})) \tag{4-25}$$

For example, suppose an image with assumed smooth grey-value variations were corrupted by an impulse or "spike"-like noise. Low-pass filtering (smoothing) would tend to distribute this noise intensity over the pixels surrounding the noise spike. In contrast, the median filter usually removes this type of image noise without other degradation. The following example illustrates the approach.

Suppose we obtain $N = 5$ image intensity samples in a neighborhood of pixel location $(x,y)$ that yield $R(\underline{x}) = \{100,110,120,130,240\}$. Clearly the pixel intensity value of 240 is either a noise spike or an image feature. In this case, the output of the rank filter yields $g(\underline{x}) = 120$.

The neighborhood, or window shape, chosen for the median filter greatly affects its filtering effects. The median filter may take an assortment of shapes. Examples are shown in Figure 4.7. The shape chosen for the window may be based on a priori knowledge of the image noise characteristics, such as horizontal or vertical orientations.

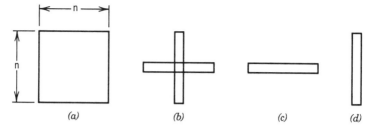

**FIGURE 4.7** Median filter window shapes
(a)   n × n window
(b)   n × n cross
(c), (d)   Horizontal and vertical strips

To avoid the computational expense of sorting large arrays of numbers, median filters often are implemented with a small size window. The image may be repeatedly filtered with multiple passes of this window.

The median operator is obviously a nonlinear filter, because, given two image functions yielding sample sequences $R_1(\underline{x})$ and $R_2(\underline{x})$,

$$\text{med}\,(R_1(\underline{x}) + R_2(\underline{x})) \neq \text{med}\,(R_1(\underline{x})) + \text{med}\,(R_2(\underline{x})) \qquad (4\text{-}26)$$

Surprisingly, however, a number of properties of the median filter allow a limited quantitative analysis. For example, given a constant $K$ and sequence $R(\underline{x})$,

$$\text{med}\,(KR(\underline{x})) = K\,\text{med}\,R(\underline{x}) \qquad (4\text{-}27)$$

$$\text{med}\,(K + R(\underline{x})) = K + \text{med}\,R(\underline{x}) \qquad (4\text{-}28)$$

The median filter has a number of other interesting properties.

1. *The median filter reduces the variance of the intensities in the image.* This is shown pictorially in the input and output "noise" images and corresponding histograms in Figure 4.8. Thus, the median filter has a capability to significantly alter image texture.

2. *Intensity oscillations with a period less than the window width are smoothed* (Nodes & Gallagher, 1982). This property is significant when considering multipass implementations of a fixed size median filter. In general, regions unchanged by the filter in a given pass are left unchanged in future passes (Pratt, 1978).

3. *Median filters will change the image intensity mean value* if the spatial noise distribution in the image is not symmetrical within the window.

4. *Median filters preserve certain edge shapes.* This is shown by the series of examples in Figure 4.9. This is important in multipass median filtering implementations, because the fixed points of a median filter are primarily edges and regions of monotonic slope (Bednar & Watt, 1984).

5. Given a symmetrical window shape, *the median filter preserves the location of edges.* This is also verified in Figure 4.9.

6. In the application of a median filter, *no new grey-values are generated.* Binary images remain binary, and the dynamic range of a median filtered image cannot exceed that of the input image.

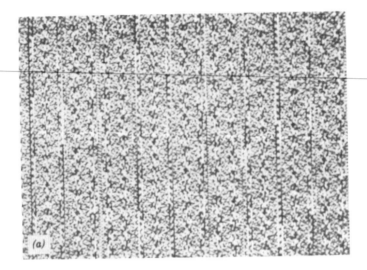

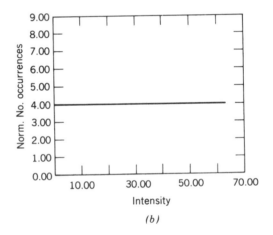

FIGURE 4.8  Median filter statistical effects
(a)  Input "noise" image
(b)  Histogram (normalized) of "noise"
(c)  Median filtered "noise" image
(d)  Median filtered "noise" histogram

**7.** *The shape chosen for a median filter may affect the processing results.* This is shown in Figure 4.10.

Figure 4.11 illustrates the typical application of a median filter to a grey-level, noise-corrupted image.

*Median Filter Practical Implementation and "Fast" Algorithms.* Unlike linear filters, which involve multiplication and summation computations, *the median filter computation requires the sorting of a list of numbers.* For large window sizes, this

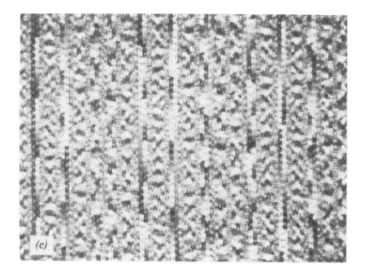

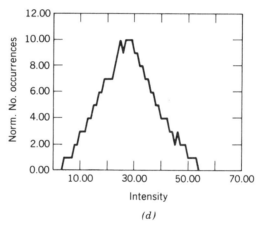

**FIGURE 4.8** *Continued*

may become a significant computational burden. The computation may be minimized several ways. One efficient approach (Huang, Yang, & Tang, 1979) for neighboring window locations (e.g., $(x, y)$ and $(x + 1, y)$) is based on *adjustment* or modification of the sorted list at the previous location, $(x, y)$. As we move the $n \times m$ window we discard $n$ points, add $n$ new points, and leave the remaining $mn - 2n$ points unchanged. This approach is only efficient if the amount of common image intensity data is significantly large from one position to the next.

A clever alternate approach (Ataman, Aatre, & Wong, 1980), based on list sorting, is to calculate the median of $R(\underline{x})$ iteratively, by bit position, starting with the MSB. After the median bit (0 or 1) for a bit position is determined, only intensity values with this bit value are retained for subsequent calculations. Notice that *this procedure terminates, for* n-*bit data, after* n *iterations, regardless of the size of the window.*

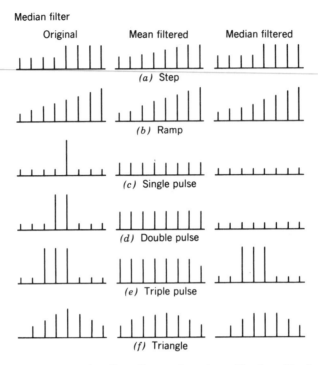

**FIGURE 4.9** Median filter effects on intensity profiles (from [Pratt])

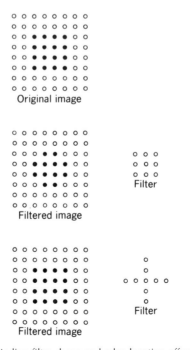

**FIGURE 4.10** Median filter shape and edge location effects (from [Pratt])

**FIGURE 4.11**  Sample median filter noise removal application (3 × 3 window)
(a)  Noise corrupted image
(b)  Median filter-processed image

*Example of the Approach.* Given the set of input values {3 9 4 7 5}, each of the unordered values is converted to binary representation. We then proceed to find the median value of each of the representation bits, starting with the MSB.

| 3 | 0011 | \| 011 | \| | \| |
|---|------|-------|----|----|
| 4 | 0100 | \| 100 | \| 00 | \| 0 |
| 5 | 0101 | \| 101 | \| 01 | \| 1 |
| 7 | 0111 | \| 111 | \| 11 | \| ↑ |
| 9 | 1001 | \| ↑ | \| ↑ | med = 1* |
| | ↑ | med = 1 | med = 0 | |
| | med = 0 | | | |

Therefore, we establish the median is $0101_2 = 5$.

## MULTIPLICATIVE MODELS AND HOMOMORPHIC FILTERING

This section considers another nonlinear approach to image enhancement that relies on conversion of a nonlinear model to a linear relationship, and linear filtering. The approach is based on the multiplicative model for radiometric image formation (Chapter 2):

$$f(x,y) = r(x,y) \, e(x,y) \qquad (4\text{-}29)$$

where $f(x,y)$ is the observed image, $r(x,y)$ is the image variation due to surface reflectivity, and $e(x,y)$ is the image grey-level variation due to the illumination source. The intensity function, $e(x,y)$, is a function of the scene illumination sources and, from Eq. 2-88:

$$0 < e(x,y) < \infty$$

Usually $e(x,y)$ varies slowly throughout the image; that is, it has low-frequency characteristics. The image histogram and consequently the dynamic range of the image is strongly a function of $e(x,y)$. The reflectance component $r(x,y)$ is constrained by

$$0 < r(x,y) < 1$$

and conveys significant information concerning the surface characteristics of scene objects. In particular, abrupt changes in $r(x,y)$ could indicate transitions to different objects, or significant edges.

The objectives of homomorphic filtering are to achieve an output image representation that uses the dynamic range of the image intensity variable and to enhance the high-frequency regions of the image. As indicated by Eq. 4-29, the image model is multiplicative, rather than additive in nature and therefore direct application of linear filtering techniques is questionable. One approach to overcoming this difficulty is to use the transformation

$$z(x,y) = \ln \{f(x,y)\} \qquad (4\text{-}30)$$

---

*Note that this requires a further description of the algorithm to handle cases of "ties." The reader is referred to Ataman, et al. (1980) for this.

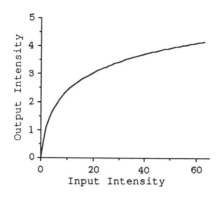

**FIGURE 4.12**  Logarithmic intensity transformation

The intensity transformation that results is shown in Figure 4.12. Note, that this represents an intensity-only contrast manipulation. From Eq. 4-29 and the properties of the natural logarithm, Eq. 4-30 becomes

$$z(x,y) = \ln\{r(x,y)\} + \ln\{e(x,y)\} \tag{4-31}$$

Thus, after the logarithmic intensity transformation, the transformed image is the sum of the logarithmically transformed reflectance and illumination components.

An aspect of this nonlinear transformation that should concern us is the frequency characteristics of $r(x,y)$ and $e(x,y)$ under the logarithmic mapping. Since this mapping is nonlinear, new frequencies are created in $\ln\{r(x,y)\}$ and $\ln\{e(x,y)\}$. This effect is shown in Figure 4.13, where the sin function of ($a$) has been logarithmically transformed to yield the periodic (nonsinusoidal) quantity of ($b$). The logarithmically transformed version of the sinusoid contains the original (fundamental) frequency, as well as a number of higher frequency harmonics. These are neglected in our subsequent analysis.

To achieve the enhancement objectives, the transformed image is filtered with a 2-D high-pass filter. Following the filtering stage, the filtered and transformed image $Z_f(x,y)$ is then inversely transformed by

$$f_0(x,y) = \exp\{z_f(x,y)\} \tag{4-32}$$

The overall sequential process is shown in block diagram form in Figure 4.14.

## EDGE DETECTION (PRODUCING EDGE IMAGES)

### INTRODUCTION

Edge information conveys image information and, consequently, scene content and is used extensively by the HVS. Edge detection contributes significantly to algorithms for feature detection, segmentation, and motion analysis.

First, we digress to attempt definition of an *edge*. In a (nonsampled) continuous image, a sharp intensity transition between neighboring pixels—for example, a step change in intensity—would be considered an edge. The waveforms shown in Figures 4.15$b$ and 4.15$c$ would probably be considered edges. A more interesting case arises when considering the sampled waveform in Figure 4.15$d$. Because of

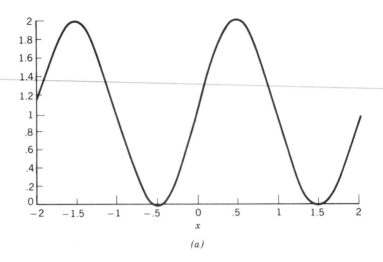

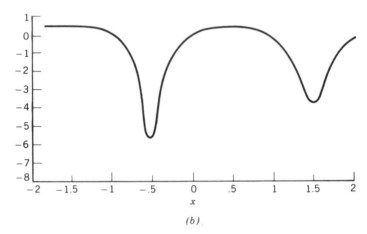

**FIGURE 4.13** Logarithmic transformation frequency effects
(a)   sin(πx) + 1
(b)   ln[sin(πx) + 1]

the high frequency components introduced by sampling (Chapter 3), every pair of pixels with differing intensities could be considered a potential edge.

## EDGE DETECTION VIA IMAGE SPATIAL GRADIENTS

*Derivative Approximations and General Combinations.* The gradient of an image function, $f(x,y)$, is defined (see Appendix 2) in terms of directionally oriented spatial derivatives as

$$\nabla f(x,y) = \begin{bmatrix} \dfrac{\partial f(x,y)}{\partial x} \\ \dfrac{\partial f(x,y)}{\partial y} \end{bmatrix}$$

$$= \frac{\partial f(\underline{x})}{\partial \underline{x}} \tag{4-33}$$

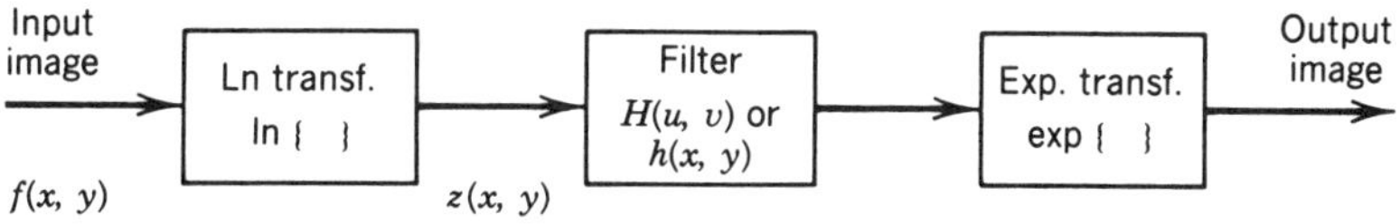

Input
image
$f(x, y)$
Ln transf.
ln { }
$z(x, y)$
Filter
$H(u, v)$ or
$h(x, y)$
Exp. transf.
exp { }
Output
image

**FIGURE 4.14** Homomorphic filtering strategy

To calculate the derivatives in Eq. 4-33, consider two-point approximations of the form

$$\frac{\partial f}{\partial x}(x,y) \approx \frac{f(x + \Delta x, y) - f(x,y)}{\Delta x} \tag{4-34}$$

$$\frac{\partial f}{\partial y}(x,y) \approx \frac{f(x, y + \Delta y) - f(x,y)}{\Delta y} \tag{4-35}$$

Note that the above operators correspond to correlation of the discretized image function with operators of the form

$$[-1 \quad 1]$$

and

$$\begin{bmatrix} 1 \\ -1 \end{bmatrix}$$

respectively. (The quantities $\Delta x$ and $\Delta y$ are left as overall window "weights.")

We examine the use of these simple operators, using a 1-D function for simplicity. Expanding a 1-D function $f(x)$ about $x$ in a Taylor series yields

$$f(x + \Delta x) = f(x) + \Delta x\, f'(x) + \frac{(\Delta x)^2}{2!} f''(x) + \cdots \tag{4-36}$$

$f(x)$
$x_e$
$x$
(a)
$f(x)$
$x_e$
$x$
(b)
$f(x)$
$x_e$
$x$
(c)
$f(x)$
$x_i$ $x_{i+1}$ $x_{i+2}$ $x_{i+3}$
(d)

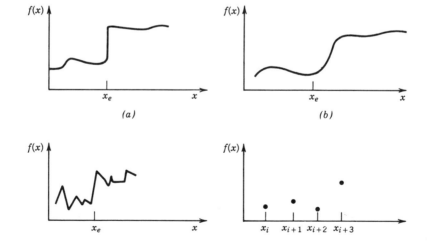

**FIGURE 4.15** Sample image edges (1-D)
(a) Ideal
(b) Approximate
(c) Noisy
(d) Sampled

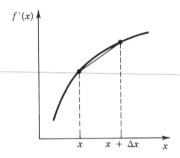

**FIGURE 4.16** Non-centered difference approximation to f'(x) = df(x)/dx

Using the mean value theorem of calculus, Eq. 4-36 may be written as

$$f(x + \Delta x) - f(x) = \Delta x \, f'(x) + \frac{(\Delta x)^2}{2} f''(\xi) \qquad (4\text{-}37)$$

where

$$\xi \varepsilon [x, x + \Delta x] \qquad (4\text{-}38)$$

Defining the forward derivative approximation, $D_1$, as

$$D_1(x) = \frac{f(x + \Delta x) - f(x)}{\Delta x} \qquad (4\text{-}39)$$

Eqs. 4-37, 4-38, and 4-39 show the error in the derivative approximation using $D_1$, and a finite interval, $\Delta x$, evolves as a function of $\Delta x$ to the first power,

$$\text{error } (D_1) \simeq \theta(\Delta x) \qquad (4\text{-}40)$$

A decrease in $\Delta x$ only linearly affects the approximation error.

Notice also from Figure 4.16 that $D_1$ is a better approximation to the slope of $f(x)$ at the *midpoint* of the interval $[x, x + \Delta x]$. Using the $D_1$ operator for $\partial f/\partial x$ and $\partial f/\partial y$ approximations in Eq. 4-33 as shown in Figure 4.17 therefore results in approximations to the gradient not at $(x, y)$, *but at different points* in the $(x, y)$ plane.

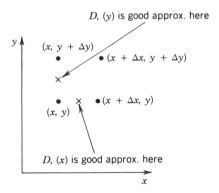

**FIGURE 4.17** Non-centered derivative approximations to df(x)/dx

An alternative *centered* difference approximation

$$D_2(x) = \frac{f(x + \Delta x) - f(x - \Delta x)}{2(\Delta x)}$$ (4-41)

has several consequences:

1. $D_2(x)$ and $D_2(y)$, due to their *centered* nature, *both* comprise good estimates for the respective derivatives of $f(\underline{x})$ at the midpoints of the interval—that is, $(x,y)$.
2. It may be shown that the error in this approximation evolves as

$$\text{error } (D_2) \simeq \mathbb{O}((\Delta x)^2).$$

3. Notice that $D_2(x)$ and $D_2(y)$ may be implemented by convolving the image function with masks

$$[-1 \quad 0 \quad 1]$$

and

$$\begin{bmatrix} +1 \\ 0 \\ -1 \end{bmatrix}$$

respectively. This concept forms the basis for extension to families of mask functions used for edge detection. Variants on $D_2$ are the $3 \times 3$ masks

$$\begin{bmatrix} -1 & 0 & 1 \\ -1 & 0 & 1 \\ -1 & 0 & 1 \end{bmatrix} \quad \text{and} \quad \begin{bmatrix} 1 & 1 & 1 \\ 0 & 0 & 0 \\ -1 & -1 & -1 \end{bmatrix}$$

which form "smoothed" or "averaged" centered difference operators and are defined as $D_{2A}(x)$ and $D_{2A}(y)$, respectively. Other smoothed operators with a weighting that emphasizes the central pixel are the Sobel weighting masks, denoted $D_s(x)$ and $D_s(y)$ and given by

$$\begin{bmatrix} -1 & 0 & 1 \\ -2 & 0 & 2 \\ -1 & 0 & 1 \end{bmatrix} \quad \text{and} \quad \begin{bmatrix} 1 & 2 & 1 \\ 0 & 0 & 0 \\ -1 & -2 & -1 \end{bmatrix}$$

respectively. An associated set of templates, with somewhat less central weighting, are $D_F(x)$ and $D_F(y)$, given by

$$\begin{bmatrix} -1 & 0 & 1 \\ -\sqrt{2} & 0 & \sqrt{2} \\ -1 & 0 & 1 \end{bmatrix} \quad \text{and} \quad \begin{bmatrix} 1 & \sqrt{2} & 1 \\ 0 & 0 & 0 \\ -1 & -\sqrt{2} & -1 \end{bmatrix}$$

General $(3 \times 3)$ masks used are of the form:

$$\begin{bmatrix} a & b & c \\ d & e & f \\ g & h & i \end{bmatrix}$$

where some of these elements may be zero (e.g., the case of $2 \times 2$ masks). It has often been hypothesized that every possible $3 \times 3$ mask has probably been considered for some image processing application!

A third operator for gradient approximation (Roberts, 1965) that is extensively employed is defined by

$$D_{+}\{(x,y)\} = f(x + \Delta x, y + \Delta y) - f(x,y)$$

$$D_{-}\{(x,y)\} = f(x, y + \Delta y) - f(x + \Delta x, y)$$

(4-42)

Notice that this operator:

1. Is a variant of the $D_1$ operator, with derivatives approximated along orthogonal orientations 45° and 135° in the image plane;
2. The midpoint of both intervals used for approximation is the *same point*; that is, it is the point $(x + \Delta x/2, y + \Delta y/2)$ located at the center of the rectangle found by the four points used; and
3. The operations in Eq. 4-42 correspond to convolution of the image function with masks:

$$D_{+} = \begin{bmatrix} 0 & 1 \\ -1 & 0 \end{bmatrix} \quad \text{and} \quad D_{-} = \begin{bmatrix} 1 & 0 \\ 0 & -1 \end{bmatrix}$$

respectively. The diagonal nature of these operators is often reflected in their being called the Roberts "cross" operator. As shown in Figure 4.18, the output intensity in the edge image is formed via

$$f_{\text{edge}}(x,y) = \max \{|D_{+}|, |D_{-}|\}$$

(4-43)

Figure 4.18(c) illustrates the visual effect of the Roberts operator on real imagery.

Although the preceding operators may be used to extract *directionally oriented* edge information (which we pursue in the next section), we further consider the combination of these operators to form *directionally invariant* or *isotropic* edge detectors.

Our immediate goal is an operator whose output is not biased by a particular edge orientation. Consider, for example,

$$f_{\text{out}}(x,y) = \mathbb{O}_{\text{edge}}\{f_{\text{in}}(x,y)\}$$

(4-44)

where

$$f_{\text{out}}(\underline{x}) = |\nabla_{\underline{x}} f(\underline{x})|$$

$$= \left[ \left( \frac{\partial f(\underline{x})}{\partial x} \right)^2 + \left( \frac{\partial f(\underline{x})}{\partial y} \right)^2 \right]^{1/2}$$

(4-45)

The square root operation represents an overall nonlinear scaling operation and may be neglected. To determine the directional sensitivity, consider application of the operator to a rotated version of an image function. Given an image $f(x,y)$, whose rotated version (see Appendix 1) is given by the affine transform

$$f_R(x,y) = f(x',y')$$

(4-46)

$$f_{\text{edge}}(x_1, x_2) = \max\{|f(x_1, x_2 + \Delta x) - f(x_1 + \Delta x, x_2)|,$$
$$|f(x_1 + \Delta x, x_2 + \Delta x) - f(x_1, x_2)|\}$$

*(a)*

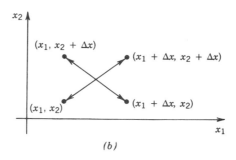

*(b)*

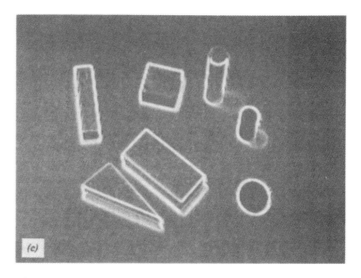

**FIGURE 4.18** Roberts 'cross'' operator for image edge enhancement
(a) Mathematical formulation
(b) Graphical interpretation
(c) Edge enhanced image using Robert's operator

with

$$\begin{bmatrix} x \\ y \end{bmatrix} = A_\theta \begin{bmatrix} x' \\ y' \end{bmatrix} \qquad (4\text{-}47)$$

and

$$A_\theta = \begin{bmatrix} \cos\theta & -\sin\theta \\ \sin\theta & \cos\theta \end{bmatrix} \qquad (4\text{-}48)$$

we compare the effect by examination of the gradient of $f(x,y)$ in the rotated coordinate system. The chain rule yields

$$\frac{\partial f_R(\underline{x})}{\partial \underline{x}} = A_\theta \frac{\partial f(\underline{x})}{\partial \underline{x}} \tag{4-49}$$

Therefore, the gradient *vector* is also rotated by θ. The magnitude (squared) of this vector, however (see the problems) yields

$$\left[\frac{\partial f_R(\underline{x})}{\partial x}\right]^2 + \left[\frac{\partial f_R(\underline{x})}{\partial y}\right]^2 = \left[\frac{\partial f(\underline{x})}{\partial x}\right]^2 + \left[\frac{\partial f(\underline{x})}{\partial y}\right]^2 \tag{4-50}$$

Therefore, the *magnitude* of the gradient is an isotropic operator.

### OTHER COMBINATIONS OF SPATIAL DERIVATIVE OPERATORS

$|\nabla_x f|$ is shown to be an isotropic edge operator. The gradient computation (approximation) is somewhat cumbersome, however, since squaring and addition of the $x$ and $y$ direction derivatives is required. For this reason it is desirable to consider other isotropic operators that are computationally simpler. A discrete set of edge types is shown in Figure 4.19. Table 4.1 summarizes the response of certain combinations of the previous operators to these edges.

Notes regarding these combinations of derivative approximation operators are:

1. Combinations 1 through 4 represent the operation of the individual operators considered previously.
2. Combinations 5 and 6 represent the use of the "RMS" value—that is, a squaring of the individual components, summation and square root operation sequence. Notice that this combination of the $D_2$ operators introduces a bias in favor of diagonal edges, whereas this combination of the $D_+$ and $D_-$ derivative approximation operators favors horizontal and vertically oriented edges. Thus, neither operator combination is isotropic.
3. Combinations 9 and 10 result in isotropic edge detection operators. In particular, combination 10 is the Roberts operator. It is frequently used because of its reasonable performance and computational simplicity.

*Second Derivative Operators and Applications.* One of the principal limitations of operators based on approximation of first spatial derivatives is *sensitivity to 2-D ramp functions*. Since 2-D edge detection operators return a function of the *slope* of the image function, ramp-like variations in the image function will result in a significant and misleading response from these operators. A way of circumventing this is based on the ideal edge property of Figure 4.15a. Since a 2-D step

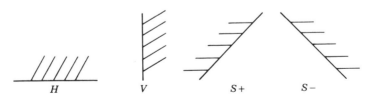

**FIGURE 4.19** Edge types used in edge detection operator analysis

■ **TABLE 4.1**
**Combinations of spatial gradients**

| | Edge type | | | |
|---|---|---|---|---|
| | $H$ | $V$ | $S+$ | $S-$ |
| Combination | Response | | | |
| 1. $D_1(x)$ or $D_2(x)$ | 0 | $h$ | $-h$ | $h$ |
| 2. $D_1(y)$ or $D_2(y)$ | $h$ | 0 | $h$ | $-h$ |
| 3. $D_+$ | $h$ | $h$ | 0 | $h$ |
| 4. $D_-$ | $h$ | $h$ | $h$ | 0 |
| 5. $\sqrt{[D_2(x)]^2 + [D_2(y)]^2}$ | $h$ | $h$ | $\sqrt{2}h$ | $\sqrt{2}h$ |
| 6. $\sqrt{[D_+]^2 + [D_-]^2}$ | $\sqrt{2}h$ | $\sqrt{2}h$ | $h$ | $h$ |
| 7. $\|D_2(x)\| + \|D_2(y)\|$ | $h$ | $h$ | $2h$ | $2h$ |
| 8. $\|D_+\| + \|D_-\|$ | $2h$ | $2h$ | $h$ | $h$ |
| 9. $\max\{\|\Delta_{2x}\|,\|\Delta_{2y}\|\}$ | $h$ | $h$ | $h$ | $h$ |
| 10. $\max\{\|\Delta_+\|,\|\Delta_-\|\}$ | $h$ | $h$ | $h$ | $h$ |

function has large (theoretically infinite) spatial derivatives of all orders, a logical starting point would be to consider edge detection operators based on discrete approximations of higher order derivatives. As before, we proceed from the 1-D case. Approximation of the first derivative of a function with noncentered difference formula and a "backward" formulation yields

$$D_{-1}(x) = \frac{f(x) - f(x - \Delta x)}{\Delta x} \tag{4-51}$$

The second (forward) difference approximation of this quantity yields

$$D_1(D_{-1}(x)) = \frac{1}{\Delta x}\left[\frac{f(x + \Delta x) - f(x)}{\Delta x} - \left(\frac{f(x) - f(x - \Delta x)}{\Delta x}\right)\right]$$

or

$$D_1^2(x) = \frac{f(x + \Delta x) - 2f(x) + f(x - \Delta x)}{(\Delta x)^2} \tag{4-52}$$

which may be represented by a $1 \times 3$ window-based operator of the form

$$[1 \quad -2 \quad 1]$$

The *Laplacian* of an image function $f(\underline{x})$ is defined to be the sum of the second spatial derivatives, denoted $\nabla^2 f(\underline{x})$, where

$$\nabla^2 f(\underline{x}) = \frac{\partial^2 f(\underline{x})}{\partial x^2} + \frac{\partial^2 f(\underline{x})}{\partial y^2} \tag{4-53}$$

The combination of $D_1^2(x)$ and $D_1^2(y)$ may then be used to form the discrete approximation to Eq. 4-53; that is,

$$\nabla^2 f(\underline{x}) = \frac{f(x + \Delta x, y) - 2f(x,y) + (x - \Delta x, y)}{(\Delta x)^2}$$
$$+ \frac{f(x, y + \Delta y) - 2f(x,y) + f(x, y - \Delta y)}{(\Delta y)^2} \qquad (4\text{-}54)$$

Assuming $\Delta x = \Delta y$, this quantity may be rewritten as:

$$\nabla^2 f(\underline{x}) = \left[\frac{1}{\Delta x}\right]^2 [f(x + \Delta x, y) + f(x - \Delta x, y) + f(x, y + \Delta y)$$
$$+ f(x, y - \Delta y) - 4f(x,y)] \qquad (4\text{-}55)$$

**FIGURE 4.20** Discrete Laplacian for edge enhancement
(a) Input image
(b) Edge enhanced image using Laplacian kernel

and represented by the $3 \times 3$ window operator:

$$\begin{bmatrix} 0 & 1 & 0 \\ 1 & -4 & 1 \\ 0 & 1 & 0 \end{bmatrix}$$

The similarity of this operator with the unsharp masking approach (page 133) is noted. Figure 4.20 illustrates the use of the discrete Laplacian approximation operator for edge enhancement.

Another significant edge detection approach is based on the use of zero crossings of second spatial derivatives (Marr & Hildreth, 1980). This is shown in Figure 4.21, where the second derivative is plotted as a function of spatial location. Clearly, two consequences result:

1. The second derivative crosses zero at the spatial location corresponding to the "midpoint" of the edge; and
2. This effect occurs in all directions (with varying magnitude) except parallel to the edge; this provides a means to determine edge orientation.

This approach is explored more fully when we consider edge detection via smoothing and the Laplacian operator (page 161).

*Edge Detection and Image Intensity Quantization.* The word length in a specific computer and the mechanics of converting an analog video intensity signal to a

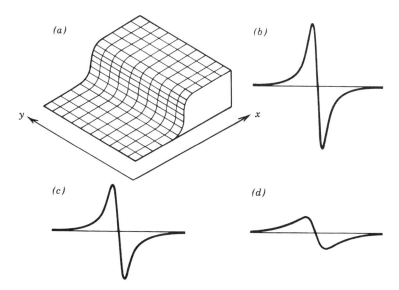

**FIGURE 4.21** 2nd derivatives, direction and zero crossings. Spatial and directional factors interact in the definition of a zero-crossing segment: (a) shows an intensity change, and (b), (c), and (d) show values of the second directional derivative near the origin at various orientations across the change. In (b), the derivative is taken parallel to the x-axis, and in (c), and (d), at 30° and 60° to it. There is zero-crossing at every orientation except for $d^2I/dy^2$, which is identically zero. Since the zero-crossings line up along the y-axis, this is the direction that is chosen. In this example, it is also the direction that maximizes the slope of the second derivative (from [Marr80]). © 1980, the Royal Society

discrete representation yield intensity samples quantified in terms of numbers of bits. For an $m$-bit representation, the number of different intensity representation levels is $2^m$; $m$ is usually in the range $1 \le m \le 12$. The case of $m = 1$ yields the extremely important class of two-valued images, which are termed *binary images*. Typical grey-value image intensity resolutions are in the range $6 \le m \le 8$. It is noteworthy that the human visual system is unable to make use of more than approximately 64 representation levels; in other words, the HVS has a dynamic range of approximately 6 bits.

Resolutions of less than 6 bits are noticeable to the HVS and, more important, may contribute to undesirable image characteristics. Too few quantization levels introduce false edges or contours into the image, as shown by Figure 4.22.

Figure 4.22a shows the "cup" image, discretized with $m = 6$. Notice that the image shading appears smooth. The shading now occurs in discernible steps; that is, visible intensity jumps or edges appear across the face of the cup. In Figure 4.22c this effect is enhanced, for $m = 2$ (four representation levels). Note, however, that even with this coarse intensity quantization, the perception of "shading" or shadows is still possible.

As shown above, images with decreasing intensity quantization levels indicate the presence of false contours, or false edges. Thus, in producing edge maps, attention to the combined effects of intensity quantization and edge detection is warranted. The effects of various bit resolutions and the threshold, $T_h$, used to create a binary image are shown below.

Assume that an image acquired with $n$-bit intensity resolution is quantized with uniform decision levels. Therefore, the modeling of a lower intensity resolution image may be accomplished as the effective "masking" of the lower order bits. For comparison purposes, let us consider $n_{\max} = 8$, and therefore assume that $n < 8$-bit pixel intensities are obtained by masking the corresponding $m = 8 - n$

FIGURE 4.22  Visual effects of varying intensity resolution
(a)  "Cup" image—6 bits intensity resolution
(b)  "Cup" image—3 bits intensity resolution
(c)  "Cup" image—2 bits intensity resolution

**FIGURE 4.22** *Continued*

lower order bits; that is,

| $x$ | $x$ | $x$ | $x$ | $x$ | $x$ | $x$ | $x$ |    8-bit image intensity

↓

| 1 | 1 | 1 | 1 | 0 | 0 | 0 | 0 |    pixel intensity mask ($m = 4$)

↓

| $x$ | $x$ | $x$ | $x$ | 0 | 0 | 0 | 0 |    corresponding 4-bit image
intensity

The derivative approximation operators used are based on simple difference approximations, or $D_1$, $D_2$ or $D_+$ and $D_-$.

When computing the gradient approximation, if the original image contains two adjacent pixels in the input image whose values differ only in the least significant $m$ (masked) intensity bits, an edge will not be detected, because the masked pixels have the same intensity value. Thus, some edges are lost.

Conversely, it may happen that *a weak difference in intensity values of the original image will result in a strong difference in the masked image.* Consider the following example, where $m = 2$

$$
\begin{array}{l}
\text{adjacent} \\
\text{pixel} \\
\text{intensities}
\end{array}
\left\{
\begin{array}{rrrrrrrr}
0 & 0 & 0 & 1 & 1 & 1 & 0 & 0 \\
-0 & 0 & 0 & 1 & 1 & 0 & 1 & 1
\end{array}
\right.
\qquad
\begin{array}{rrrrrrrr}
0 & 0 & 0 & 1 & 1 & 1 & 0 & 0 \\
-0 & 0 & 0 & 1 & 1 & 0 & 0 & 0
\end{array}
$$

$$
\text{difference} \quad
\begin{array}{rrrrrrrr}
0 & 0 & 0 & 0 & 0 & 0 & 0 & 1
\end{array}
\longleftrightarrow
\begin{array}{rrrrrrrr}
0 & 0 & 0 & 0 & 0 & 1 & 0 & 0
\end{array}
$$

unmasked pixel          masked pixel

intensities             intensities

Therefore, edges at different intensity resolutions may be strengthened, weakened, or unaffected. The reader is encouraged to verify these results with other examples. This result corresponds with intuition in viewing the images of Figure 4.22, because some edges are in fact enhanced (the "false" contours), whereas others are eliminated (e.g., subtle background variations).

### EDGE DETECTION VIA SURFACE FITTING AND TEMPLATE MATCHING

*Surface Fitting.* Noise in the image function is the nemesis of edge detection operators. Derivative operators are essentially high-pass filters, and the typical frequency domain characterization of commonly encountered noise suggests a high-frequency nature. The (theoretically infinite) response of ideal differentiators at infinite frequency is thus a severe limitation of simply derivative approximation operators.

One solution to this problem would be the smoothing or low-pass filtering of the image data prior to application of an edge operator. An alternative is the fitting of low-order functions to the local image intensity data to smooth noise effects. An example of this is an operator (Haralick, 1984) that fits orthogonal polynomials to the intensities in a $3 \times 3$ image region. The derivatives (including the second derivative) of these polynomials may be computed and combined to form directional derivative information. Analogous to the Marr and Hildreth (1980) approach, zero crossings and directions of zero second directional derivatives may be computed.

*Template Matching.* Using the basis function approach (Chapter 3), we may develop "transforms" of $3 \times 3$ (and theoretically, larger) image neighborhoods that are designed to extract edge orientation information. Nine (orthogonal) $3 \times 3$ "edge functions" are chosen as basis functions for the $3 \times 3$ subimage. The coefficients of this $3 \times 3$ transform indicate the contribution of the intensities in the $3 \times 3$ image region from the various basis functions. Perhaps the best-known example of this approach is the set of nine orthogonal templates proposed by Frei and Chen (1977).

The templates are summarized in Figure 4.23$a$, and a set of images separately processed with each of these nine pixel templates are shown in Figure 4.23$b$.

The Frei-Chen templates provide a limited classification of the type of discontinuity present in the $3 \times 3$ window by *grouping* the response due to sets of windows. For example, templates $T_1$ through $T_4$ in Figure 4.23$a$ represent a set of basis functions corresponding to edge types $H$, $V$, $S_+$, and $S_-$ considered previously. In addition, "lines" present in the image may be detected, without regard to orientation, using templates $T_5$ to $T_8$.

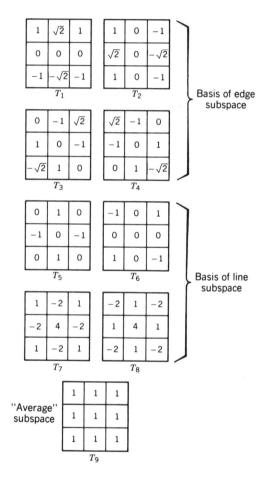

FIGURE 4.23 Frei-Chen edge templates
(a) Templates
(b) Imagery processed with Frei-Chen templates [F] (photos)
    (i) Using $T_1$
    (ii) Using $T_2$
    (iii) Using $T_3$
    (iv) Using $T_4$
    (v) Using $T_5$
    (vi) Using $T_6$
    (vii) Using $T_7$
    (viii) Using $T_8$
    (ix) Using $T_9$

*Continued on next page*

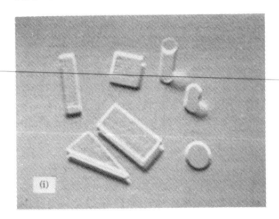

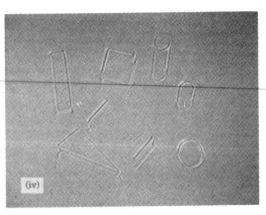

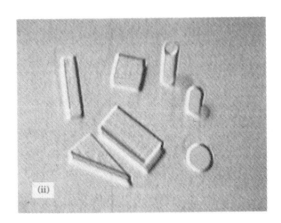

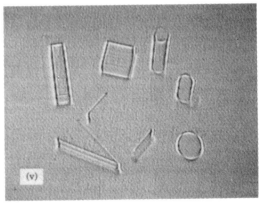

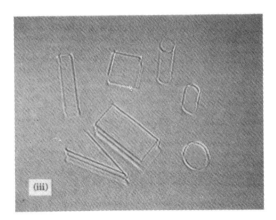

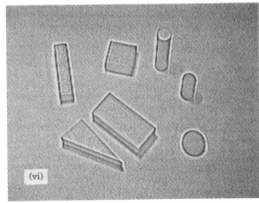

**FIGURE 4.23** *Continued*

*Continued on next page*

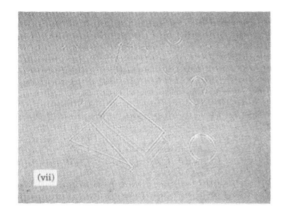
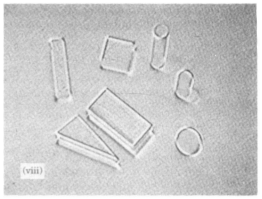

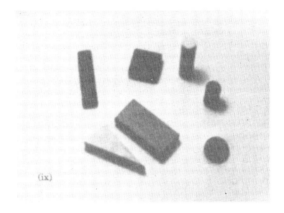

**FIGURE 4.23** *(Continued)*

### Edge Detection Via Smoothing and Laplacian

The previously described edge detection operators perform well with some images and poorly with others. As noted, a prominent source of performance degradation in these operators is noise in the input image. In this section an approach to edge detection is introduced which minimizes noise effects by smoothing the image prior to edge enhancement. This approach is conceptually obvious. Henceforth, we will refer to the specific implementation of the operator studied here as the Laplacian-of-the-Gaussian (LOG) operator.

The LOG operator smooths the image through convolution with a Gaussian-shaped kernel to minimize noise. This operation may improve the connectivity of extracted edges. The Gaussian kernel guarantees zero crossings of the second derivative are preserved. More is said about this in studying multiple resolution or pyramidal image analysis in relation to the Gaussian kernel in Chapter 7.

Following Gaussian smoothing, the Laplacian operator is applied. Although this sequential operation appears somewhat counterproductive (i.e., the second operation, to some extent, "undoes" the first), the resulting operator has high-frequency emphasis characteristics (see the problems).

*1-D Example of the Approach.* The operation of the LOG operator is first shown in a 1-D example. Referring to Figure 4.21, the location of a zero crossing of the second derivative is used to signify the location of an edge.

Modeling the edge as negative step via a 1-D image function of the form yields

$$f(x) = -2 u_{-1}(x) + 1 \tag{4-56}$$

which corresponds to a function with a step discontinuity at $x = 0$ where the intensity changes from $+1$ to $-1$. (Note that $u_{-1}$ is the unit step function.) Convolving this function with a 1-D Gaussian smoothing function, $g(x)$, of the form

$$g(x) = (1/(\sqrt{2\pi} \, \sigma)) \exp(-x^2/2\sigma^2) \tag{4-57}$$

yields the blurred 1-D output image, $f_2(x)$

$$f_2(x) = 1 - 2 \int_{-\infty}^{x} (\sigma \sqrt{2\pi})^{-1} \exp(-\tau^2/2\sigma^2) \, d\tau \tag{4-58}$$

The second derivative of $f_2(x)$ is

$$f_2''(x) = (2x/\sigma^3\sqrt{2\pi}) \exp(-x^2/2\sigma^2) \tag{4-59}$$

which has a zero crossing at $x = 0$.

Figure 4.24 depicts this result graphically. Note that Figure 4.24*d* represents, by definition, the step response of the LOG operator.

*2-D LOG Operator Development.* The kernel for a 2-D Gaussian smoothing operator in $(x,y)$ coordinates is

$$G(x,y) = (1/2\pi\sigma^2) \exp(-(x^2 + y^2)/2\sigma^2) \tag{4-60}$$

$G(x,y)$ is circularly symmetric and the smoothing effect may be controlled through $\sigma$. A scaled plot of this kernel for the case of $\sigma = 3$ is shown in Figure 4.25*a*. This function is convolved with the image function, $f(x,y)$, to produce the smoothed image

$$f_s(x,y) = f(x,y) * G(x,y) \tag{4-61}$$

The circular symmetry of the filter often leads to a polar representation, $G(r)$, where radius $r$ and $(x,y)$ are related by

$$r = (x_1^2 + x_2^2)^{1/2} \tag{4-62}$$

The discrete version of Eq. 4-61 is implemented in practice. *It is important to note that* G(r) *may not be cast as a fixed size window*, but rather the significant spatial extent of the operator varies with $\sigma$. The exponential operator in Eq. 4-60 decreases with increasing $r$, however, so that discrete convolution is truncated when values of the smoothing kernel become numerically insignificant.

As mentioned above, the conceptual basis for the algorithm is the Gaussian smoothing of the image followed by the application of the Laplacian operator ($\nabla^2$). This sequential process is unnecessary, however. The Laplacian of the convolution of $f(x,y)$ and $G(x,y)$ may be written as the convolution of $f(x,y)$ with the Laplacian of $G(x,y)$. Thus, the edge-enhanced image may be computed in a single operation

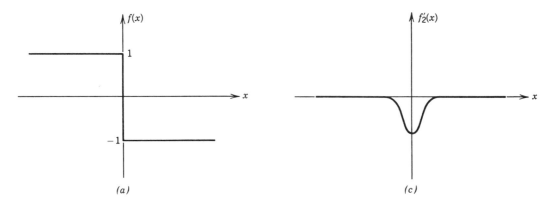

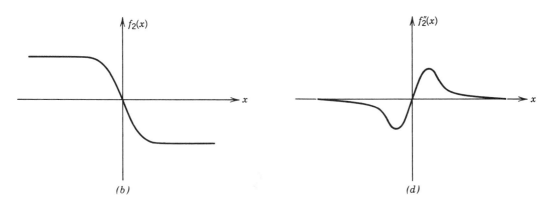

**FIGURE 4.24** LOG processing sequence (1-D)
(a) Ideal step (eq. 4-56)
(b) Smoothed 1-D step
(c) First derivative
(d) Second derivative (note: this represents the overall step response of the LOG operator)

by forming the convolution

$$f_{\text{edge}}(x,y) = (\nabla^2 G(x,y)) * f(x,y) \tag{4-63}$$

where $\nabla^2 G(x,y)$ is the composite LOG operator, which may be computed a priori. Recall the Laplacian of a function was defined previously as

$$\nabla^2 (\cdot) = \partial^2 (\cdot)/\partial x^2 + \partial^2 (\cdot)/\partial y^2 \tag{4-64}$$

Therefore, we compute the Laplacian of $G(r)$ as (see the problems)

$$\nabla^2 G(r) = (1/\pi\sigma^4) (r^2/2\sigma^2 - 1) \exp(-r^2/2\sigma^2) \tag{4-65}$$

Figure 4.25$b$ shows the characteristics of the Laplacian of the Gaussian (LOG), again for the case $\sigma = 3$. Several observations can be made:

**1.** The operator, as shown in Figure 4.25$b$, resembles the unsharp masking operator from the discussion on pages 135–136 in the sense that a smoothed portion of the image function (in the central region of the kernel or mask) is subtracted from positively weighted pixel intensities around the periphery of the mask.

2. Often, because the resultant zero crossings are of primary significance, the constant term $(1/\pi\sigma^4)$ is replaced with an arbitrary scale factor. This scale factor may be negative, yielding an inverted version of Figure 4.25b, which some think resembles a "Mexican hat."

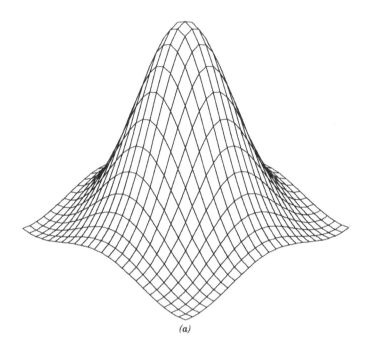

*(a)*

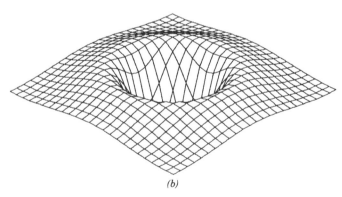

*(b)*

**FIGURE 4.25**
(a)  Gaussian smoothing kernal ($\sigma = 3$)
(b)  Laplacian Gaussian function
(c)  LOG filtered images
    (i)  Original
    (ii)  $\sigma = 0.5$
    (iii)  $\sigma = 1.0$

**FIGURE 4.25** *Continued*

■ TABLE 4.2
Mask size of LOG operator as function of $\sigma$

| $\sigma$ | $6\sqrt{2}\,\sigma$ | Mask Size (pixels) |
|---|---|---|
| 0.5 | 4.24 | $5 \times 5$ |
| 1 | 8.48 | $9 \times 9$ |
| 2 | 17.0 | $17 \times 17$ |
| 3 | 25.4 | $26 \times 26$ |
| 4 | 33.9 | $34 \times 34$ |
| 5 | 42.4 | $43 \times 43$ |

3. Although the spatial extent of the LOG operator is theoretically infinite, the numerically significant extent of the operator is easily bounded. Because more than 99% of the area under the Gaussian curve lies within a distance of $\pm 3\sigma$ from the origin, this provides some guidance in choosing the effective window extent.

4. The extent of the negative portion of the LOG operator is easily shown from Eqs. 4-64 and 4-65 to be within a distance of $\sqrt{2}\,\sigma$ from the origin; thus, the distance between zero crossings of the LOG operator is $w = 2\sqrt{2}\,\sigma$, or approximately $w \approx 3\sigma$. To achieve the desired edge-enhancement effect (Huertas & Medioni, 1986; Marr & Hildreth, 1980), one should use mask dimensions in the range of 3 to 4 $w$ to provide a suitable trade-off between reasonable mask size and operator performance. This is shown in Table 4.2.

5. The frequency response of the LOG operator also warrants investigation; this is addressed in the problems.

Table 4.2 illustrates one of the potential flaws in the LOG approach; the effective mask size is not constant and becomes unwieldy when $\sigma$ becomes large. For example, the LOG operator in the case $\sigma = 6$ requires a $57 \times 57$ pixel region. Fortunately, the LOG has an extremely useful separable decomposition, as shown in Huertas and Medioni (1986). Writing $\nabla^2 G(x,y)$ in Eq. 4-65 as

$$\nabla^2 G(x,y) = K(2 - (x^2 + y^2)/\sigma^2)\exp(-(x^2 + y^2)/2\sigma^2) \tag{4-66}$$

where $K$ is a scale factor, the operator may be decomposed into the sum of two operators, each of which, in turn, is separable in $x$ and $y$. This decomposition is achieved as follows

$$\nabla^2 G(x,y) = h_{12}(x,y) + h_{21}(x,y) \tag{4-67}$$

where

$$h_{12}(x,y) = h_1(x)\,h_2(y) \tag{4-68}$$

$$h_{21}(x,y) = h_2(x)\,h_1(y) \tag{4-69}$$

and

$$h_1(\beta) = \sqrt{K}\,(1 - \beta^2/\sigma^2)\exp(-\beta^2/2\sigma^2) \tag{4-70}$$

$$h_2(\beta) = \sqrt{K}\,\exp(-\beta^2/2\sigma^2) \tag{4-71}$$

(The proof of this is left to the problems.)

6. Historically, the LOG operator implementation has been approximated by forming the difference of two images, each filtered with the Gaussian operator but with different σ values. There is evidence that biological systems use this approach (Huertas & Medioni, 1986; Marr & Hildreth, 1980).

Several examples of the LOG operator, convolved with the image function, are provided in Figure 4.25c.

*The LOG operator, in addition to edge enhancing an image, yields directional edge information through the orientation of the zero crossing.* This information may be used to link directionally oriented edge pixels and thus form connected edges. One such predicate-based scheme is shown in Huertas & Medioni (1986).

### INTENSITY-ONLY TRANSFORMATIONS AND APPLICATIONS

In this section, we explore algorithmic approaches for image enhancement and restoration that place little significance on the geometric (spatial) dependence of pixels and thus are "intensity-only" approaches. The first approach, which may be based on either a stochastic or a deterministic model, leads to a grey-level processing algorithm of the form shown in Figure 4.26. Input pixel intensities, denoted $r$, are mapped to output intensities, denoted $s$, through the transformation

$$s = T(r) \tag{4-72}$$

The relationship $s = T(r)$ is easily implemented via a hardware or software lookup table. We begin with an examination of the underlying characteristics of this transformation as shown in Figure 4.27. Three cases are significant:

1. The case $s = T(r) = r$ is the "do nothing" transformation in which input pixel intensities are merely passed through to the output.
2. Cases where the slope of $T(r)$ ($ds/dr$) is less than 1.0 (i.e., as shown at point $a$ in Figure 4.27) result in pixel intensities in the neighborhood of $a$ being "darkened." (This assumes that $T(r)$ does not change the DC level of the intensities.) More important, **differences in pixel intensities (i.e., local contrast)** are *decreased* or compressed where $ds/dr < 1$.
3. Cases where $ds/dr > 1$ (e.g., at point $b$ in Figure 4.27) yield a "lightening" of the image due to output of an intensity value greater than the input. (This, again, ignores DC level changes.) Similarly, **differences (or local contrast) are** *increased* **or expanded.**

An arbitrary transformation, $T(r)$, will consist of a combination of the above cases. $T(r)$ may consist, for example, of piecewise linear segments. A limiting case

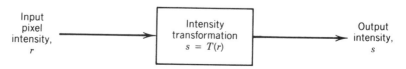

**FIGURE 4.26** Intensity-only image transformations

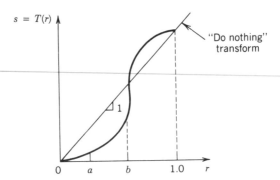

**FIGURE 4.27**  s = T(r) relationship characteristics

of the proceeding analysis, shown in Figure 4.28, is the case in which $T(r)$ is chosen as

$$T(r) = \begin{cases} A \text{ for } r > T \\ 0 \text{ otherwise} \end{cases}$$

This transformation is known as *thresholding* and is quite useful in a number of applications.

### DETERMINISTIC TECHNIQUES

An example of an application that employs the $s = T(r)$ transformation in the deterministic case was shown previously using the logarithmic transformation (Figure 4.12). $f(\underline{x})$ is first preprocessed via the intensity-only transformation using the natural logarithm. Figure 4.12 shows that for small $r$, $ds/dr > 1$ and, conversely, that larger $r$ values correspond to areas where $ds/dr = 0$. Therefore, the logarithmic transform expands the image contrast in dark regions and compresses it in lighter intensity regions. This is verified by the transformed image shown in Figure 4.29.

### STOCHASTIC MODELS AND ENHANCEMENT

We now consider the probabilistic ramifications of Eq. 4-72. Assume, without loss of generality, that the input values are represented by a *random variable*, $r$, which takes on values in the range

$$0 < r < 1 \qquad (4\text{-}73)$$

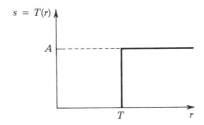

**FIGURE 4.28**  Grey-level transformation (thresholding)

**FIGURE 4.29** Logarithmic intensity transformation image example

Furthermore, assume $T(r)$ is single valued and monotonically increasing; it is also normalized—that is,

$$0 < T(r) < 1 \qquad (4\text{-}74)$$

and the inverse transformation $T^{-1}(s)$ exists.

$s = T(r)$ may be given the interpretation of a transformation of a random variable and thus probability density functions (pdfs) of the random variables (rvs) $r$ and $s$ may be related. Specifically, we quantify $p_s(s)$ as a function of $p_r(r)$ and $T(r)$. Elementary probability theory may be used to show that, if $T(r)$ satisfies the conditions stated above, the pdfs of $r$ and $s$ are related via

$$p_s(s) = p_r(r) \, dr/ds \,\Big|_{r \,=\, T^{-1}(s)} \qquad (4\text{-}75)$$

Thus, *$T(r)$ provides a way to modify the pdf of the input image intensities.* This leads to histogram equalization.

*Histogram Equalization.* $p_r(r)$ may be approximated by a histogram of pixel intensity values. The general subjective brightness and contrast characteristics of an image may be determined from this histogram. For example, if $p_r(r)$ is skewed such that nonzero values of $p_r(r)$ cluster about small values of $r$, we would tend to say the image is fairly dark. Conversely, if $p_r(r)$ is nonzero for a range of large values of $r$, the subjective evaluation would be that of an overly bright or perhaps "washed out" image. The cause of either of these effects may have been improper scene illumination or incorrect sensor sensitivity levels. Neither of these cases is desirable for subjective viewing, since the range of image intensities is quite narrow and therefore the perceived image contrast is poor, as shown in Figure 4.30(*a*). Thus, it is argued that an approximately uniform pdf is most desirable because it provides maximum contrast and utilizes the dynamic range of the sensor and display equipment.

An alternative and quantitative rationale for the desirability of a uniform image

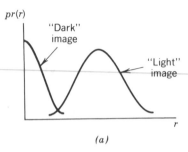

(a)

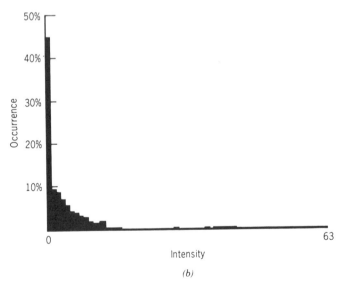

(b)

**FIGURE 4.30**   Histogram equalization
(a)   Histogram (pdf) interpretation
(b)   Sample results
    (i)   Input image
    (ii)   Histogram
    (iii)   Enhanced image
    (iv)   Histogram of output image

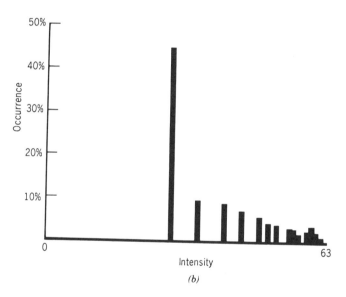

**FIGURE 4.30** *Continued*

intensity pdf may be developed by considering performance metrics for the representation of continuous data ranges by a set of discrete values (Gonzales & Wintz, 1987). For example, given image intensities in the range

$$0 < f < A \qquad (4\text{-}76)$$

a set of $L$ quantization levels, each with representation values $R_i$ and decision or threshold values $D_{i-1}$ and $D_i$, may be determined to minimize a performance measure of the form:

$$J = \sum_L \int_{D_{i-1}}^{D_i} (r - R_J)^2\, P_r(r)\mathrm{d}r \qquad (4\text{-}77)$$

It is relatively easy to show (see the problems) that *a uniform pdf for* p_r(r)*yields equally spaced decision values* $D_i$ *with representation values* $R_i$ *taken as the midpoint of the regions delineated by the decision values.* Returning to the actual equalization process, Eq. 4-75 indicates, for an arbitrary input pdf (i.e., $p_r(r)$) how $T(r)$ may be chosen. Since $p_s(s) = 1$ is desired, an obvious solution might be, given $p_r(r)$, to choose

$$dr/ds = [p_r(r)]^{-1} \tag{4-78}$$

However, cases of $P_r(r) = 0$ would be intractable in this formulation. As an alternative, consider the grey-level transformation function

$$s = T(r) = \int_0^r p_r(a)da \tag{4-79}$$

which is recognized as the cumulative probability distribution of the random variable $r$. Differentiation of Eq. 4-79 using Liebnitz's rule yields

$$ds/dr = p_r(r) \tag{4-80}$$

which is the desired relationship. The algorithm we have just derived is referred to as *histogram equalization* and consists of the following three steps:

1. Compute the histogram of intensity levels in the input image (this is an approximation to $p_r(r)$).
2. Integrate (sum) this approximation of $p_r(r)$ to obtain an approximation to the cumulative distribution function, $F_r(r)$.
3. Use $F_r(r)$ as the intensity transformation function, $T(r)$; that is,

$$s = F_r(r) \tag{4-81}$$

Figure 4.30 illustrates the result of histogram equalization of a typical low-contrast image. It is only possible to approximate a uniform pdf in the output image due to finite intensity resolution (6 bits).

*Histogram Specification.* Other cases exist wherein it is desired to develop an intensity transformation such that the output image pdf *matches* that of a pre-specified pdf. A typical application requiring this type of transformation involves comparing two images of a scene (taken by the same sensor with fixed geometric parameters) where the scene illumination conditions under which each image was acquired were different [Wong, 1977]. This type of pdf-matching transformation is termed *histogram specification.* Given an input image with intensities given as realizations of the rv $x$, and arbitrary pdf $p_x(x)$, a grey-level transformation $s = T(x)$ is derived which yields an output image with the desired pdf, denoted pdf $p_s(s)$. The procedure is a modified version of that used for histogram equalization:

1. Transform the input image intensities to achieve a uniform pdf. This results in an intensity mapping $s_1 = T_1(x)$ yielding a uniform (0,1) pdf for $s_1$ (Figure 4.31, Part 1).

2. Transform the output image intensities, with prespecified pdf, to yield a uniform pdf. This yields a second transformation $s_2 = T_2(s)$ (Figure 4.31, Part 2).

3. Invert the transformation in 2., and combine with the results of 1. As shown

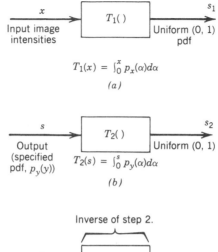

$$T_1(x) = \int_0^x p_x(\alpha)d\alpha$$

*(a)*

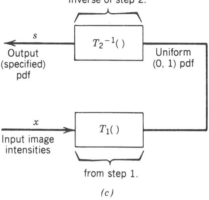

*(b)*

Inverse of step 2.

*(c)*

**FIGURE 4.31** Histogram specification process
(a)  Input image pdf transformed to uniform (step 1)
(b)  Output image (desired) pdf transformed to uniform (step 2)
(c)  Composite operation (step 3)

in Figure 4.31, Part 3, this yields a structure for transformation of input image intensities, $x$, to output image intensities, $s$, (with $p_s(s)$ specified) of the form:

$$s = T_2^{-1}(T_1(x)) \tag{4-82}$$

Note that the inversion of $T_2(s)$ in step 2 is necessary. $T_2$ is the cumulative distribution function of an rv. Seldom do the inverses of these distributions exist in closed form. (A primary example is the Gaussian cdf.) However, the inverse may be determined in the digital implementation by an "inversion" of the lookup table process, in either hardware or software.

## MODEL-BASED ENHANCEMENT AND RESTORATION

The previous approaches for image enhancement using smoothing, sharpening, and equalization operators employed relatively simple underlying models for the image function. A broader class of enhancement and restoration approaches exist which is based on more sophisticated or complete underlying models for image origin or characteristics. If a more accurate characterization of the image degradation process is available, more precise enhancement or restoration processing may be undertaken. We look briefly at two examples of these models.

## A LINEAR SYSTEM MODEL FOR ENHANCEMENT

In this section we model the source of the image degradation as a linear operation on the undegraded image function. In this context, the overall restoration problem involves two models—one for the underlying degradation and another for the restoration process. When these models involve filtering operations, and the restoration filter is designed to "undo" the (undesirable) effect of the degradation model, the concepts of *inverse filtering* and *deconvolution* arise. Unfortunately, the process of inverse filtering or deconvolution is not easy to formulate or implement. A principal reason for this difficulty is the potential lack of knowledge concerning the degradation model parameters. These may need to be estimated from the degraded image. The process of developing inverse filters is usually underconstrained. Furthermore, the resulting deconvolution operator often is difficult to implement; for example, it may require a spatially variant filter.

Recall from Chapter 3 that a general model to describe a linear operation on an image could be written in terms of the input image, $f_1(\underline{x})$, an impulse response function, $h(\underline{x},\beta)$ (which represents the response, in image coordinates, $\underline{x}$, to a unit impulse at location $\beta$), to yield the output image, $f_2(\underline{x})$, as

$$f_2(\underline{x}) = \int f_1(\beta) \, h(\underline{x},\beta) \, d\beta \qquad (4\text{-}83)$$

When the system is space invariant, $h(\underline{x},\beta)$ becomes $h(\underline{x} - \beta)$, and we may formulate this operation in the frequency domain as

$$F_2(\underline{u}) = F_1(\underline{u}) \, H(\underline{u}) \qquad (4\text{-}84)$$

where $F_1$, $F_2$, and $H$ are the Fourier transforms of the functions $f_1$, $f_2$, and $h$, respectively, and $\underline{u} = (u,v)$ is the frequency domain coordinate.

The first example involves the modeling and restoration of imagery degraded by motion blur [Sawchuck, 1972]. This example shows how a time-varying effect may be cast as a spatial filtering operation.

An image, $f_2(\underline{x})$, is given, which is measured with respect to an $(x_1, x_2)$ coordinate system. $f_2(\underline{x})$ is a degraded version of another (the integrated) image, $f_1(\beta)$, measured with respect to a $(\beta_1,\beta_2)$ coordinate system. The $(\beta_1,\beta_2)$ coordinate system may be assumed to be moving in time with respect to the $(x_1,x_2)$ system to achieve motion blur. A conservation of image energy is postulated; that is, over small regions $d\underline{x}$ and $d\beta$,

$$f_2(\underline{x})d\underline{x} = f_1(\beta)d\beta \qquad (4\text{-}85)$$

Therefore,

$$f_2(\underline{x}) = f_1(\beta)|d\beta/d\underline{x}| \qquad (4\text{-}86)$$

where the determinant in Eq. 4-86 is denoted $J_x(\beta)$, the Jacobian of the transformation. The time varying geometric distortion is given by

$$\beta = g(\underline{x},t)$$

or $\qquad\qquad\qquad\qquad\qquad\qquad\qquad\qquad\qquad\qquad\qquad\qquad (4\text{-}87)$

$$\beta_1 = g_1(\underline{x},t)$$

$$\beta_2 = g_2(\underline{x},t)$$

Note that the $J_x = I$ for translational motion. In what follows, assume that the motion is constant velocity translation only, with velocities $V_1$ and $V_2$ in the $\beta_1$ and $\beta_2$ directions, respectively. Therefore,

$$\beta_1 = x_1 - V_1 t$$

and

$$\beta_2 = x_2 - V_2 t \qquad (4\text{-}88)$$

Furthermore, the output image intensity, $f_2(\underline{x})$, is modeled as the value of the moving input image integrated over an exposure interval of duration $T$

$$f_2(\underline{x}) = \int_{t=0}^{T} f_2(\underline{x},t) \, dt = \int_{t=0}^{T} f_1(g(\underline{x},t)) \, dt \qquad (4\text{-}89)$$

This form, involving temporal, rather than spatial integration, is not in the desired convolution form of Eqs. 4-83 and 4-84. Note from Eq. 4-87 that fixing the spatial argument $\underline{x}$ forces a time-varying relationship between $\beta$ and $t$; in fact, a curve is traced in $(\beta_1,\beta_2)$ space for varying $t$. This relationship may be written in terms of a function $k$ as

$$t = k(\underline{x},\beta) \qquad (4\text{-}90)$$

If both $\beta_1$ and $\beta_2$ are functions of time (i.e., the time-varying geometric distortion is in both the $\beta_1$ and $\beta_2$ directions), the relationship in Eq. 4-90 may be written in terms of two related functions, $k_1$ and $k_2$, obtained from Eq. 4-87

$$t = k_1(\underline{x},\beta_1) = k_2(\underline{x},\beta_2) \qquad (4\text{-}91)$$

This relationship among $\underline{x}$, $\beta_1$, and $\beta_2$ is shown in the general case in Figure 4.32. Using the example of constant velocity translation from Eq. 4-88, the Eq. 4-91 relationship becomes

$$t = (1/V_1) \, (x_1 - \beta_1) = (1/V_2) \, (x_2 - \beta_2) \qquad (4\text{-}92)$$

Therefore, the path constrained by Eq. 4-90 in the $(\beta_1,\beta_2)$ coordinate system must be

$$\begin{aligned}
\beta_2 &= (V_2/V_1) \, \beta_1 + x_2 - (V_2/V_1) \, x_1 \\
&= x_2 + (V_2/V_1) \, (\beta_1 - x_1)
\end{aligned} \qquad (4\text{-}93)$$

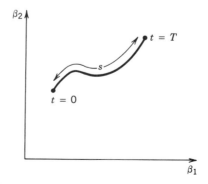

**FIGURE 4.32** Model-based restoration example: trajectory in $(\beta_1, \beta_2)$ system for fixed x

Notice that for constant velocities and fixed $\underline{x}$, the $\beta_1$–$\beta_2$ relationship is a line. Thus, the intensity of each pixel location $\underline{x}$ in the output image, from Eq. 4-87 and Eq. 4-89, is determined by integration along the $(\beta_1,\beta_2)$ path in the $(\beta_1,\beta_2)$ plane traversed over time $T$. The significance of this result is that we can relate the incremental length of the path, denoted $dS_\beta$, in $(\beta_1,\beta_2)$ coordinates, to the incremental time interval, derived from Eq. 4-90, as

$$dS_\beta = [(d\beta_1/dt)^2 + (d\beta_2/dt)^2]^{1/2} \, dt \qquad (4\text{-}94)$$

(This is due to an elementary application of differential calculus to plane curves.) We reformulate Eq. 4-89 in a form somewhat closer to the desired result as

$$f_2(\underline{x}) = \int_{\underline{\beta}=g(\underline{x},0)}^{\underline{\beta}=g(\underline{x},T)} f_1(\underline{\beta}) \, \frac{dS_\beta}{[(d\beta_1/dt)^2 + (d\beta_2/dt)^2]^{1/2}} \qquad (4\text{-}95)$$

where the limits on the integral are rewritten to show the equivalent constraint on $\beta$. Finally, we can relate the integral above to our objective form of Eq. 4-83 by converting the path integral to an area integral. Employing the delta function, denoted $\delta(\ )$, the path is specified via

$$f_2(\underline{x}) = \iint_{\underline{\beta}=g(\underline{x},0)}^{\underline{\beta}=g(\underline{x},T)} \frac{f_1(\underline{\beta}) \, \delta[\beta_2 - (V_2/V_1)\,\beta_1 - (x_2 - (V_2/V_1)\,x_1)] \, d\underline{\beta}}{[(d\beta_1/dt)^2 + (d\beta_2/dt)^2]^{1/2}} \qquad (4\text{-}96)$$

For simplicity, assume that the motion is only in the horizontal direction, or $V_2 = 0$. The path of integration therefore (from Eq. 4-93) simplifies to $\beta_2 = x_2$. Equation 4-96 then reduces to

$$f_2(\underline{x}) = \iint f_1(\underline{\beta}) \, \delta[\beta_2 - x_2] \, (1/V_1) \, d\underline{\beta} \qquad (4\text{-}97)$$

Therefore, by analogy with Eq. 4-83, the point spread function for this case in Eq. 4-97 is

$$h(\underline{x},\underline{\beta}) = h(x_1 - \beta_1) = \begin{cases} (1/V_1) & 0 \leq x_1 - \beta_1 \leq V_1 T \\ 0 & \text{elsewhere} \end{cases} \qquad (4\text{-}98)$$

The above convolution-based model derivation is illustrative and somewhat tedious. To complete and unify our understanding of these types of image degradation models, an alternate and equivalent frequency domain approach is developed. Taking the 2-D Fourier transform of Eq. 4-89 yields

$$F_2(\underline{u}) = \iint_{-\infty}^{\infty} f_2(\underline{x}) \, \exp[-j2\pi\langle \underline{x},\underline{u}\rangle] \, d\underline{x} \qquad (4\text{-}99)$$

Again assume, for simplicity, $V_2 = 0$. Using Eqs. 4-89, 4-97, and 4-98, interchanging the order of temporal and spatial integrations, and using the shifting property of Fourier transforms (Appendix 3), the reader may verify that Eq. 4-99 reduces to

$$F_2(u,v) = F_1(\underline{u}) \int_0^T \exp[-j2\pi(uV_1 t)] \, dt \qquad (4\text{-}100)$$

Therefore, the degradation model transfer function, $H(u,v)$, is given by the second term in the right hand side of Eq. 4-100.

$$H(u,v) = \int_0^T \exp[-j2\pi(uV_1 t)] \, dt \qquad (4\text{-}101)$$

The inverse transform of this function is, by definition, the point spread function of the system. The solution to this integral is

$$H(u,v) \; = \; \exp(-j\pi u V_1 T) \; T \; \text{sinc} \; (\pi u T V_1) \tag{4-102}$$

This quantity in Eq. 4-102 represents the transform of a pulse of width $V_1 T$, centered at $x = V_1 T/2$, with amplitude $(1/V_1)$. This impulse response of the system is the same as the result from the spatial domain approach, Eq. 4-98. Thus, the Fourier domain derivation of the linear systems model is equivalent to and complements the spatial domain approach.

Up to this point, the formulation of the degradation model has been considered. The corresponding restoration algorithm is now developed. The degraded image, $f_2(\underline{x})$, may be formulated in the Fourier domain as

$$F_2(\underline{u}) \; = \; F_1(\underline{u}) \; H(\underline{u}) \tag{4-103}$$

from which we note that

$$F_1(\underline{u}) \; = \; F_2(\underline{u})/H(\underline{u}) \tag{4-104}$$

It would be tempting to formulate the inverse or restoration process directly as a linear filtering operation using Eq. 4-104. Denoting the restoration operator or filter as $H_R(u,v)$ and the restored image as $f_R$ in the frequency domain, we may represent the restoration as

$$F_R(\underline{u}) \; = \; F_2(\underline{u}) \; H_R(\underline{u}) \tag{4-105}$$

Therefore, using Eq. 4-104, a reasonable choice for $H_R(\underline{u})$ would be

$$H_R(u,v) \; = \; [H(u,v)]^{-1} \tag{4-106}$$

This represents a simplistic *inverse filtering* formulation. However, the fact that the value of $H(u,v)$ is zero at

$$u \; = \; (n/TV_1) \; \text{for} \; n \; = \; 1,2,\ldots$$

precludes the practical application of this unmodified approach at these frequencies. A simple modification is to define $H_R(u,v) = 0$ when this occurs.

*Algebraic Formulation of the Linear Systems Approach.* In practice discrete versions of the linear system degradation models are employed. In the linear, space invariant, discrete degradation case, a conceptually simple and computationally practical result may be obtained. (This result is explored more fully in the problems.)

A linear, space invariant, discrete model as the source of image degradation is of the form

$$f_2(i,j) \; = \; \sum_{-\infty}^{\infty} \sum_{-\infty}^{\infty} h(i-k, j-l) \, f_1(k,l) \; + \; n(i,j) \tag{4-107}$$

where $n(i,j)$ is a 2-D noise process. Therefore, the degradation model involves the linear filtering of the undegraded image, followed by the addition of a noise process. Furthermore, it is assumed that $h$ is known and has compact support; that is, it is nonzero in some bounded region of 2-D space. Converting the sampled input and output image functions $f_1$, $f_2$ and noise $n$ to vectors (perhaps by row or column concatenation) allows Eq. 4-107 to be reformulated in vector-matrix notation as

$$\underline{f}_2 = H \underline{f}_1 + \underline{n} \tag{4-108a}$$

where $H$ is determined from $h(i,j)$ and the matrix to vector conversion strategy. Note that neither $\underline{f}_1$ nor $\underline{n}$ is directly measurable. We may formulate our objective, in the case of restoration, as the determination of an approximation to $\underline{f}_1$, denoted $\underline{f}_R$, using the degraded image, $\underline{f}_2$, and $H$. One reasonable criterion is to minimize the vector distance between the undegraded and restored functions, or to minimize $\|\underline{f}_R - \underline{f}_1\|^2$. In addition, it would be convenient if the resulting restoration algorithm employed a linear operation on $\underline{f}_2$. One way to accomplish this is through least-squares techniques (Appendix 2), thereby forming the restoration solution as

$$\underline{f}_R = H^+ \underline{f}_2 \tag{4-108b}$$

where $H^+$ denotes the pseudoinverse of $H$. Note that $H$ in general contains many repetitions of the parameters of $h$, and this leads to efficient solutions based on the resultant "block circulant" properties of $H$ (Andrews and Hunt, 1977).

# ■ CONVERSION OF GREY-LEVEL TO BINARY IMAGES

Conversion of grey-level images to binary representations is important for a number of reasons:

1. To identify the extent of objects, represented as a region in the image. For example, we may wish to separate a visual target from its background.

2. To concentrate on shape (or morphological) analysis, in which case the intensities of pixels are less significant than the shape of a region.

3. To display an image on an output device which has only one bit intensity resolution, that is, a binary or two-level display device, such as a printer. The objective is to convert the grey-level image so that the subjective appearance is that of a multi-intensity image. The advent of desktop publishing makes this an area of growing significance.

4. To convert an edge-enhanced image to a line drawing of the imaged scene. It is necessary to distinguish strong edges that correspond to object outlines (and features) from weak edges due to illumination changes, shadows, etc.

## THRESHOLDING

Thresholding has previously been shown to be the limiting case of an intensity-only transformation (p. 168). It has a significant role in the low-level processing of images. The idea of using simply the pixel intensity or grey-level to produce either an ON (or "1") or OFF (or "0") intensity in the output image is both conceptually obvious and simple to implement; however, unless the class of images under consideration has appropriate characteristics (e.g., the image is formed from a clearly backlighted matte black object), this approach alone is seldom successful.

GREY-LEVEL IMAGES

*Global Image Thresholding.* An obvious approach to converting a grey-level image to a binary image is to form an input/output relationship (implemented in hardware via a lookup table) of the form

$$f_o(\underline{x}) = \begin{cases} A \text{ if } f_i(\underline{x}) \leq T \\ B \text{ if } f_i(\underline{x}) > T \end{cases} \qquad (4\text{-}109)$$

where $f_i$ and $f_o$ are the respective input and output image functions.

The values of the threshold, $T$, and the bilevel output image intensity values, $A$ and $B$, are chosen a priori. The autonomous determination of a suitable threshold for a wide class of images is a nontrivial task. A typical algorithm is based on the formation of a global histogram of image intensity values and consequent selection of a threshold that yields a desired fraction (typically 10–50%) of ON output pixels. Another related approach simply sets $T$ to be a fraction of the maximum image intensity (denoted $R$). A reasonable choice is $T = R/2$. An example of the use of a global threshold is shown in Figure 4.33.

*Locally Adaptive Image Thresholding.* In this case, thresholding is accomplished locally. The threshold level is varied to suit local or neighborhood input image grey-level variations. The intuitive result is the preservation of local contrast, thus yielding an output image with a subjectively pleasing appearance, as well as less loss of information.

Several techniques to implement a local threshold include:

1. Line- or edge-sensitive local thresholding: (The detection of an edge and its corresponding intensity are used to determine the local threshold value).

2. Average grey-level based thresholding: The threshold is determined as a function of the average input image grey-value in a local region (usually 3 × 3 or 5 × 5 pixels in spatial extent). Pixel intensities that differ significantly from this average are assumed to contain local contrast information and are thus distinguished in the output image.

An example of the local average thresholding strategy is shown in Figure 4.33*b*.

EDGE-ENHANCED IMAGES

As shown in Figure 4.34, the production of a usable edge image or *edge map* following edge enhancement involves another processing step. The discrimination between extraneous edges and those that contribute to a higher level of processing is necessary. For example, the identification and classification of edge junctions, which may correspond to object vertices in the scene, is often the next processing step.

Global or local thresholds may be determined by looking at histograms of the global or local edge intensity data, with the hope that these histograms are bimodal. An alternative technique is to force the output binary image to have a predetermined percentage of ON pixels. The thresholding of an edge-enhanced image with varying threshold levels is shown in Figure 4.35. The application of thresholding to the edge-enhanced image is seldom sufficient to generate a useful edge image or map, but it provides a starting point for more sophisticated algorithm devel-

*(a)*

**FIGURE 4.33**
(a)  Binary image produced with global threshold
   (i)   T = 20
   (ii)  T = 30

*(b)*

**FIGURE 4.33** (b) Binary image produced using locally adaptive threshold

opment. Often a *thinning* algorithm is employed to attempt minimization of su-perfluous edges (Chapter 6).

## HALFTONING

At the present time, virtually all printed pictorial information consists of a binary (bilevel) microstructure. Three printing technologies dominate; lithography, let-terpress, and gravure; all of these produce bilevel output. All pictorial imagery in the mass printed media are produced using *halftone* approaches. The halftone process allows the approximation of a grey-scale image appearance at normal

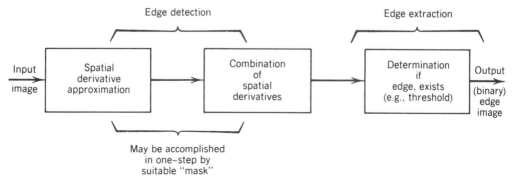

**FIGURE 4.34** Creating a binary edge image or "edge map" via isotropic operators

**FIGURE 4.35** Thresholding edge-enhanced images
(a)  T = 15
(b)  T = 20

viewing distances (about 14 inches from the document). We begin our examination of halftoning with some definitions.

*Continuous tone imagery* is imagery whose intensity quantization involves multiple grey-levels with no perceptible quantization. Examples are television images and photographs. *Halftone imagery* is (bilevel) imagery which appears to have multiple grey-levels due to the microstructure (halftone dots) that vary locally over the area of coverage. Halftone techniques are successful since the human visual system spatially integrates on and off intensity values to create perceived greyscale. Examples are newspaper, magazines, and book images.

Normally, the bilevel output medium used for halftoning has a much higher spatial resolution than that of the corresponding grey-level image. The mapping from a grey-level image to a bilevel image is a one-to-many transformation, since each input image grey-value does not yield a unique output dot or dot pattern. Assume (Saghri, et al., 1986) the input grey-level image, modeled as the discrete function $f(x,y)$, or $m \times n$ matrix $[f]$, is composed of $n_i$ columns and $m_i$ rows, indexed by $x$ and $y$, respectively, and the dynamic range of image intensity is $2^p$ where $p$ is the number of intensity bits per pixel. Therefore,

$$> 0 \leq f(x,y) < 2^p - 1 \approx 2^p \text{ (for large } p) \qquad (4\text{-}110)$$

where

$$1 \leq x \leq n_i \quad \text{and} \quad 1 \leq y \leq m_i$$

A halftone rendition of this image, denoted $h(i,j)$, is represented on a bilevel device with $n_h$ and $m_h$ columns and rows, respectively, with

$$h(i,j) \in \{0,1\}$$

and

$$1 \leq i \leq n_h \quad \text{and} \quad 1 \leq j \leq m_h$$

This is shown in Figure 4.36. The objective of halftoning is to determine a mapping from $f(x,y)$ to $h(i,j)$ that is "subjectively" pleasing. A fundamental objective in the development of halftone mapping strategies is the determination of pattern codings that do not exhibit a false textural contour or other "artifacts."

A useful measure of the dynamic resolution of the halftone is the number of halftone dots allocated per input pixel, given by the ratio $R_h$

$$R_h = (n_h m_h)/(n_i m_i) \qquad \text{dots/pixel} \qquad (4\text{-}111)$$

For example, given an input grey-level image of $256 \times 256 \times 6$ bit resolution, and an output display device with $1024 \times 1024 \times 1$ bit resolution,

$$R_h = 16 \text{ dots/pixel}$$

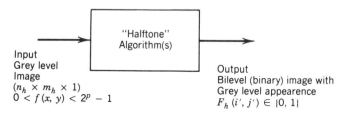

**FIGURE 4.36** Grey level-binary image halftone conversion process

This does not mean that each mapped pixel could be represented by the equivalent of $2^{16}$ intensities (i.e., ON or OFF combinations of 16 dots), since it is the aggregated visual effect of these dot intensities that gives the resulting halftone a "grey-level-like" appearance. From the point of view of aggregated grey-level effect, many of these $2^{16}$ patterns are indistinguishable.

### HALFTONING STRATEGIES

The typical halftone process relies on a conversion from a grey-level pixel (single value or local region) in the input image to a region of bilevel pixels in the output image. This region ($n \times n$ array) of bilevel pixels may be determined in a multitude of ways. Some are:

1. *Creation of grey-scale character fonts.* A set of "character" fonts for an $n \times n$ pixel region, are used to map individual input image grey-scale intensities

*(a)*

$$\begin{bmatrix} 0 & 0 \\ 0 & 0 \end{bmatrix} \qquad \begin{bmatrix} 1 & 0 \\ 0 & 1 \end{bmatrix} \qquad \begin{bmatrix} 1 & 1 \\ 0 & 1 \end{bmatrix} \qquad \begin{bmatrix} 1 & 1 \\ 1 & 1 \end{bmatrix}$$

$$0 \qquad\qquad 1/3\, f_{\max} \qquad 2/3\, f_{\max} \qquad f_{\max}$$

**FIGURE 4.37** Halftone creation using graphics character set
(a) Resulting halftone image
(b) Character set

into suitable $n \times n$ binary regions or characters in the output image. This yields a conceptually and practically simple implementation scheme, but the appearance of false contours often precludes the use of this process alone. An example of this process is shown in Figure 4.37.

2. *Pseudorandom thresholding and the application of dither.* The visual appearance of false contours generated in the halftone process is reduced by introduction of random noise (on/off pixel values) to the halftone image. The perceptual effect of the introduction of this noise is decreased concentration on high-frequency image information. This spatially distributed noise causes the observer to locally integrate the intensity in a local region. In practice, noise may be added to the input grey level prior to conversion to a bilevel image. Additionally, optimization of this process is possible, since *the process of pseudorandom noise addition followed by fixed (global) thresholding is equivalent to the thresholding of the signal with a pseudorandom threshold. This is the basis of "dither" matrices.*

Furthermore, the incorporation of local spatial dependence into the process may be shown to yield subjectively more pleasing halftone images. This pseudorandom thresholding with spatial threshold dependence is termed *ordered dither.*

Assume for simplicity that each thresholded grey-level pixel generates one output binary pixel, or $n_i = n_h$ and $m_i = m_h$. The more general case of $n_i \leq n_h$ and $m_i \leq m_h$ may be handled by appropriately modifying the scale (or, more generally, the scale and aspect ratio) of the input image prior to application of the halftoning process.

For small spatial regions, *dither matrices* are used. Using dither matrices, the output image is formed by a pixel-by-pixel comparison of the input intensity and the corresponding $n \times n$ dither matrix threshold. The dither matrix is assumed to be replicated so that it covers the entire source image. For an $n \times n$ dither matrix, $D^n$, image pixel threshold elements are selected on the basis of the current pixel location $(i,j)$ as

$$T_{ij} = D^n (i \bmod n, j \bmod n) \tag{4-112}$$

The output halftone image is therefore formed as

    For $i := 1$ TO $n_h$ DO

        FOR $j : = 1$ TO $m_h$ DO

            BEGIN form_threshold_from_dither_matrix;

            IF $f(i,j) > T_{ij}$

                THEN $f_{out}(i,j) = $ ON;

                ELSE $f_{out}(i,j) = $ OFF

        END;

Several choices for dither matrices exist. In the $2 \times 2$ case, for example, a suitable choice (Jarvis, et al., 1976) is

$$D^2 = \begin{bmatrix} 0 & 2 \\ 3 & 1 \end{bmatrix} \tag{4-113}$$

Two reasonable choices for $D^4$ are

$$\begin{bmatrix} 0 & 14 & 3 & 13 \\ 11 & 5 & 8 & 6 \\ 2 & 12 & 1 & 15 \\ 9 & 7 & 10 & 4 \end{bmatrix}$$

and

$$\begin{bmatrix} 0 & 8 & 2 & 10 \\ 12 & 4 & 14 & 6 \\ 3 & 11 & 1 & 9 \\ 15 & 7 & 13 & 5 \end{bmatrix}$$

Note that dither matrices are usually formed using integer-valued elements starting at 0. For example, in the case of $D^2$, the threshold values are in the range $[0 . . 3]$. Thus, in practice, the actual threshold is determined by scaling the dynamic range of the dither matrix elements to match that of the input image dynamic range.

The number of distinct thresholds in an $n \times n$ dither matrix is $N = n^2$. Thus, these $N$ thresholds allow the thresholding of the input grey-level image at most $N + 1$ distinct grey-levels. Table 4.2 shows this relationship.

Thus, the dither matrix dimension, which may be viewed as analogous to a spatial sampling rate, must be chosen to provide a good trade-off between spatial and intensity quantization. It is desirable to avoid both "oversampling" (i.e., too large a dither matrix dimension) in regions of nearly constant image intensity, and "undersampling" (choosing too small a dither matrix dimension) in image regions with significant high frequency content. These conflicting requirements suggest a possible solution based on a spatially adaptive dither matrix dimension (Besslich and Carlsohn, 1985).

The derivation of $4 \times 4$ and larger dither matrices with desirable properties has been studied by a number of researchers (Jarvis, et al., 1976, Lippel and Kurland, 1971). Recursive relationships exist to generate dither matrices of dimension $2^P$ from those of order $P$. Jarvis (1976) indicates one recursive formulation to form a

■ **TABLE 4.2**
**Dither matrix dimension and corresponding grey-level thresholds**

| $n$ (matrix dimension) | $N$ (thresholds) | $N + 1$ (grey-levels) |
|:---:|:---:|:---:|
| 2 | 4 | 5 |
| 3 | 9 | 10 |
| 4 | 16 | 17 |
| 5 | 25 | 26 |
| 6 | 36 | 37 |
| 7 | 49 | 50 |
| 8 | 64 | 65 |
| . | . | . |
| . | . | . |
| . | . | . |
| 15 | 225 | 226 |
| 16 | 256 | 257 |

dither matrix of order $n$ as

$$D^n = \begin{bmatrix} 4D^{n/2} + D_{00}^2 \ U^{n/2} & 4D^{n/2} + D_{01}^2 \ U^{n/2} \\ 4D^{n/2} + D_{10}^2 \ U^{n/2} & 4D^{n/2} + D_{11}^2 \ U^{n/2} \end{bmatrix} \tag{4-114}$$

where $U^n$ is an $n \times n$ matrix of all "1"'s, and $D_{ij}^2$ represents the $i,j^{th}$ element of the $D^2$ matrix.

Properties of a $4 \times 4$ dither matrix derived using Eq. 4-114 are as follows:

1. The threshold patterns in the dither matrix are regular in the horizontal, vertical, and diagonal directions, thus allowing periodic spatial extensions.

(a)

(b)

**FIGURE 4.38**  Image of size (240 × 768 × 1), derived from the size of (240 × 256 × 6)
(a)  2 × 2 dither matrix
(b)  4 × 4 dither matrix

2. The patterns are invariant under dyadic shifting.

3. The sum of the elements in either the rows, columns, or the nine $2 \times 2$ submatrices is the "magic" number 30.

When the output bilevel device resolution exceeds that of the input grey-level image (i.e., $R_h > 1$), the dithering technique is modified. One approach is to interpolate grey-levels in the input image to create an input grey-level image with resolution equal to that of the output device. For example, given $n_i = m_i = 256$ and $n_h = m_h = 512$ ($R_h = 4$ from Eq. 4-111), replication of rows and columns in the input image is a computationally efficient manner in which to produce the equivalent resolution input image. Of course, other interpolation strategies are possible—for example, linear interpolation. The output image is formed by thresholding with the appropriate dither matrix. Computationally, the process would be performed locally—that is, in the $n \times n$ image region corresponding to the dither matrix.

Examples of halftone imagery produced using dither are shown in Figure 4.38. Other modifications of the dither scheme are possible, such as calculation of regional "entropy" [Shiozaki, 1988] to minimize artifacts.

## ■ IMAGE COMPRESSION AND ENCODING TECHNIQUES

In this section, a brief introduction to the subject of image data compression and the companion process of image data encoding is presented. We consider approaches for image archiving and image transmission, since these represent the majority of applications for compression and encoding technology.

Image compression techniques basically involve the processing of the image prior to transmission or archiving. The image data is then transmitted (or stored, in the archival application) and decoded, decompressed, or reconstructed prior to use. The heart of any of the image compression techniques centers on two entities:

1. The development of an image representation that removes a significant amount of the inherent redundancy in the image data. From a statistical viewpoint, we seek a transformation of the image data such that the transformed image consists, ideally, of uncorrelated data.

2. The achievement of a reconstruction scheme that "undoes" the compression or encoding scheme. Most important, this reconstruction scheme, together with the chosen compression technique, is chosen to minimize subjective distortion in the resulting image.

### IMAGE DATA REQUIREMENTS AND ALGORITHM PERFORMANCE MEASURES

As a preliminary example, consider an image with $512 \times 512$ pixel spatial resolution and 8 bits (256 levels) intensity resolution. This represents 0.25 Mbyte (1 M byte = (1 K byte)$^2$; 1 K = 1024) of image data. At what is sometimes referred to as "real-time" rates (i.e., the RS-170 frame rate; see Chapter 8) this amount of data over time represents a data rate of almost 63 million bits per second. Compression techniques seek to reduce this data rate.

Measures of compression algorithm performance are basically composed of three entities:

1. A quantitative measure of the amount of data reduction expressed in terms of memory bits per image or bits per pixel (e.g., reduced to 1 bit/pixel, etc.).
2. A quantitative or qualitative assessment of the degradation (if any) of the image data.
3. A measure of the algorithm complexity, particularly with respect to compression/expansion processing speed.

## ELEMENTARY COMPRESSION APPROACHES

An obvious approach for the reduction of image data is to undersample the image. The implicit assumption in subsampling is that adjacent lines or adjacent pixels contain information that is so highly correlated it may be assumed to be replicated and that the replication of this data during the reconstruction phase results in an image that is, subjectively speaking, close to the original. Subsampling methods exist in several forms; the most popular is to sample one of the image frame fields and discard the other (Chapter 8). Most (1988) home videocassette recorders (VCRs) employ this technique.

## TRANSFORM APPROACHES

### GLOBAL AND BLOCK TRANSFORMS

If the majority of the image content could be represented using relatively few of (some) transform basis functions, the image could be transmitted or archived in transformed form, with a significant data reduction. This type of approach was considered in Chapter 3. Other approaches partition the image into smaller regions, or blocks, and encode these blocks of local data. Block coding of data usually results in greater success, since the likelihood of a small block containing highly correlated data is probably greater in a local region than over the entire image.

Another popular transform is known as the Karhunen-Loeve (KL) principal component, or Hotelling transform. In contrast with the deterministic approaches treated previously, the KL transform is based on the statistical characterization of the image data. The KL transformation is based on representation of a sampled image function as a vector and statistical characterization of this vector to determine ("principal") components which represent most of the image intensity variation.

## DIFFERENTIAL COMPRESSION AND ENCODING APPROACHES

The differential approach to image data compression exploits the redundancy of intensities in a normally highly (spatially) correlated image function. This correlation implies that the signal does not change rapidly between adjacent pixel locations (or at least it does not change as rapidly as if it were completely uncorrelated). An uncorrelated signal—for example, one in which adjacent intensity samples were statistically independent—requires each of the intensity samples to represent the signal; encoding in this case may not be accomplished without information loss. Due to the line-by-line generation of images (a historical carryover from electron beam scanning), often this correlation is only exploited on a line-by-line basis. Significant correlation usually does exist, however, between lines.

## DIFFERENTIAL ENCODING SCHEMES

The difference of highly correlated image function intensity samples will have less variance than the variance of the sample set itself. Thus, coding of the interpixel intensity difference (i.e., the difference between adjacent pixels) yields a set of samples whose transmission bandwidth is less than that of the raw image intensity data. This may be shown simply by considering the variance of two correlated scalar random variables, denoted $X$ and $Y$. From the definitions in Appendix 4, it may be shown that the variance of a linear combination of $X$ and $Y$ is given by

$$\sigma^2_{aX+bY} = a^2\sigma^2_X + b^2\sigma^2_Y + 2ab\sigma_{XY} \tag{4-115}$$

Therefore, if we model the intensities of adjacent pixels along a line as realizations of these random variables—that is,

$$X = f(i,j)$$

and

$$Y = f(i,j + 1)$$

$$\tag{4-116}$$

the variance of the *difference* between $X$ and $Y$ is given by Eq. 4-115, or ($a = 1, b = -1$):

$$\sigma^2_{X-Y} = \sigma^2_X + \sigma^2_Y - 2\sigma_{XY} \tag{4-117}$$

In the case where $\sigma^2_X = \sigma^2_Y$, this reduces to

$$\sigma^2_{X-Y} = 2(\sigma^2_X - \sigma_{XY}) \tag{4-118}$$

indicating that for large values of $\sigma_{XY}$ (i.e., strong values of the correlation between $f(i,j)$ and $f(i,j + 1)$) the variance of the intensity difference may be significantly smaller than that of the random variable itself.

Figure 4.39 illustrates the basic idea of differential encoding using prediction applied to a discrete image function. Letting $f_D(i,j)$ represent the encoded pixel intensity difference, where, for pixel intensity $(i,j)$,

$$f_D(i,j) = f(i,j) - f_{PE}(i,j) \tag{4-119}$$

where $f(i,j)$ is the original (uncoded) image intensity and $f_{PE}(i,j)$ is a predicted value of the intensity at $(i,j)$. The predicted $f_{PE}(i,j)$ may be formed as a linear combination of the intensities in the neighborhood surrounding $(i,j)$; an obvious simple choice is to let

$$f_{PE}(i,j) = f(i,j - 1) \tag{4-120}$$

As indicated in Figure 4.39, (the quantized value of) $f_D(i,j)$ is then used by the decoder, along with a predicted value of the previous line intensity, to reconstruct the signal intensity from the compressed (difference) signal. This process is then repeated for all pixels in the image. Although conceptually simple, this process is not workable in the form shown in Figure 4.39e. The design represents an unstable system; small differences (due either to quantization error or other "noise" sources) between $f(i,j)$ and the reconstructed intensity, $f_R(i,j)$, are *accumulated* in this design. The reader may use $z$-transform or algebraic techniques to verify this. This effect is due to the fact that, as shown in Figure 4.39$e$, the quantization and prediction error corrupted signal is used "open-loop" by the decoder in reconstruction of the signal. A solution is shown in Figure 4.39$f$, where the operation of the decoder is simulated as a part of the encoding process to alleviate the aforementioned problem.

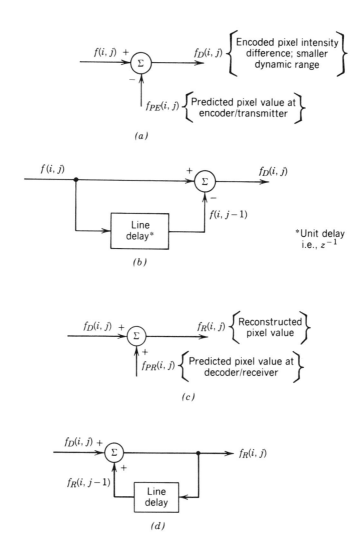

FIGURE 4.39   Basic concept of differential encoding (discrete image)
(a)   Encoder operation
(b)   Encoder using prediction
(c)   Decoder operation (noiseless case)
(d)   Decoder using prediction (noiseless case)
(e)   Composite system with possible noise/error
(f)   Revised encoder for workable system

*Continued on next page*

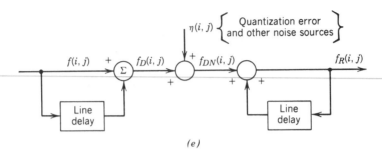

(e)

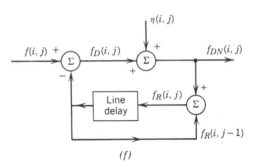

(f)

FIGURE 4.39  Continued

RUN-LENGTH ENCODING AND COMPRESSION

This section considers line-based run-length encoding, where pixel intensities are not stored or transmitted individually, but rather on a given line:

1. The intensity of the first pixel on line a is stored and denoted as reference pixel $f(a, x_2)$. A line or run counter is set to 1, indicating that the current "run" consists of 1 pixel.

2. Intensities of the pixels to the right of $f(a, x_2)$ along the line (e.g., $f(a, x_2 + 1)$, $f(a, x_2 + 2)$, . . . etc.) are then sequentially compared to the reference pixel intensity. If the intensity difference magnitude exceeds a threshold, $T$, a new reference value is stored and the run counter is reset to 1 (indicating a new run). Otherwise the run counter is simply incremented by 1 to extend the existing run. Note that candidate pixels are compared to the reference value, so that intensity functions with ramp characteristics will not be falsely encoded as constant intensity runs.

3. The process is repeated for all pixels on the line, thereby generating a data set consisting of an intensity and threshold-dependent set of pairs representing the encoded image of the form $\{f(a, x_2), rl\}$ where $rl$ is the length of the given run (in pixels) with intensity $f(a, x_2)$.

Because there are likely to be runs of length $\gg 1$ in the compressed image representation, the resulting compressed data set will be smaller than the raw image data. These effects are highly dependent on the threshold, $T$, which must be chosen to yield both a reasonable image representation (i.e., the reconstructed image should appear subjectively "close" to the uncompressed image) and a reasonable number of runs, each consisting of a reasonable number of pixels. Note that the requirements on $T$ are conflicting; small threshold values tend to maximize the retained image representation while minimizing compression, whereas large thresholds produce significant compression while introducing significant distortion. A more complete analytical treatment of image compression via run length encoding may be found in Pratt (1978).

*Image Example.* Figure 4.40a shows an example of run-length encoding. Using the technique, with a threshold of $T = 10$, the resulting reconstruction image is

**FIGURE 4.40** Run length encoding example
(a) Original image (64 grey levels)
(b) Reconstructed image with run-length compression threshold = 10

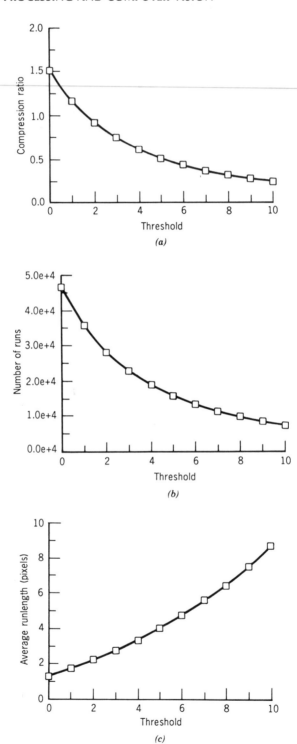

**FIGURE 4.41** Sample run length encoding results using image of Figure 4.40
(a) Compression ratio vs. threshold
(b) Number of runs vs. threshold
(c) Average run length vs. threshold

shown in Figure 4.40*b*. Note that although the required image data storage amount has been reduced significantly due to the compression technique, the reconstructed image exhibits significant distortion in the form of "block-ness" along lines. Table 4.3 and Figure 4.41 quantify compression results for the image of Figure 4.40*a*.

The case of $T = 0$ is interesting. Since one byte for intensity and one byte to indicate the run length is allocated in this case, one might expect the resulting data file to be twice as large as the original image data file. This is not the case, due to a "natural compression" caused by the redundant nature of image data. In the example of Figure 4.40, for example, Table 4.3 indicates an expected "natural" run length of 1.3 pixels.

*Theoretical Assessment and Extensions.* A relatively simple probabilistic argument is used to quantify the sample results. Assume the probability of occurrence of a pixel difference that exceeds the threshold $T$ is independent from pixel to pixel along a line. Thus,

$$P(\text{occurrence of adjacent pixel difference}) > T) = P_T \qquad (4\text{-}121)$$

The probability of a run length 1 is therefore $P_T$. The probability of a run of length 2 is $(1 - P_T)P_T$, etc. Thus, probability of a run of length $L$ is given by

$$\text{Prob}\{\text{run of length } L\} = (1 - P_T)^{(L-1)}P_T \qquad (4\text{-}122)$$

Thus, if $P_T$ is small, the average run length tends to be large and vice versa. If $P_T$ is inversely proportional to $T$, the linear characteristic of Figure 4.41*c* is explained. This result also appeals to our intuition.

Since the number of bits, not bytes, actually determines storage requirements (although the computational requirements of the manipulations required to "pack" the bytes must be considered), a more exact compression ratio would be in terms of relative numbers of bits.

■ TABLE 4.3
Sample compression results (image of Figure 4.40*a*)

| Threshold | Compression Ratio* | No. Runs | Avg. Run Length |
|---|---|---|---|
| 0 | 1.5135 | 46589 | 1.3188 |
| 1 | 1.1595 | 35711 | 1.7205 |
| 2 | 0.9105 | 28053 | 2.1901 |
| 3 | 0.7371 | 22719 | 2.7043 |
| 4 | 0.6077 | 18740 | 3.2785 |
| 5 | 0.5054 | 15590 | 3.9410 |
| 6 | 0.4261 | 13148 | 4.6730 |
| 7 | 0.3628 | 11201 | 5.4852 |
| 8 | 0.3148 | 9722 | 6.3197 |
| 9 | 0.2693 | 8333 | 7.3731 |
| 10 | 0.2331 | 7200 | 8.5333 |

*Bytes in original image/bytes in compressed image.

## ■ PROJECTIONS AND RECONSTRUCTION

### BACKGROUND

The objective of reconstruction from projections is to *reconstruct* either a 2-D (image) or 3-D (object function) from a finite number of either 1-D (line) or 2-D (image) *projections*, respectively. For simplicity, we consider the case of reconstruction of 2-D images from 1-D projections; the theory involved in the higher-order case is similar.

Applications for this approach are found in several areas, perhaps the most predominant of which is medical diagnosis (CAT scanners and ultrasound) (Herman, 1979). Three-dimensional views of internal organs are created for analysis by the physician with minimal risk or discomfort to the patient. In addition, the use of projections as features facilitates visual target tracking, scene and/or camera orientation determination (Alliney, 1986), and image data compression (Fraser, 1985).

Figure 4.42 shows the origin of the projection-based model. The projection data is generated by a family of line integrals parallel to the projected beams. Reconstructing $N$-dimensional entities from some number of $(N - 1)$-dimensional projections immediately raises questions related to uniqueness, or even more fundamentally, feasibility.

Two primary approaches to reconstruction are employed. The first, termed the

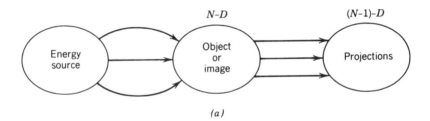

(a)

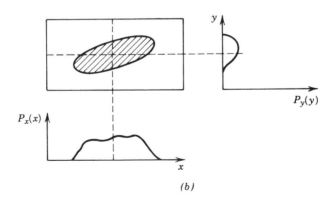

(b)

FIGURE 4.42  Origins of the projection/reconstruction problem
(a)  Medical/seismic problem
(b)  Image features as projections

*algebraic* approach, is relatively simple to implement, uses spatial domain computations, and is successful in a limited number of applications. The alternative, the *Fourier domain* approach, employs computations in the transformed (Fourier) domain, is typically more complicated, and is based on the *projection theorem*. Prior to investigating either approach, it is first necessary to define precisely the *projections*.

Perhaps the most common approach is based on parallel projections, as shown in Figure 4.43. A parallel projection along a prespecified line at an angle of $\theta$ with respect to the $x$-axis is shown. This projection is the summation or integration of $f(x,y)$ intensities onto a line with an orientation of angle $\theta$ with respect to the $x$-axis. The $(s,t)$ coordinate system shown is obtained as an affine (Appendix 1) transformed version of the $(x,y)$ system; that is, image point locations may be related by

$$\begin{bmatrix} s \\ t \end{bmatrix} = A_\theta \begin{bmatrix} x \\ y \end{bmatrix} \tag{4-123}$$

where $A_\theta$ is a rotation matrix of an angle, $\theta$. The projection of the image function onto this line for any value of $s$ is given by the line integral

$$g(s,\theta) = \int_t f(x,y)\mathrm{d}t \tag{4-124}$$

Several comments regarding this model are in order.

1. In projecting onto the $s$-axis, we are integrating along lines parallel to the $t$-axis, that is, the range of $(x,y)$ values determined by a fixed value of $s$. Figure 4-43 illustrates the case $s = s'$.

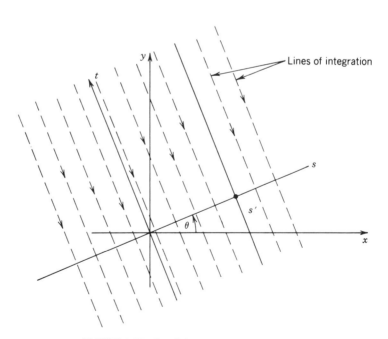

**FIGURE 4.43** Parallel projection formation model

2. The $(x,y)$ locations comprising the axis as shown in Figure 4.43, along which $f(x,y)$ is summed, are given by writing this line in *normal form* (Appendix 1) through the parameters $s'$, $\theta$ as

$$s' = x \cos \theta + y \sin \theta \qquad (4\text{-}125)$$

Therefore, we can use the constraint of Eq. 4-125 to rewrite the line integral of Eq. 4-124 for any value of $s$ using the sifting property (Chapter 3) of the dirac delta function as:

$$g(s,\theta) = \iint_{xy} f(x,y)\, \delta(s - x \cos \theta - y \sin \theta)dxdy \qquad (4\text{-}126)$$

The quantity $g(s,\theta)$ is known as the *Radon* transform of $f(x,y)$.

Prior to investigating reconstruction algorithms based on this model, we consider several examples. Due to the sampled nature of image data, the discrete equivalent of Eq. 4-126 is employed. In the case of projections onto the $x$- and $y$-axes, $g(s,\theta)$ becomes the following quantities

$$g(x, \theta) \stackrel{\Delta}{=} p_x(x) = \sum_y f(x,y) \qquad (4\text{-}127)$$

$$g(x, \pi/2) \stackrel{\Delta}{=} p_y(y) = \sum_x f(x,y) \qquad (4\text{-}128)$$

We now explore the algebraic ramifications of image reconstruction with a simple example. Given a 4-element ($2 \times 2$) image function:

$$\begin{matrix} f_{00} & f_{01} \\ f_{10} & f_{11} \end{matrix}$$

Equations 4-127 and 4-128 become

$$\begin{aligned} p_x(0) &= f_{00} + f_{01} \\ p_x(1) &= f_{10} + f_{11} \\ p_y(0) &= f_{00} + f_{10} \\ p_y(1) &= f_{01} + f_{11} \end{aligned} \qquad (4\text{-}129)$$

Notice that (for an $N \times N$ image) each discrete projection generates $N$ equations. A formulation to recover the 4 image elements is to rewrite Eq. 4-129 in vector-matrix form as

$$\begin{bmatrix} 1 & 1 & 0 & 0 \\ 0 & 0 & 1 & 1 \\ 1 & 0 & 1 & 0 \\ 0 & 1 & 0 & 1 \end{bmatrix} \begin{bmatrix} f_{00} \\ f_{01} \\ f_{10} \\ f_{11} \end{bmatrix} = \begin{bmatrix} p_x(0) \\ p_x(1) \\ p_y(0) \\ p_y(1) \end{bmatrix} \qquad (4\text{-}130)$$

where the image function matrix is converted to a vector via row concatenation. A simple matrix inversion would thus allow "reconstruction" of $f$.

A difficulty with this approach is that an $N \times N$ image requires the estimation of $N^2$ pixel values. Since each projection equation yields $N$ equations, the number of needed projections $p$, is

$$p \geq N \qquad (4\text{-}131)$$

For example, a $512 \times 512$ image requires $p \geq 512$ projections, which is an unwieldy and unrealistic number. An alternative is to employ *a priori information* concerning the quantity to be reconstructed in the form of *constraints*. For example, given that it is known the image displays symmetry about some axis, the number of pixel intensities to be estimated is reduced to $N(N + 1)/2$ or approximately half.

### SPATIAL DOMAIN RECONSTRUCTION TECHNIQUES AND ANALYSIS (THE ALGEBRAIC APPROACH)

An alternative, suboptimal, but conceptually and computationally straightforward approach is referred to as the *summation* method or *method of back-projection*. The basic idea involves redistributing $g(s,\theta)$, for all discrete values of $s$, over the $N$ locations $(x,y)$ or "cells" that fall along the projection path. Therefore, the value of a given cell in the reconstructed image results from the summation of the back-projected values of all the projections.

The redistribution of projection values may be implemented in a number of ways, some of which involve iteration. A straightforward approach is to redistribute the value of $g(s',\theta)$ *uniformly* to all $N$ cells lying along the discretized line $s = s'$ that is, the quantity

$$\frac{1}{N} g(s',\theta)$$

is added to each cell. In the case of projections of a binary image, a thresholding operation is needed to restore the binary nature of the reconstructed image. This process results in a blurred or low-pass filtered approximation to $f(x,y)$ (see the problems).

Figure 4.44*a* shows an original binary image with the "object" shape outlined. The horizontal and vertical intensity projections, given by Eqs. 4-127 and 4-128 are shown in part *b*. Using a uniform redistribution function, the reconstructed image is shown in Figure 4.44*c* (note it is no longer binary). Reconstructed binary images result from thresholding the image of Figure 4.44*c* with varying thresholds and are shown in Figures 4.44*d*–4.44*g*. Notice that the reconstructed image in part *e* represents the closest match to the original. Note, in part *e*, the smoothing or low-pass filtering effect of the reconstruction algorithm.

The non-exact reconstruction results from this example suggest several modifications to the approach, including:

1. Non-uniform back projection of $g(s,\theta)$;
2. Combining the information in a cell due to several back-projections in a manner other than a simple sum (for example, the use of RMS and multiplicative combinations) and;
3. Iterative approaches that form the reconstructed image, calculate projections based on this approximate image, and use the difference between the exact projections and those estimated to refine the back-projection and thresholding process. (This is left to the problems.)

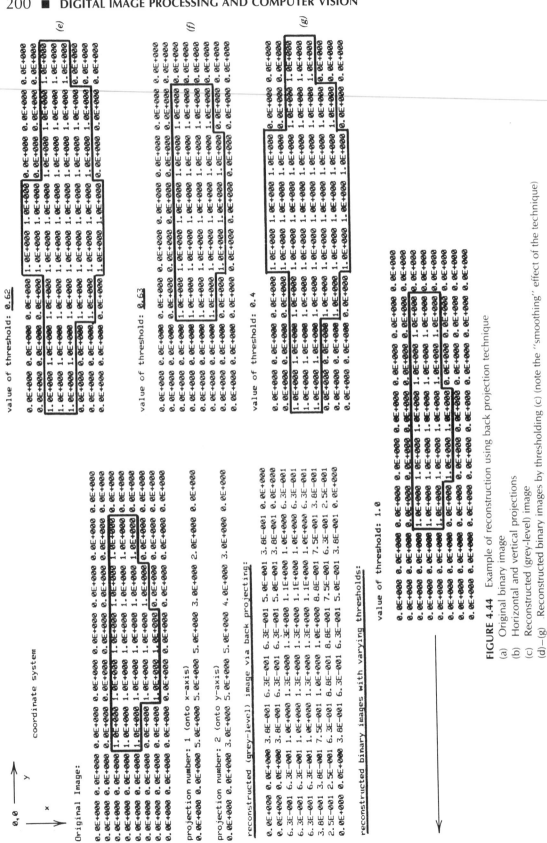

**FIGURE 4.44** Example of reconstruction using back projection technique

(a) Original binary image

(b) Horizontal and vertical projections

(c) Reconstructed (grey-level) image

(d)–(g) Reconstructed binary images by thresholding (c) (note the "smoothing" effect of the technique)

## FOURIER DOMAIN RECONSTRUCTION TECHNIQUES

The basis of the Fourier domain approach to reconstruction is relatively simple to state:

1. Determine the equivalent frequency domain information inherent in the given projections of $f(x,y)$, i.e., $g(s, \theta)$.
2. *Interpolate* reconstruct $F(u,v)$.
3. Inverse transform $F(u,v)$ to obtain $f(x,y)$.

Recall from Chapter 3 the 2-D Fourier transform of an image function $f(x,y)$ is defined as

$$F(u,v) = \iint f(x,y)\exp[-j2\pi(ux + vy)]dxdy \qquad (4\text{-}132)$$

We consider first, for illustration, the projection of the image function onto the $x$-axis; that is,

$$g(x, 0) \overset{\Delta}{=} g_0(x) = \int_Y f(x,y)dy \qquad (4\text{-}133)$$

where $Y$ is the image spatial extent in the $y$-direction. It is extremely important to observe that the 1-D Fourier transform of the quantity in Eq. 4-133

$$G_0(u) \overset{\Delta}{=} F\{g_0(x)\} = \int_X g_0(x)\exp[-j2\pi ux]dx \qquad (4\text{-}134)$$

may be shown, using Eqs. 4-133 and 4-132 to be equivalent to evaluation of the 2-D Fourier transform of $f(x,y)$ along the $v = 0$ axis in the $(u,v)$ plane, i.e.,

$$F(u,0) = G_0(u) \qquad (4\text{-}135)$$

*Thus, given the projection of an image function onto the x-axis, an alternative and equivalent viewpoint is that we are given information to form F(u,0).*
Referring to the results of Appendix 3, note that a rotation of the image about the origin by an angle of $\theta$ yields a corresponding rotation of $F(u,v)$ by the same angle in Fourier space. Thus, given the transform pair

$$f(\underline{x}) \Leftrightarrow F(\underline{u}) \qquad (4\text{-}136)$$

a rotation of the image plane via an affine rotation matrix $A_\theta$, as given by Eq. 4-123 yields the transform relationship

$$f(A\underline{x}) \Leftrightarrow F(A\underline{u}) \qquad (4\text{-}137)$$

Therefore, the Fourier transform of the projection function is given by Eq. 4-126,

$$F\{g(s,\theta)\} \overset{\Delta}{=} G_\theta(r) = F(u',v') \qquad (4\text{-}138)$$

where $(u',v')$ is loci of all points in $(u,v)$ space along a line rotated by $\theta$ degrees, as shown by Figure 4.45. Therefore, given values of a projection of $f(x,y)$ along a line oriented at an angle of $\theta$ with respect to the $x$-axis, an equivalent interpretation is that we are given information to form values of $F(u,v)$ along a line in $(u,v)$ space *with the same angular orientation*. This observation is the basis of Fourier transform reconstruction and is often referred to as the *projection slice theorem*. The recon-

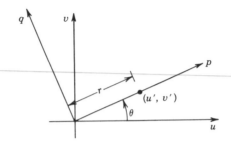

**FIGURE 4.45**   Fourier transform of g(s,θ) "Projection Slice Theorem"

struction of $F(u,v)$, and consequently $f(x,y)$, from projection data involves the following steps:

1. Fourier transform the projections
2. reconstruct $F(u,v)$ from 1 and Eq. 4-138
3. invert $F(u,v)$ to get $f(x,y)$.

One difficulty in the preceding approach is that the discrete nature of the data (both due to discrete data samples and a discrete number of θ values) yields only a finite number of points in the discrete Fourier domain. Some values of $(u,v)$ may not have corresponding values; therefore, *interpolation in the Fourier domain is required.*

## ■ SUMMARY

We note in closing that much of the content of this chapter is considered to represent the core of low-level image processing concerns. This does not preclude further research into alternate and enhanced algorithms for the tasks cited. The large amount of current research in these topical areas is fueled by the need to achieve more accurate and robust algorithms as well as the hypothesis that more reliable early preprocessing results yield less processing and greater reliability at higher processing levels.

Furthermore, the complexity of the underlying models and the resulting algorithms needs to be weighed in the process of choosing among the approaches presented. Storage and computational speed requirements of the complex model-based algorithms vis-à-vis suboptimal, yet reasonable ad hoc approaches often warrant a study of the associated trade-offs in algorithm selection.

## ■ REFERENCES

Alliney, S., and Morandi, C. (1986) Digital image registration using projections, *IEEE Trans. Pattern Analysis and Machine Intelligence*, **8**(2), 222–233.

Andrews, H. C., and Hunt, B. R. (1977) *Digital Image Restoration*, Prentice-Hall, N. J.

Ataman, E., Aatre, V. K., and Wong, K. M. (1980) A fast method for real time median filtering. *IEEE Trans. Acoust., Speech, Signal Process.*, **28**, 415–420.

Bednar, J. B., and Watt, T. L. (1984) Alpha trimmed means and their relationship to median filters. *IEEE Trans. Acoust., Speech, Signal Process.*, **32**, 145–153.

Besslich, P. W., and Carlsohn, M. F. (1985) Adaptive selection of threshold matrix size for pseudogray rendition of images. *Optical Engineering*, **24**(4), 655–662.

Bovik, A. C., Huang, T. S., and Munson, D. C. (1987) The effect of median filtering on edge estimation and detection. *IEEE Trans. Pattern Analysis and Machine Intelligence*, **9**(2), 181–194.

Carlsohn, M. F., and Besslich, P. W. (1985) Adaptive selection of threshold matrix size for pseudogrey rendition of images. *Optical Engineering*, **24**(4), 655–662.

Cooper, D. B. (1979) Maximum likelihood estimation of Markov-process blob boundaries in noisy images. *IEEE Trans. Pattern Analysis and Machine Intelligence*, 372–384.

Fraser, D., Hunt, B. R., and Su, J. C. (1985) Principles of tomography in image data compression. *Optical Engineering*, **24**(2), 298–306.

Frei, W., and Chen, C. C. (1977) Fast boundary detection: a generalization and a new algorithm. *IEEE Trans. Computers*, **26**(10), 988–998.

Gonzales, R., and Wintz, P. (1987) *Digital Image Processing*, (2nd Ed.), Addison Wesley.

Haralick, R. M. (1984) Digital step edges from zero crossing of second directional derivatives. *IEEE Trans. Pattern Analysis and Machine Intelligence*, **6**(1), 58–68.

Herman, G. T., ed. (1979) *Image Reconstruction from Projections*, **33**, Springer-Verlag, Berlin.

Hodgson, R. M., Bailey, D. G., Naylor, M. J., Ng, A. L. M., and McNeill, S. J. (1985) Properties, implementations, and applications of rank filters. *Image and Vision Computing*, **3**(1).

Huang, T. S., Yang, G. Y., and Tang, G. Y. (1979) A fast two dimensional median filtering algorithm. *IEEE Trans Acoust., Speech, Signal Process.*, **27**, 13–18.

Huertas, A., and Medioni, G. (1986) Detection of intensity changes with subpixel accuracy using Laplacian–Gaussian masks. *IEEE Trans. Pattern Analysis and Machine Intelligence*, **8**(5), 651–664.

Jarvis, J. F., Judice, C. N., and Ninke, W. H. (1976) A survey of techniques for the display of continuous tone pictures on bilevel displays. *Computer Graphics and Image Processing*, **5**, 13–40.

Justusson, B. I., and Huang, T. S. (1981) Median filtering statistical properties. *Two Dimensional Digital Signal Processing II, Top. Appl. Phys.*, **43**, 161–196.

Lippel, B., and Kurland, M. (1971) The effect of dither on luminence quantization of pictures. *IEEE Trans. Commun. Technology*, **19**(6), 879–848.

Marr, D., and Hildreth, E. (1980) Theory of edge detection. *Proc. Royal Soc. London*, **207**, 187–217.

Merserean, R. M., and Dudgeon, D. E. (1984) *Multidimensional Digital Signal Processing*, Prentice-Hall, N.Y.

Narendra, P. M. (1980) A separable median filter for image noise smoothing. *IEEE Trans. Pattern Anal. Mach. Intell.*, **3**, 20–29.

Nodes, T. A., and Gallagher, N. C. (1982) Median filters: some modifications and their properties. *IEEE Trans. Acoust., Speech, Signal Process.*, **30**, 739–746.

Pratt, W. (1978) *Digital Image Processing*, John Wiley.

Roberts, L. G. (1965) Machine perception of three-dimensional solid. *Optical and Electro-Optical Information Processing*, (J. T. Tippell, ed.), MIT Press, 159–197.

Saghri, J. A., Hou, H. S., and Tescher, A. G. (1986) Personal computer image processing with halftoning. *Optical Engineering*, **25**(3), 499–504.

Sawchuck, A. A. (1972) Space-variant image motion degradation and restoration. *Proc. IEEE*, **60**, 854–861.

Shiozaki, A. (1988) Image enhancement in a dithered picture. *Computer Vision, Graphics and Image Processing*, **24**, 107–113.

Sondhi, M. M. (1972) Image restoration: the removal of spatially invariant degradations. *Proc. IEEE*, **60**(7), 842–853.

Stoffel, J. C., and Moreland, J. F. (1981) A survey of electronic techniques for pictorial image reproduction. *IEEE Trans. Commun.*, **29**(12), 1898–1925.

Tukey, J. W. (1977) *Exploratory Data Analysis*, Addison-Wesley.

Wong, R. Y. (1977) Image sensor transformations. *IEEE Trans. Syst. Man Cyber.*, **7**(12), 836–841.

# ■ PROBLEMS

1. Verify the derivation in the section on discrete linear operators (p. 132) leading up to Eq. 4-13.

2. In the frequency domain analysis of smoothing (p. 134), the image size, $N$, was chosen to be much larger than the window size, $n$ (cf. Eq. 4-13). Repeat this analysis, discussing the frequency domain results as $n \to N$.

3. In a manner analogous to that of the smoothing filter, derive the frequency domain behavior of the window function used for *unsharp masking*.

4. Using the mask values for a $3 \times 3$ unsharp masking filter, explore the response of this filter to various edge orientations.

5. Determine the effect of an unsharp masking filter, described where the $n \times n$ pixel neighborhood used for computing $\bar{f}(x,y)$ is larger than $3 \times 3$. Compare this to the $3 \times 3$ case. What happens as $n \to N$, the image extent?

6. An extension of the unsharp masking concept that is often used for target enhancement and background suppression is shown in Figure P.6. For simplicity, assume the intensities in regions $R_1$ and $R_2$ are constant, and the output pixel intensity (the center of $R_1$) is formed via

$$f_{out}(x,y) = \sum_{R_1} f_{in}(x,y) - \sum_{R_2} f_{in}(x,y)$$

(a) Determine the frequency response of this filter.

(b) Given that $R_1$ is $n \times n$ pixels and $R_2$ is $m \times m$ pixels, compare the response of this filtering approach for image targets for the cases:

(i) the target intensity is greater than the local background and the target size is less than the dimension of $R_1$.

(ii) same as (i) except the target intensity is less than that of the local background.

(iii) same as (i) except the target size is greater than the dimension of $R_1$ but less than the dimension of $R_2$.

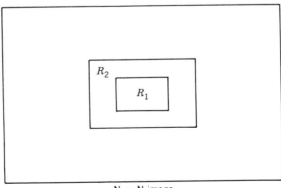

N × N image

**FIGURE (P.6)**  (note $R_1 \subset R_2$)

7. Choose two sequences of pixel intensity samples to verify the nonlinear nature of the median filter (4.5-6); that is, prove

$$\text{med } (R_1 (\underline{x}) + R_2 (\underline{x})) \neq \text{med } (R_1 (\underline{x})) + \text{med } (R_2 (\underline{x}))$$

for arbitrary pixel intensity sample sets $R_1$ and $R_2$.

8. Show, by example, that a median filter with an asymmetrical choice of window (about the center) may change the position of image edges.

9. Compute the frequency content of

$$\ln (\sin x + 1).$$

Note the introduction of new frequencies due to the nonlinear transformation.

10. Prove: (a) $|\nabla_x f(\underline{x})|$ is *sensitive* to edge *location*; and (b) that $|\nabla_x f(\underline{x})|$ is a shift-invariant operator.

11. Show, via examples, that the first derivative operators proposed in the text are sensitive to 2-D ramp functions, whereas second derivative operators (e.g., the Laplacian) are not.

12. Rederive the Laplacian operator approximation by using a Tayor series expansion of $f(\underline{x})$ about $\underline{x}$.

13. Viewing the Laplacian operator as linear filtering, determine the Fourier transform of the Laplacian mask: What is the frequency response characteristic of this operator?

14. Prove Eq. 4-50; that is, that

$$\left(\frac{\partial f(\underline{x})}{\partial x}\right)^2 + \left(\frac{\partial f(\underline{x})}{\partial y}\right)^2 = \left(\frac{\partial f_R(\underline{x})}{\partial x}\right)^2 + \left(\frac{\partial f_R(\underline{x})}{\partial y}\right)^2$$

15. Compute and compare the frequency response characteristics of
    (i) the $D_1(x)$ and $D_1(y)$ operators;
    (ii) the $D_2(x)$ and $D_2(y)$ operators; and
    (iii) the $D_s(x)$ and $D_s(y)$ operator.

16. Compute the response of the Frei-Chen template set to the edge samples $H$, $V$, $S_+$, and $S_-$.

17. Determine a set of nine edge templates, analogous to the Frei-Chen operators, which return a measure of
    (i) edge orientation in the directional sense (e.g., $H$, $V$, $S_+$, or $S_-$); *and*
    (ii) edge transition direction (e.g., a high-to-low or low-to-high change).

    First consider any set of templates with this property, then attempt to determine an *orthogonal* set.

18. To continue our examination of edge detection operators, we extend Table 4.1. Specifically, show the edge orientation effects of the Sobel operator ($D_s(x)$ & $D_s(y)$) with the previously considered edge types ($H_1$ $V$, $S_+$, $S_-$). Consider the following combinations of the operators:
    (i) RMS
    (ii) max.

19. (i) Verify, via examples, the effect of "masking," or different intensity resolutions, on derivative approximations.

    (ii) Derive an analytical analysis of the effects of the masking (or multiple resolution) process on edge detection.

20. The objective of this problem is to verify the characteristics of the LOG operator.

    (a) Derive the Fourier transform of the Laplacian of $G(r)$ as in Eqs. 4-64 and 4-65.

    (b) Show that the extent of the negative or "central" portion of the LOG operator from Eqs. 4-64 and 4-65, measured between zero crossings, is $2\sqrt{2}\sigma$.

    (c) Verify, by substitution, the separability of the LOG using Eq. 4-66 through Eqs. 4-70 and 4-71.

21. Show that the performance measure of Eq. 4-77 is minimized, in the case of a uniform pdf for $p_r(r)$, by equally spaced decision values, $D_i$, and representation values $R_i$ taken as the midpoint of the regions delineated by the decision values.

22. (a) Show, by example, why the thresholding operation is inherently nonlinear; that is, the result of thresholding an image with $T = a + b$ is not, in general, equal to the summation of two images, each thresholded with $T = a$ and $T = b$, respectively.

    (b) Show, by example, the noncommutative nature of the threshold and edge-enhancement operators.

23. Indicate, in detail, two reasons why the run-length encoding technique should rely on a comparison between the *reference* pixel intensity and each of those to the right (along the scan direction), as opposed to comparing adjacent pixels. Show an example of the problem that results from the latter approach when the intensity varies linearly along a scan line.

24. Based on the algebraic reconstruction examples presented on page 200, develop an iterative strategy for modification of the back-projection and thresholding strategies using the difference between the reconstructed image projections and the exact projections. Apply this technique to the data given in the text example.

25. The back projection example on page 200 of the text reconstructed each pixel intensity by a *summation* of the redistributed projection values. Repeat this example, but instead of summation, reconstruct each pixel intensity using:

    (i) the *RMS value* of the total of the redistributed intensities; and

    (ii) the *product* (multiplicative combination) of the redistributed intensities.

    Predict modified algorithm performance with other types of images (e.g., binary images of objects with a "hole" in the center).

26. If an image is circularly symmetric about the origin, using an affine model (Appendix 1) for the rotated image, show that the Radon transform of the rotated image is identical to that of the unrotated image. On this basis, show that a single projection is sufficient to reconstruct the image.

**27.** The case of image reconstruction given product separability of the image function is an interesting case. Suppose

$$f(x,y) = f_1(x) f_2(y)$$

Compute the Radon transform of $f(x,y)$ for the cases of $\theta = 0$ and $\theta = \pi/2$, and show that these horizontal and vertical projections are sufficient to reconstruct $f(x,y)$. Specifically, apply the approach to the $2 \times 2$ image functions used on page 000.

**28.** The use of Fourier domain reconstruction techniques on page 201 indicated that the bandlimited nature of $f(x,y)$ was valuable a priori information that could be incorporated into the reconstruction process. This yields at least three important consequences:

(i) Show that if the image function $f(x,y)$ is bandlimited, with nonzero values of $F(u,v)$ confined to a region $R$ in the $(u,v)$ plane, then all the projections of $f(x,y)$ are also bandlimited. (Use the projection-slice theorem.)

(ii) Show the converse of (i): if *all* projections of $f(x,y)$ are bandlimited, then $f(x,y)$ must also be bandlimited.

(iii) Suppose the region of support for $F(u,v)$, denoted $R$, is given by

$$R = \{(u,v) \mid u^2 + v^2 < r_0^2\}$$

Given a rectangular lattice over which $f(x,y)$ is sampled, what is the maximum distance between samples of the *projection* in order to reconstruct $f(x,y)$ with no loss of information?

**29.** In this problem we consider the pitfalls of carelessly applied inverse filtering. For simplicity, consider the undegraded "image" to be a 1-D step function,

$$f(x_i) = \begin{cases} 0 & x_i < \alpha \\ 1 & x_i \geq \alpha \end{cases}$$

Suppose the degradation model is that of a smoothing operator (perhaps to simulate a defocused optical system). Specifically, suppose we use a $3 \times 1$ smoothing window of the form

$$[1/3 \quad 1/3 \quad 1/3]$$

which we know has "low-pass" frequency characteristics.

(i) Plot the degraded image as a function of $x$.

(ii) Suppose we attempt to "undo" the smoothing model operation by application of an edge-enhancement operator such as the centered difference operator or the Laplacian operator—either

$$[-1 \quad 0 \quad +1] \quad \text{or} \quad [-1/2 \quad 1 \quad -1/2]$$

respectively. Recall that we know these operators have high-frequency emphasis properties. Apply these operators to the degraded "image" computed in (i). Is the resulting image the desired restored image? (Hint: Consider the frequency response, in particular, $F(0,0)$ of each of the operators used in the process.)

**30.** Repeat problem 29, but instead assume an algebraic formulation, to restoration,

$$f_2(x_i) = \sum_{-\infty}^{\infty} h(x_i - u_i) f_i(u_i)$$

(i) Using the $3 \times 1$ smoothing window from problem 31, determine $h(x_i - u_i)$.

(ii) Formulate this degradation, for a finite extent input image, as a vector-matrix equation of the form

$$\underline{f}_2 = H \underline{f}_1$$

where $\underline{f}_2$ and $\underline{f}_1$ represent vectors of samples of the original and degraded images, respectively, and $H$ incorporates $h(x_i - u_i)$.

(iii) Given $f(x)$ as in problem 30, apply least squares inversion techniques (Appendix 2) to the formulation in (ii) to determine an approximation to the undegraded image.

**31.** We have considered the application of dither-based halftoning algorithms in cases where $n_i = m_i = 4p$ and $n_h = m_h$, with $n_h >> n_i$ and $n_h = k\, n_i$ where $p$ and $k$ are integers. As noted in the text, we could magnify the input image, $f_i$ prior to application of the dither matrices. Consider the "reasonableness" of the following two alternate halftoning approaches:

(i) Replication (based on $k$) of lines and pixels in $f_i$ instead of interpolation, followed by application of dither; or

(ii) Using the dither matrices on $f_i$ directly, and replication of this result (by $k$) to form $f_h$.

Are (i) and (ii) equivalent?

**32.** We define the *entropy*, $H$, of an $n \times n$ region $R$, comprised of $n^2$ pixels with intensity values $a_1, a_2, \ldots a_{n^2}$, to be

$$H = -\sum_{i=1}^{n^2} P_i(\log_2 P_i)/\log_2 n^2$$

where

$$P_i = a_i \bigg/ \sum_{j=1}^{n^2} a_j$$

$H$ is a measure of the grey-value variation or "busyness" in $R$.

(i) Suppose $a_1 = a_2 = \ldots = a_n^2 = \bar{a}$, i.e., the region is of uniform intensity. Compute $H$. Is it a function of $\bar{a}$?

(ii) Suppose instead, $R$ consists of $n^2$ pixels with alternating intensities, i.e., $a_{min}, a_{max}, a_{min} \ldots a_{max}$, where

$$a_i = \begin{cases} a_{min} & i \text{ odd} \\ a_{max} & i \text{ even} \end{cases}$$

Compute $H$ in this case. Does it depend on $a_{min}$ or $a_{max}$? Why?

(iii) Can two regions with radically different perceived contrasts have the same $H$? Why?

**33.** Verify the result of Eq. 4-63, i.e.,

$$\nabla^2(G(x,y) * f(x,y)) = (\nabla^2 G(x,y)) * f(x,y)$$

in both the spatial and frequency domains.

**34.** Derive the Laplacian of $G(r)$, i.e., Eqs. 4-64 and 4-65.

**35.** The purpose of this problem is to investigate the frequency (Fourier) domain behavior of the LOG filter used for edge enhancement. Given the radially symmetric version of the LOG operator

$$\nabla^2 G(r) = \frac{1}{\pi r^4} \left( \frac{r^2}{2\sigma^2} - 1 \right) \exp\left( -r^2/2\sigma^2 \right)$$

(i) Derive $F(u)$ for this Kerel.
(ii) Is the shape of $|F(u)|$ versus $u$ as expected?
(iii) How does $F(u)$ vary with $\sigma$? Is this variation as expected?
(iv) What is the DC value of $F(u)$?

**36.** Show analytically that the back-projection approach to reconstruction using uniform redistribution of the projections yields a blurred or low-pass filtered approximation to $f(x,y)$.

**37.** (i) Repeat the spatial-domain derivation on page 175 for the impulse response in the case of uniform motion blur, with $v_1$ and $v_2$ nonzero.
(ii) How does the analysis and derivation of an impulse response function model change when the motion is described by

$$\underline{\beta}(t) = A_{\theta(t)} \, \underline{x}$$

That is, the time-varying motion is a rotation. Take the derivation as far as possible. (Hint: see Sawchuck 1972).

**38.** Given an input grey-scale image resolution

$$f_{in} : n_i \times m_i \times p$$

and a corresponding halftone rendition

$$f_h : n_h \times m_h \times 1$$

Assume the input image is $512 \times 512$ pixels, with 8 bits intensity quantization. Compute $R_n$, and comment on the halftoning difficulty, in the following cases:

(i) "Newspaper" Halftoning: 300 dots/inch and a $8\frac{1}{2}'' \times 8\frac{1}{2}''$ page
(ii) "workstation": $n_h = m_h = 1024$
(iii) "monochrome graphics board": $n_h = 350$; $m_h = 720$
(iv) "reduced area (quadrant) of (iii)": $n_h = 200$; $m_h = 360$

# 5

# IMAGE MOTION: MODELING, DETECTION, INTERPRETATION, AND UNDERSTANDING

## ■■ DYNAMIC OR TIME-VARYING IMAGE ANALYSIS

## ■ INTRODUCTION

### DYNAMIC IMAGERY ALGORITHMS AND APPLICATIONS

The subject of this chapter is referred to as dynamic imagery, time-varying imagery, or motion analysis. The time-varying nature of the 3-D world introduces motion concerns in many image processing and computer vision applications. Motion analysis capabilities are required for robotic visual guidance systems used on typical assembly lines containing moving objects. Other motion-based guidance applications include satellite tracking, anti-aircraft weapons firing systems, and autonomous aircraft landing and navigation.

Motion analysis yields significant information on the structure of the 3-D scene under observation (e.g., "time-to-adjacency," p. 225). Observed relative motion between the sensor and scene objects indicates relative depth and 3-D surface or contour information.

The quantitative estimation as well as qualitative interpretation of the motion in image sequences is an emerging research area of interdisciplinary interest and

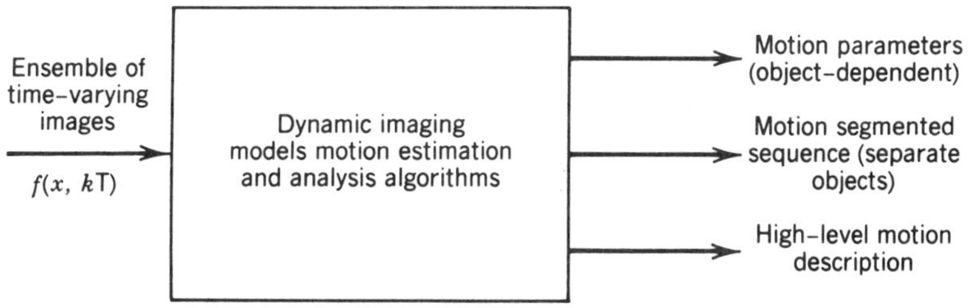

**FIGURE 5.1** Overall dynamic imagery analysis objective(s)

contributions. Many different (but perhaps interrelated) viewpoints exist on how to automate this task. In this chapter, we seek to model and estimate qualitative and quantitative measures of perceived change in the scene as a consequence of observed image plane spatiotemporal change. Thus, our measures of "motion" may not directly quantify object movement in the sense of velocities or other dynamic quantities, but they may be estimates of the parameters of a transformation that relates object (or, perhaps as an intermediate step, image) point locations.

Although motion analysis is itself a bona fide subfield of computer vision, it also embodies or extends a number of topics, including feature extraction, correspondence, and matching; edge detection; and 3-D geometric transformations.

The ability to use image motion is a basic low-level capability of the HVS. It has a significant relationship with stereopsis. Later in this chapter, we relate the 3-D measurement problem of Chapter 2 with that of the motion estimation problem to develop combined approaches for solving both problems simultaneously.

The previously developed model for the grey-level representation of imagery is enhanced by the addition of an independent variable to represent the time-dependence of the image function. This yields an image function representation $f(x_1, x_2, t)$. Manipulation of this model is the basis for most of the low-level image motion estimation approaches, including optical flow. One of the key problems that arises in dynamic image analysis is a result of the fact that motion concepts are *geometric* in nature but their effect is manifest as a change of image pixel *intensity*. Therefore, the core of the image motion estimation problem concerns relating time-varying image intensity or image feature changes to the movement of objects in the scene. A likely intermediate step is relating image intensity changes to the movement (or geometric distortion) of pixel locations. Figure 5.1 illustrates the overall motion estimation problem.

### "STATIC IS BASIC" VS. "MOTION IS BASIC" APPROACHES

One interesting aspect of image motion interpretation is its relationship to that of corresponding high-level static image analysis; that is, it spawns the "static is basic" versus "motion is basic" question (Ballard & Brown, 1982). Given an image sequence (i.e., an ensemble of images with time-varying characteristics and temporal correlation of information), the static-is-basic paradigm approaches the problem as a succession of unrelated image-to-image static analysis problems, followed by some type of feature matching procedure. The dynamic or time-varying nature of the image sequence is inconsequential. Conversely, the motion-is-basic approach attempts to model and exploit the time-varying features or dynamics of the image sequence; that is, dynamic or spatiotemporal models are employed and the static nature of the images is secondary. For example, processing may concern the determination of the "velocity" of points in the image plane. Motion-is-basic models are usually based on differential analysis and therefore constrained to "small" motion applications. Often a gradient approach is used to characterize pixel or feature spatiotemporal variation. Numerous instances of human visual system performance may be used to justify either approach. For example, a motion-is-basic operation is exemplified by the observation that people tend to automatically duck to avoid being struck by flying objects. This action occurs prior to any structural analysis of the object. In this chapter, both approaches are explored.

## THE CORRESPONDENCE PROBLEM, MODELING, AND QUANTITATIVE VS. INEXACT VISION

In either the motion-is-basic or static-is-basic approaches, *a fundamental requirement is that of information regarding image plane locations of corresponding object points or features*. Thus, a matching problem is implied in dynamic imagery analysis. This is precisely the same information that was required for the stereo vision solution in Chapter 2. In fact, stereo vision could be viewed as a motion problem with a static world and a camera that moves between acquisition of images.

Since time-varying imagery is derived from the imaging of object(s) motion in a 3-D world, a useful place to start is in determining how the time-varying geometry of 3-D objects generates this imagery. This avenue gives rise to a number of approaches and concepts, including the focus of expansion (FOE), model-based matching, and geometric motion constraints.

The analysis of dynamic or time-varying imagery is approached from two interrelated viewpoints:

1. By considering the projection of moving points in 3-D onto the image plane to generate a sequence of time-varying images. In this manner, we seek to develop a motion model that allows us to infer (or perhaps even quantitatively estimate), from image data, the motion of objects in the 3-D world.

2. By considering the image plane to image plane perturbations of pixel data caused by the motion of objects in the 3-D world. In developing a model of this type, we may proceed as in 1 above. Alternately, we may conclude that it is unrealistic to assume the availability of the parametric and correspondence information necessary to accomplish 3-D motion inference from 2-D images and instead seek only a way to relate the spatiotemporal changes in pixel intensities, and perhaps then seek techniques to estimate 3-D motion parameters. This approach parallels some aspects of the HVS and has significant utility in the segmentation of images containing moving objects.

### QUANTITATIVE VS. INEXACT VISION

This chapter explores a number of quantitative approaches to determining image or object motion. The motion is estimated through determination of precise geometric parameter values. This is computationally intensive, sensitive to error, and most significantly, yields more information than is often necessary. In simple cases all that is required is an algorithm to parametrically estimate regional image motion (e.g., "region 1 motion parameters using an affine motion model are . . . "). Alternately, higher-level motion descriptions that are more qualitative may be desired (e.g., "The *person* on the *left* is *walking down the street*, and the *person* on the *right* is *jogging* up the hill"). Both the static and dynamic nature of the high-level conclusions of the latter example are apparent. An even higher-level example is the rule-based paradigm for the conversion of low-level local motion descriptors into the simultaneous quantitative and structural description of image motion (developed in Chapter 7).

# ■ ELEMENTARY APPROACHES TO IMAGE MOTION FEATURE EXTRACTION

The approaches to dynamic image analysis presented in this section are conceptually obvious, model-based, and implementable (see Chapter 8). They serve as useful preprocessing approaches and lead to more sophisticated extensions. We begin by considering several low-level models used to generate image change.

### DIFFERENCE IMAGES

*Image motion implies image change.* The change of image intensities is the basis for algorithms for motion estimation. A starting point is the computing of a *difference image* from a pair of images. This operation is easily stated as

$$f_d(x_1, x_2, t_1, t_2) = f(x_1, x_2, t_2) - f(x_1, x_2, t_1) \tag{5-1}$$

where $f_d$ is the difference image. The operation is computationally straightforward because it involves only the subtraction of corresponding pixel intensities and has obvious potential for parallel implementation. In computing a difference image, new intensities may be created, some of which may be negative. This is important to recognize for display purposes. Difference images alone reveal little useful information as to the higher-level nature of the scene and/or sensor change as reflected in the image plane. For example, in the case of several independently moving objects and a moving sensor, the difference images will reflect the combination of a number of motion effects.

Figure 5.2 illustrates graphically the computation of a difference image. Figure 5.3 shows an example of difference images and shows a visual display of both the utility and limitations of the approach. Several important notes regarding difference images are in order:

1. *Difference images may be used as a scaled approximation of the time derivative of the image function.* A simple 2-point finite difference represents an approximation to $df(\underline{x}, t)/dt$ at the midpoint of the time interval $t_2 - t_1$.

2. *Difference images where the difference in image intensities is due to (or may be modeled as) slight shifts in image plane points (in nearly orthogonal directions) have the visual characteristics of edge images* due to their analogy with image gradient function operators (Chapter 4).

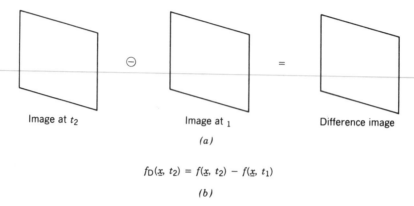

Image at $t_2$ $\ominus$ Image at $_1$ = Difference image

(a)

$$f_D(x,\, t_2) = f(x,\, t_2) - f(x,\, t_1)$$

(b)

**FIGURE 5.2**  Difference image formation
(a)  Graphical interpretation $f_D(x,t_2) = f(x,t_2) - f(x,t_1)$
(b)  Mathematical formulation

3. *The difference image (just as in the case of the static edge image) will, in realistic images, not consist of ideal closed contour regions, but rather will often reflect incomplete change information.* An obvious example of this is the case where an object moves along a background whose image plane intensity (or perhaps texture) is nearly the same as that produced by the object. Such cases (e.g., the familiar "polar bear in a snowstorm") will not produce useful difference image information.

TERNARY IMAGE MOTION DESCRIPTIONS

Difference images convey information not just about the absolute image change, but also concerning the type of change. A simple example leads to ternary image descriptions of image motion (Jain, Martin, & Aggarwal, 1979). As shown in Figure 5.4, an image at time $t_1$ contains a square region of positive intensity value, $f_p$, which is moving to the right (in the image) with constant horizontal velocity $v$. The background is assumed homogeneous with intensity 0. A subsequent image at time $t_2$ therefore contains this region shifted to the right. The difference image is therefore ternary (contains three intensities) and contains four regions:

1. A region of intensity $-f_p$, of horizontal dimension $v(t_2 - t_1)$, because of the "uncovering" of the 0 intensity background over this time interval;
2. A region of intensity $f_p$, of horizontal dimension $v(t_2 - t_1)$, because of "covering" of the 0 intensity background over this time interval;
3. A region between the above two of intensity 0, because of the presence of the object in this region in both images; and
4. A region of intensity 0, because of the (assumed) unchanged background in both images.

By segmenting the difference image into these regions, the direction of the motion may be estimated. This is left to the problems. Note that this approach requires the preprocessing (segmentation) of grey-level images to be of use.

**FIGURE 5.3**  Difference image examples
(a)   $f(x,t_1)$
(b)   $f(x,t_2)$
(c)   $f_d(x,t_1,t_2)$

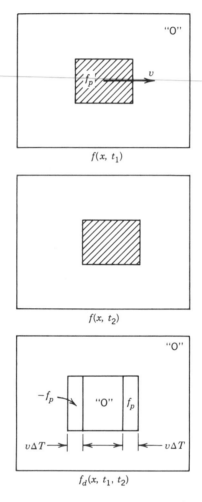

**FIGURE 5.4** Ternary image example

### ACCUMULATIVE DIFFERENCE IMAGES

The previous procedure employs two successive time samples (or frames) of time-varying image data. Consider first the example of Figure 5.5. In this case an output image is computed which indicates the cumulative motion history over the time interval of interest, again using the differencing approach. However, image change information is propagated throughout the resultant image. Assume the image temporal samples are available at times $t_1, t_2, \ldots, t_n$. Defining the difference image $f_d(\underline{x}, t_i, t_j)$ as in Eq. 5-1, we create the cumulative output image at time $t_n$, denoted $f_T(\underline{x}, t_n)$ using the equations

$$f_T(\underline{x}, t_2) = f_d(\underline{x}, t_1, t_2) \tag{5-2}$$

and

$$f_T(\underline{x}, t_n) = f_d(\underline{x}, t_{n-1}, t_n) - f_T(\underline{x}, t_{n-1}) \tag{5-3}$$

$$n \geq 3$$

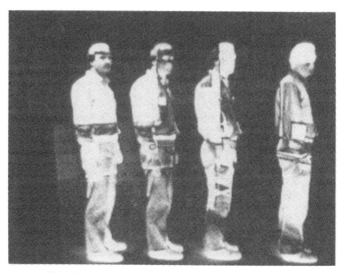

**FIGURE 5.5** Accumulative difference image example

This recursive process allows $f_T$ to convey motion information over the entire interval, as shown in Figure 5.5. The equations above could be modified to employ the absolute value of the difference; however the output image dynamic range would become successively smaller as $t$ increased. An alternative approach for using accumulative image change information in image ensembles is shown in Nagel and Jain (1979).

IMAGE CHANGE DETECTION

A variant of Eq. 5-1 is to form the output image, $f_{out}$, as

$$f_{out}(\underline{x}, t_1, t_2) = \begin{cases} f(\underline{x}, t_2) \text{ if } f_d(\underline{x}, t_1, t_2) \geq T_d \\ 0 \text{ otherwise} \end{cases} \qquad (5\text{-}4)$$

This operation employs a change detection threshold, $T_d$, and is equivalent to forming the difference image, thresholding this difference image using an unsigned (magnitude) comparison, and then multiplying $f(\underline{x}, t_2)$ by this result. A consequence of this operation is that only regions displaying significant change are retained as regions of interest for subsequent processing. An example of this operator is shown in Figure 5.6.

## MOVING EDGE DETECTION

In Chapter 4 considerable emphasis was given to the extraction of static edges, due to the strong relationship between edge information and image feature and structural information. The edge-based approach is extended to the time domain, and the utility of this approach is examined.

The motion of a moving object with discernible static edges will affect the difference image and thus provide a response in both static and dynamic processing steps. The combination of this information is used to extract *moving* edges.

A family of moving edge detectors (med's) may be derived; one (Jain, Martin,

**FIGURE 5.6**   Image change detection example

& Aggarwal, 1979) is considered here. This moving edge detector achieves the required AND-ing operation of spatial and temporal intensity changes by forming an output image where the intensity of any pixel location is the *product* of the magnitude of the image gradient and the difference image values at $\underline{x}$; that is,

$$f_{med}(\underline{x},t_1,t_2) = |df(\underline{x})/d\underline{x}| \, |f_d(\underline{x},t_1,t_2)| \tag{5-5}$$

The operation of this operator is shown in Figure 5.7. The med, because of its local nature, fails in certain nontrivial cases. For example, the motion of an edge of a binary region in either the horizontal or vertical direction will result in zero difference image intensities along this edge.

**FIGURE 5.7**   Moving edge detector example

# ▪ OPTICAL FLOW FORMULATIONS AND RAMIFICATIONS

## *FLOW MODEL ORIGIN*

### INTRODUCTION TO DYNAMIC IMAGE MODELING

There is a great deal of both spatial and temporal redundancy, in a sequence of images containing moving objects (so-called "dynamic imagery"). The information contained in $500 \times 500$ pixel images sampled at a 60-Hz rate might be transmitted via systems with far less bandwidth than is required to transmit the raw data. Furthermore, moving image plane features (which may be spatially discontinuous) are perceived as *changing* "smoothly." The HVS makes use of significant scene-to-scene feature temporal dependence (assuming an appropriate temporal sampling rate).

Optical flow research concerns the determination of the "motion" of the individual pixel locations by using intensity data in a sequence of images. The resultant optical flow field is the field of 2-D pixel "velocity" vectors. The optical flow field conveys valuable information concerning the characteristics (e.g., curvature and orientation) and depth of surfaces as well as the relative motion among scene objects and the sensor system.

### THE BASIC GEOMETRIC MODEL

Recalling the *p-p* based geometric model of Chapter 2, consider the motion of an object point in physical coordinates from $\underline{x}_o$ to $\underline{x}'_o$. This yields a 3-D motion vector $(\underline{x}'_o - \underline{x}_o)$. This 3-D motion vector has a 2-D image plane projection, since (in homogeneous coordinates)

$$\hat{\underline{x}}_i = A \, \hat{\underline{x}}_o \tag{5-6}$$

where

$$\hat{\underline{x}}_o = \left[ \frac{\underline{x}_o}{1} \right] \tag{5-7}$$

and

$$\hat{\underline{x}}'_i = A \, \hat{\underline{x}}'_o \tag{5-8}$$

with

$$\hat{\underline{x}}'_o = \left[ \frac{\underline{x}'_o}{1} \right] \tag{5-9}$$

The primed coordinate system indicates the object point location after the 3-D motion. $A$ is the $3 \times 4$ imaging system geometric calibration matrix. A choice of global coordinate system coincident with the image plane-centric system yields $A = P$, where $P$ is the projection matrix defined in Chapter 2.

In physical coordinates the image plane motion is expressed via a "perturbation," "flow," or "disparity" vector for each point $\underline{x}_i$ in the image plane, in the form

$$\underline{b}(\underline{x}_i) = \underline{x}'_i - \underline{x}_i \tag{5-10}$$

The agglomeration of all the $\underline{b}$ vectors represents a flow or disparity field. This

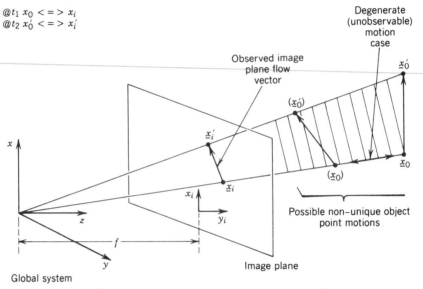

**FIGURE 5.8**   3-D geometrical constraints from observed image plane motion (front projection pp model)

change of pixel locations yields a change in the corresponding pixel intensities, as seen in a difference image. *It is fundamentally difficult to relate the perceived intensity changes to the coordinate (geometric) motion.* In addition, note that Eqs. 5-6 through 5-9 do not determine a unique 3-D or object coordinate flow vector from the image plane flow vector. Given the image plane flow vector, the corresponding 3-D motion vector is constrained to lie in a plane in 3-D space (with the exception of the degenerate case presented below). The trajectory from $\underline{x}_o$ to $\underline{x}_o'$, in the absence of additional constraints on the motion, is not unique. Any 3-D trajectory that yields a curve from $\underline{x}_o$ to $\underline{x}_o'$ will yield the same image plane flow vector. This effect is shown in Figure 5.8. Furthermore, when the motion is along the ray determined by the center of projection and $\underline{x}_o$, the motion is geometrically indistinguishable and yields the image plane flow vector $\underline{b} = \underline{0}$. Although it is geometrically indistinguishable, this motion may be observable from radiometric (intensity) effects.

The motion of all $n$ object points of interest projected in the image plane yields a field of flow vectors, with each given by Eq. 5-10. Properties of this field are useful in making inferences about the motion represented. Figure 5.9 illustrates the case of a simple flow field.

## OPTICAL FLOW CHARACTERISTICS

Up to this point, image plane motion has been described as a difference or displacement-based process. It is useful to explicitly introduce the notion of time in the model. Given a front-projection based imaging model with image coordinates $(x_i, y_i)$ and the assumed object point to image plane distance $z_o \gg f$, and $f = 1$ yields

$$\begin{bmatrix} x_i \\ y_i \end{bmatrix} = \begin{bmatrix} x_o/z_o \\ y_o/z_o \end{bmatrix} \tag{5-11}$$

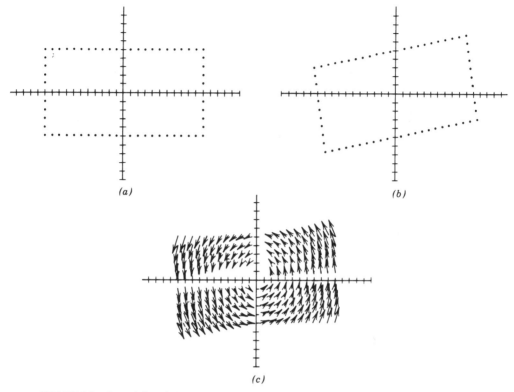

**FIGURE 5.9** Optical flow field example
(a) Original object (outline only)
(b) Perturbed object
(c) Optical flow field

Assume object point motion is constant velocity (and common to all object points) with respective velocities in the $x$, $y$, and $z$ directions given by $u$, $v$, and $w$. The time-varying evolution of a specific object point is

$$\begin{bmatrix} x_o(t) \\ y_o(t) \\ z_o(t) \end{bmatrix} = \begin{bmatrix} x_o + ut \\ y_o + vt \\ z_o + wt \end{bmatrix} \tag{5-12}$$

where $(x_o, y_o, z_o)$ is the location of the specific object point at $t = 0$. Thus, as a function of $t$, the motion of this object point in 3-D space generates a line (see the problems). Using Eq. 5-11, the corresponding image plane motion is

$$\begin{bmatrix} x_i(t) \\ y_i(t) \end{bmatrix} = \begin{bmatrix} (x_o + ut)/(z_o + wt) \\ (y_o + vt)/(z_o + wt) \end{bmatrix} \tag{5-13}$$

### THE FOCUS OF EXPANSION (FOE)

Assume that the motion of the point is toward the image plane (i.e., $w = dz/dt < 0$). Due to the foreshortening property of the $p$-$p$ transform, as $t \to -\infty$ the motion of this object point appears to emanate from a fixed point in the image plane, given by

$$\lim_{t \to -\infty} \begin{bmatrix} x_i(t) \\ y_i(t) \end{bmatrix} = \begin{bmatrix} u/w \\ v/w \end{bmatrix} \equiv \underline{e} \tag{5-14}$$

This point in the image plane, denoted as $\underline{e}$, is referred to as the *focus of expansion*, or FOE. With this model, the motion of all object points (notice the FOE is independent of $(x_o, y_o, z_o)$), as seen in the image plane, appears to emanate from (or toward, if $w > 0$) the FOE. Figure 5.10 illustrates the significance of the FOE for a simple case. Figure 5.11 illustrates the concept with real imagery.

Several approaches to calculate the FOE exist, based on exploitation of the fact that for constant velocity object motion all image plane flow vectors intersect at the FOE. An obvious approach involves plotting of the extracted flow vectors and extrapolation backwards (or forwards) to find this intersection. An alternate approach is shown in Jain (1983).

In closing, we note that if the object point motion is not simple constant velocity translation (e.g., the object is rotating), a FOE may not exist (see the problems).

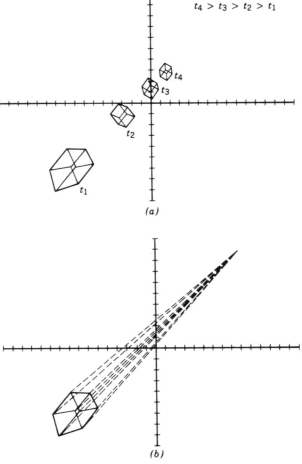

**FIGURE 5.10** Example of the FOE
(a) Motion sequence
(b) Calculation of FOE

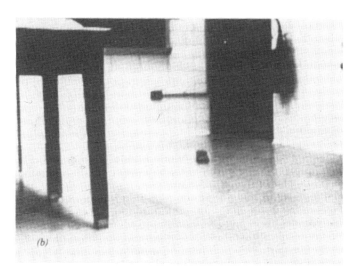

**FIGURE 5.11**   Calculation of the FOE from real imagery
(a)   $f(x, t_1)$
(b)   $f(x, t_2)$
(c)   $f(x, t_3)$
(d)   $f(x, t_4)$
(e)   FOE using (a)–(d)

*Continued on next page*

The case of multiple translating objects is also of interest; in this case each object has a FOE.

### THE TIME-TO-ADJACENCY EQUATION AND DEPTH FROM MOTION

It is useful to define the time-varying distance, $D(t)$, in the image plane, of an image point from the FOE. This is given as

$$D(t) = \|\underline{x}_i - \underline{e}\| \tag{5-15}$$

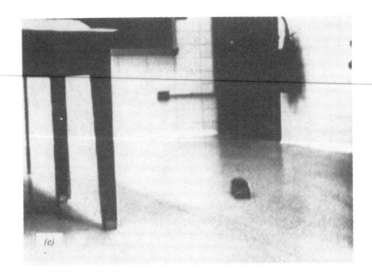

**FIGURE 5.11** *Continued*

or, from Eq. 5-14,

$$D(t) = [(x_i(t) - u/w)^2 + (y_i(t) - v/w)^2]^{1/2} \qquad (5\text{-}16)$$

This is shown in Figure 5.12. Clearly, as $t \to -\infty$, $D(t) \to 0$. What is even more useful, however, is the quantity (expressed in units of time)

$$T_A = D(t)/(d\ D(t)/dt) \qquad (5\text{-}17)$$

It is left for the reader, through differentiation and suitable algebraic manipulation, to show that this quantity reduces to

$$D(t)/[d\ D(t)/dt] = -z(t)/w \qquad (5\text{-}18)$$

Defining the rate of change of the distance $D(t)$ as

$$V(t) = d/dt\ [D(t)] \qquad (5\text{-}19)$$

we arrive at the result

$$D(t)/V(t) = -z(t)/w \qquad (5\text{-}20)$$

Note that the quantity $D(t)$ is specific to each pixel location, $\underline{x}_i$, in the image. This yields several consequences, including:

1. At any particular time (i.e., $t_1$) the ratio $-z(t_1)/w$ (recall $w$ is negative if $z$ is positive, since the point is moving toward the image plane) is the distance of the object point from the image plane divided by the (constant) velocity of the point. This is the time, measured from $t_1$, until the object point intersects the image plane, or the "time-to-adjacency". Equation 5-20 is denoted the time-to-adjacency equation.

2. Equation 5-20 holds for each corresponding object and image point pair. Computing $D(t)/V(t)$ for all points of interest and noting that $w$ is assumed constant, a measure of the relative depth of all moving object points is obtained. For example, consider two object points with $z$ coordinates $z_1(t)$ and $z_2(t)$, $z$-direction velocities, $w$, and corresponding $D_i(t)$ and $V_i(t)$ values

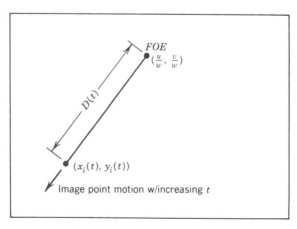

**FIGURE 5.12**   D(t) and the FOE

measured from the image plane. Equation 5-20 yields, for each of these points

$$[D_1(t)/V_1(t)] = [z_1(t)/w] \qquad (5-21)$$

and

$$[D_2(t)/V_2(t)] = [z_2(t)/w] \qquad (5-22)$$

Therefore,

$$z_2(t) = z_1(t) [D_2(t)/D_1(t)] [V_1(t)/V_2(t)] \qquad (5-23)$$

*Thus, under the above assumptions, we are able to determine the* relative 3-D *distances* $[z_2(t)/z_1(t)]$ *of these two object points solely from their image plane motion.* This property yields information on the moving object static structure and introduces the concept of Structure From Motion (SFM).

## ANALYTICAL ORIGIN OF AN OPTICAL FLOW MODEL

There exist several ways to develop spatiotemporal image models that relate time-varying image intensity changes to the "flow" or motion of the image pixels. Here, we take an image-plane centric approach to optical flow and develop analytical model(s) for the flow field—specifically, a spatiotemporal differential relationship between image spatial and temporal gradients. This facilitates solution of the correspondence problem, enables estimation of flow fields through parameter estimation, and provides a basis for flow vector aggregation. This model also provides constraints for the estimation of flow vectors. Note that *in spatiotemporal models derived from differential approaches, the motion must be assumed to be "small."* Therefore, global image changes are not directly representable. Evolution over time might possibly be represented with this approach.

### DERIVATION OF REDUCED DIMENSION OPTICAL FLOW MODEL

We begin our derivation of optical flow models with a simple 1-D example. This model relates the time-varying image plane intensity variations, the time-varying geometric transform parameters, and image plane spatial intensity variations. (The reader may wish to consult Appendix 2 for background.)

*A Spatiotemporal Model Via a Geometric Distortion Model and Taylor Series Expansion (1-D Time-Varying Spatial Function Example).* Consider the following 1-D (spatial dimension) time-varying model

$$f(x,t) = f(g(x,t),t_0) \qquad (5-24)$$

Time evolution of the 1-D image function is thus governed by $f(x,t_0)$ and $g(x,t)$. (Implied in $g(x,t)$ is dependence on the initial time, $t_0$. We could write this function as $g(x,t, t_0)$.) In this model, the intensity that appears at spatial location $x$ at time $t$ is the same intensity that appeared at location $x' = g(x,t)$ at time $t_0$. $f(x,t)$ will be a constant along a family of curves in $(x,t)$ space defined by $g(x,t) = c$.

Assume that $g(x,t)$ in Eq. 5-24 is given simply as a constant velocity translation of the form

$$g(x,t) = x + b(x,t) \qquad (5-25)$$

$$= x + \dot{b}(t - t_0) \qquad (5-26)$$

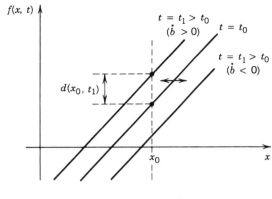

$$f(x, t) = f(x + \dot{b}(t - t_0))$$

**FIGURE 5.13**   Simple example of optical flow model (1-D intensity "Ramp")

where $\dot{b}$ denotes the time derivative of $b(x,t)$. This has the form of a velocity, and is shown in Figure 5.13. Viewing $f(x,t)$ in the $x$-coordinate system, for $\dot{b} > 0$ (i.e., a positive velocity), the apparent motion is to the left; the converse holds for $\dot{b} < 0$. Therefore, from Eq. 5-24,

$$f(x,t) = f(x + b(x,t), t_0) \tag{5-27}$$

Expanding this function about $x$ in a Taylor's series yields

$$f(x + b(x,t),t_0)) \approx f(x,t_0) + [\partial f(x,t_0)/\partial x] \, b(x,t) \tag{5-28}$$

Equation 5-28 may be rewritten as

$$f(x + b(x,t),t_0)) - f(x,t_0) = [\partial f(x,t_0)/\partial x] \, b(x,t) \tag{5-29}$$

or

$$\begin{aligned} f(x,t) - f(x,t_0) &= [\partial f(x,t_0)/\partial x] \, b(x,t) \\ &= d(x,t,t_0) \end{aligned} \tag{5-30}$$

From Eq. 5-30 we observe that the difference image is related to the image spatial gradient and $b(x,t)$. Consider the limiting argument

$$\lim_{t \to t_0} \{d(x,t,t_0)/(t - t_0)\} = \lim_{t \to t_0} [\partial f(x,t_0)/\partial x] \, (b(x,t)/(t - t_0)) \tag{5-31}$$

which yields the spatiotemporal relationship

$$\partial f(x,t_0)/\partial t = [\partial f(x,t_0)/\partial x] \, [\partial b(x,t)/\partial t] \tag{5-32}$$

or, from Eq. 5-26,

$$\partial f(x,t_0)/\partial t = [\partial f(x,t_0)/\partial x] \, b \tag{5-33}$$

Thus, the image spatial and temporal derivatives are related through this velocity or "motion parameter." From Figure 5.13, this is confirmed intuitively. As shown, $f(x,t)$ has a positive and constant spatial derivative (i.e., slope). For $\dot{b} > 0$, Eq. 5-33 indicates that the time change of the image function (i.e., the value of the difference image) at $x_0$ would be positive. This analytical observation is confirmed graphically. Similarly, for $\dot{b} < 0$ (motion to the right), with the image spatial gradient as shown in Figure 5.13, both Eq. 5-33 and the figure predict decreasing image intensity at $x_0$ for $t > t_0$. Note that estimates of the difference image and the image spatial gradient may be used to determine $\dot{b}$.

*A Spatiotemporal Model Via a Geometric Distortion Model and Spatiotemporal Differentiation and the Chain Rule (1-D Time-Varying Spatial Function Example).* An alternate derivation is presented prior to delving into the 2-D (spatial) case. Differentiation of $f(x,t)$ in Eq. 5-24 with respect to $x$ and $t$, and employing the chain rule for differentiation, yields

$$\partial f(x,t)/\partial x = \partial \ (f(g(x,t),t_0)/\partial x \tag{5-34}$$
$$= (\partial f/\partial g) \ (\partial g/\partial x)$$

and

$$\partial f(x,t)/\partial t = \partial (f(g(x,t),t_0)/\partial t \tag{5-35}$$
$$= (\partial f/\partial g) \ (\partial g/\partial t)$$

where we have omitted function arguments for clarity. Elimination of $\partial f/\partial g$ in the above equation, noting that $\partial g/\partial x$ is a 1-D Jacobian, yields the relationship

$$f_t = f_x \ (J_x^{-1} \ \partial g/\partial t) \tag{5-36}$$

From Eq. 5-26

$$\partial g/\partial x = 1 + (\partial \dot{b}(x)/\partial x) \ (t - t_0) \tag{5-37}$$

and

$$\partial g/\partial t = \dot{b}(x) \tag{5-38}$$

Note that the term $(\partial \dot{b}(x)/\partial x)$ in Eq. 5-37 represents a measure of the divergence of the velocity field, which may be of use in regional models. Assuming that $(\partial \dot{b}(x)/\partial x) = 0$ locally, Eqs. 5-36 and 5-37 yield

$$f_t = f_x \ \dot{b} \tag{5-39}$$

which is identical to Eq. 5-33. Thus, the two approaches are consistent.

### EXTENSION TO THE 2-D CASE (THE SPATIOTEMPORAL MODEL)

Our development of the full-spatial dimension model follows from the preceding section. We choose a model for the image evolution as follows

$$f(\underline{x},t) = f(\underline{g}(\underline{x},\underline{a},t),t_0) \qquad t \geq t_0 \tag{5-39}$$

In this model, the motion parameters are represented by a time and space varying parameter vector $\underline{a}$. One method to derive the spatiotemporal dynamics model is to differentiate Eq. 5-39 with respect to $\underline{x}$ and $t$ and relate the resulting partial differential equations, as shown previously. The increased dimensionality of $\underline{g}$ (it is a $2 \times 1$ *vector* function) necessitates care with vector-matrix manipulations. Recall (although it is not shown explicitly in Eq. 5-39), $\underline{g}(\underline{x},t)$ is a function of $t_0$. This yields a distributed parameter system spatiotemporal model of the form

$$f_t(\underline{x},t) = f_{\underline{x}}^T \ (\underline{x},t) \ J_x^{-1} \ \underline{\dot{g}}'(\underline{x},t) \tag{5-40}$$

where $J_x$ is the $2 \times 2$ Jacobian matrix of the time-varying geometric transformation and $\underline{\dot{g}}(\underline{x},t) = \partial \underline{g}(\underline{x},t)/\partial t$. A simple application is in an optical flow model where

$g(\underline{x},\underline{a},t) = \underline{x} + \underline{b}(t)$ (assuming locally $J_x = I$); thus

$$f_t\,(\underline{x},t) = \underline{f_x^T}\,(\underline{x},t)\,\dot{\underline{b}}(t) \tag{5-41}$$

Notice the motion parameters at each point $(\underline{x},t)$ consist of a $2\times 1$ vector of velocities, namely $\dot{\underline{b}} = [\dot{b}_1, \dot{b}_2]^T$. Estimating $f_t$ and $f_x$ for each point of interest, yields a method to *constrain* $\underline{b}$. Unfortunately, each point only provides one constraint equation on the values of two parameters $\dot{b}_1$ and $\dot{b}_2$. Thus, the flow estimation problem is underconstrained.

*Relation to the Model of Horn and Schunk (Optional).* Another spatiotemporal model (Horn & Schunk, 1980) is of the form

$$f(\underline{x},t) = f(\underline{x} + \delta\underline{x}, t + \delta t) \tag{5-42}$$

Expanding the righhand side of Eq. 5-42 in a Taylor's series about $(\underline{x},t)$ and neglecting higher order terms (the reader should verify this) with $\underline{x} = [x_1,x_2]^T$ yields

$$(\partial f/\partial x_1)\,(\partial x_1/\partial t) + (\partial f/\partial x_2)\,(\partial x_2/\partial t) + \partial f/\partial t = 0 \tag{5-43}$$

Notice that Eq. 5-43 may be written as

$$f_t = -f_x^T\,[\partial\underline{b}/\partial t] \tag{5-44}$$

Therefore, only the negative sign distinguishes this model from our previous spatiotemporal result. The key to unification of the models is to compare Eq. 5-39 with the model of Eq. 5-42, or

$$f(\underline{x},t) = f(g(\underline{x},t), t_0) \tag{5-45}$$

$$t \geq t_0$$

using

$$g(\underline{x},\underline{a},t) = \underline{x} + \underline{b}(t),$$

with

$$f(\underline{x},t) = f(\underline{x} + \underline{b},t_0) \tag{5-46}$$

These may be related by

$$t_0 = t + \delta t \tag{5-47}$$

and

$$\underline{x} + \delta\underline{x} = \underline{x} + \underline{b} \tag{5-48}$$

Thus, the Horn and Schunk model represents a "forward" formulation of the image spatiotemporal evolution (in the sense that the intensity at $(\underline{x},t)$ moves to $(\underline{x} + \delta\underline{x}, t = t + \delta t)$, whereas in Eq. 5-46, a reverse formulation is shown (i.e., $\underline{x}$ moves from $\underline{x} + \underline{b}$ at $t = t_0$ to $\underline{x}$ at $t = t$). The approaches may be shown to be equivalent by noting that $t - t_0 = -\delta t$; therefore, the sign of the differential is the only change. Conversion between the two models may also be accomplished by changing the signs of the motion velocity vector components, because we could shift the spatial indices and rewrite Eq. 5-42 as

$$f(\underline{x} - \delta\underline{x},t) = f(\underline{x}, t + \delta t) \tag{5-49}$$

which is in the form of Eq. 5-39, with $g(\underline{x},\underline{a},t) = \underline{x} - \delta\underline{x}$. Thus, the models are consistent.

### REMARKS ON THE SPATIOTEMPORAL MOTION MODEL

In concluding the derivation of the spatiotemporal model, note the following:

1. The model implies a conservation of pixel intensities (neglecting effects at the finite image boundary), because the intensities merely"shift" or move about the image.

2. No effort is made to incorporate radiometric information resulting from the 3-D imaging geometry into the model. This has been considered by Schunk (1986).

## MOTION ESTIMATION APPROACHES AND RAMIFICATIONS

With the model formulated in the previous section, we now consider the flow field estimation, or the determination of the motion parameters. Attention is restricted to the determination of estimates for the local flow vectors, and the model is of the form of Eq. 5-41

$$f_t(\underline{x},t) = f_x^T(\underline{x},t) \, \underline{\dot{b}}(\underline{x},t) \tag{5-50}$$

The value of $\underline{\dot{b}}(\underline{x},t)$, for all pixel locations in the image, is desired. Note that $\underline{\dot{b}}(\underline{x},t)$ is not required, in general, to be constant with respect to either $\underline{x}$ or $t$. Two time samples, or frames $f(\underline{x},t_1)$ and $f(\underline{x},t_2)$ are used. The time interval $t_2 - t_1$ is assumed sufficiently small such that differential approximations hold. The under-constrained nature of the problem becomes evident by expanding the vector form of Eq. 5-50 in terms of the two unknowns, $\dot{b}_1(\underline{x},t)$ and $\dot{b}_2(\underline{x},t)$. We assume these unknowns are constant over the time interval $t_2 - t_1$, and define

$$\dot{b}_1 \, (\underline{x},t) = u \tag{5-51}$$

$$\dot{b}_2 \, (\underline{x},t) = v \tag{5-52}$$

Therefore, Eq. 5-50 is expanded. We have used the negative of the velocities, as shown in the previous section (in order that results correspond with the literature) as

$$\delta f(\underline{x},t)/\delta t - (\delta f(\underline{x},t)/\delta x_1) \, u - (\delta f(\underline{x},t)/\delta x_2) \, v = 0 \tag{5-53}$$

which shows that, given estimates of the spatial and temporal derivatives in Eq. 5-53, we arrive at a single *linear* constraint equation for the two unknowns, $u$ and $v$. In fact, Eq. 5-53 constrains $u$ and $v$ to lie along a line in the solution space, with the parameters of the line given by the spatial and temporal derivatives (see the problems). Spatial derivatives may be approximated using any of the approaches in Chapter 4. The temporal derivative is approximated using the difference image, $f_d(\underline{x},t_2,t_1)$ as

$$\partial f(\underline{x},t)/\partial t \approx f_d(\underline{x},t_2,t_1)/t_2 - t_1 \tag{5-54}$$

Estimation approaches for this problem, in one manner or another, introduce additional constraints that allow mathematical solutions.

### SOLUTIONS ASSUMING LOCAL MOTION PARAMETER HOMOGENEITY

Clearly, given only the constraint of Eq. 5-53, we are left in the unpromising position of attempting to estimate two independent unknowns from a single (linear) equation. One solution to this dilemma is to assume that in the local image region there are two values of $\underline{x}$ that indicate the same image motion parameters. This assumes that adjacent pixels exhibit similar image motion. Defining these two points as $\underline{x}_1$ and $\underline{x}_2$, we write the set of two linear equations

$$\partial f(\underline{x}_1,t)/\partial t - (\partial f(\underline{x}_1,t)/\partial x_1)\, u - (\partial f(\underline{x}_1,t)/\partial x_2)\, v = 0 \qquad (5\text{-}55)$$

$$\partial f(\underline{x}_2,t)/\partial t - (\partial f(\underline{x}_2,t)/\partial x_1)\, u - (\partial f(\underline{x}_2,t)/\partial x_2)\, v = 0 \qquad (5\text{-}56)$$

The matrix equation

$$\underline{f}_t = S\,\underline{u} \qquad (5\text{-}57)$$

where $\underline{u} = [u\ v]^T$, and the vector and matrix above are formed with the appropriate values from Eqs. 5-55 and 5-56. Inverting $S$ yields $[u\ v]^T$. However, note that any errors in the values of the spatial or temporal derivative estimates may have a severe effect on the velocity estimates. Furthermore, there is no guarantee that $S$ is invertible; that is, for some functions Eqs. 5-55 and 5-56 yield a set of linearly independent equations. For example, one or more of the spatial derivatives in Eqs. 5-55 and 5-56 may be zero (i.e., $f$ may be regionally constant with respect to $\underline{x}$, or "textureless"), and therefore no motion information is obtainable.

The local motion homogeneity assumption, although perhaps valid for image points corresponding to object points that are close together on the moving object, is not a valid assumption when adjacent image points correspond to the motion of independently moving and occluding objects. We show later in this chapter (p. 238) that image motion discontinuity provides an important clue as to the 3-D scene motion.

An alternate approach (Horn & Schunk, 1980) is to explicitly formulate a *local smoothness constraint* on the velocity vector—that is, to assume that $u$ and $v$ vary slowly with changing $\underline{x}$. This may be formulated mathematically as an optimization problem wherein the objective is to minimize a function of the form

$$C_1 = (\partial^2 u/\partial x_1^2) + (\partial^2 v/\partial x_2^2) + (\partial^2 v/\partial x_1^2) + (\partial^2 v/\partial x_2^2) \qquad (5\text{-}58)$$

which is observed, from Chapter 4, to be the sum of the Laplacians of the functions $u$ and $v$. $C_1$ is only one possible form of the local smoothness constraint: forcing the second derivatives of the local flow velocities to be small (ideally zero) implies that the solution velocities will at most vary linearly (and, consequently, smoothly) in the local region. Note that the Laplacian of a spatially varying quantity, as shown in Chapter 4 (p. 155), may be approximated as the difference of this quantity with a local spatial average, or

$$C_2 \approx (u - u_{\text{avg}}) + (v - v_{\text{avg}}) \qquad (5\text{-}59)$$

The minimization of $C_1$ or $C_2$, or other similarly formulated measures, is a *constrained minimization process*, with satisfiability the flow equation of Eq. 5-53 constraining the minimization. This may be formulated using the method of Lagrange multipliers in several different ways. (Note that the minima of either $C_i$, as formulated, is insufficient since $-\infty$ is a solution.) The constraint is reformulated such that a minimum of zero is obtained. For example,

$$C_3 = (u - u_{\text{avg}})^2 + (v - v_{\text{avg}})^2 \qquad (5\text{-}60)$$

Our chosen formulation for the estimation of $u$ and $v$ is a function of the desired relative "satisfiability" of the total problem constraints. One approach is to force

$C_3$ to be zero and also minimize the quantity

$$M^2 = [\partial f(\underline{x},t)/\partial t - (\partial f(\underline{x},t)/\partial x_1) u - (\partial f(\underline{x},t)/\partial x_2)v]^2 \qquad (5\text{-}61)$$

thus yielding a problem of minimizing

$$E(\underline{u},\lambda) = M^2 + \lambda\, C_3 \qquad (5\text{-}62)$$

where $\lambda$ is a Lagrange multiplier used to append constraint, $C_3$. Alternately, we could formulate the problem as

$$E(\underline{u},\lambda) = C_3 + \lambda\, M^2 \qquad (5\text{-}63)$$

The solution to Lagrange formulations is given by finding values of $\underline{u} = [u,v]^T$ that satisfy

$$\partial E/\partial \underline{u} = 0 \qquad (5\text{-}64)$$

and

$$\partial E/\partial \lambda = 0 \qquad (5\text{-}65)$$

Equations 5-64 and 5-65 represent three equations, the last of which is equivalent to $C_3 = 0$. Using the criteria of Eq. 5-62, with $C_3$ as defined in Eq. 5-62, the reader should verify that Eq. 5-64 yields two solution equations that may be solved for $\lambda$

$$\lambda = -[f_1 f_2 v + f_1^2 u + f_1 f_t]/(u - u_{avg}) \qquad (5\text{-}66)$$
$$= -[f_1 f_2 u + f_2^2 v + f_2 f_t]/(v - v_{avg})$$

where $f_1 = \partial f(\underline{x},t)/\partial x_1$ and $f_2 = \partial f(\underline{x},t)/\partial x_2$. Notice that Eq. 5-66 constrains $u$ and $v$, but Eq. 5-65 returns no new information; it yields

$$C_3 = 0 \qquad (5\text{-}67)$$

We might attempt solution of Eq. 5-63 for $u$ and $v$, directly. Note however, that Eq. 5-67 is quadratic in $u$ and $v$, and, more important, we don't have $u_{avg}$ and $v_{avg}$. Therefore, an iterative solution is developed. Manipulating Eq. 5-66 as shown below (the algebra is lengthy, but straightforward)

$$u = u_{avg} - [f_1^2\, u_{avg} + f_1 f_2\, v_{avg} - f_1 f_t]/[\lambda + f_2^2 + f_1^2]$$

and

$$v = v_{avg} - [f_2^2\, v_{avg} + f_1 f_2\, u_{avg} - f_2 f_t]/[\lambda + f_2^2 + f_1^2] \qquad (5\text{-}68)$$

yields righthand quantities (with the exception of $\lambda$) that are functions of $f_1$, $f_2$, and $f_t$ and the local averages of $u$ and $v$. An iterative solution, using Eq. 5-68, is based on refinement of $u$ and $v$ estimates through refinement of $u_{avg}$ and $v_{avg}$ and $\lambda$. This may be stated as a procedure to update estimates of $u$ and $v$ at the $(n + 1)^{st}$ iteration

$$u^{n+1} = u^n_{avg} + U^n$$

and

$$\qquad (5\text{-}69)$$

$$v^{n+1} = v^n_{avg} + V^n$$

where $U^n$ and $V^n$ in Eq. 5-69 are the corresponding terms in Eq. 5-68, based on values of $u$, $v$, $u_{avg}$, and $v_{avg}$ at step $n$, and $u_{avg}$ and $v_{avg}$ are also obtained from these previous estimates. The algorithm stops when convergence is obtained; that is, when, for all $\underline{x}$,

$$u^n(\underline{x}) - u^{n-1}(\underline{x}) \leq \varepsilon_1$$

and

$$v^n(\underline{x}) - v^{n-1}(\underline{x}) \leq \varepsilon_2$$

where $\varepsilon_1$ and $\varepsilon_2$ are predetermined estimate tolerances.

Sample results using this approach are shown in Figure 5.14.

ALTERNATE SOLUTIONS

As mentioned, all solutions to the optical flow field determination problem rely on the use of supplementary assumptions which lead to additional constraints. Two such approaches are mentioned here:

1. The use of an explicit model for $f(\underline{x})$. An example would be fitting local image grey-value data to a 2-D polynomial. This constrains the relationship between spatial derivatives at neighboring image plane locations.

2. The derivation of more local constraints—for example, additional spatial differentiation of the image function to achieve additional constraint equations. An example is so-called second-order models (Nagel, 1983). The reader may suspect that this approach leads to a formulation for the motion parameters with at least two equations per point, which therefore may be solved without any local homogeneity assumptions. However, two practical difficulties arise: (a) The estimation of higher order derivatives is a numerically sensitive process; and (b) data from a pixel neighborhood is still needed to estimate higher-order derivatives.

Any additional constraints on the underlying image motion must be chosen carefully. While enabling numerical solutions for optical flow, these assumptions must retain a basis of reasonableness or suitability.

## REGIONAL MOTION MODELING, ESTIMATION APPROACHES, AND DIFFERENTIABILITY CONCERNS

In this section, we consider several alternate approaches for the modeling and estimation of image motion, which is regionally, as opposed to pointwise, varying. This type of image motion behavior is reinforced by Figure 5.9, where it is usually obvious that the flow vectors are related. Specifically, they are related by: the object (region) shape, the object (region) spatial texture (i.e., spatial derivatives), the temporal sampling rate, and the motion parameters.

Additional justification for this type of model is based on the theory of spatio-temporal aggregation in the HVS (Chandrasekaran & Flinchbaugh, 1981). This theory seeks to explain the grouping together of elements (i.e., image regions or features) in an image sequence whose motions have consistent interpretations as a cluster of "particles" in the physical world. For example, the Gestalt law of "common fate" has been used to explain why points in space that are perceived to be moving in a similar manner are considered part of a single entity or object.

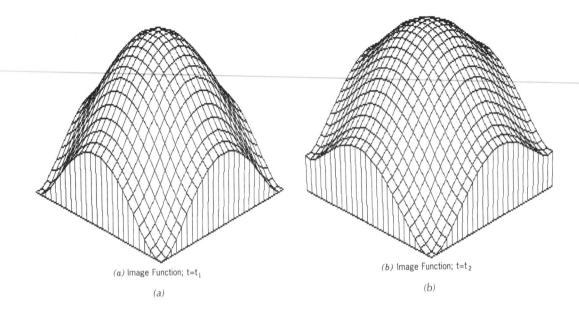

(a) Image Function; t=t₁

(a)

(b) Image Function; t=t₂

(b)

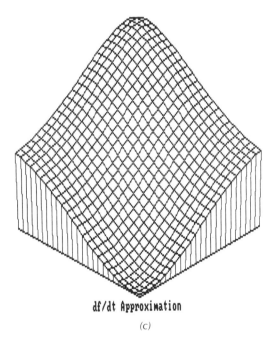

df/dt Approximation

(c)

**FIGURE 5.14** Optical flow (2-D) example
(a)  Image function; t = t₁
(b)  Image function; t = t₂
(c)  df/dt approximation
(d)  df/dx approximation
(e)  df/dy approximation
(f)  u estimates
(g)  v estimates
(h)  u estimates
(i)  v estimates (enlarged to show numerical error detail)

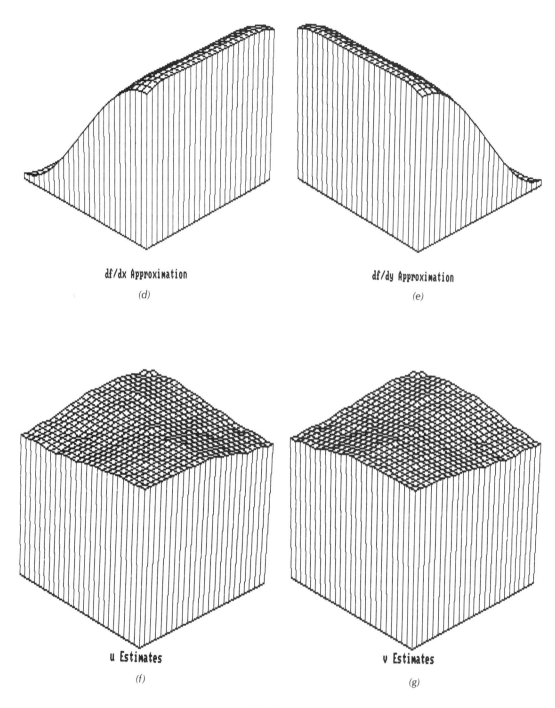

df/dx Approximation

(d)

df/dy Approximation

(e)

u Estimates

(f)

v Estimates

(g)

**FIGURE 5.14** *Continued*

*Continued on next page*

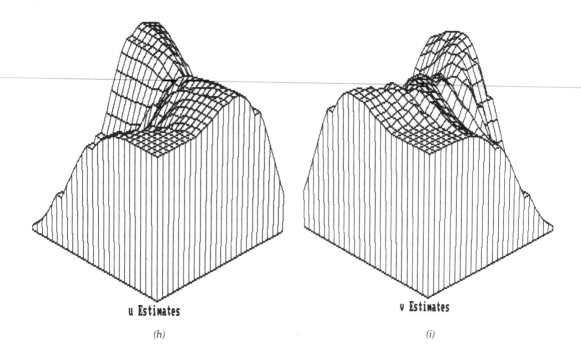

u Estimates

(h)

v Estimates

(i)

**FIGURE 5.14** *Continued*

This is similar to the assumption of object rigidity. A set of image plane locations that undergo a 2-D transformation may be used to derive a 3-D interpretation of a rigid body moving in space. This type of motion parameter agglomeration, while two-dimensional in nature, may be useful as an intermediary solution to the 3-D motion estimation case (Adiv, 1985).

SOLUTIONS EMPLOYING THE HOUGH TRANSFORM

An alternate approach to motion parameter estimation is based on the Hough transform (refer to Appendix 2, part d), alternately referred to as the "clustering" approach (Thompson & Barnard, 1981). This approach is based on the simultaneous solution of a number of linear equalities. Recall that a pseudoinverse solution is not appropriate when the number of motion parameter classes is greater than one, since the pseudoinverse will "blend" the individual solutions to achieve a minimum error parameter estimate that satisfies all motion classes simultaneously. The basic idea of clustering is discrete enumeration of all possible solutions for each constraint. In the solution parameter space, regions of joint intersection of these constrained solutions (or "clusters" of the solutions) are taken as likely solutions. Computationally speaking, the approach is:

1. $p$-parameter solution space is discretized for each of the solution parameters. This yields a partitioning into (hopefully small) $p$-dimensional hypercubes or "bins." The value of each of these bins is initialized to zero.
2. The discretized $p$-1 dimension solution space for each constraint equation is

$$c_{i1}b_1 + c_{i2}b_2 = c_{i3} \quad i = 1, \ldots m$$
$$(c_{ij} \text{ given})$$

(a)

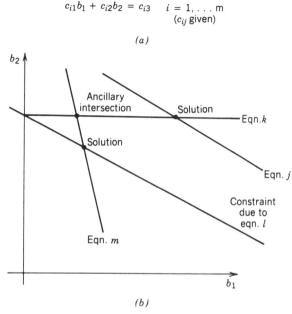

(b)

**FIGURE 5.15** Hough transform approach to motion parameter determination ($p = 2$)
(a)  Constraint
(b)  Solution space (typical example)

then computed by enumeration. When the $p$-1 dimensional solution passes through a particular bin, the bin is then incremented by one. This process is repeated for all constraint equations, yielding a $p$-dimensional array of solution bins. The enumeration of all possible solutions for each constraint (particularly if the solution parameters may require a relatively fine discretization interval) is not computationally efficient, particularly as $p$ becomes large (see Appendix 2, part d).

An example of this process is shown in Figure 5.15 for the commonly encountered case of $p = 2$ (e.g., 2 velocity parameters). Each equation of the form of Eq. 5-50 (or, more generally, Eq. 5-40) provides a linear constraint on the solution parameters. In the absence of noise corruption, two constraint equations that correspond to the same motion parameters will intersect. This is true for each motion class. Resulting bins with large values (i.e., a significant number of intersecting constraint equation solutions) are assumed to represent solution parameters for a motion class. There may be ancillary intersections of the constraints that do not correspond to solutions. "Sidelobes" in the accumulator peaks (Brown, 1983) may occur. Since the number of distinct solutions (e.g., the number of independently moving objects) is not known a priori, some mechanism (e.g., a threshold test on bin values) is used to determine true solutions. Note that using the Hough approach, for example, an affine parameter motion model requires a six-dimensional solution space. This is noteworthy for computational requirements.

An alternative regional approach, based on the concept of "weak solutions" to Eq. 5-40 is shown elsewhere (Schalkoff, 1983, 1987a, 1987b).

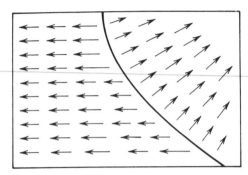

**FIGURE 5.16** Dynamic occluding boundary example in optical flow field

REGIONAL FLOW FIELD DISPARITIES DUE TO MOVING OBJECT OCCLUSION

The origin of optical flow, in particular the geometric model of Figure 5.8, suggests that discontinuities in the optical flow field are likely to result from the occlusion of two or more objects, or object motion against a stationary background. This is shown in Figure 5.16. These situations yield a *dynamic occlusion boundary*, where flow field properties differ across the boundary. The significance of this motion discontinuity boundary is threefold:

1. It causes problems in the optical flow estimation algorithms that assume spatially smooth flow;
2. The dynamic occlusion boundary identifies spatial regions in the image plane that may correspond to the motion of different 3-D objects (or perhaps different surfaces of 3-D objects); and,
3. This boundary contains information on the shape of the silhouette of the object(s), as a function of the viewing geometry. This again indicates the relationship between motion and static structural information.

Thus, techniques to determine dynamic occluding boundaries are useful. A simple approach is an extension of the LOG operator considered in Chapter 4 (p. 161) and assumes the optical flow field has been previously determined. The problem of determining the dynamic occluding boundary location from the flow field is obviously analogous to the problem of 2-D edge detection. Application of the LOG operator to a 2-D flow field requires a somewhat modified interpretation, since the optical flow field is a 2-D *vector* valued quantity, as opposed to grey-level images, which are 2-D scalar valued entities. Fortunately, as shown in Thompson, Muntch, and Berzins (1985), this modification is straightforward.

## APPLICATION OF THE FOURIER TRANSFORM TO SPATIOTEMPORAL MOTION ANALYSIS

The 3-D Fourier domain analysis of image motion is useful for several purposes, in particular:

1. It allows the design of frequency domain filters for spatiotemporal interpolation (Bliss, 1986); and

**2.** It suggests a method for determining the motion (velocity) parameters by examination of the nonzero region of support of $F(u,v,w)$.

A time varying image function of the form

$$g(x,y,t) = f(x - v_x t, y - v_y t) \tag{5-70}$$

would be perceived, in time, as moving in a spatial direction determined by velocity vector $[v_x \; v_y]^T$. As shown in Appendix 3, one consequence of a 2-D Fourier transform of Eq. 5-70 is a *phase term* of the form

$$F_{2\text{-D}}\{g(x,y,t)\} = e^{-j2\pi(uv_x + vv_y)t} F_{2\text{-D}}\{g(x,y,t)|_{t=0}\}$$
$$= e^{j2\pi(uv_x + vv_y)t} F(u,v) \tag{5-71}$$

where $F(u,v)$ is the Fourier transform of $f(x,y)$. The existence of the phase component in the above equation enables the estimation of image velocity. This phase term is linearly dependent on $t$ and the inner product of the 2-D Fourier indices $(u \; v)^T$ with the velocity vector $(v_x \; v_y)^T$. Determining the 3-D Fourier transform of the image function in Eq. 5-70 only requires an extension of the 2-D transform in Eq. 5-71. Assuming *constant* velocity (i.e., $v_x$ and $v_y$ are fixed in time)

$$F_{3\text{-D}}\{g(x,y,t\} \triangleq F(u,v,w) = \int_{\infty}^{\infty} F_{2\text{-D}}\{g(x,y,t)\} e^{-j2\pi wt} dt$$
$$= F(u,v) \int_{\infty}^{-\infty} e^{-j2\pi(uv_x + vv_y)t} e^{-j2\pi wt} dt \tag{5-72}$$

The integral in Eq. 5-72, using the properties of the Fourier transform developed in Chapter 3, may be shown to yield

$$F(u,v,w) = F(u,v) \, \delta \, (uv_x + vv_y + w) \tag{5-73}$$

where $\delta(\;)$ is the dirac delta function. Thus, the 3-D Fourier transform of $g(x,y,t)$ is nonzero only in a *plane*. This plane in $(u,v,w)$ space is given by

$$uv_x + vv_y + w = 0 \tag{5-74}$$

where the slope of this plane is given by the values of $v_x$ and $v_y$. Intuitively, this result is expected by analogy with the 1-D case. Recall the Fourier transform of a 1-D constant function yields an impulse; in the case of Eq. 5-70, $g(x,y,t)$ is constant in $(x,y,t)$ space along a trajectory given by

$$\begin{bmatrix} x \\ y \end{bmatrix} = \begin{bmatrix} x_0 + v_x t \\ y_0 + v_y t \end{bmatrix} \tag{5-75}$$

where $(x_0, y_0)$ is a particular spatial index at $t = 0$. Thus, for all possible values of $(x_0, y_0)$, Eq. 5-75 generates a family of curves (they are lines in the case of constant velocities) in $(x,y,t)$ space, along which the intensity is constant. These are often referred to as the characteristics or characteristic traces of $g(x,y,t)$ (Schalkoff, 1983). Thus, $g(x,y,t)$ may be visualized as a 3-D "solid" of constant intensities, which propagate in time with a slope determined by $(v_x \; v_y)^T$. This analysis therefore indicates that the constant nature of $g(x,y,t)$ along these trajectories should give rise to Fourier domain impulse characteristics; Eq. 5-73 confirms this.

# ■ 3-D TO 2-D MOTION MODELS AND ESTIMATION APPROACHES

In this section, a model for the representation of observed 3-D object motion in image sequences is derived. Using extracted point features (incomplete) information regarding the motion of the 3-D object is determined. Since these point or feature correspondences will most likely contain errors, we consider the origin and effects of these errors on the 3-D motion estimation process.

## *MODEL ORIGINS*

### THE RIGID OBJECT ASSUMPTION

The formal definition of a *rigid* 3-D object is one for which the 3-D distances between any pair of points on the object do not change with time; that is, for all pairs of points on the 3-D object

$$\|x_i - x_j\|^2 = c_{ij} \ \forall \ t, \ \forall \ (i, j) \tag{5-76}$$

where $c_{ij}$ are constants. The assumption of rigid, or nondeformable, objects is often reasonable, because many man-made objects are, in fact, nondeformable, and is used to develop additional constraints for motion estimation. Rigidity constrains the motions of individual object points to be strongly coupled, although the need for point correspondence information is still present. For example, the 3-D translation of a rigid object (which is only translating) may be determined by the estimation of the translation of a single object point.

We begin by showing the motion estimation problem in the case that corresponding *object* points are known in two successive time frames, at $t_1$ and $t_2$, where $t_2 > t_1$. Recall from Chapter 2 that the motion or path of the rigid object over a time interval could have occurred in an infinite number of ways (e.g., rotation followed by translation, or the converse, as well as a succession of perturbations). One particularly handy and compact model (Rogers & Adams, 1976) involving direction cosines relates object points (in homogeneous coordinates) at times $t_1$ and $t_2$ by

$$\hat{\underline{x}}(t_2) = M \, \hat{\underline{x}}(t_1) \tag{5-77a}$$

where $M$ is the $4 \times 4$ matrix

$$M = \begin{bmatrix} n_1^2 + (1 - n_1^2)\cos\theta & n_1 n_2(1 - \cos\theta) - n_3\sin\theta & n_1 n_3(1 - \cos\theta) + n_2\sin\theta & l_1 \\ n_1 n_2(1 - \cos\theta) + n_3\sin\theta & n_2^2 + (1 - n_2^2)\cos\theta & n_2 n_3(1 - \cos\theta) - n_1\sin\theta & l_2 \\ n_1 n_3(1 - \cos\theta) - n_2\sin\theta & n_2 n_3(1 - \cos\theta) + n_1\sin\theta & n_3^2 + (1 - n_3^2)\cos\theta & l_3 \\ 0 & 0 & 0 & 1 \end{bmatrix}$$

$$\tag{5-77b}$$

The $l_i$ and $\theta$ are the parameters of the translation and rotation perturbation about an axis through the origin, and the $n_i$ are the directional cosines that relate this axis to the global coordinate system orientation. Mitiche and Bouthemy (1985) show that a minimum of four corresponding object points at times $t_1$ and $t_2$ arranged in $4 \times 4$ matrices:

$$A(t_i) = [\hat{\underline{x}}_1(t_i) \ \hat{\underline{x}}_2(t_i) \ \hat{\underline{x}}_3(t_i) \ \hat{\underline{x}}_4(t_i)] \tag{5-78}$$

may be used to estimate the 12 parameters of $M$ using least squares techniques. For example, given corresponding object points arranged in $A(t_i)$ at $t_1$ and $t_2$, we may formulate the estimation of $M$ via

$$A(t_2) = M \, A(t_1) \tag{5-79}$$

A pseudoinverse formulation of Eq. 5-79 may then be used to estimate $M$. Constraints on these points are explored in the problems. Writing $M$ as

$$M = [m_{ij}] \tag{5-80}$$

once the $m_{ij}$ parameters in $M$ are determined, it is possible to recover the geometrical parameters from

$$l_i = m_{i4} \qquad i = 1,2,3$$

$$\cos\theta = (m_{11} + m_{22} + m_{33}^{-1})/2$$

$$\sin\theta = (m_{32} - m_{23})/(2n_1)$$

$$n_1 = [(m_{11} - \cos\theta)/(1 - \cos\theta)]^{1/2} \tag{5-81}$$

$$n_2 = (m_{21} + m_{12})/(2n_1(1 - \cos\theta))$$

$$n_3 = (m_{31} + m_{13})/(2n_1(1 - \cos\theta))$$

Thus, knowledge of four corresponding object point pairs allows determination of a unique set of motion parameters for the rigid object over the interval. Practically speaking, a larger number of corresponding points would be used in order to obtain minimum error parameter estimates.

This result, while illustrative, masks a significant problem in the single sensor case. *Object point correspondences are not generally available; rather, corresponding points in the image plane are assumed known.* This, as we will show, is insufficient to determine exact motion parameter estimates.

Recall the model that related image and object points in Chapter 2. We augment this model to show the time dependence

$$\hat{\underline{x}}_i(t) = P \, R^{i-g} \hat{\underline{x}}_o^g(t) \tag{5-82}$$

where $P$ is the projection matrix that implements the perspective-projective transformation, and $R^{i-g}$ relates the image plane and object point coordinate systems. The product of $P$ and $R^{i-g}$ is the sensor calibration matrix, $A$. Using the fact that any 3-D motion of a rigid 3-D body may be described by a 3-D translation vector and three rotation angles chosen with respect to a suitable coordinate system, six parameters completely describe the object motion. Formulating the rotations using three rotation matrices, the rigid body assumption yields a geometric model of the form of Eq. 5-77, where, in physical coordinates

$$\underline{x}_o(t_2) = R_P \, \underline{x}_o(t_1) \tag{5-83}$$

$R_P$ is the $3 \times 3$ matrix comprising the composite rotations underlying the rigid body 3-D motion. For example, object motion consisting of a series of 3-D rotations of angles $\alpha$, $\beta$, and $\theta$ about the respective axis in a Cartesian coordinate system could be modeled using an $R_P$ matrix of the form

$$R_P = R_\theta R_\beta R_\alpha \tag{5-84}$$

The resultant object is denoted motion in homogeneous coordinates (i.e., the combined rotations and translations) by matrix $R$. Using $R_P$ and a translation vector,

$\underline{T}$, $R$ (actually, $R(t_2,t_1)$) has the form

$$R = \left[ \begin{array}{ccc|c} & R_P & & \underline{T} \\ \hline 0 & 0 & 0 & 1 \end{array} \right] = [r_{ij}] \tag{5-85}$$

Consequently,

$$\underline{\hat{x}}_o(t_2) = R\, \underline{\hat{x}}_o(t_1) \tag{5-86}$$

Although the 12 unknown parameters of $R$ are derived from six unknowns, namely the three rotation angles and the three elements of the translation vector, $\underline{T}$, we consider the motion estimation problem to be that of estimating the 12 unknowns, without regard to their relationship. We now seek to determine the significance of this 3-D motion in the image plane.

### 3-D MOTION INFORMATION IN THE IMAGE PLANE

The following assumptions are employed:

1. The image plane coordinate system and the global (object point) coordinate systems differ only in the $z$-direction by $f_p$ as shown in Figure 5.8. This allows investigation of motion concepts without the obscuring effects of a general calibration matrix.
2. $f_p = 1$. This is used to eliminate $f_p$ from the algebra.
3. The object points are sufficiently far from the image plane, or, equivalently, the magnification ratio is sufficiently large so that we may approximate the p-p effects by:

$$x_i(t) = x_o(t)/z_o(t) \tag{5-87}$$
$$y_i(t) = y_o(t)/z_o(t)$$

Note that the third assumption does not eliminate the effect of perspective distortion.

Define $R_p$ from Eq. 5-83

$$R_p = [r_{ij}] \qquad i,j = 1,2,3 \tag{5-88}$$

and the vector $\underline{T}$ as

$$\underline{T} = \begin{bmatrix} t_x \\ t_y \\ t_z \end{bmatrix} \tag{5-89}$$

Using the assumptions above, the homogeneous relationship in Eq. 5-86 is converted into physical coordinates in the image plane

$$x_i(t_2) = \frac{(r_{11}\, x_i(t_1) + r_{12}\, y_i(t_1) + r_{13})\, z_o(t_1) + t_x}{(r_{31}\, x_i(t_1) + r_{32}\, y_i(t_1) + r_{33})\, z_o(t_1) + t_z}$$

and $\hspace{10cm}$ (5-90)

$$y_i(t_2) = \frac{(r_{21}\, x_i(t_1) + r_{22}\, y_i(t_1) + r_{23})\, z_o(t_1) + t_y}{(r_{31}\, x_i(t_1) + r_{32}\, y_i(t_1) + r_{33})\, z_o(t_1) + t_z}$$

Solving for $z_o(t_1)$ in Eq. 5-90, and equating the result yields (this is left to the reader), after a little algebraic manipulation, the matrix-vector result

$$[x_i(t_2) \quad y_i(t_2) \quad 1] \; E \begin{bmatrix} x_i(t_1) \\ y_i(t_1) \\ 1 \end{bmatrix} = 0 \qquad (5\text{-}91)$$

where the elements in $E$ are comprised of the $r_{ij}$ and elements of $\underline{T}$. (The reader should verify this.) The estimation of unique values of these elements is not possible since Eq. 5-91 is homogeneous. This agrees with intuition, due to the lack of invertibility of the 3-D to 2-D image transformation. Thus, the motion of object points cannot be determined uniquely from only image plane data. Suppose we arbitrarily normalize element $e_{33}$ of $E$ in Eq. 5-91; that is, we set $e_{33} = 1$. (This is similar to our solution of the camera calibration problem.) It is then possible to manipulate Eq. 5-91 into the form

$$\underline{c}^T \, \underline{e} = -1 \qquad (5\text{-}92)$$

where the vector $\underline{c}^T$ is comprised of only combinations of the corresponding image plane coordinates; that is, for one point pair

$$\underline{c}^T = [x_i(t_2)x_i(t_1) \quad x_i(t_2)y_i(t_1) \quad x_i(t_2) \quad y_i(t_2)x_i(t_1)$$

$$y_i(t_2)y_i(t_1) \quad y_i(t_2) \quad x_i(t_1)y_i(t_1) \quad x_i(t_2)y_i(t_2)] \qquad (5\text{-}93)$$

Therefore, a minimum of eight image point correspondences could be used to form a system of equations of the form

$$\begin{bmatrix} \underline{c}_1^T \\ \underline{c}_2^T \\ \underline{c}_3^T \\ \underline{c}_4^T \\ \underline{c}_5^T \\ \underline{c}_6^T \\ \underline{c}_7^T \\ \underline{c}_8^T \end{bmatrix} \; \underline{e} = \begin{bmatrix} -1 \\ -1 \\ -1 \\ -1 \\ -1 \\ -1 \\ -1 \\ -1 \end{bmatrix} \qquad (5\text{-}94)$$

from which the elements of the vector $\underline{e}$ and, consequently, the matrix $E$, and ultimately $R$, may be determined.

Extensions of this model may be derived for camera mount motion. One shortcoming of models obtained using this derivation, however, is the inability to represent frame-to-frame occlusion effects as well as radiometric changes in 3-D space. The geometric model only considers the evolution of object points into image plane points, and, therefore, some assumption about the mapping of scene intensity values into image plane intensities is also necessary.

# ■ COMBINING DYNAMIC IMAGE ANALYSIS WITH MULTIPLE CAMERA VISION (MOTION AND STEREO)

## INTRODUCTION

As we saw in Chapter 2, the use of two or more spatially distributed and calibrated sensors enables the determination of 3-D scene attributes, such as object depth or range. In addition, the use of dynamic image information from a single sensor

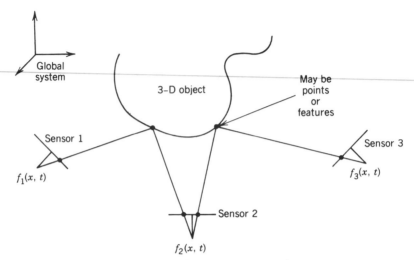

**FIGURE 5.17**   3-D motion/multiple sensor processing objective (passive case)

allows the determination of scene characteristics such as relative depth, rigidity, and the like. We now consider the combination of these two approaches in systems that are designed to process time-varying imagery obtained from a spatially distributed set of sensors. The duality of the approaches becomes evident. Figure 5.17 illustrates the situation.

Recall that the Focus of Expansion (FOE) and the time-to-adjacency formulation (Eq. 5-20) together with the knowledge of the $z$-coordinate of a single object point yields knowledge of the $z$-location of other corresponding object points with the same velocity. Thus, *image motion conveys object structure*. Similarly, the static stereo vision solution enables determination of the 3-D location of an object point. Thus, image plane locations in two views corresponding to a single object point at times $t_1$ and $t_2$ may be used to determine the values of $\underline{x}_o(t_1)$ and $\underline{x}_o(t_2)$. From these, the motion of the object point may be determined. In this sense, *structure conveys motion*. Interestingly, correspondences arise when simultaneously considering time- and space-varying image data (i.e., motion and stereo). For example, in the case of two spatially disparate sensors at times $t_1$ and $t_2$ we may extract the set of $n$ ordered pairs $\{[\underline{x}_i(t_1), \underline{x}_j(t_2)]\}$ that indicate the correspondences between points in the $i^{th}$ and $j^{th}$ sensors at times $t_1$ and $t_2$. For $t_1 = t_2$, this formulation becomes the static stereo case. Figure 5.18 illustrates the overdetermined nature of combined motion and stereo imaging models in the 1-D case.

### A MODELING AND ESTIMATION FRAMEWORK

We develop a modeling and estimation framework that indicates the strong coupling between motion estimation and object structure determination. The geometric model for the projection of 3-D points into the image plane, is (^ denotes homogeneous coordinates)

$$\hat{\underline{x}}_i(t) = A \, \hat{\underline{x}}_o(t) \tag{5-95}$$

Furthermore, given constant velocity motion and a constant temporal sampling

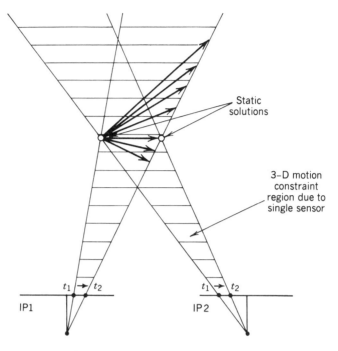

**FIGURE 5.18**  Stereo and motion constraints (1-D example) in the combined formulation

interval, object point motion may be modeled as

$$\hat{\underline{x}}_o(t + T) = R\,\hat{\underline{x}}_o(t) \tag{5-96}$$

where the $R$ matrix represents the rigid body motion. In general, $R$ may be time varying (assume here it is constant over the time interval of interest).

Assuming that all sensors are calibrated with respect to a chosen global coordinate system, the following formulation holds for each of the $j$ distributed sensors

$$\hat{\underline{x}}_i^k(t) = A^k\,\hat{\underline{x}}_o(t) \qquad k = 1, 2, \ldots, j \tag{5-97}$$

From Eq. 5-96

$$\hat{\underline{x}}_i^k(t + T) = A^k\,\hat{\underline{x}}_o(t + T) = A^k R\,\hat{\underline{x}}_o(t) \qquad k = 1, 2, \ldots j \tag{5-98}$$

Note if $R = I$, there is no motion, and the formulation degenerates to the static multiple-sensor case. In particular, if $j = 2$, we have the stereo vision case.

The availability of $m$ time samples of corresponding image points yields an even more redundant or overdetermined system of the form

$$\hat{\underline{x}}_i^k(t + nT) = A^k\hat{\underline{x}}_o(t + nT) = A^k R^n \hat{\underline{x}}(t) \qquad k = 1, 2, \ldots j \text{ (sensors)} \atop n = 0, 1, \ldots m \text{ (time samples)} \tag{5-99}$$

Unless (see the problems) the matrix $R$ is of a particular form, Eq. 5-99 is not of practical use, since $R^n$, while conveying information about $R$, does so in a highly nonlinear manner.

Choosing a more specific case, namely, $j = 2$ and $m = 2$, yields a stereo vision, two time-frame motion example. Given two consecutive time samples or "frames" in each sensor, as well as image point correspondences spatially and over time, we may write

$$\hat{\underline{x}}_i^1(t) = A^1 \hat{\underline{x}}_o(t) \tag{5-100}$$

$$\hat{\underline{x}}_i^2(t) = A^2 \hat{\underline{x}}_o(t) \tag{5-101}$$

$$\hat{\underline{x}}_i^1(t + T) = A^1 \hat{\underline{x}}_o(t + T) = A^1 R \hat{\underline{x}}_o(t) \tag{5-102}$$

$$\hat{\underline{x}}_i^2(t + T) = A^2 \hat{\underline{x}}_o(t + T) = A^2 R \hat{\underline{x}}_o(t) \tag{5-103}$$

Therefore, in physical coordinates, we have a total of $8n$ equations per object point, where $n$ is the number of object points. The total number of unknowns is $12 + 3n$ (12 elements of $R$ and 3 elements for each $\underline{x}_o$). This yields the constraint on the solution:

$$12 + 3n \leq 8n \tag{5-104}$$

Since $n$ must be an integer, $n \geq 3$. Note the equations are assumed linearly independent; this is not guaranteed. Thus, three corresponding image points from two views in two frames are sufficient to determine both the motion parameters and the 3-D location of the object points. An alternate formulation is pursued in the problems.

# ■ SUMMARY

The topic of dynamic imagery analysis, because of the disparity of approaches, is currently one of the most prolific and volatile areas of image processing and computer vision research. The references cited below serve merely as starting points. *The successful motion estimation and understanding algorithm determines and exploits the best information available from a variety of sources such as edge images, segmented images, difference images, and world models employing rules or constraints.* The design of these algorithms for general applications embodies a superset of many of the unsolved problems in image analysis and is therefore expected to challenge researchers for some time. Other difficult motion estimation problems concern the Webb and Aggarwal (1981) tracking of jointed objects.

Fundamental modeling and solution techniques for multiple camera vision systems where the scene is time-varying have been presented. The duality of the motion and stereo vision formulations is apparent. It is worth noting that other approaches to this combined problem exist, including surface-dependent techniques, motion in structured light fields, and region-based techniques.

# ■ REFERENCES

Adiv, G. (1985) Determining three dimensional motion and structure from optical flow generated by several moving objects. *IEEE Trans. Pattern Analysis and Machine Intelligence,* July, 384–401.

Ballard, D. H., and Brown, C. M. (1982) *Computer vision.* Englewood Cliffs, NJ: Prentice-Hall.

Barnard, S. T., and Thompson, W. B. (1979) Disparity analysis of images. *IEEE Trans. PAMI*, **2**, 333–340.

Bliss, J. G. (1986) Velocity-tuned filters for spatio-temporal interpolation. *Proc. IEEE Workshop on Motion: Representation and Analysis*, Kiawah Island, SC, 61–66.

Brown, C. M. (1983) Inherent bias and noise in the Hough transform. *IEEE Trans. Pattern Analysis and Machine Intelligence*, Sept., **PAMI-6**(5), 493–505.

Chandrasekaran, B., and Flinchbaugh, B. E. (1981) A theory of spatio-temporal aggregation for vision. *Artificial Intelligence*, **17**, 387–407.

Horn, B. K., and Schunk, B. G. (1980) Determining optical flow. A. I. Memo No. 572, MIT Artificial Intelligence Laboratory. Cambridge, MA.

Jain, R. (1983) Direct computation of the focus of expansion. *IEEE Trans. Pattern Analysis and Machine Intelligence*, **5**(1), 58–63.

Jain, R., Martin, W. N., and Aggarwal, J. K. (1979) Segmentation through the detection of changes due to motion. *Computer Graphics and Image Processing*, **11**, 13–34.

Labuz, J., and Schalkoff, R. J. (1984) New results using an integrated model and recursive algorithm for image motion estimation. *Pattern Recognition Letters*, **2**(3), 179–183.

Mitiche, A. (1984) On combining stereopsis and kineopsis for space perception. *Proc. IEEE 1st AI Conf*. Denver, CO.

Mitiche, A., and Bouhemy, P. (1985) Tracking modelled objects using binocular images. *Computer Vision, Graphics and Image Processing*, **32**, 384–396.

Mitiche, A., Seida, S., and Aggarwal, J. K. (1986) Interpretation of structure and motion from line correspondences. *Proc. Eighth International Conference on Pattern Recognition*, Paris, France, Oct. 27–31, 1986, pp. 1110–1112.

Nagel, H. H. (1981) Image sequence analysis: What can we learn from application? In T. S. Huang (ed.), *Image sequence analysis*. New York: Springer Verlag.

Nagel, H. H. (1983) Overview on image sequence analysis. In T. S. Huang (ed.), *Image Sequence Processing and Dynamic Scene Analysis*, New York: Springer Verlag.

Nagel, H. H., and Jain, R. (1979) On the analysis of accumulative difference pictures from image sequences of real-world scenes. *IEEE Trans. Pattern Analysis and Machine Intelligence*, **1**(2), 206–214.

Rogers, D. F., and Adams, J. A. (1976) *Mathematical elements for computer graphics*. New York: Mc-Graw Hill.

Schalkoff, R. J. (1987a) Analysis of the weak solution approach to image motion estimation. *Pattern Recognition*, **20**(2), 189–197.

Schalkoff, R. J. (1987b) Dynamic imagery modelling and motion estimation using weak formulations. *IEEE Transactions on Pattern Analysis and Machine Intelligence*, **9**(4), 578–583.

Schalkoff, R. J. (1983) Distributed parameter systems approach to feature extraction and motion estimation in image sequences. *Image and Vision Computing*, **1**(4), 227–233.

Schalkoff, R. J. (1984) Contextual image motion estimation and analysis using spatio-temporal primitives. *Applications of Artificial Intelligence*, **485**, 180–188.

Schalkoff, R. J. and McVey, E. S. (1982) A model and tracking algorithm for a class of video targets. *IEEE Transactions on Pattern Analysis and Machine Intelligence*, **4**(1), 2–10.

Schunk, B. G. (1986) The image flow constraint equation. *Computer Vision, Graphics and Image Processing*, **35**, 20–46.

Snyder, W. E. (guest editor) (1981) Special Issue on Computer Analysis of Time-Varying Images, *Computer*, August.

Thompson, W. B. (1981) Lower-level estimation and interpretation of visual motion. *Computer*, **14**(8), 20–28.

Thompson, W. B., and Barnard, S. T. (1981) Lower-level estimation and interpretation of visual motion. *Computer*, **14**(8), 20–28.

Thompson, W. B., Muntch, K. M., and Berzins, V. A. (1985) Dynamic occlusion analysis in optical flow fields. *IEEE Trans. Pattern Analysis and Machine Intelligence*, **7**(4), 374–383.

Webb, J. A., and Aggarwal, J. K. (1981) Visually interpreting the motion of objects in space. *Computer*, **14**(8), 40–49.

# ■ PROBLEMS

1. Given the constant velocity motion of a point in 3-D, that is, in physical coordinates

$$\underline{x}(t) = \underline{x}o + \begin{bmatrix} u \\ v \\ w \end{bmatrix} t$$

   (a) Show that this motion generates a line in 3-D over time.
   (b) Using the p-p imaging model, with an appropriate choice of coordinate system, determine the time-varying trajectory in the image plane. Does this make sense?
   (c) Does constant velocity motion result in the image plane?
   (d) Repeat (b) and (c) for the case of an orthographic projection.

2. It is postulated that the image plane projection of a smooth 3-D trajectory will be a smooth 2-D trajectory in both orthographic and p-p projections.
   (a) Verify this by considering the respective projection equations and the first and second derivatives of the projected points.
   (b) Is the converse true?

3. Suppose two imaging systems, with respective foci $f_1$ and $f_2$, are separated by a simple translation in the $x_1$ direction. Using some (unspecified) technique, the FOE corresponding to a particular object is computed in each image.
   (a) How are the FOE's related?
   (b) What constraint does the knowledge of the FOE in each image plane place on the 3-D trajectory of the object motion?

4. Derive the time-to-adjacency equation (Eq. 5-18).

5. Does a FOE exist in the case of nonconstant 3-D velocities?

6. The concept of the FOE was developed on pages 221–222. Modify this derivation for the case of a more general (i.e., $f \neq 1$) but known value of $f$.

7. Suppose we are observing the motion of a nonrigid (i.e., deformable) body. Which equations from pages 242–243 are still valid, and which need to be modified? If some information regarding the deformation of the body is available, how could this be incorporated into the motion estimation process?

8. Suppose we are interested in estimating the parameters of motion for a rigid body over a longer *succession* of time samples (i.e., more than two successive frames). Consider the case wherein the 3-D motion is constrained to constant velocity translation only (no rotations). Show the evolution of the parameters in $R^n$.

9. On page 215 we considered ternary images for motion detection. Show:
   (1) An approach, given the segmental ternary image, for determination of the region velocity. (Choose an example.)

(2) The modified derivation for this motion estimation approach where the background intensity is:

   (i) greater than $f_p$; and

   (ii) less than $f_p$.

(3) The possible consequences of:

   (i) incorrect segmentation; and

   (ii) a nonhomogeneous background.

10. Consider the geometric model for 3-D motion as reflected in the image plane (^ denotes homogeneous coordinates):

$$\hat{\underline{x}}_i(t) = \overset{3\times 4}{[A]}\, \hat{\underline{x}}_o(t) \tag{1}$$

Assume a constant velocty motion and constant sampling interval, $T$, i.e.,

$$\hat{\underline{x}}_o(t + T) = \overset{4\times 4}{[R]}\, \hat{\underline{x}}_o(t) \;\forall\, t \tag{2}$$

It is an objective to consider the ramifications of this model for combined motion estimation and stereo vision. For all parts, assume the motion to be due to that of a single, rigid 3-D body.

 (i) How is a rigid body defined, and how does this motion lead to (2)?

 (ii) Suppose initially, we knew $A$ and only wished to determine $R$, where $R$ reflects general 3-D motion of the object.

   —How many parameters determine this motion?

   —Suppose we choose, instead, to estimate the parameters of $R$. How many are there? How are they related?

(Assume for parts (iii) through (v) that *our objective is to estimate* R *and the object structure*, specifically $\underline{x}_o(t)$.

(iii) Given two frames and a single sensor, what is the maximum information (in terms of the objective above) which may be obtained, and how many points are required (two frames/sensor)?

(iv) Given two frames and two (noncoincident) sensors, repeat part (iii). In the case of $R = I$ (no motion) does this solution degenerate to static stereo?

 (v) Repeat the model based analysis of parts (iii) and (iv) for the following additional cases?

   —2 frames/3 sensors

   —3 frames/2 sensors.

   In both cases, given that the problem becomes overdetermined, indicate how this redundant information may be used effectively. In addition, remark on the need for correspondence information.

(vi) In this point, we assume that, in each sensor, we are given a set of corresponding image points in the corresponding temporal image ensemble.

   —How would we determine the FOCUS of EXPANSION (FOE) in each sensor*, and what is its significance?

---

*Assume the problem is overdetermined, i.e., one aspect of the problem is to formulate a reasonable solution.

—How could we relate the FOE's in the different sensors (given calibration and/or relative sensor geometry parameters), and what could the image trajectories, FOE's, and FOE relationships reveal about the nature of the 3-D motion?

11. This problem considers the extension of optical flow techniques using a "forward-backward" approach. This approach is an attempt to use spatiotemporal derivatives in the second image (i.e., $f(\underline{x}, t_2)$) to develop an additional constraint on the flow vector. An integrated form of this is found in [Lab/Sch 1984]. The approach is based on the following observation:

$$f(\underline{x}, t_2) = f(A\underline{x} + \underline{b}, t_1) \qquad (\text{P.11-1})$$

Assuming shift-invariance in $f$ (with respect to the spatial indices), (P.11-1) may be written as:

$$f[A^{-1}(\underline{x} - \underline{b}), t_2] = f(\underline{x}, t_1) \qquad (\text{P.11-2})$$

Note (P.11-2) represents a "reverse" version of (P.11-1). Alternately, from (P.11-1) and (P.11-2) we observe:

(i) point $A\underline{x} + \underline{b}$ at $t_1$ moves to $\underline{x}$ at $t_2$; and

(ii) point $A^{-1}(\underline{x} - \underline{b})$ at $t_2$ moves to $\underline{x}$ at $t_1$.

This is shown in Figure (P.11-1).

For simplicity, we consider only the case of translation ($A = I$) in what follows:

(a) Derive the optical flow estimation equations corresponding to (P.11-1) and (P.11-2).

(b) Under what situations does (P.11-2) yield additional constraint information? (Show in detail the constraints on $f(\underline{x}, t)$, its derivations and $\underline{b}$ for this).

(c) Sketch the "forward-backward" approach for the 1-D spatial case.

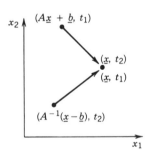

FIGURE P.11-1 "Forward/reverse" optical flow estimation

12. (a) From Eqs. 5-77 and 5-78 derive the estimation equation for $M$.

(b) What are the constraints on the object points used in part (a)?

13. The purpose of this problem is to explore the use of *line correspondences* (as opposed to point correspondences) for motion estimation. For illustration, we initially distinguish between 2-D (image plane) and 3-D cases.

(a) Consider first the 2-D (image plane) case. Suppose we are modeling image motion using the affine transform, i.e.,

$$\underline{x}'_i = A\underline{x}_i + \underline{b}$$

where $\underline{x}'_i$ is the motion-perturbed location (at time $t_2$) of point $\underline{x}_i$ (at time $t_1$).

(i) How many corresponding image point pairs of the form $(\underline{x}_i, \underline{x}'_i)$ are necessary for the estimation of $A$ and $\underline{b}$?

(ii) Consider instead of using isolated point pairs of the form $(\underline{x}_i, x'_i)$ the use of corresponding point quadruples of the form

$$(\underline{x}_{1i}, \underline{x}_{2i}, \underline{x}_{1i}, \underline{x}_{2i})$$

where $(\underline{x}_{ki}, \underline{x}'_{ki})$ correspond as in part (i). Assuming points $\underline{x}_{1i}$ and $\underline{x}_{2i}$ and $\underline{x}'_{1i}$ and $\underline{x}'_{2i}$ *determine corresponding line segments* $l_i$ and $l'_i$ as shown in Figure (P.13-1), show how the parameters of these lines segments lead to an estimation algorithm. Does the equation of the intervening segment contribute anything new to the estimation approach? In assuming spatially connected points $\underline{x}_{1i}$ and $\underline{x}_{2i}$ are we enforcing a form of motion rigidity on the intervening points? For what cases of line orientation does this approach fail?

(b) For the case of 3-D motion, show how corresponding 3-D line segments lead to a motion parameter estimation approach.

(c) Consider the case of 3-D motion of line segments and 2-D image plane observations. Develop a motion estimation strategy using image plane line segment correspondences. What are the limitations?

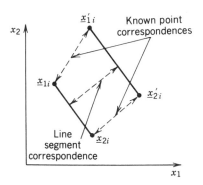

**FIGURE P.13-1**   2-D line segment correspondences

14. Repeat the 3-D Fourier transform derivation of page 239 for the case where the translation velocity is not constant. Specifically, consider the case where an acceleration occurs, i.e.,

$$g(x, y, t) = f(x - g_x(t), y - g_y t)$$

and

$$g_x(t) = a_x t^2$$

$$g_y(t) = a_y t^2$$

How does this affect $F(u, v, w)$? Does this make intuitive sense?

**15.** Repeat problem 14; however, consider a time-varying *rotation* of the image, i.e.,

$$g(x,y,t) = f(\underline{\S}\,(\underline{x},t))$$

where

$$\underline{\S}\,(\underline{x},t) = \begin{bmatrix} \cos{(wt)}\,\sin{(wt)} \\ -\sin{(wt)}\,\cos{(wt)} \end{bmatrix}$$

What is noteworthy about $F(u,v,w)$? Does this make intuitive sense?

**16.** In this problem, we design a set of *spatiotemporal masks*, for the detection of time-varying edges in $f(x,y,t)$. Suppose we are given three time samples, i.e., $f(x,y,t), f(x,y,t_2)$ and $f(x,y,t_3)$ as shown in Figure P.16-1. Assume also a $3 \times 3$ spatial region will be used. (We are therefore extending the Frei-Chen approach onto the time dimension.) Assume the parametric form of the $3 \times 3$ masks corresponding to $\partial f/\partial x, \partial f/\partial y$ and $\partial f/\partial t$ at $t_1, t_2$, and $t_3$ is as shown in Fig. P.16-2. We would like to determine the $a$ and $b$ values such that the quadrant magnitude of $f(x,y,t)$, i.e., $\partial f^2/\partial x + \partial f^2/\partial y + \partial f^2/\partial t$ is isotropic. Note this yields a $3 \times 3 \times 3$ mask or "cube" with 27 parameters to be chosen.

(i) For an ideal step, perpendicular to the $x$-axis and invariant w.r.t. time, i.e.,

$$f(x,y,t) = u_{-1}(x) = \begin{cases} 1 & \text{for } x \geq 0 \\ 0 & \text{for } x < 0 \end{cases}$$

Show the magnitude of the gradient, in this case is simply

$$\frac{\partial I}{\partial x}^2 = 4 + 4a + b \qquad (\text{P.16-1})$$

(ii) What is $\partial f^2/\partial y$ for $f(x,y,t) = u_{-1}(y)$?

(iii) For an ideal step oriented diagonally and which is stationary, i.e.,

$$f(x,y,t) = u_{-1}(x + y)$$

show the gradient magnitude

$$\frac{\partial f}{\partial x}^2 + \frac{\partial f}{\partial y} = \sqrt{2}\,(2 + 3a + b) \qquad (\text{P.16-2})$$

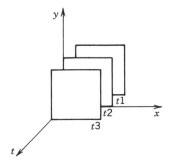

**FIGURE P.16-1**  Spatiotemporal edge templates

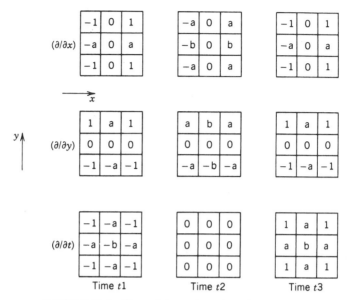

**FIGURE P.16-2** Slices of the "cube" along the x, y at t axes.

(iv) Finally, consider a moving step of the form

$$f(x,y,t) = u_{-1}(x + y + t)$$

—sketch $f(x,y,t)$
—show the gradient magnitude in this case is

$$\frac{\partial f}{\partial x}^2 + \frac{\partial f}{\partial y}^2 + \frac{\partial f}{\partial t}^2 = \sqrt{3}\,(2 + 2a + b) \qquad \text{(P.16-3)}$$

(Note—due to symmetry of the masks, other orientations of the spatiotemporal edges do not need to be considered.)

(v) Using (P.16-1), (P.16-2) and (P.16-3) determine the values of $a$ and $b$ which makes the gradient magnitude the same for the three cases above.

17. Using 5-90 and 5-91, i) derive the relation between the $e_{ij}$ (elements of $E$) and the $r_{ij}$ and $t_x$, $t_y$, $t_z$ parameters. ii) Does knowledge of $E$ allow exact recovery of the $r_{ij}$ and $t_x$, $t_y$, $t_z$ parameters?

# 6

# IMAGE ANALYSIS, PART I

## ■ INTRODUCTION

In Chapter 6 we explore the first of two higher levels of computer vision. The emphasis in Chapter 6 is on lower-level feature extraction. Higher-level vision tasks are covered in Chapter 7, where more "intelligence" needs to be focused on the problem. Thus, we address the problem of *image analysis* from a model-based viewpoint, as shown in Figure 6.1a.

The HVS is adept at reasoning about the contents and structure of a complex scene from images that may be noisy or contain incomplete information. These types of conclusions employ data from other sources—sources of knowledge perhaps based on past experience or learning. Exploiting these additional sources of information, through suitable techniques to represent, manipulate, and integrate this knowledge, is an application of artificial intelligence techniques to computer vision problems.

We may succinctly state our objective in the next two chapters as follows:
In image analysis, we are concerned with *relating image grey-levels to scene objects*. This generally involves the matching of image-derived information with object models that incorporate a priori known constraints.

This is shown in Figure 6.1b and may involve a number of intermediate steps. The concepts explored involve significantly less "signal processing" and more pattern recognition and artificial intelligence–related concepts.

### TOP DOWN AND BOTTOM UP APPROACHES

Image analysis may be accomplished in a number of ways. For example, low-level features may be extracted from the raw grey-level image data, and this feature information processed sequentially, at increasingly higher levels. This is the *bottom up* or data-directed approach. Conversely, we might hypothesize at the highest level scene characteristics and then proceed sequentially toward lower levels, extracting other supporting entities, until the raw image grey-levels have been reached. This is an example of a *top down approach*. In practice, algorithmic approaches employ both of these approaches. Figure 6.1*a* and 6.1*b* show the potential interaction of the models and processing algorithms in this context.

### *RELATIONSHIP TO STATISTICAL AND SYNTACTIC PATTERN RECOGNITION*

Pattern recognition (PR) is the science that concerns the description or classification (recognition) of measurements, usually based on an underlying model. The two major approaches to pattern recognition are the statistical (or decision theoretic) and the syntactic (or structural) approaches. Of particular interest are the following concerns:

    **1.** Reducing the general, statistically based pattern or feature classification approach to a *practical* formulation that is of use in image processing.

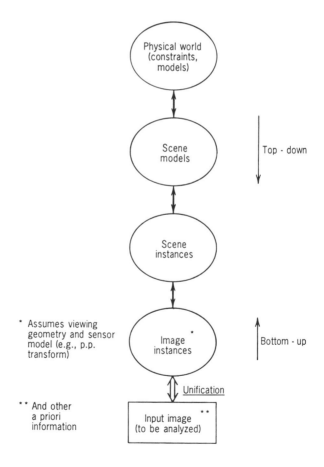

**FIGURE 6.1**
(a)  Model-based image understanding overview
(b)  Sample processing sequence for image analysis (single 2-D image)    *Continued on next page*

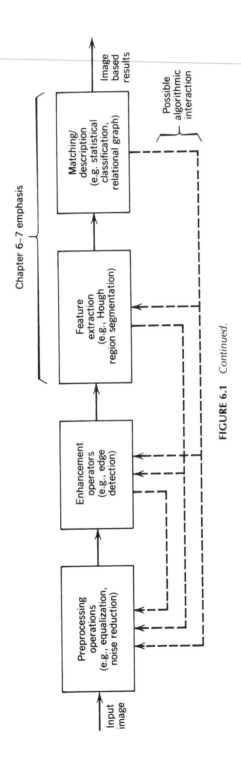

**FIGURE 6.1** *Continued.*

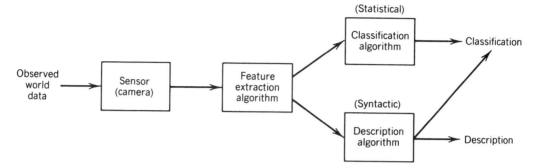

**FIGURE 6.2** Typical pattern recognition system

2. The selection of the lowest-level features to be used. The selection of features or primitives in general pattern recognition problems is typically more art than science, although the principles presented here provide some theoretical guidelines.

3. The development and application of syntactic approaches to image processing problems from the point of view of *grammars and productions*. These may be integrated with a rule-based system.

Complete coverage of pattern recognition involves entire books and courses on either syntactic or statistical pattern approaches; therefore, only approaches that are immediately useful for image processing are covered, with a minimum of derivations.

The structure of a typical pattern recognition system is shown in Figure 6.2. Notice that it consists of a sensor (an image sensor or camera in our case), a feature extraction mechanism (algorithm), and a classification or description algorithm (depending on the approach). In addition, usually some data that has already been classified or described is assumed available in order to train the system (the so-called "training set").

### FEATURES

Broadly speaking, *features* are any extractable measurement of use. Examples of low-level image features are pixel intensities or geometric distances between pixels. Features may also result from applying a feature extraction algorithm or operator to the image data. An example is motion parameter estimates. Additionally, features may be higher-level entities, for example geometric descriptors of either an image region or a 3-D object appearing in the image. For example, aspect ratio and Euler number are higher-level geometric features. Note that significant computational effort may be required in image feature extraction.

Features generally come from a number of information domains. Examples are:

1. *The spectral domain.* Here, for example, visible and infrared spectra may be used to generate independent object features. The independence of these features is due to the independent origin of the sensed energy; that is, the former is based on the visible appearance of an object whereas the latter is a function of its temperature.

2. *The spatial domain.* For example, the spatial distribution of a pattern of intensities over a region (i.e., its "texture") is used as a regional feature to characterize particular regions. These regions, in turn, characterize scene types; for example, the spatial frequencies and orientation of farmland are distinguishable in aerial imagery. Texture is only one example of spatial features. Other examples are geometric attributes such as length and width.

3. *The temporal domain.* For example, the change or motion of image attributes is a dynamic or time-varying feature which, in the case of stationary sensors, provides a method of discrimination between moving scene entities' motion and those that are stationary.

Typically, features are represented via a feature vector, which yields a multi-dimensional measurement space. This large dimensionality compounds feature extraction and application of pattern recognition approaches in image processing applications. For example, it is impractical to directly use all the pixel intensities in an image as a feature vector; a $512 \times 512$ pixel image yields a $262,144 \times 1$ feature vector.

Statistical pattern recognition is explored in depth in Duda and Hart (1973). Syntactic pattern approaches are presented in Fu (1982). A unified view is shown in Fu (1980).

# ■ STATISTICAL PATTERN RECOGNITION

## *ELEMENTARY THEORY*

### INTRODUCTION

We begin with a simplistic example, similar to Duda and Hart (1973). Suppose we wish to design an autonomous system to identify two types of machine parts. One part, which is denoted a "shim," is typically dark and has no surface intensity variation or "texture." Another part, denoted a "machine bolt," is predominantly bright and has considerable surface intensity variation. For illustration, we consider only texture and brightness as features, thus yielding a 2-D feature space. (A plethora of other possible features, such as shape, may be used.) The problem, as formulated, is difficult because these features are only *typical* of each part type. There exist cases of shims which are bright and textured and bolts which are dark and have little texture.

Specifically, define

$x_i$ as a *feature* of the entities, which has a measured value (here we choose $x_1$ as measured brightness and $x_2$ as measured texture)

and

$w_i$ as a class, or a "state of nature," (here $w_1$ is taken to be shim and $w_2$ is bolt).

Thus, if the underlying class is $w_1$ (shims), we expect typical measurements of

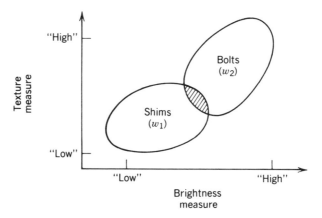

**FIGURE 6.3** Typical ranges of feature values for the "shim-bolt" example

$x_1$ and $x_2$ to be small, whereas if the object under observation is from $w_2$ (bolts), we expect the values of $x_1$ and $x_2$ to be, on the average, large (or at least larger than those of $w_1$). This relationship is shown graphically in Figure 6.3. Of particular importance is the region where values of the features overlap. In this region errors in classification are likely.

Given a particular sample, the extracted features are arranged as a $2 \times 1$ feature vector, $\underline{x}^T = [x_1, x_2]$. Suppose the class conditioned probability density functions for the feature vector (i.e., $p(x_1, x_2 | w_i)$, or simply $p(\underline{x} \mid w_i)$ where $i = 1,2$) are available. Finally, assume that something is known about the a priori (i.e., before measurement) likelihood of the occurrrence of class $w_1$ or $w_2$, specifically, assume the a priori probabilities $P(w_i)$, $i = 1,2$, are known. For example, if we know that on a given day we inspect four times as many shims as bolts, then $P(w_1) = 0.8$ and $P(w_2) = 0.2$. In the absence of this information, an often reasonable assumption is that $P(w_1) = P(w_2)$; that is, the a priori probabilities are equal.

The statistical pattern recognition classification problem may now be cast succinctly as follows:

Determine a strategy for classifying samples, based on the measurement of $\underline{x}$, such that classification error is minimized.

To enable rigorous development of this solution, Bayes' theorem is used. The a priori estimate of the probability of a certain class is converted to the a posteriori (or measurement conditioned) probability of a state via

$$P(w_i \mid \underline{x}) = [p(\underline{x} \mid w_i) \, P(w_i)]/p(\underline{x}) \tag{6-1}$$

where

$$p(\underline{x}) = \sum_i p(\underline{x} \mid w_i) \tag{6-2}$$

Although we omit the details here, minimization of almost any reasonable choice of classification error requires that a given sample, $\underline{x}$, is classified by choosing the state of nature, $w_i$, for which $P(w_i \mid \underline{x})$ is largest. This is also intuitively reasonable. Notice in Eq. 6-1 the quantity $p(\underline{x})$ is common to all class-conditioned probabilities; therefore, it represents a scaling factor that may be eliminated. Thus, in our shim-bolt example above, the decision or classification algorithm is to decide

$$w_1 \quad \text{if} \quad p(\underline{x} \mid w_1) \, P(w_i) > p(\underline{x} \mid w_2) \, P(w_2)$$

or                                                                          (6-3)

$$w_2 \quad \text{if} \quad p(\underline{x} \mid w_2) \, P(w_2) > p(\underline{x} \mid w_1) \, P(w_1)$$

Note also that any monotonically nondecreasing function of $P(w_i \mid \underline{x})$ may be used for this test.

### EXTENSIONS

Consider a multidimensional Gaussian distribution

$$p(\underline{x}) = (2\pi)^{-n/2} \mid \Sigma \mid^{-1/2} \exp\left[-1/2 \, (\underline{x} - \underline{\mu})^T \, \Sigma^{-1} \, (\underline{x} - \underline{\mu})\right] \quad (6\text{-}4)$$

where $\underline{x}$ is $n \times 1$ with mean $\underline{\mu}$ and covariance matrix $\Sigma$. The symmetry of the co-variance matrix allows complete specification of this distribution by $n + n(n + 1)/2$ parameters, which may prove impractical for large $n$. Assume the class conditional density functions are given by Eq. 6-4, and class dependence is through class specific mean vectors and covariance matrices, i.e., $\underline{\mu}_i$ and $\Sigma_i$. Define a *discriminant function* for the $i^{\text{th}}$ class from Eq. 6-1 as

$$g'_i(\underline{x}) = P(\underline{x} \mid w_i) \quad (6\text{-}5)$$

Given a feature vector, $\underline{x}$, classification is based on finding the largest discriminant function. Assuming equal a priori probabilities, this means choosing the class for which $p(\underline{x} \mid w_i)$ is largest. As indicated above, any monotonically increasing function of $g_i(\underline{x})$ is also a valid discriminant function. The log function meets this requirement; that is, an alternative discriminant function is

$$g'\,i(\underline{x}) = \log \{p(\underline{x} \mid w_i)\} \quad (6\text{-}6)$$

which, in the Gaussian case (the derivation is left for the reader) with equal co-variance matrices (i.e., class dependence is only through the mean vectors), yields

$$g'_i(\underline{x}) = -1/2 \, (\underline{x} - \underline{\mu}_i)^T \, \Sigma^{-1} \, (\underline{x} - \underline{\mu}_i) - n/2 \, \log(2\pi) - 1/2 \, \log \mid \Sigma \mid \quad (6\text{-}7)$$

In the equal covariance matrix case, the second and third terms in Eq. 6-7 are constant biases and may be eliminated. Observe, however, that $\Sigma$ influences classification through the first term, which is the squared distance of the feature vector from the $i^{\text{th}}$ mean vector, weighted by the inverse of the covariance matrix. In the case where $\Sigma = I$, a Euclidean distance norm results. The factor in Eq. 6-7

$$d_i^2 = (\underline{x} - \underline{\mu}_i)^T \, \Sigma^{-1} \, (\underline{x} - \underline{\mu}_i) \quad (6\text{-}8)$$

is extremely significant. Given $\underline{x}$, $g'_i(\underline{x})$ is largest when $d_i^2$ is smallest. Another viewpoint is that we are matching $\underline{x}$ against each of the $\underline{\mu}_i$, to classify based on the best match. Assuming $\Sigma = I$ in Eq. 6-8, we expand $d_i^2$ as

$$\| \underline{x} - \underline{\mu}_i \|^2 = \underline{x}^T \underline{x} - 2\underline{\mu}_i^T \underline{x} + \underline{\mu}_i^T \underline{\mu}_i \quad (6\text{-}9)$$

This formulation yields a linear discriminant function or correlation detector of the form

$$g_i(\underline{x}) = \underline{m}_i^T \underline{x} + m_{i0} \quad (6\text{-}10)$$

where

$$m_{i0} = -1/2 \; \underline{\mu}_i^T \underline{\mu}_i \tag{6-11}$$

and

$$\underline{m}_i = \underline{\mu}_i \tag{6-12}$$

## EXTENSIONS AND RAMIFICATIONS

One of the problems not addressed in the previous section is determination of the parameters for the class-conditioned probability density functions. In the case of Gaussian pdf models, a labeled set of *training samples* (i.e., sets of labeled feature vectors with known class) are used. This training set is denoted $H$ and used to estimate $\underline{\mu}_i$ and $\Sigma_i$. Large-dimension feature vectors, and consequently density functions, lead to situations wherein this approach is impractical. For example, if we use the grey-level measurements directly as features, an image with $10 \times 10$ pixel spatial resolution yields a $100 \times 1$ feature vector, and requires estimation of a $100 \times 100$ covariance matrix.

One (suboptimal) alternative, which is related to the minimum distance classification approach, is the use of a nonparametric technique known as nearest neighbor classification. We illustrate the concept of a 1-nearest neighbor classification rule (1-NNR) first. Given a feature vector, $\underline{x}$, we determine the vector in $H$ that is closest in distance to $\underline{x}$, denoted $\underline{h}$. $\underline{x}$ is classified by assigning the class corresponding to $\underline{h}$. A variation is the $k$-NNR, where the $k$ samples in $H$ that are nearest to $\underline{x}$ are determined, and the class of $\underline{x}$ is based on some measure of the labels of these samples (e.g., a voting scheme may be employed). This approach, although conceptually and computationally straightforward, may be shown to have a greater error rate than the minimum distance classifier. However, the concept of classification based on nearness, or similarity, of features is significant.

The previous approaches are predicated on the training set, $H$, being given. Consider the application of pattern recognition to image segmentation—that is, the classification of image pixels into groupings that represent some higher entity or information in the images. Unfortunately, it is rare to have either a statistical model to aid in this grouping or a training set. Therefore, so-called unsupervised learning techniques are applied. One unsupervised learning approach that embodies a more general measure of feature vector similarity and does not require $H$ is known as hierarchical clustering. A set of feature vectors is sequentially partitioned (or merged) on the basis of dissimilarity (or similarity). Thus, given only a similarity measure, we either aggregate feature vectors into a single class or sequentially subdivide feature vector partitions. This is the basis of the region growing, splitting, and merging approaches to segmentation.

## ELEMENTARY APPLICATIONS OF STATISTICAL PATTERN RECOGNITION TO IMAGE DATA (REMOTE SENSING)

Satellite-based sensors in orbit around the earth are one of the largest sources of quantitative image data. The acquired earth images, which may be spectrally distributed, contain information that has significant military, economic, and humanitarian application. For example, the identification of earth areas containing likely mineral deposits or the classification of areas on the basis of vegetation (i.e., specific crops) is possible. A comprehensive bibliography of remote sensing research is presented in Landgrebe (1981).

A series of satellites used for earth remote sensing comprise the Landsat program, initiated in 1972. Landsat satellites are equipped with multispectral scanner systems (MSS), which generate a feature vector for every pixel in the Landsat image, with the $i^{th}$ component of the feature vector representing the intensity response in a particular spectrum at this location. For example, the table below shows nominal spectral parameters for the early generation Landsat sensors:

*Nominal Landsat Spectral Parameters*

| feature | wavelength | band |
|---------|------------|------|
| $x_1$ | 0.50–0.60 μm | visible |
| $x_2$ | 0.60–0.70 μm | visible |
| $x_3$ | 0.70–0.80 μm | near IR |
| $x_4$ | 0.80–1.10 μm | near IR |

LAND TYPE DETERMINATION

One of the most useful applications of the Landsat data is in cartography. Development of a map that indicates type of land (e.g., sand, trees, mountains, water, etc.) is possible. As a result of the different spectral responses of these types of land (e.g., the response of sand in the spectra cited above is different from that of water), it is possible to postulate a class specific model, train the model, and then allow the system to autonomously classify pixels into one of these regions. As shown in Landgrebe (1981), experiments with Landsat image data, using these four features alone (following a training phase) yields a classification error of approximately 17%. Since we have only considered *spectral* features, it is natural to seek even smaller error rates by extraction of other features (e.g., spatial and temporal features). Features typically used in Landsat data classification, and more generally image segmentation, include texture, context, shape, and structural relationships. Examples of textural features are the grey-scale co-occurrence matrix and Fourier transform techniques, which are discussed in the next section. Note that generally an increase classification accuracy requires a corresponding increase in the computational cost.

# ■ SEGMENTATION/RECOGNITION

## INTRODUCTION

The process of *segmentation* groups pixels to form higher-level regional image structures (which may be associated with entities in a higher-level model). Through segmentation, parts or regions of an image are identified prior to determining what they represent in the 3-D scene. The success of the segmentation algorithm often determines the success or failure of the overall image analysis algorithm. A good quantitative summary of segmentation is found in Zenzo (1983).

The general problem of segmentation may be considered in the context of a pattern recognition classification problem, where the entities to be classified may be either pixels or regions (groups of pixels). Generally, *clustering* or unsupervised learning approaches are employed under the conditions that

1. Each resulting segmented region or pixel group is as homogeneous as possible with respect to some measure of feature similarity;
2. Pixels in different subdivisions (or different regions) are inhomogeneous; and
3. The resulting groupings have some meaning in terms of further processing. They are not "artificial" groupings of pixels, but rather constitute image subregions with meaningful interpretations as part of a higher-order concept, such as road, trees, water, etc.

We explore two approaches to segmentation. In *noncontextual* segmentation, relations among features (pixels or regions) are ignored. In *contextual* segmentation the segmentation process employs neighboring relations among the features. Contextual classification is often more successful, because the local image information may reinforce a classification decision. However, it is also theoretically difficult to quantify, as well as practically cumbersome to implement.

A good example of a noncontextual approach is the classification of pixels using statistical pattern recognition approaches where the feature vector is intensity-based. An example is the use of simple thresholding of pixel data to assign pixels to either the ON or OFF classes in the processed image. In contrast, edge detection and region growing approaches typify contextual classification approaches in that support for a segmentation decision comes from the local pixel region content, rather than from an individual pixel.

## EXAMPLES OF SEGMENTATION APPLICATIONS

1. *CAT Preprocessing.* In Computer Aided Tomography (CAT) applications (the related reconstruction algorithms are addressed in Chapter 4), 2-D images of 3-D body parts are acquired and used to form 3-D representations of these parts. One often necessary preprocessing step, prior to reconstruction, is the segmentation of these images, perhaps to separate image regions corresponding to bone from those corresponding to soft tissue.
2. *Colorization of Motion Pictures.* One potential (and controversial) segmentation application involves the "colorization" of older motion pictures, which were originally acquired in monochrome ("black and white"). Some viewers find color versions of these films preferable; marketing studies have confirmed this. To colorize (discretized) films, it is necessary to determine a specific color to be assigned to each pixel at each frame. Because film is typically generated at 25 frames (or images) per second, the amount of manual labor necessary to colorize a 90-minute film is formidable. Digital image processing techniques enable an operator to accomplish this task in a reasonable time, by specifying the color of an image region. The system then automatically determines the location of this region in subsequent frames and assigns this color to these regions. The determination of these regions in subsequent frames involves segmentation.
3. *Object/background discrimination.* In many tracking applications, the objec-

tive is to automatically process time-varying data and generate camera mount control signals to track a 3-D object in a sequence of images. A prerequisite for the generation of control signals is the extraction of the object region of the image, thus necessitating segmentation.

## EDGE-BASED APPROACHES TO SEGMENTATION

As described previously, all low-level segmentation algorithms are based on the concept of similarity (or, conversely, dissimilarity) of attributes. One approach to detect dissimilarity is to identify grey-level intensity discontinuities, or edges. The edge-based segmentation problem becomes more difficult if we require that an image be segmented by determining regions with edges forming closed contours in the image plane.

### BOUNDARY DETECTION VIA GREY-LEVEL VALUES

Using only pixel intensity values, classification is successful when the intensities of the different classes cluster into separate regions in 1-D space, as shown in Figure 6.4b. This is equivalent to requiring that the class-conditioned intensity pdf's are unimodal and have well-separated means. This is seldom the case, as shown in Figure 6.4c, for the image of Figure 6.4a. Practical results using this approach are shown in Figure 6.4d. An extreme example of this is the case of binary images (with assumed intensities 0 and $i_{max}$). The pdf's are dirac delta functions at 0 and $i_{max}$ in this case. Choosing a decision threshold midway between these intensities yields the *thresholding* approach, which was explored in Chapter 4. Other intensity features that might aid in classification, such as color, may be similarly employed.

### FREI-CHEN AND DIRECTED EDGES

Any grey-level disparity between spatially adjacent pixels represents a potential edge, which may be marked with directional information. Another conceptually obvious approach to segmentation is the determination of region edge locations, followed by the agglomeration of this edge information into regions. The classical approach of Brice and Fenneman (1970) illustrates the potential complexity of this procedure. In this approach, a discrete image (matrix of intensities), $F$, of spatial dimension $n \times n$ is mapped into a larger array, of dimension $(2n + 1) \times (2n + 1)$, denoted $S$. This is shown in Figure 6.5. For example, the intensity of pixel $(i, j)$ is mapped to location $(2i + 1, 2j + 1)$ in $S$. For each pixel in $S$ (shown as a circle in Figure 6.5), the intensity is compared with that of its north and east intensity neighbors (or the pixels above and to its right, respectively). The magnitude and sign of this difference are used to compute a value for the two respective " + " cells, as shown. Thus, directional edge segments are produced. This approach provides a global perspective on the image segmentation process, since it enumerates all potential interpixel edges. The representation allows the efficient merging of edge segments into regions, as shown in Figure 6.5c.

### EDGE FOLLOWING AND EDGE CODING

A difficulty that arises with applying edge operators followed by (attempted) agglomeration of edge data into regions is that resulting regions (if any) are not required to be connected (i.e., enclosed by a closed contour of edge segments).

(a)

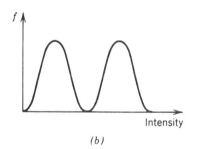

(b)

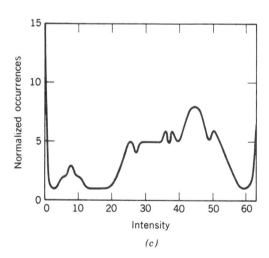

(c)

**FIGURE 6.4** Segmentation via thresholding
(a) Tank image [F]
(b) Ideal histogram
(c) Actual grey-level histogram

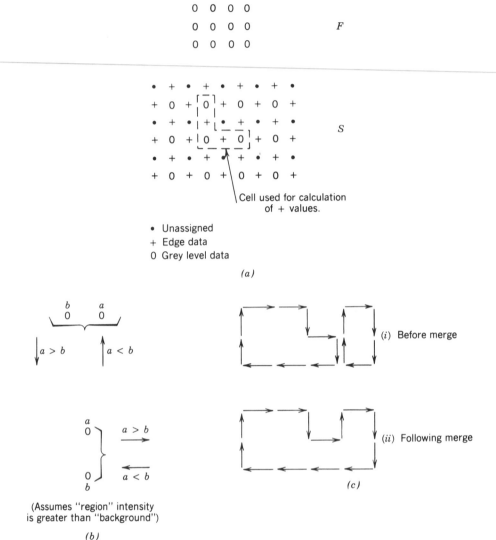

FIGURE 6.5    Brice/Fennema edge enumeration approach for region contour determination
(a)    Grid structure for potential edge representation and merging
(b)    Determination of edge direction for right and above + cells
(c)    Edge merging

An example is an image that has been preprocessed using a LOG kernel. The resultant edge locations and orientation information is insufficient, in typical image applications, to produce a closed contour of significance.

A related approach for the generation of a closed (or at least connected) contour is similar to the region growing process and involves successively growing an edge contour, given an edge seed. This approach is referred to as edge tracking (Ashkar & Modestino, 1978). Given an image of (previously extracted) potential edge element features, as shown in Figure 6.6, with a chosen seed we proceed to grow or track the edge by finding potential paths or contours. The combinatorial explosion inherent in this type of approach is evident; however, with good feature

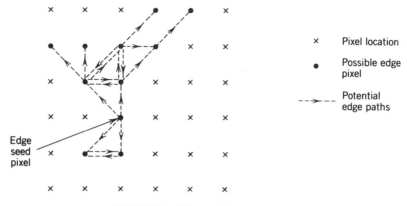

**FIGURE 6.6** Edge tracking or growing

extraction methodologies and evaluation functions (which choose only reasonable paths to investigate), edge tracking attention may remain focused. Typical evaluation functions might be based on:

1. *Edge magnitude and direction.* For example, we may only choose to pursue edge paths using adjacent pixels whose edge strength and direction feature similarity is above a suitable threshold.

2. *Curvature of a segment.* For example, we may know a priori some constraints on the maximum (or minimum) curvature of the contours of the class of objects under investigation.

3. *Closeness to a known a priori contour.* For example, if we know a priori that we are extracting circular or elliptical contours, this information constrains possible tracking directions.

An equivalent viewpoint for the edge tracking or growing approach is that potential edge paths constitute a tree of possible tracking decisions in which one or more paths through the tree are correct. Thus, search is involved.

## Thinning Edge Images

The previous section considered generating a closed contour from an edge-enhanced image, under the assumption that the low-level enhancement process yielded unconnected region boundaries. An analogous and strongly related task is that of thinning edge-enhanced images to produce a single region edge. As shown in the edge-enhancement examples of Chapter 4, the resulting edge maps contain superfluous edges. As in edge growing, the conceptual basis for edge determination via thinning is the extraction and application of additional constraints on the edge elements that are to be preserved. In other words, features other than edge magnitude are used to classify a pixel as being a true edge. An algorithm similar to that of Nevatia and Babu (1980) is used as an example. In this approach, the input grey-level image is correlated with a set of masks (similar to the Frei-Chen approach) corresponding to ideal (step) edges each with a directional orientation. Figure 6.7 shows the case of six $5 \times 5$ pixel masks, which, including the sign of the response, indicate one of 12 possible edge orientations. Correlating these masks

| | | | | |
|---|---|---|---|---|
| −13 | −13 | 0 | 13 | 13 |
| −13 | −13 | 0 | 13 | 13 |
| −13 | −13 | 0 | 13 | 13 |
| −13 | −13 | 0 | 13 | 13 |
| −13 | −13 | 0 | 13 | 13 |

(a) 0°

| | | | | |
|---|---|---|---|---|
| −13 | 4 | 13 | 13 | 13 |
| −13 | −10 | 12 | 13 | 13 |
| −13 | −13 | 0 | 13 | 13 |
| −13 | −13 | −12 | 10 | 13 |
| −13 | −13 | −13 | −4 | 13 |

(b) 30°

| | | | | |
|---|---|---|---|---|
| 13 | 13 | 13 | 13 | 13 |
| −4 | 10 | 13 | 13 | 13 |
| −13 | −12 | 0 | 12 | 13 |
| −13 | −13 | −13 | −10 | 4 |
| −13 | −13 | −13 | −13 | −13 |

(c) 60°

| | | | | |
|---|---|---|---|---|
| 13 | 13 | 13 | 13 | 13 |
| 13 | 13 | 13 | 13 | 13 |
| 0 | 0 | 0 | 0 | 0 |
| −13 | −13 | −13 | −13 | −13 |
| −13 | −13 | −13 | −13 | −13 |

(d) 90°

| | | | | |
|---|---|---|---|---|
| 13 | 13 | 13 | 13 | 13 |
| 13 | 13 | 13 | 10 | −4 |
| 13 | 12 | 0 | −12 | −13 |
| 4 | −10 | −13 | −13 | −13 |
| −13 | −13 | −13 | −13 | −13 |

(e) 120°

| | | | | |
|---|---|---|---|---|
| 13 | 13 | 13 | 4 | −13 |
| 13 | 13 | 12 | −10 | −13 |
| 13 | 13 | 0 | −13 | −13 |
| 13 | 10 | −12 | −13 | −13 |
| 13 | −4 | −13 | −13 | −13 |

(f) 150°

**FIGURE 6.7** Edge masks in six directions
(a)  0°
(b)  30°
(c)  60°
(d)  90°
(e)  120°
(f)  150°

with the image function yields six numerical features for each pixel, one for each mask. The response of each of these masks is therefore associated with a directional code. Recording the correlation magnitude and direction code of the mask yielding the largest response at each pixel location, two output images are obtained. One indicates edge strength, the other edge direction. Figures 6.8b and 6.8c show a sample result. These magnitude and edge direction images are then used to accomplish thinning. A $3\times3$ pixel region is used for the thinning algorithm. Each candidate edge pixel is compared with its four nearest (NSEW) neighbors in a $3\times3$ region. A reasonable thinning procedure is as follows:

Thinning Algorithm
IF　　　　{for pixel location at the center (p5 in Figure 6.8a) of the $3\times3$ region}
1. the magnitude of the central pixel is larger than the edge magnitudes of its two neighbors in the direction normal to the direction of p5 (note this implies the direction normal to a 30° or 60° edge orientation may be determined in the $3\times3$ region)
AND
2. the edge directions of the two neighbors to p5 in the direction of p5 are within 30° of the direction of p5.

THEN

> p5 is marked as an edge element
>
> AND
>
> the two edge pixels identified in step 1 as being in a direction normal to p5 are removed as candidates for further processing.

ELSE

> p5 is not a "significant" edge pixel.

The operation of the above algorithm is conceptually appealing in the sense that spurious edges are eliminated by requiring a peak in local edge magnitude and consistency of direction. Constraint 1. forces the edge response to be a (directionally sensitive) local peak and constraint 2. eliminates edges with extreme variations in curvature by requiring smooth variations in the output edge direction code. Sample thinning algorithm results are shown in Figure 6.8.

Many alternative edge-based approaches for the generation of line drawings from grey-level imagery have been proposed. In Chapter 7 we address this subject from the point of view of a rule-based system application.

| p1 | p2 | p3 |
|----|----|----|
| p4 | (p5) | p6 |
| p7 | p8 | p9 |

*(a)*

| 0 | 5 | 0 |
|---|---|---|
| 4 | 5 | 3 |
| 0 | 5 | 0 |

*(b)* Magnitude

| 0 | 0 | 0 |
|---|---|---|
| 1 | 0 | 0 |
| 0 | 0 | 0 |

*(c)* D

| 0 | 5 | 0 |
|---|---|---|
| 0 | 5 | 0 |
| 0 | 5 | 0 |

*(d)* M

**FIGURE 6.8** Example of the thinning process
(a)  3 × 3 grid matrix, p5 is the candidate of edge element
(b)  Sample edge magnitude before the process
(c)  Sample edge direction
(d)  Edge magnitude after the thinning process
(e)  Actual results of edge thinning algorithm
    (i)   Input image
    (ii)  Preliminary edges
    (iii) Edge map after thinning

*Continued on next page*

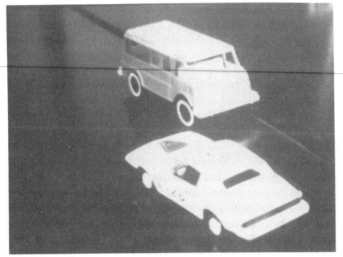

(e) i

(e) ii

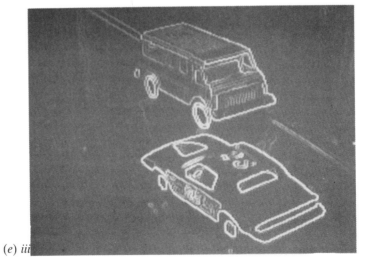

(e) iii

**FIGURE 6.8** *Continued.*

## REGIONAL APPROACHES (TEXTURAL SEGMENTATION)

Regional approaches attempt segmentation of the image into regions through a consideration of regional image data similarity (or dissimilarity), as opposed to edge-enhancing the image and linking edges. We hereafter assume that a segmentation operator is applied to a relatively small image subregion. This has two implications:

1. From a theoretical viewpoint, we desire sufficient "resolution" of a segmented image on the basis of the extracted feature, such that we are able to reliably determine region size, shapes, and boundaries. This suggests that a trade-off exists concerning the region size used for feature extraction. Too small a region (particularly in the presence of noise) may lead to operators with large errors (or variances) in the extracted features, whereas too large a region may lead to extracted features that represent grey-level variations across dissimilar regions.

2. From a practical standpoint, the computational effort required in computing the regional features is significant. Since each feature results from a sequence of operations on an image subregion (e.g., a $p \times q$ pixel rectangular region), it is desirable to keep these regions small.

Although a strict, universally accepted definition of texture does not exist, the notion of image texture is familiar to most viewers. Texture typically refers to the perceived grey-value variations in an image subregion. Clearly, in the visible spectrum, images of the desert (i.e., sand) have a noticeably different overall spatial characteristic than those of forests. Furthermore, certain objects may have a texture that is directionally dependent (e.g., stripes with a certain orientation), which facilitates discrimination of these entities from other image regions.

### TEXTURE FEATURES

Textural segmentation agglomerates or partitions an image into nonoverlapping regions on the basis of textural homogeneity. Fundamental to any textural discrimination approach is a model for the spatial evolution of the texture—that is, a vehicle that allows the *quantitative* assessment of textural features.

### FOURIER DOMAIN SEGMENTATION

*Fourier Domain Textural Features.* The Fourier transform of an image function is defined in Chapter 3 as

$$F(u,v) = \iint_R \exp[-j2\pi(ux + vy)] \, f(x,y) \, dx \, dy \qquad (6\text{-}13)$$

Here, as noted above, we restrict the region over which the transform is computed to $R$. Whereas $F(u,v)$ is in general complex, the power spectrum, denoted $|F(u,v)|^2$ of $F(u,v)$ is given by:

$$|F(u,v)|^2 = F(u,v) \, F^*(u,v) \qquad (6\text{-}14)$$

where the * denotes complex conjugate. This quantity has zero phase for all spatial frequencies; that is, it is a real quantity. It spawns several textural feature extraction approaches. First, for simplicity, consider Eq. 6-14 in polar coordinates, or $|F(r,\theta)|^2$. One measure of the local texture in image region $R$ is in the radial distribution of $|F(r,\theta)|^2$. The reader is left to verify the intuitively plausible observation that a "coarse" texture (predominantly low frequency components) in an image will yield high values of $|F(r,\theta)|^2$ for small values of $r$, whereas a predominantly fine texture will cause values of $|F(r,\theta)|^2$ to be spread throughout the $(r,\theta)$ plane, Thus, without considering orientation of the texture, a useful texture coarseness feature generator is

$$t(r) = \int_0^{2\pi} |F(r,\theta)|^2 \, d\theta \qquad (6\text{-}15)$$

A set of texture features for region $R$ results from computing Eq. 6-15 for various values of $r$.

The spatial or angular orientation of texture may be a significant feature for textural discrimination. For example, consider the case of an image function with edges oriented at an angle of $\theta$ with respect to the $x$-axis. Traversing a direction perpendicular to these edges in $(x,y)$ space, we encounter significant texture. Therefore, the Fourier transform of this function has significant components in a direction $\theta \pm \pi/2$ in $(u,v)$ space, thus providing an orientation-specific texture measure. For example, suppose a function has texture only in the horizontal direction; for example,

$$f(x,y) = \cos(2\pi\alpha x) \qquad (6\text{-}16)$$

This function has contours of constant intensity in directions parallel to the $y$-axis—that is, along lines that form an angle of $\theta = \pi/2$ with respect to the $x$-axis. In Chapter 3 we saw that the Fourier transform of this function is

$$F(u,v) = 1/2 \left[\delta(u - \alpha,v) + \delta(u + \alpha,v)\right] \qquad (6\text{-}17)$$

Thus, Eq. 6-17 indicates that the only nonzero component of $F(u,v)$ is along the $u$-axis, or at an angle of $\theta = 0$ in the $(u,v)$ plane. Thus, one orientation-specific texture feature extraction approach is

$$t(\theta) = \int_0^\infty |F(r,\theta)|^2 \, dr \qquad (6\text{-}18)$$

Note that the approach in Eq. 6-15 is orientation insensitive and frequency sensitive, whereas that of Eq. 6-18 is frequency insensitive and orientation sensitive. Of course, a combination of these features could also be developed. (This is left to the problems.)

### PROBABILISTIC APPROACHES (INCLUDING CO-OCCURRENCE MATRICES)

Statistical models for image grey-value variation play a significant role in the process of segmentation of images (Cooper, et al., 1981; Nahi & Jahanshahi, 1977; Pratt, et al., 1978; Woods, 1978). For example, region segmentation may be accomplished on the basis of regional stochastic properties (e.g., model parameters), and images may be partitioned into regions that are statistically homogeneous.

*Co-occurrence Matrices.* The co-occurrence or "grey-tone spatial dependence" (Zucker & Terzopoulos, 1981) matrix, is a second order statistical measure of image variation. It provides a basis for a number of textural features. The matrix evolves from a consideration of the joint probability density function of two pixel locations. The probability function $P((x_1,x_2),f)$ represents the probability that the image function $f(x_1,x_2)$ has an intensity value $\leq f$ at a location $\leq(x_1,x_2)$. The latter (inexact) statement illustrates the difficulty in extending 1-D probabilistic concepts to 2-D and higher dimensions; there is no unique ordering of the 2-D plane. Temporarily neglecting this difficulty, the density function corresponding to $P((x_1,x_2),f)$ is denoted $p((x_1,x_2),f)$. Eliminating the effect of location $(x_1,x_2)$ in $p$ yields the marginal probability density function $p(f)$, which is recognized as the image intensity pdf, and often approximated by a histogram (Chapter 4). A second order (joint) probability density function for two pixels is

$$p((x_1^1,x_2^1), f^1, (x_1^2,x_2^2), f^2)$$

which represents the density of the joint occurrence of the events $f^1 = f(x_1^1,x_2^1)$, and $f^2 = f(x_1^2,x_2^2)$. This function has four arguments, two of which are spatial locations and two of which are (corresponding) intensities. The domain of this function is therefore the cartesian product of the argument sets. Given an $N \times N$ image with $m$ grey-levels, the enumeration of this domain requires $N^2 \times m \times N^2 \times m$ elements. To achieve a practical representation, the relationship between pixel locations $(x_1^1,x_2^1)$ and $(x_1^2,x_2^2)$ is often restricted, simplified, or ignored. This results in a local representation characterized by a simpler pdf. For example, a matrix of entries, each of the form $p(f^1,f^2)$ and an assumed underlying relationship between the corresponding spatial coordinates is used. This is known as a *co-occurrence matrix*.

Let $\underline{\delta} = (\delta x_1, \delta x_2)^T$ be a vector in the $(x_1,x_2)$ plane. We use this formulation to yield statistical measures of intensity co-occurrence that do not involve $(x_1^1,x_2^1)$ and $(x_1^2,x_2^2)$, but rather the difference between these quantities. Fixing $\underline{\delta}$ at a specific value (e.g., $\underline{\delta} = (1,0)^T$ in the example below), with an intensity resolution of $m$ grey-levels, we form an $m \times m$ matrix $H_\delta$, which indicates the joint probability of occurrence of grey-levels occurring in the image at a separation of $\underline{\delta}$. Thus,

$$H_\delta = [h_\delta(i,j)] \tag{6-19}$$

Element $h_\delta(i,j)$ is a measure of the joint (or co-occurrence) of intensities $i$ and $j$ with an image plane pixel separation of $\underline{\delta}$. Actual implementation of this measure is achieved by restricting elements of $\underline{\delta}$ to integer multiples of the spatial sampling increments and counting the number of times that intensities $i$ and $j$ occur at a separation of $\underline{\delta}$. We now consider an extended example using simple sample texture cases, with $m = 3$ grey-levels and $4 \times 4$ pixel subregions, as shown in Figure 6.9. Note that:

1. Region $(a)$ is a gradually increasing function with a slope of approximately $+45°$.
2. Region $(b)$ has a rippling texture with only a horizontal $(x_1)$ component.
3. Region $(c)$ is a 90° rotated version of $(b)$.
4. Region $(d)$ contains a step oriented at 0°.
5. Region $(e)$ is similar to $(d)$ except that the magnitude of the step is less.

We now compute and examine several co-occurrence matrices corresponding to these regions. Since $m = 3$, these are $3 \times 3$ matrices. The above definition does

```
0 0 0 1      1 2 1 2      1 1 1 1
0 0 1 1      1 2 1 2      2 2 2 2
0 1 1 2      1 2 1 2      1 1 1 1
1 1 2 2      1 2 1 2      2 2 2 2

   (a)          (b)          (c)

        0 0 2 2      1 1 2 2
        0 0 2 2      1 1 2 2
        0 0 2 2      1 1 2 2
        0 0 2 ·2     1 1 2 2

           (d)          (e)
```

**FIGURE 6.9**   Sample image texture functions ($4 \times 4$ subregions; $m = 3$ grey-levels)

not require the co-occurrence matrix to be symmetric. Denote $\underline{\delta} = (i,j)^T$ as $\underline{\delta}_{ij}$. For example, Figure 6.10 shows the results for the $\underline{\delta}_{10}$ case. Several observations regarding Figure 6.10 are as follows:

1. The cases of relatively smooth texture appear to yield co-occurrence matrices with significant values clustered around the diagonal (e.g., cases $(c)$ and $(e)$). This assumes that the magnitude of $\underline{\delta}$ is small compared with the texture spatial variation. Conversely, if the texture is large vis-à-vis $\underline{\delta}$, the values of $H_{\delta}$ will be spread more uniformly throughout the matrix.

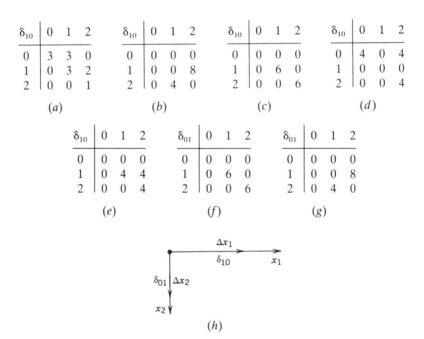

| $\delta_{10}$ | 0 | 1 | 2 |
|---|---|---|---|
| 0 | 3 | 3 | 0 |
| 1 | 0 | 3 | 2 |
| 2 | 0 | 0 | 1 |

(a)

| $\delta_{10}$ | 0 | 1 | 2 |
|---|---|---|---|
| 0 | 0 | 0 | 0 |
| 1 | 0 | 0 | 8 |
| 2 | 0 | 4 | 0 |

(b)

| $\delta_{10}$ | 0 | 1 | 2 |
|---|---|---|---|
| 0 | 0 | 0 | 0 |
| 1 | 0 | 6 | 0 |
| 2 | 0 | 0 | 6 |

(c)

| $\delta_{10}$ | 0 | 1 | 2 |
|---|---|---|---|
| 0 | 4 | 0 | 4 |
| 1 | 0 | 0 | 0 |
| 2 | 0 | 0 | 4 |

(d)

| $\delta_{10}$ | 0 | 1 | 2 |
|---|---|---|---|
| 0 | 0 | 0 | 0 |
| 1 | 0 | 4 | 4 |
| 2 | 0 | 0 | 4 |

(e)

| $\delta_{01}$ | 0 | 1 | 2 |
|---|---|---|---|
| 0 | 0 | 0 | 0 |
| 1 | 0 | 6 | 0 |
| 2 | 0 | 0 | 6 |

(f)

| $\delta_{01}$ | 0 | 1 | 2 |
|---|---|---|---|
| 0 | 0 | 0 | 0 |
| 1 | 0 | 0 | 8 |
| 2 | 0 | 4 | 0 |

(g)

(h)

**FIGURE 6.10**   Sample co-occurrence matrices corresponding to textures in Figure 6.9 ($\delta_{10}$)
(a)–(e)
(f)   $\delta_{01}$ for subregion of part (b)
(g)   $\delta_{01}$ for subregion of part (c)
(h)   Graphical description of $\delta_{10}$ and $\delta_{01}$

2. It is possible to distinguish between the texture of subregions with identical *distributions* of intensities (such as would be indicated by a histogram). This is exemplified by cases (*b*) and (*c*).

The co-occurrence matrix $H_\delta$ does not directly provide a single feature that may be used for texture discrimination. Two measures that have been proposed (Haralick, 1979; Haralick, Shanmugam, & Dinstein, 1973) for extraction of textural features from $H_\delta$ are as follows:

1. *Contrast*. The contrast operator is:

$$C = \Sigma (i - j)^2 h(i,j). \tag{6-20}$$

   This operator yields an indication of the coarseness of the texture.

2. *Entropy*. Entropy is a commonly employed measure of the variance of a set of data. The entropy operator is

$$E = -\Sigma h(i,j) \log\{h(i,j)\} \tag{6-21}$$

It is left for the reader to verify that equal $h(i,j)$ yield large values of $E$, whereas $E$ is small when the $h(i,j)$ are unequal. Entropy therefore yields an indication of the homogeneity of the co-occurrence matrix. (The entropy operator is also applied to grey-value data to yield an indication of the prominence and/or edginess of the texture, as described in Chapter 4, p. 208.)

Numerous other features may be extracted from $H_\delta$. Examples of cluster prominence, local homogeneity, energy (Trevedi & Harlow, 1985), and run length statistics (Weszka, Dyer, & Rosenfeld, 1976).

REGION GROWING/SPLITTING, MERGING

We now turn our attention to a class of segmentation algorithms that embodies region growing, region splitting, region merging, and associated combinations.

The objective of these algorithms (collectively referred to as "region growing") is shown in Figure 6.11. The basic concept involves locally growing a "seed" to "annex" similar pixels into the region. Region splitting, on the other hand, starts

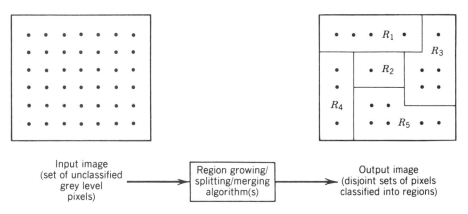

FIGURE 6.11 Region growing objective

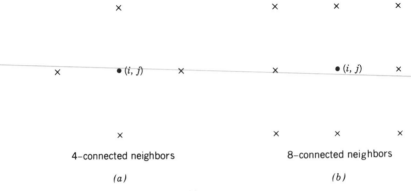

**FIGURE 6.12** "Connectedness" and neighbors
(a)   4-connected neighbors
(b)   8-connected neighbors

with the entire image, which is subsequently split into smaller regions on the basis of dissimilarity.

The connectedness of two pixels may be defined in several ways. Most often, the concept of minimum spatial distance is used. Referring to Figure 6.12, pixel $(i,j)$ is connected to its nearest N,S,E, and W neighbors (4-NN) on the sampling grid, in the case of 4-connectedness (part $(a)$), whereas pixel $(i,j)$ is connected to its eight nearest neighbors (8-NN) in the case of 8-connectedness (part $(b)$).

*Definitions*

*Connected*: Pixels $\underline{x}_i$ and $\underline{x}_j$ are said to be *connected* in region $R$ iff:

1. There exists ($\mathrm{+}$) a sequence $\{\underline{x}_i, \ldots, \underline{x}_j\}$ such that adjacent pixels in the sequence are connected, and
2. All points in this sequence are in region $R$.

Region $R$ is said to be connected (a connected region) if every pair of points in $R$ is connected. Note that regions with concave boundaries may still be connected.

The objective of a region growing/splitting/merging algorithm is to partition the set of all pixels in the input image, denoted $x$, into subsets $\{R_1, R_2, \ldots, R_n\}$ such that:

1. The sets are disjoint—that is, the intersection of sets $R_i$ and $R_j$ is the empty set; and
2. The union of the $R_i$ is $X$; that is, we classify all pixels through the development of regions.

In order to group or classify pixels into a region, a measure of similarity (or dissimilarity) is required. This measure, as described previously, may be based on features such as intensity, color (if available), local texture, or other measures.

The following approaches are developed without specific enumerations of this similarity measure. Instead, the similarity measure is embedded in a predicate function, $H$, which determines homogeneity or region uniformity via

$$H(R_i) = \begin{cases} \text{TRUE if } R_i \text{ is homogeneous} \\ \text{FALSE otherwise} \end{cases} \qquad (6\text{-}22)$$

For example, one $H$ function, based solely on intensity, is

$$H(R_i) = \begin{cases} \text{TRUE if } \forall \text{ 8-connected neighbors, } n, \text{ of all} \\ \quad \text{pixels } (i,j) \in R_i, \ |f(i,j) - f(n)| \leq T \\ \text{FALSE} \end{cases}$$

Note in the above measure that the test threshold, $T$, need not be fixed and perhaps could be updated throughout the segmentation process (e.g., the average of pixels already classified in $R_i$ could be used).

Once $H(R)$ and an initial image partition have been chosen, the segmentation of images is based on noting that:

*Observation 1.* If $H(R_i)$ = FALSE, then one or more pixels do not belong in $R_i$; and

*Observation 2.* If $H(R_i \cup R_j)$ = TRUE, then there is nothing to distinguish regions $R_i$ and $R_j$, and they should be merged.

*Region Growing.* Region growing is a bottom-up procedure for generation of a segmented image. It is based on Observation 2 above. The methodology for region growing is as follows:

*Sample Region Growing Algorithm*

> BEGIN
> choose seeds, $s_i$. $i = 1,2, \ldots , n$. {these are the initial regions}
> UNTIL no further classification of pixels is possible[1]
>> DO
>> FOR all current regions, $R_i$,
>>> DO
>>> FOR each pixel in $R_i$ that has unclassified 8-neighbors[2] {this forces the growing of connected regions}
>>>> DO
>>>> examine each of these unclassified 8-neighbors and assign to $R_i$, if possible[3]
>
> END.

*NOTES*:

[1]This implies that no unclassified pixels remain or the choice of $H$ does not allow any more pixels to be included.

[2]Possible contention for pixels from adjacent regions must be addressed.

[3]Typically, a method of "tagging" classified pixels is necessary.

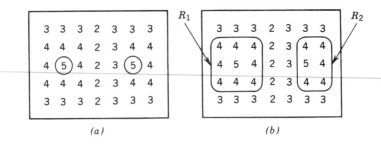

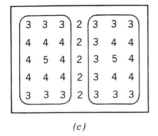 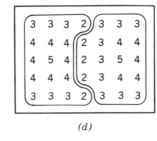

Assign $(i, j)$ to $R_i$ iff

1. abs $|f(i, j) - c| < 2$

2. $c$ in $R_i$

3. $(i, j)$ is 8-neighbor of $c$

(e)

**FIGURE 6.13** Region growing example
(a) Initial image seeds (local intensity maxima) circled
(b) Regions after examination of 8-neighbors of seeds ($R_1$ first)
(c) Regions after consideration of 8-neighbors of $R_1$ and $R_2$ in (b)
(d) Final regions
(e) Similarity measure

An example of this process applied to a simple image is shown in Figure 6.13.

*Region Splitting.* Region splitting is a divisive, or top-down procedure, based on Observation 1. Beginning with all pixels in the same region, nonhomogeneous regions are recursively divided into smaller subregions, and the homogeneity test reapplied to these regions. When all regions satisfy the homogeneity criteria (or perhaps the number of desired regions is established), the process stops.

In addition to the choice of $H$, *two major problems with region splitting are choice of a splitting or region subdivision methodology and choice of a stopping criteria.* A function $H$ that is overly restrictive will result in a final segmented image where each pixel is a unique region.

*Iterative Region Merging and Splitting.* The combination of splitting and merging algorithms to form an iterative procedure is possible. We consider a conceptually simple split and merge procedure similar to Horowitz and Pavlidis (1974). A region homogeneity measure, $H$, and a region splitting methodology (i.e., the geometrical relationship of regions to split subregions) are chosen. The algorithm proceeds as follows:

*Sample Region Splitting-Merging Algorithm*

BEGIN
initialize the input image as one region

UNTIL no more merging or splitting is possible
    DO for all currently existing regions $R_i$
        BEGIN
            IF $H(R_i)$ = FALSE
                THEN split $R_i$ into smaller regions
            IF regions $R_i, R_j, R_k, \ldots$ exist such that
                $H(R_i, R_j, R_k, \ldots)$ = TRUE
                THEN merge $R_i, R_j, R_k, \ldots$ into a larger region
    END.

The skeletal algorithm description above obscures many important implementation details, such as choice of $H$ and the splitting geometry.

## MATCHING FOR SEGMENTATION/RECOGNITION

We begin by considering matching based solely on comparisons of grey-levels. This approach is derived from the correlation and convolution approaches cited in Chapter 3. Matching involving higher (information) level symbolic entities and hierarchical approaches are discussed in Chapter 7.

### TEMPLATE MATCHING

In *template matching*, the intensity profile of the entity we seek to match the image forms a *template*. The segmentation process consists of searching for regions in the image where the image grey-levels and the template grey-levels regionally coincide. Figure 6.14 shows a simplistic interpretation of the process, where the viewer may visually "slide" the template over the image until the template and image intensity levels coincide.

The template is defined in a template-specific coordinate system, as $g(x_1, x_2)$, and the image function, again in terms of a chosen coordinate system, is denoted $f(x_1, x_2)$. Assume that $g(x_1, x_2)$ is nonzero only over a region, denoted $R$, in the template system.

The determination of a good measure of match, or *metric*, is important. The value of the metric should be large when the template and image region coincide in intensity levels over $R$, and small otherwise. For analysis purposes, we may wish to use an alternate measure of mismatch. *The template g is shifted over all possible locations in f, and a measure of match is computed at each of these locations.* The following are two candidate metrics indicating *mismatch* (indices are omitted for simplicity):

**1.** $m_1 = \Sigma \Sigma |f - g|$                                             (6-23)
**2.** $m_2 = \Sigma \Sigma (f - g)^2$                                          (6-24)

$m_1$ and $m_2$ will be small when $f$ and $g$ are identical over $R$, and large when they are significantly different. Whereas metric 1 is easy to compute, a closer examination of Eq. 6-24 leads us to some interesting results. Expanding the second order term in Eq. 6-24 yields

$$m_2 = \Sigma \Sigma f^2 - 2 \Sigma \Sigma f g + \Sigma \Sigma g^2 \qquad (6-25)$$

*Template*

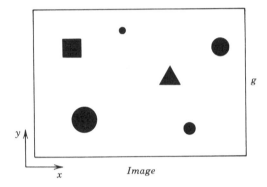

*Image*

**FIGURE 6.14**   Simple template matching concept
(a)   Template, $g(x_1, x_2)$
(b)   Image, $f(x_1, x_2)$

In Eq. 6-25 the intensities of $f$ and $g$ *individually* contribute to $m_2$, through the $\Sigma \Sigma f^2$ and $\Sigma \Sigma g^2$ terms. For a fixed template, $\Sigma \Sigma g^2$ is constant throughout the matching process. Conversely, the term $\Sigma \Sigma f^2$ varies throughout the matching process.

The $\Sigma \Sigma fg$ term Eq. 6-25 is of fundamental interest. Since the coefficient of this term is negative, when this term is large, $m_2$ will be small. Therefore, where $m_2$ provides a good measure of mismatch, the $\Sigma \Sigma fg$ term provides a reasonable measure of match. This operation, hereafter referred to as the *unnormalized correlation* of $f$ and $g$ (over $R$), amounts to an element-by-element multiplication followed by a summation over $R$.

Assume, without loss of generality, that the coordinate system for the template and the image representations are coincident. Since the template is only nonzero in region $R$, the unnormalized correlation may be computed via

$$C_{\text{un}}(\alpha, \beta) = \underset{\text{over } R'}{\Sigma \Sigma} \ g(x_1 + \alpha, x_2 + \beta) \, f(x_1, x_2) \tag{6-26}$$

over all possible locations (values of $\alpha, \beta$) of $g$, relative to $f$. $R'$ is the extent of the nonzero region in the image plane of the shifted template $g$. Peaks in $C_{\text{un}}(\alpha, \beta)$ indicate the potential regions where the template is present. The finite extent of $R$ causes some difficulty in actually computing this metric at the edges of the images, since image data that is "off the image plane" is required.

Furthermore, note the strong relationship of the unnormalized correlation with that of 2-D linear convolution.

Due to the relation between convolution in the spatial domain and multiplication in the Fourier domain, the correlation of Eq. 6-26 may be implemented in the discrete Fourier domain. Finally, as noted in Chapter 3, unnormalized correlation may be viewed as a linear filtering operation, wherein the filter impulse response is a 180° rotated version of the template. This type of filtering is referred to as *matched filtering*. Matched filtering is a well studied area (Papoulis, 1962).

An example of the use of unnormalized correlation in an image is shown in Figure 6.15.

*Normalized Correlation.* To begin, note that zero intensity values in either $f$ or $g$ contribute nothing to the unnormalized correlation measure of match in Eq. 6-26.

This is one indication of a more serious shortcoming of the unnormalized approach. For example, in regions where both $f$ and $g$ have significant numbers of corresponding pixels with zero intensity, $C_{un}$ does not reflect this match or correspondence. This effect would be most pronounced in applying $C_{un}$ to binary images, where only "1"s would contribute to the matching metric. In addition, note that the local energy in the image function, $f$, over $R'$ is reflected in $C_{un}$.

For this reason a *normalized correlation metric* $C_n(\alpha,\beta)$ is used

$$C_n(\alpha,\beta) = (1/E) \, \Sigma \, \Sigma_{R'} \, g(x_1 + \alpha, x_2 + \beta) \, f(x_1,x_2) \qquad (6\text{-}27)$$

where

$$E = \Sigma \, \Sigma_{R'} \, f(x_1,x_2) \qquad (6\text{-}28)$$

Other normalizations of the correlation match measure are possible; for example, dividing by

$$[\Sigma \, \Sigma g(x_1 + \alpha, x_2 + \beta)]^{1/2} \, [\Sigma \, \Sigma f(x_1,x_2)]^{1/2}$$

keeps the normalized correlation measure in the interval $(-1,1)$. An example of matching using normalized correlation is shown in Figure 6.16.

*Matching with Generalized Geometric Distortions.* When the relative geometric orientation of the region to be matched and the template is allowed to be other than translation, the matching process becomes more complex. For example, one significant problem with regional segmentation approaches based on grey-level correlation is varying geometric orientation. We restrict our attention here to relative 2-D orientations. Referring to Figure 6.17, numerous geometric distortions of the template may occur in practical imagery. Various solutions to this problem may be pursued. For example, regional features that are invariant to orientation could be used for matching. An example is the use of moments (see p. 304). An alternative is to store all possible rotated and scaled versions of the template and use or match metric with each of these. This approach is often impractical.

Geometric perturbations of the template, such as rotation and dilation (or more generally affine parameters in the model), have significant effects on metrics that are chosen simply to indicate position. As shown in Figure 6.18, rotations >3° or dilutions ≥3%, cause a loss of the correct correlation peak. This is an unacceptable aspect of correlation-based designs.

## MATCHING INVARIANT TO POSITION, SCALE, AND ORIENTATION

The goal of this section is to develop a matching technique that is invariant to translation, rotation, and scale (T, R, and S, respectively) differences between the template and the image. The approach is in three steps and begins with translation

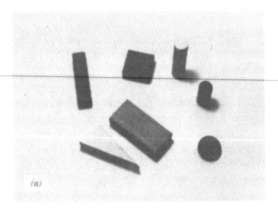

**FIGURE 6.15** Example of unnormalized correlation
(a) Input image
(b) Template (shown in box)
(c) Results of unnormalized correlation

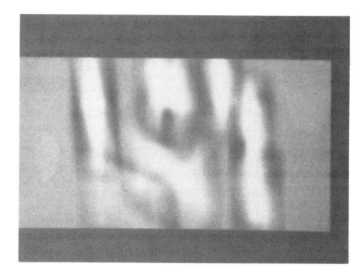

**FIGURE 6.16** Example of normalized correlation

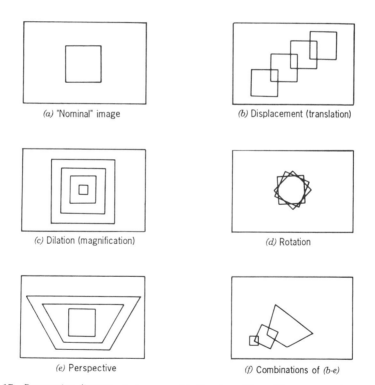

(a) "Nominal" image

(b) Displacement (translation)

(c) Dilation (magnification)

(d) Rotation

(e) Perspective

(f) Combinations of (b-e)

**FIGURE 6.17** Perspective distortion in image registration (matching with geometric distortions)
(a)  "Nominal" image
(b)  Displacement (translation)
(c)  Dilation (magnification)
(d)  Rotation
(e)  Perspective
(f)  Combinations of (b–e)

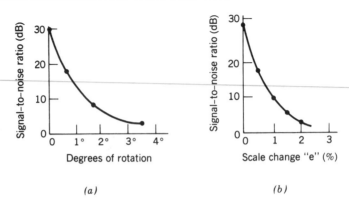

**FIGURE 6.18** Effect of geometric distortions on correlation. (Copyright © 1977 IEEE)
(a) Rotation
(b) Dilation

effects. It is easy to verify (see Appendix 3) that the *magnitude* of the Fourier transform, $|F(u,v)|$, is invariant to translation. Computing the Fourier transform of the template and the image and ignoring the phase yields a matching approach insensitive to position. Note, however, that a rotation of $f(x_1,x_2)$ rotates $|F(u,v)|$ by the same amount and a scale change in $f(x_1,x_2)$ by $\alpha$ scales $|F(u,v)|$ by $1/\alpha$.

Separation of rotational and scale effects is achieved by transforming $|F(u,v)|$ from rectangular coordinates to polar form—that is, from $(u,v)$ coordinates to $(r,\theta)$ coordinates. Any rotation of $f(x_1,x_2)$ manifests itself as a shift in $\theta$ in $F(r,\theta)$. A scale change in $f(x_1,x_2)$ of $\alpha$ affects only the $r$ coordinate of $|F(r,\theta)|$. Thus, a two-dimensional scaling of the image function is reduced to a scaling of only one coordinate in the polar representation of $|F(r,\theta)|$.

One scale invariant transformation is the *Mellin transform*, the 2-D version of which we consider. The Mellin transform of image function $f(x_1,x_2)$, denoted $M(u,v)$, is given by

$$M(u,v) = \iint f(x_1,x_2)\, x_1^{-ju-1}\, x_2^{-jv-1}\, dx_1\, dx_2 \qquad (6\text{-}29)$$

To see the scale invariance property, note the Mellin transform of $f_2 = f(\alpha x_1, \alpha x_2)$, denoted $M_2(u,v)$ is

$$M_2(u,v) = \alpha^{-ju-jv}\, M(u,v) \qquad (6\text{-}30)$$

where $M(u,v)$ is the Mellin transform of $f(x_1,x_2)$. Thus,

$$|M_2(u,v)| = |M(u,v)| \qquad (6\text{-}31)$$

For example, consider a 2-D rect function with variable spatial extent expressed in the form

$$f(x_1,x_2) = \text{rect}\, \frac{(x_1 - (x_{1L} - x_{1R})/2)}{(x_{1R} - x_{1L})}\, \text{rect}\, \frac{(x_2 - (x_{2L} - x_{2R})/2)}{(x_{2R} - x_{2L})} \qquad (6\text{-}32)$$

The Mellin transform of this quantity is

$$|M(u,v)| = |(4/(uv)) \sin [u \ln(x_{1R}/x_{1L})]\, \sin [v \ln(x_{2R}/x_{2L})]| \qquad (6\text{-}33)$$

which, in terms of the scale of $f(x_1,x_2)$, is seen to be only a function of the *ratios* $x_{1R}/x_{1L}$ and $x_{2R}/x_{2L}$, and thus scale invariant.

Table 6-1 below summarizes the Mellin transform of several commonly encountered 1-D functions.

■ **TABLE 6-1**
**Mellin transforms**

| $f(x)$ | $M(u)$ |
|---|---|
| $\delta(x - 1)$ | 1 |
| $u_{-1}(x - 1)$ | $1/ju$ |
| $x$ | $1/(ju - 1)$ |
| $x^{-a}$ | $1/(ju + a)$ |

A final remark regarding the Mellin transform concerns its implementation. Fortunately, the Mellin transform may be computed by an appropriate prescaling of the image function. Specifically, a logarithmic scaling of the coordinates of the input function followed by a Fourier transform of this result yields the Mellin transform (Robbins & Huang, 1972). We illustrate this property and some common Mellin transforms using the 1-D spatial analogy. Using the 1-D version of Eq. 6-29 and a transformation of coordinates.

$$M(u) = \int_0^\infty f(x)\, x^{-ju-1}\, dx \tag{6-34}$$

Letting

$$\gamma = \ln(x) \tag{6-35}$$

yields

$$x = \exp[\gamma] \tag{6-36}$$

therefore

$$M(u) = \int_{-\infty}^\infty f(\exp[\gamma])\, x^{-ju-1}\, dx \tag{6-37}$$

Also, $dx = \exp[\gamma]\, d\gamma$, so

$$M(u) = \int_{-\infty}^\infty f(\exp[\gamma])\, \exp[\gamma]^{-ju}\, \exp[\gamma]^{-1}\, \exp[\gamma]\, d\gamma \tag{6-38}$$

or simply,

$$M(u) = \int_{-\infty}^\infty f(\exp[\gamma])\, \exp[-ju\gamma]\, d\gamma \tag{6-39}$$

which is the desired result.

Thus, combining the Fourier and Mellin transforms with a rectangular to polar conversion yields a computationally attractive RST-invariant matching scheme. The approach makes use of the individual invariance properties of a sequence of operators. A summary of the sequential steps is shown in Figure 6.19. The potential for optical implementation of the Fourier transform makes two of the three steps computationally attractive.

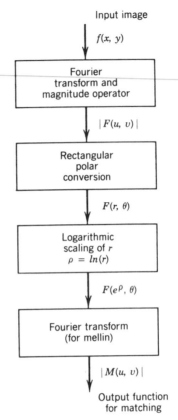

**FIGURE 6.19** Sequential processing steps in an RST-invariant matching technique (operations on one image shown)

# ■ SYNTACTIC PATTERN RECOGNITION

### *THEORY*

The statistical pattern recognition methodology attempts to segment image data using a set of extracted features and an underlying statistical model for the evolution of these features. In this section, syntactic pattern recognition is introduced. Syntactic pattern recognition is strongly founded in formal languages and parsing and differs from the statistical approach principally in that the structure (determined application of productions or rules) of the entity is used for classification or segmentation.

The use of formal grammars in computer vision applications is reasonable if the problem exhibits a discernible structure and if extraction of a set of primitive structural elements is possible.

FORMAL LANGUAGE THEORY

Consider the following simple example of an English-language sentence:

The quarterback throws accurately.

This sentence has both a meaning and a structure and is produced using the following "rewriting" rules (which involved successive replacement):

1. (sentence)
2. (noun phrase) (verb phrase)
3. (article) (noun) (verb phrase)
4. the (noun) (verb phrase)
5. the quarterback (verb phrase)
6. the quarterback (verb) (adverb)
7. the quarterback throws (adverb)
8. the quarterback throws accurately

A *grammar* consists of the following four entities:

1. A set of terminal or *primitive symbols* (primitives), denoted $\Sigma$ (or, alternately, $V_T$).
2. A set of *nonterminal symbols*, or *variables*, which are used as intermediate quantities in the generation of an entity consisting solely of terminal symbols. Often this set is denoted as $N$ (or, alternately, $V_N$).
3. A set of *productions*, or production or rewriting rules. This set of productions, coupled with the terminal symbols, gives the grammar its "structure." The set of productions is denoted $P$.
4. A *starting* (or root) *symbol*, denoted $S$. $S$ is a member of $N$. In the previous example, $S = $ (sentence).

Having defined such a grammar, it may be used in one of two modes:

1. *Generative*: The grammar is used to create a string of terminal symbols using $P$; a *sentence* in the language of the grammar is thus generated.
2. *Analytic*: Given a sentence (typically, but not always, in the language of the grammar), together with $\Sigma$ and $P$, one seeks to determine (a) if the sentence was generated by this grammar, and, if so, (b) the structure (usually characterized as the sequence of productions used) of the sentence.

Thus, we formally denote a grammar, $G$, as

$$G = (\Sigma, N, P, S)$$

The *language* generated by $G$, denoted $L(G)$, is the set of all strings subject to the following:

1. Each string consists solely of terminal symbols; and
2. Each string was produced from $S$ using $P$.

We consider only context-free grammars, which allow use of the productions in $P$ independent of the *context* of the symbols.

### PARSING

Parsing is a fundamental concept related to the syntactic or structural approach of image analysis. It is the process of determining the structure of a sentence produced in the language of some grammar. It is worth noting that the descriptor "language" connotes a far broader meaning than "spoken words"; for example, we consider languages used to describe the structure of visible objects. An excellent example of this is the *picture description language* (PDL) (Shaw, 1969, 1970).

### GRAPHICAL CONSTRUCTS

The use of graphical constructs for a grammar in either the generative or analytic mode is common. The generative mode yields a derivation tree, whereas the analytic mode yields a parse tree.

*Graphical Constructs: The Derivation Tree.* Consider the enumeration of the steps used to construct the sentence

The quarterback throws accurately.

Figure 6.20 shows this sequence and is referred to as a *derivation tree*. The process starts at the topmost portion of the tree with the root or starting symbol $S$ (in $N$) and terminates with the final substitutions of terminals (in $\Sigma$) at the leaves of the tree. The productions occur by traversing the tree from the root to the leaves.

*Abstract View of Parsing.* Given a sentence $x$, and a grammar $G$, specified as

$$G = (\Sigma, N, P, S)$$

we construct a triangle of the form:

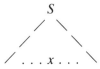

The process of filling the interior of this triangle with a tree of productions that link $S$ to $x$ is called a parse. If successful, $x$ is a member of $L(G)$; the structure (e.g., sequence of production) of $x$ is determined; otherwise it is not. If the interior

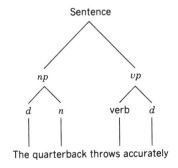

**FIGURE 6.20**   Derivation tree example

of the triangle is filled from the top down (i.e., from the root of the tree), a top-down parse results. Alternately, working from the bottom up (beginning with the terminal symbols), a bottom-up parse is achieved. More details on formal grammars, applications, and the process of designing a parser (in PROLOG) may be found in Schalkoff (in press).

## APPLICATION TO IMAGES (A LINE DRAWING DESCRIPTION GRAMMAR)

Suppose an image is preprocessed to provide a line drawing of some object or set of objects in a scene. This line drawing is the input to our grammatically based analysis of the scene. Consider the cylinder description grammar, $G_{cyl}$, as follows:

$$G_{cyl} = (\Sigma_{cyl}, N_{cyl}, P_{cyl}, S_{cyl})$$

where

$\Sigma_{cyl} = \{t,b,u,o,s\}$ as described in Figure 6.21

$N_{cyl} = \{\text{top, body, cylinder}\}$

$P_{cyl}$:

cylinder $\Rightarrow$ top + body
top $\Rightarrow t + \neg b$
body $\Rightarrow \neg u + b + u$

+ represents head-to-tail concatenation
$\neg$ represents head-and-tail reversal
$\Rightarrow$ means "may be replaced by"

and

$S_{cyl} = \{\text{cylinder}\}$

This grammer allows the representation of the class of cylinders shown in Figure 6.22*b*. This approach is useful for:

1. Classification of line drawings. The problem is to discriminate between a line drawing of a cube and a cylinder. Given a suitable description, denoted $d_x$, of the line drawing of a scene, and given the cylinder and cube grammars $G_{cyl}$ and $G_{cube}$, respectively, the problem becomes that of determining whether $d_x \in L(G_{cyl})$, $d_x \in L(G_{cube})$, or $d_x \in$ some other language. This is accomplished via parsing.

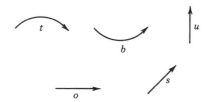

**FIGURE 6.21** Picture description grammar primitives

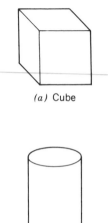

(a) Cube

(b) Cylinder

**FIGURE 6.22** Sample line drawings for the grammar-based approach
(a) Cube
(b) Cylinder

2. Determining the *structure* of the entity under observation, perhaps for descriptive purposes. The identity and spatial relationship of "side," "top," and perhaps the shape of the entity (i.e., cylindrical or cubical) is useful; again, a parse of the description provides this. The structural description and recognition of an entity avoids many of the problems due to varying orientations; that is, it should be possible to recognize a cylinder in any orientation.

## ■ LOW LEVEL OR EARLY DESCRIPTION

The key to segmentation of image data into regions of pixels that correspond to discernible entities is the choice of information *representations*. These representations may include raw pixel intensities, regional boundary models, regional features, such as geometric properties, moments, 2-D topological descriptors, region intensity statistical descriptors (e.g., co-occurrence matrices), regional frequency characteristics, as well as representations obtained by syntactically combining extracted lower-level features.

Our objective is to develop representational approaches that have desirable properties, the two most important of which are computational practicality and invariance to geometric distortions that are expected. Thus, we are dealing with the area of invariant numerical shape modeling (INSM).

### CONTOUR BASED DESCRIPTIVE APPROACHES

The shape representation of an entity presupposes that we are able to extract the boundary of the 2-D region, as shown in Figure 6.23. The principle underlying most of contour parameterization is the conversion of a 2-D shape, represented as a closed contour, to a (periodic) 1-D signal.

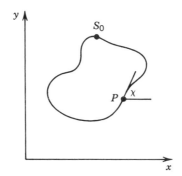

**FIGURE 6.23** Typical extracted region contour for parameterization

BOUNDARY DESCRIPTION AND ENCODING

The boundary in Figure 6.23 may be described or parameterized in a number of ways. Clearly, since planar curves are generally not single-valued functions, representations of the contour in forms

$$y = f(x) \tag{6-40}$$

are, at best, valid locally. An alternative representation derived from differential geometry is the use of curvature. This involves the representation of a curve parametrically in terms of its arc or path length. By considering path length of the curve, expressed in terms of a variable, $s$, (with some reference point, denoted $(x(s_0), y(s_0))$, we may express an arbitrary curve, $C$, in the form

$$C = \{x(s), y(s)\} \qquad s \in [s_0, L] \tag{6-41}$$

where $L$ is the total path length of the curve. If $C$ is a closed curve, $x(s)$ and $y(s)$ are periodic. We define the curvature, $k$, of a curve at point $P$ to be the instantaneous rate of change of the slope (or tangent) angle $\phi$ (measured with respect to the coordinate system shown in Figure 6.23) with respect to curve length, $s$; that is,

$$k(s) = d\phi(s)/ds \tag{6-42}$$

where

$$ds = \sqrt{dx^2 + dy^2} \tag{6-43}$$

Knowing $k(s)$ over the interval $[0, L]$ and the reference point $(x(s_0), y(s_0))$ allows exact reconstruction of the contour function $C$. Contour representations allow classification of regions based on this measure of shape. For example, it is possible to show that the curvature of a circle is constant, whereas that of a line is zero (see the problems). Discarding the dependence of $k(s)$ on $(x(s_0), y(s_0))$, we obtain a parameterization that is insensitive to translation since translation merely manifests itself as a variation in $(x(s_0), y(s_0))$. Similarly, if we normalize the curve length parameter to be, for example, over the interval $[0,1]$, the representation becomes scale invariant. Note, however, that this representation is not invariant to rotation; this is due to the fact that $k(s)$ depends on the starting value of $s$ along the curve.

We may compute $k$, given $x(s)$ and $y(s)$, by recalling the following standard definitions of spatial derivatives

$$y' = dy/dx \tag{6-44}$$
$$y'' = d^2y/dx^2$$

from which we may show

$$k(s) = y''/(1 + (y')^2)^{3/2} \tag{6-45}$$

$k(s)$ is periodic with period $L$, or $k(s) = k(s + L)$. On this basis, the use of 1-D Fourier coefficients is appropriate. We may expand $k(s)$ as

$$k(s) = \sum_{n=-\infty}^{\infty} a_n \exp [jn2\pi s/L] \tag{6-46}$$

where

$$a_n = \int_0^L k(s) \exp [-jn2\pi s/L] \, ds \tag{6-47}$$

Recalling (Appendix 3) that translations of a function manifest themselves as an additive (but linear) phase term in the Fourier transform, and assuming that the first few terms of the Fourier series are adequate to represent $k(s)$, we see that modification[1] of several low-order Fourier series coefficients yields a translation invariant curvature description methodology.

### FOURIER (AND OTHER) BOUNDARY ENCODING

*Fourier Approach.* A more direct approach (i.e., which does not require calculation of boundary curvature) is to assume that the figure is represented in a complex coordinate system, and thus each point on the boundary is represented by a complex number (Granlund, 1972). We choose our coordinate system in the complex plane, or $z = x + jy$. As shown in Figure 6.24, traversing the length of the curve (from some starting point) generates a parameterization of the curve as a complex (but 1-D) signal, in terms of a "velocity" of transversal, $v$. Assuming constant velocity, $C$ may be encoded as a time-varying complex quantity $u(t)$, which is periodic (since the contour is closed). Thus,

$$u(t) = u(t + nT) \tag{6-48}$$

where $T$ is the time required to transverse $C$, and $n$ is a positive integer. We note that this parameterization is similar to that of the previous section in that arc length ($vt$) is involved; however, the representational feature chosen is not an angle, but rather a complex number with respect to some chosen origin in the complex plane. For simplicity of analysis, we may choose $v$ such that

$$T = (\text{length of } C)/v = 2\pi \tag{6-49}$$

From Eqs. 6-48 and 6-49, $C$ may be parameterized in terms of a function $u(t)$, which has a Fourier series representation, with coefficients obtained via

$$a_n = \int_0^L u(t) \exp [-jnt] \, dt \tag{6-50}$$

---

[1]This modification could be accomplished by simply using the transform magnitude only.

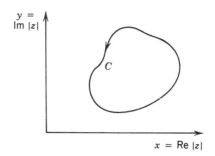

**FIGURE 6.24** Parameterization of region contour using complex variable

Similarly, knowing the Fourier series representation of the contour, $u(t)$ is recoverable via

$$u(t) = \sum_{-\infty}^{\infty} a_n \exp[jnt] \tag{6-51}$$

As before, this representation is sensitive to the starting point chosen for the contour representation, or $u(t_0)$. Any choice of a starting point, however, merely represents a time shift relative to $t_0$, which therefore introduces a linear (in $n$) phase term in the $a_n$ coefficients, since for any shift, $\tau$,

$$a_n = a_{n,0} \exp[jn\tau] \tag{6-52}$$

where $a_{n,0}$ denotes the $\tau = 0$ case. Similarly, the choice of coordinate system origin may be represented via addition of a complex offset, denoted $z$, to $u(t)$; that is,

$$u(t) = u_0(t) + z \tag{6-53}$$

where $u_0$ is a reference contour. The feature extraction approach in Eq. 6-50 may be shown to yield (this is left to the problems):

$$a_n = \frac{a_{n,0} \text{ for } n \neq 0}{a_{0,0} \text{ for } n = 0} \tag{6-54}$$

Thus, translation affects only the "DC value" or "center of gravity" of the contour representation. A rotation of an angle $\theta$ about the center of gravity of the complex contour is modeled as

$$u(t) = u_0(t) \exp[j\theta] \tag{6-55}$$

which, using Eq. 6-50, yields

$$a_n = a_{n,0} \exp[j\theta] \tag{6-56}$$

Finally, a dilation by a factor of $\alpha$ (with respect to a coordinate system whose origin is at the center of gravity) yields

$$a_n = \alpha \, a_{n,0} \tag{6-57}$$

The combination of all these effects on the features (Fourier coefficients) is thus

$$a_n = \{\exp[jn\tau] \exp[j\theta] \alpha\} a_{n,0} \tag{6-58}$$

By defining a new feature sequence, $b_n$, Granlund (1972) showed that the following function of the $a_n$ coefficients is invariant to translation, rotation, and dilation:

$$b_n = (a_{1+n,0} \, a_{1-n,0})/(a_1)^2 \qquad (6\text{-}59)$$

While insensitive to RST transformation of the curve, the $b_n$ coefficients are nonetheless sensitive to the contour shape and are thus useful features for description and classification.

ALTERNATIVE BOUNDARY ENCODING ("CHAIN CODES")

As mentioned, the curvature-based contour representation approach must be modified to allow use with the discretized pixel data encountered in actual application. One popular extension is the use of discrete boundary codes. This encoding is similar in concept to the use of curvature, in the sense that we develop a local measure of the boundary orientation as the curve is traversed (i.e., as a function of curve length). Thus, given a set of discrete boundary orientation (and perhaps length) primitives, we use a polygonal representation of the boundary to generate the code. Since we are dealing with discrete samples, the resultant parameterization is in terms of a sequence or "chain" of discrete descriptors, or "chain code." Several popular chain codes exist.

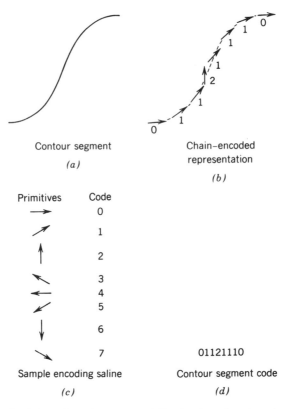

Contour segment

(a)

Chain-encoded representation

(b)

| Primitives | Code |
|---|---|
| → | 0 |
| ↗ | 1 |
| ↑ | 2 |
| ↖ | 3 |
| ← | 4 |
| ↙ | 5 |
| ↓ | 6 |
| ↘ | 7 |

Sample encoding saline

(c)

01121110

Contour segment code

(d)

FIGURE 6.25  Sample chain code contour representation (portion of contour shown)
(a)  Contour segment
(b)  Chain-encoded representation
(c)  Sample encoding scheme
(d)  Contour segment code

## INTEGER CODES FOR INSM ALGORITHM

| Relative Condition Between Line Segments | Integer Code |
|---|---|
| RIGHT | |
| Shorter | 1 |
| Equal | 2 |
| Longer | 3 |
| LEFT | |
| Shorter | 4 |
| Equal | 5 |
| Longer | 6 |

**(a)**

Figure 1. The polygonal representation of an airplane profile.

The coding is done starting from the circled node:

1. right, equal:  2      4. right, longer:  3
2. left, longer:  6      5. right, shorter:  1
3. right, shorter:  1    6. right, shorter:  1

**(b)**

261311 (raw)
613112 (normalized via circular rotation)

**(c)**

**FIGURE 6.26** Differential chain encoding (from [Badi'i/Majd] Copyright © 1985 IEEE).
(a)   Code strategy
(b)   Sample polygonal outline (airplane). Starting point shown circled
(c)   Resulting code

Referring to Figure 6.25, we develop a piecewise linear approximation to the contour using a set of orientation-only primitives. Thus, the chain encoding approach is similar to generation of a syntactic description of the boundary, using the primitives shown in the figure. An alternate mechanism for viewing this approach is derived from a "neighborhood matrix," with each neighbor coded to correspond to the primitives in the figure. This matrix appears as follows:

$$
\begin{array}{ccc}
3 & 2 & 1 \\
4 & \cdot & 0 \\
5 & 6 & 7
\end{array}
$$

Differential encoding schemes are possible, where we pick a starting point and generate successive boundary segment codes based on the relative direction and length of the edge segments (Badi'i & Majd, 1985). We use consecutive line segments and six possible simple relations, namely shorter, longer, equal in conjunction with left and right, as shown in part (*a*) of Figure 6.26. Note the descriptor "left" or "right" indicates the direction to which the current line segment turns, relative to the previous segment. A sample application of this scheme is shown in part (*c*). As the contour is traversed, each line segment is assigned one of the six codes. For an *n*-sided polygon, an *n*-digit code results. Note that although this approach is RST invariant, it is sensitive to the choice of starting point. To eliminate this sensitivity, the raw code may be normalized. An example is circularly rotating the raw code until the largest code value is leftmost.

### THE HOUGH TRANSFORM AND EXTENSIONS

The concept and basic implementation of the Hough transform is shown in Appendix 2.d and applied to motion in Chapter 5. Hough techniques are particularly useful for computation of sets of global description parameters from (perhaps noisy) local measurements. The idea behind using Hough techniques for geometric figure recognition is quite simple: Each extracted feature (e.g., point) indicates its contribution to a globally consistent solution. *The Hough approach is especially useful in applications where the number of solution classes is not known a priori.* For example, given a set of points, it is generally not known a priori how many lines are determined by these points.

We consider Hough transform applications to the extraction and fitting of geometric shapes from a set of extracted image points. First, consider the conceptually simple problem of fitting a set of line segments to a set of discrete image points. Possible ramifications of this problem are shown in Figure 6.27, where we note that our definition of a line segment and the lack of a priori knowledge about the number of desired line segments yields an underconstrained problem. If we simply decide that a line segment is determined by a minimum of two points, a multitude of possible solutions results, as shown in parts (*b*) and (*c*) of Figure 6.27. Conversely, if we determine a priori that the set of points contains a single line (which must be fitted to the point set in some fashion), a solution similar to part (*d*) of the figure may result. Note in the case of part (*d*) none of the given points actually falls on the fitted line. Finally, as shown in Figure 6.27*e*, a line fitting procedure (developed in the problems) such as least squares, which seeks to fit a single line to the given points, may result in a poor fit vis-à-vis the use of two line segments.

Any 2-D line may be mathematically quantified in a number of ways, as shown in Appendix 1, part a. For example, given a set of points $(x_i, y_i)$, $i = 1, 2, \ldots n$, we may attempt to fit a line in the slope intercept form; that is,

$$y_i = a x_i + b \tag{6-60}$$

However, this approach has two shortcomings. Vertical lines (lines with $a = \infty$) are not representable. Furthermore, only the parameters of a single line may be determined in this manner. To overcome these shortcomings, we instead choose the normal form for line representation; that is, a line is represented by the parameters $(p, \theta)$

$$p = x_i \cos \theta + y_i \sin \theta \tag{6-61}$$

Any point $(x_i, y_i)$ on a line determined by $(p, \theta)$ will be constrained by Eq. 6-61, as shown in Figure 6.27*f*. More important, we may revise or "invert" our viewpoint of Eq. 6-61 and observe that any choice of a fixed point $(x_i, y_i)$ constrains $p$ and $\theta$. This represents *a point-to-curve transformation.* Thus, the straight line version of the Hough transform maps points into sinusoids. Since each point in the given point set generates a curve in $p$-$\theta$ space, it is possible to show (see the problems) that any common point (i.e., intersection) of the $p$-$\theta$ curves for two points determines the parameters of a line determined by these two points. More important, we may extend this concept to the case of three colinear points; the $p$-$\theta$ curves for these lines share a common point $(p', \theta')$, which represents the normal form characterization for this 3-point line. Therefore, if we generate the $n$ $p$-$\theta$ curves for all points in the given set, points of intersection of large numbers of curves present strong evidence that a line should be fitted to these points. Moreover, these specific points in $(p, \theta)$ space are the line parameters. The Hough approach therefore yields both an indicator of the number of lines and their parameters.

Actual computer implementation of the $p$-$\theta$ curve calculation and recording of intersections involves discretization of 2-D $p$-$\theta$ space into finite intervals or 2-D

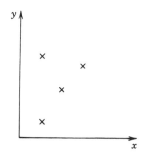

*(a)* Extracted points

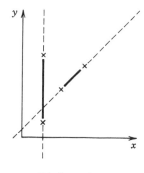

*(b)* One solution
(2 lines)

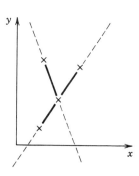

*(c)* Alternate solution
(2 lines)

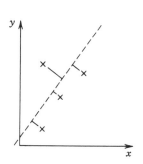

Alternate solution:
(1 line–not on sampling
grid)

*(d)*

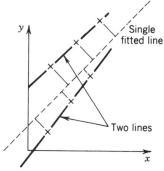

Case of 1 Fitted line segment
vs. 2 segments

*(e)*

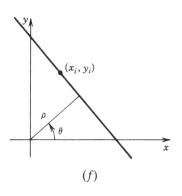

*(f)*

**FIGURE 6.27** Fitting line segments to extracted image plane points
(a)  Extracted points
(b)  One solution (2 lines)
(c)  Alternate solution (2 lines)
(d)  Alternate solution: (1 line—not on sampling grid)
(e)  Case of 1 fitted line segment vs. 2 segments
(f)  Normal parameterization of a line

"bins." Each of these bins in $p$-$\theta$ space is an accumulator, which is initialized to zero. The discretized $p$-$\theta$ curves are generated and each bin that lies along a specific $p$-$\theta$ constraint curve is augmented by one to indicate membership in this possible solution curve. Resulting peaks in the $(p, \theta)$ accumulator array indicate strong evidence of lines in the image. Bounds on the values of $p$ and $\theta$ to be considered may be determined. For a square image of extent $n \times n$,

$$p_{max} = \sqrt{2}\, n \qquad (6\text{-}62)$$

and

$$0 \le \theta \le 2\pi \qquad (6\text{-}63)$$

*An Example of the Hough Approach.* We consider an application of the Hough approach as a tool for geometric distortion correction. Consider an image that is distorted by optical effects—for example, a combination of pincushion and barrel distortion. The data is shown in Figure 6.28. We hypothesize that the geometric distortion is minimal in the interior of the image and determine the parameters of two lines that intersect at the center of the distorted image using the Hough approach. Choosing the nine points shown in Figure 6.28a, we apply the Hough transform, as indicated in Figure 6.28b. Two peaks, each containing five $p$-$\theta$ curves, result in $p$-$\theta$ parameter space. The resultant parameters for these two lines are in excellent agreement with the figure: One is nearly horizontal and the other is nearly vertical.

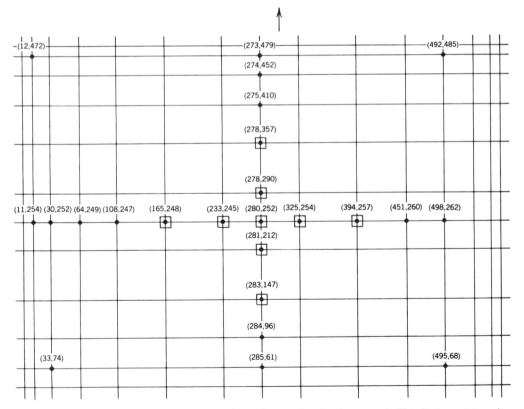

**FIGURE 6.28(a)**  Geometrically distorted image for Hough approach (□ Indicates point used)

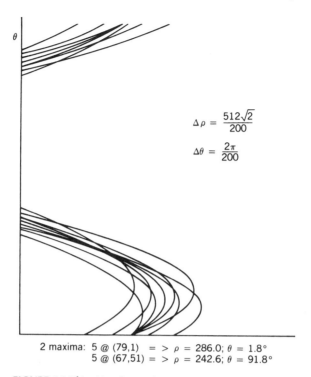

$\theta$

$$\Delta\rho = \frac{512\sqrt{2}}{200}$$

$$\Delta\theta = \frac{2\pi}{200}$$

2 maxima: 5 @ (79,1)  = > $\rho$ = 286.0; $\theta$ = 1.8°
          5 @ (67,51) = > $\rho$ = 242.6; $\theta$ = 91.8°

**FIGURE 6.28(b)**   Hough transform for points in Figure 6.28

*Extensions and Generalizations of the Hough Approach.* A more general interpretation of the Hough transform gives rise to consideration of the invertability of the approach (Casasent & Krishnapuram, 1987). Furthermore, the Hough-based feature extraction method may be extended to geometric shapes more complex than lines. For example, the detection of circles (i.e., the fitting of a set of given image plane points to a parametrically defined circle) using a modified Hough procedure is possible. A circle of radius $r$ and centered at $(a_1, a_2)$ containing point $(x_i, y_i)$ is given by

$$(x_i - a_1)^2 + (y_i - a_2)^2 = r^2 \qquad (6\text{-}64)$$

Three parameters are necessary to parameterize a circle. By analogy with the point to curve transformation cited above, we may alternately view a fixed point from the given set $(x_i, y_i)$ in Eq. 6-64 as forcing a constraint on the possible circle parameters $(a_1, a_2, r)$. This is equivalent to constraining the loci of points $(a_1, a_2)$ that lie a distance of $r$ from $(x_i, y_i)$. In other words, the alternate viewpoint of the constraint in Eq. 6-64 is that a point constrains the loci of $(a_1, a_2)$ to be a family of circles, with the value of $r$ generating the family. Thus, we may discretize $r$ (over a range of a priori chosen positive values), $a_1$ and $a_2$ and use each of the $n$ $(x_i, y_i)$ points to generate solutions in a 3-D accumulator array, where each accumulator bin is indexed by a discrete value of $(a_1, a_2, r)$. We increment $(a_1, a_2)$, for fixed $r$, by traversing a circle in discrete increments of $\theta$—that is, $\delta\theta$, where

$$a_1 = r \cos\theta + x_i$$
$$a_2 = r \sin\theta + y_i \qquad (6\text{-}65)$$

From this array, as in the line detection approach, peaks correspond to values of $(a_1, a_2, r)$, which likely represent circular representations for the points whose point-to-curve transformation contributes to these peaks. However, the dimensionality of the problem and the need for good precision in the discretization of the parameters spawn a problem (see Appendix 2) of considerable computational complexity and with significant memory requirements. Therefore, some way to minimize this complexity is desired. As shown in Kimme, Ballard, and Sklansky

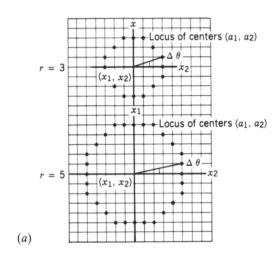

(a)

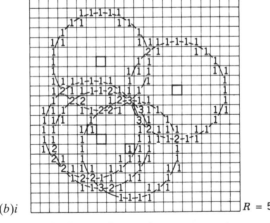

(b)i      R = 5

From Kimme, Ballard, and Sklansky, "Finding Circles in an Array of Accumulators," *Communications of the ACM*, February 1975, copyright © 1975, Association for Computing Machinery, Inc., reprinted by permission.

**FIGURE 6.29** Hough transform application to circle detection. (ACM to advise on format of copyright acknowledgement)
(a)    $\Delta\theta$ as a function of r
(b)    Contents of accumulator array
     (i)    No gradient direction information R = 5
     (ii)    Gradient direction information for circle $\Delta\phi = 45$
     (iii)    Gradient direction information for artifact $\Delta\phi = 45$
(c)    Grey scale digitized radiograph
(d)    Same radiograph after Fourier filtering
(e)    Gradient modulus of Fourier filtered radiograph (white = large modulus)
(f)    Threshold results of applying algorithm to Figure 5 data (with gradient direction)

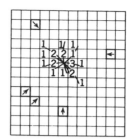

(b)ii

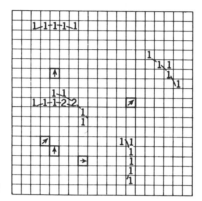

(b)iii

□ Denotes a pixel in $P(x)$ superimposed on accumulator array
↗ Denotes the gradient direction

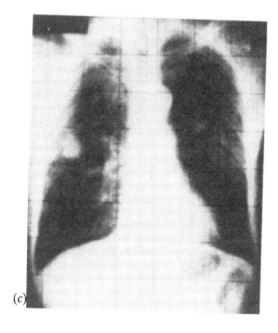

(c)

**FIGURE 6.29** Continued.

Continued on next page

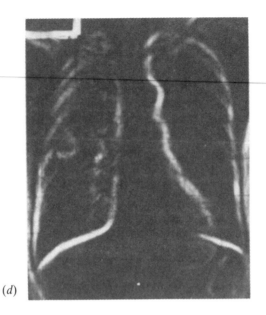

(d)

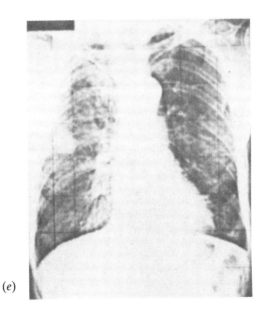

(e)

**FIGURE 6.29** *Continued.*

(1975) and Figure 6.29, one way to achieve data reduction in this computation is to employ an additional constraint, namely that the normal to the tangent of the circle (i.e., the gradient) should point toward the center. Implementation of this constraint is shown graphically in Figure 6.30. It is important to note that this additional constraint exemplifies the use of local image information, or regional information around $(x_1, x_2)$.

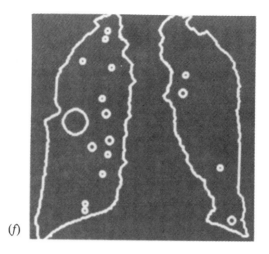

*(f)*

**FIGURE 6.29** *Continued.*

The Hough transform approach may be further generalized (Ballard, 1981) for arbitrary shapes. For example, consider an ellipse centered at $(x_0, y_0)$, with major and minor axes $a$ and $b$. If the major axis is parallel to the $x$-axis, any point $(x_i, y_i)$ on this ellipse may be described by

$$(x_i - x_0)^2/a + (y_i - y_0)^2/b = 1 \qquad (6\text{-}66)$$

Adding a fifth parameter, namely an angle Ø, to handle orientation, allows application of the Hough technique, albeit in a 5-D parameter solution space. However, as shown in Ballard (1981), the use of gradient information may reduce the required number of computations. More important, the Hough approach may be generalized to nonanalytic curves and composite shapes.

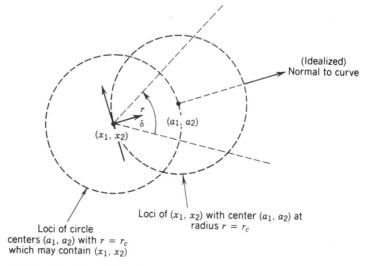

**FIGURE 6.30** Use of the gradient to eliminate false accumulator peaks (fixed r)

### APPROACHES BASED ON MORPHOLOGY

Recall that morphology is the study of forms and shape. This broad area includes the topics of integral geometry, topology, set theory, and cellular automata. Historically, morphological operators have been applied to binary images. Hereafter, we assume this is the case. Description of the geometric attributes of preprocessed images is useful in image understanding.

#### ELEMENTARY GEOMETRIC DESCRIPTORS

An example of an elementary geometric region descriptor is region area, denoted $A_R$. Clearly, this feature is invariant to $RT$ transformations, but not $S$; that is, the area is sensitive to scale changes. Others include the enclosing rectangle, the "minimum bounding rectangle" (Nevatia, 1982), and the region convex hull (defined as the minimal convex hull enclosing the region), as shown in Figure 6.31. These features are conceptually obvious and relatively straightforward to compute, as well as sensitive to $RS$ transformations.

#### MOMENTS

Moments are a descriptive technique with an intuitive basis in the study of the mechanics of bodies. The initial approach is usually credited to Hu (1961, 1962). Properties of invariance to $R$, $S$, and $T$ transformations may be derived using functions of moments. We begin by considering the continuous version of the moment transform and then consider the formulation and ramifications of discrete

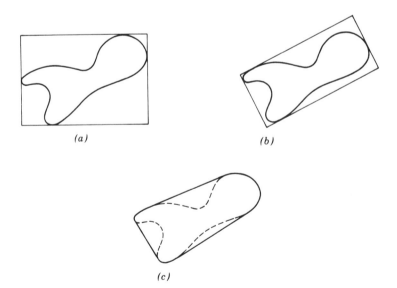

*(a)*

*(b)*

*(c)*

**FIGURE 6.31** Simple geometric figure descriptors
(a) Enclosing rectangle
(b) Minimum bounding rectangle
(c) Convex hull

implementations. The moment transform of an image function, $f(x,y)$, is given by

$$m_{pq} = \int_{-\infty}^{\infty} \int_{-\infty}^{\infty} x^p\, y^q\, f(x,y)\, dx\, dy \qquad p,q = 0, 1, 2, \ldots, \infty \qquad (6\text{-}67)$$

Thus, the image function may be thought of as being represented by an infinite set of transform coefficients, $m_{pq}$, which are derived from projecting the image onto a set of 2-D polynomial basis functions. Practical application of the transform thus requires that we employ a finite number. In the case of a spatially discretized $M \times N$ image, denoted $f(i,j)$, Eq. 6-67 may be formulated using an approximation of double summations:

$$m_{pq} = \sum_{i=0}^{M} \sum_{j=0}^{N} i^p\, j^q\, f(i,j) \qquad (6\text{-}68)$$

We briefly digress to apply this approach to a region from a segmented binary image. Assume that region $R$ appears in the binary image as a region of intensity "1." The $p,q^{\text{th}}$ moment of this region, or figure, $R$, is given by

$$m_{pq} = \sum_{i,j \ \in R} i^p\, j^q \qquad (6\text{-}69)$$

That is, all points $(i,j)$ used in this computation are either boundary or interior points of $R$. In this example, $m_{00}$ is simply the total number of points in the region, and the centroid is given by $m_{10}$ and $m_{01}$. The higher-order moments are not invariant to translation. A translation of the origin to the centroid of the region, and recomputation of the so-called central moments yields

$$\mu_{pq} = \sum_{i,j \ \in R} (i - \hat{i})^p\, (j - \hat{j})^q \qquad (6\text{-}70)$$

where, using Eq. 6-69,

$$\hat{i} = (m_{10}/m_{00}) \qquad (6\text{-}71)$$

$$\hat{j} = (m_{01}/m_{00}) \qquad (6\text{-}72)$$

The reader may verify that Eq. 6-70 yields $\mu_{10} = \mu_{01} = 0$.

The central moments from Eq. 6-70 are still sensitive to $R$ and $S$ transformations. Note that scale invariance may be obtained by further normalizing $\mu_{pq}$, or forming

$$\eta'_{pq} = \mu_{pq}/\mu_{00}^{[(p+q)/2+1]} \qquad p + q = 2, 3 \ldots \qquad (6\text{-}73)$$

In the continuous formulation, the central moments of $f(x,y)$ are defined by analogy with (6-70), and given by

$$\mu_{pq} = \int_{-\infty}^{\infty} \int_{-\infty}^{\infty} (x - \hat{x})^p\, (y - \hat{y})^q f(x,y)\, dx\, dy \qquad p,q = 0, 1, 2, \ldots \qquad (6\text{-}74)$$

where $\hat{x}$ and $\hat{y}$ are the continuous equivalents of $\hat{i}$ and $\hat{j}$ in Eqs. (6-71) and (6-72). As shown in Hu (1962) and Wong and Hall (1977) the central moments, $\mu_{pq}$, may be expressed and computed in terms of the noncentral moments, $m_{pq}$.

*Geometric Interpretation of Central Moments.* The significance of moments computed from Eq. 6-74 is not immediately apparent from the algebra. To relate the moment approach to other geometric descriptors, the following interpretations of several low-order central moments for a region, $R$, are shown to have a direct analogy with the mechanics of bodies (Giuliano, et al., 1961):

| central moment | interpretation |
|---|---|
| $\mu_{20}$ | "horizontal centralness" |
| $\mu_{02}$ | "vertical centralness" |
| $\mu_{11}$ | "diagonality"; indication of quadrant w.r.t. centroid where $R$ has more "mass" |
| $\mu_{12}$ | "horizontal divergence"; indicates the relative extent of the left of $R$ compared to the right |
| $\mu_{21}$ | "vertical divergence"; indicates the relative extent of the bottom of $R$ compared to the top |
| $\mu_{30}$ | "horizontal imbalance"; location of center of gravity with respect to half horizontal extent |
| $\mu_{03}$ | "vertical imbalance"; location of center of gravity with respect to half vertical extent |

*Sample Application.* Using Eq. 6-73, a set of normalized central moments, denoted $\eta'_{pq}$, may be developed. From these, constraining $p, q \leq 3$, and using the tools of invariant algebra, we may develop a set of seven *RST* invariant features, as shown in Table 6.2. (Note that $\phi_7$ is actually only *ST* invariant; it changes sign for a reflection.)

*Effects of Digital Approximations on Moment Invariance Properties.* The actual implementation of Eq. 6-74 on spatially sampled images is accomplished using the discrete approximation:

$$\mu_{pq} = \sum_{\substack{i,j \\ \in R}} (i - \hat{i})^p (j - \hat{j})^q f(i,j) \tag{6-75}$$

It is possible to show that the set of invariant moments shown in Table 6.2 is invariant to translation even though the moments are computed discretely. Due to the non-1:1 nature of general discrete geometric transformations (including rotations and scale changes), we should not expect the moments computed on the basis of Eq. 6-75 to be strictly invariant under rotation and scale changes. As

■ **TABLE 6.2**
**Seven derived moment invariants (see text)**

$$\phi_1 = \eta_{20} + \eta_{02}$$
$$\phi_2 = (\eta_{20} - \eta_{02})^2 + 4\eta_{11}^2$$
$$\phi_3 = (\eta_{30} - 3\eta_{12})^2 + (3\eta_{21} - \eta_{03})^2$$
$$\phi_4 = (\eta_{30} + \eta_{12})^2 + (\eta_{21} + \eta_{03})^2$$
$$\phi_5 = (\eta_{30} - 3\eta_{12})(\eta_{30} + \eta_{12})[(\eta_{30} + \eta_{12})^2 - 3(\eta_{21} + \eta_{03})^2]$$
$$+ (3\eta_{21} - \eta_{03})(\eta_{21} + \eta_{03})[3(\eta_{30} + \eta_{12})^2 - (\eta_{21} + \eta_{03})^2]$$
$$\phi_6 = (\eta_{20} - \eta_{02})[(\eta_{30} + \eta_{12})^2 - (\eta_{21} + \eta_{03})^2]$$
$$+ 4\eta_{11}(\eta_{30} + \eta_{12})(\eta_{21} + \eta_{03})$$
$$\phi_7 = (3\eta_{21} - \eta_{03})(\eta_{30} + \eta_{12})[(\eta_{30} + \eta_{12})^2 - 3(\eta_{21} + \eta_{03})^2]$$
$$- (\eta_{30} - 3\eta_{12})(\eta_{21} + \eta_{03})[3(\eta_{30} + \eta_{12})^2 - (\eta_{21} + \eta_{03})^2]$$

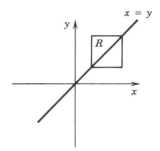

$f(x, y) = 1, (x, y) \in R;$ $O$ elsewhere

**FIGURE 6.32** Example of region used for $\phi_1$ calculation

before, the culprit is sampling and quantization, which introduces both intensity steps and errors in the contour representation of the discretized image. A simple example illustrates this concern. Consider the square region of dimension $a \times a$ spatial units and intensity 1.0 in Figure 6.32. For this function,

$$f(x,y) = \text{rect}[(x - a/2)/a] \text{ rect } [(y - a/2)/a] \qquad (6\text{-}76)$$

Using Eq. 6-74 and Table 6.2 (see the problems), the first invariant feature for this region (using the continuous formulation) is $\phi_1 = 1/6$. $\phi_1$ is independent of $a$ and thus the region size. Consider now the sampled version of this image function, $f(i,j)$, where we assume rectangular sampling with $a > 1.0$, thus forming

$$f(i,j) = f(x,y) s(x,y) \qquad (6\text{-}77)$$

The sampling function $s(x,y)$ is given by

$$s(x,y) = \sum_{m=-\infty}^{\infty} \sum_{n=-\infty}^{\infty} \delta(x - m, y - n) \qquad (6\text{-}78)$$

and assumes unity $x$ and $y$-axis sampling intervals. From (6-77) and (6-78) it is possible to evaluate $\phi_1$ for the discrete image function in closed form, yielding

$$\phi_1 = (1 - 1/a^2)/6 \qquad (6\text{-}79)$$

As the ratio of the region size to the sampling interval ($a$ in this example) $\rightarrow \infty$, the discrete and continuous moment calculations for $\phi_1$ coincide. A finite ratio, however, introduces an error in $\phi_1$. For reasonable sampling intervals, however, this effect is minimal. A similar error derivation may be shown for the discretization effects in the case of rotation. These and other topics are discussed in Teh and Chin (1986).

TOPOLOGICAL APPROACHES

Topology is the study of geometric configurations with specific properties, foremost of which is invariance under certain transformations (usually any deformation except tearing or joining). Simple examples of topological regions descriptors include area/shape measures such as the ratio $D_1$:

$$D_1 = A_R/(P_R)^2 \qquad (6\text{-}80)$$

where $A_R$ is the area (in pixel units) of region $R$, and $P_R$ is the corresponding perimeter, or length of the boundary of $R$. It is straightforward to show that this

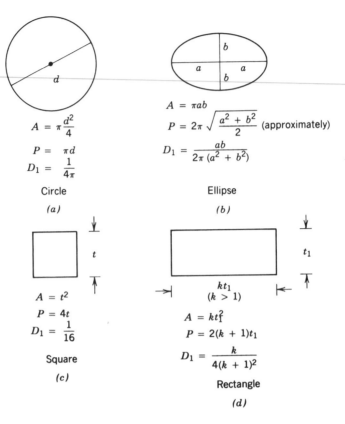

**FIGURE 6.33** Example of the topological descriptor $D_1 = A_R/(P_R)^2$
(a) Circle
(b) Ellipse
(c) Square
(d) Rectangle

measure is invariant with respect to *RST* transformations. Furthermore, it provides a descriptor for the "elongation" of a region shape, being a maximum for circles and smaller for elongated shapes. For example, as shown in Figure 6.33, as an ellipse is "pulled" to form a circle—that is, as

$$a \to d/2$$

$$b \to d/2$$

then

$$D_1 \text{ (ellipse)} \to D_1 \text{ (circle)}$$

Clearly, as the ratio of the major to minor axes of the ellipse increases, $D_1$ becomes smaller. Similar remarks may be made concerning the rectangle shown in Figure 6.33*d*.

Another somewhat more complicated useful geometric feature extraction methodology is the medial axis transform (Agin & Binford, 1976; Blum, 1967). This computationally intensive transformation, although important in itself, when interpreted as fitting maximal circular neighborhoods inside the figure, serves as an

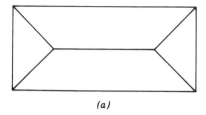
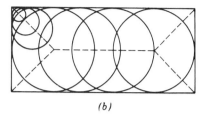

(a)                                         (b)

**FIGURE 6.34** Medial axis feature extraction (rectangle example)
(a)  Medial axes
(b)  Circle-based interpretation of the transform (sample circles shown)

introduction to 3-D modeling using generalized cones (Chapter 7). There are two ways in which to define the generation of medial axes of a figure. First, given a region $R$ with boundary $B$, for any point, $x$, in the interior of the figure, we define a function

$$q(x, B) = \min(d(x, y)) | y \in B \qquad (6\text{-}81)$$

where $d$ is the Euclidean distance between points $x$ and $y$. Each point $x$, interior to $B$, for which there exist two or more points $y$ on $B$ yielding equal $q(x, B)$ (from Eq. 6-81), lies on the medial axis. This means that two or more points on $B$ are at equal and minimum distances to $x$, and therefore these points, together with the value of $x$ that satisfies Eq. 6-81, describe a circle that is completely enclosed by the figure, and whose radius is $q(x, B)$. The medial axis may alternately be viewed as the loci of the centers of all circles that are enclosed by the region and not totally contained within other circles, as shown in Figure 6.34. Note that the region has been "skeletonized" with the relative length and direction of the longest axis extracted indicating the orientation and elongation of the figure in simple cases. Skeletonization is pursued further in the next section.

The medial axis transform is nontrivial to compute (Montanari, 1968). Furthermore, it is sensitive to small boundary perturbations. The medial axes for a given figure may change substantially with only slight changes in local edge curvature.

*Euler Numbers and Holes.*  Another topological-based feature extraction methodology is founded on the concepts of connected components and holes. A segmented image may be viewed as being composed of subregions containing connected components, which are subsets of a region such that any two points in the connected component may be joined by a *curve* lying entirely within the connected component. Figure 6.35 shows two examples of images, each containing a single connected component. If we define a hole as a region completely enclosed by a connected component, this same figure shows the cases of one and two holes (cases (a) and (b)), respectively. We designate the number of connected components in an image as $C$, and the number of holes in an image as $H$. Once these concepts have been defined, we develop the concept of an image Euler number, $E$, defined as

$$E = C - H \qquad (6\text{-}82)$$

For example, Figure 6.35a shows an image with one connected component and one hole, thus yielding a Euler number of zero. Similarly, Figure 6.35b indicates

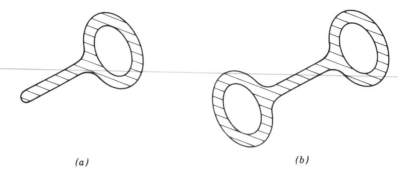

(a)                                    (b)

**FIGURE 6.35**  Topological descriptor using Euler number
(a) Image 1
$E = 1 - 1 = 0$
(b) Image 2
$E = 1 - 2 = -1$

a Euler number of $-1$. As shown in the example, the Euler number provides a simple approach to discriminating between certain classes of objects. It is apparent that the Euler number is invariant to *RST* transformations.

## IMAGE MORPHOLOGY USING MINKOWSKI OPERATORS

### INTRODUCTION

The formal mathematical analysis of morphology may be formulated using the so-called Minkowski algebra. Specifically, the operations of *Minkowski addition and Minkowski subtraction* are fundamental. Images are analyzed in terms of shape and size using elementary patterns or *structuring elements*. The operation is analogous to, but not the same as, discrete convolution, where the *structuring element* is analogous to the convolution kernel. The difference is that convolution involves multiplication and addition, whereas morphological operations involve the equivalent of set operations on the data and other *measurements* such as number of changed or unchanged pixel values between iterations. Binary images, as we show, enable direct application of these operators.

### MINKOWSKI OPERATORS

The Minkowski algebra is heavily dependent on set theoretic concepts, particularly union (∪), intersection (∩) and complementing (C). In addition, in order to represent Minkowski operations, the concept of two point sets, denoted $A$ and $B$ in $R^2$ and their *translation* is defined as using simple vector addition as

$$A + \underline{x} = \{\underline{a}_i + \underline{x} | \underline{a}_i \in A\} \qquad (6\text{-}83)$$

where $\underline{x} \in R^2$. On this basis, the *Minkowski addition* of $A$ and $B$ is denoted $[+]$ and defined as

$$A [+] B \equiv \bigcup_{\underline{x} \in B} (A + \underline{x}) \qquad (6\text{-}84)$$

or,

$$A [+] B = \bigcup_{\substack{\underline{a}_i \in A \\ \underline{y} \in B}} (\underline{a}_i + \underline{y}) \qquad (6\text{-}85)$$

Similarly, *Minkowski subtraction* is denoted $[-]$ and defined as

$$A \, [-] \, B = \bigcap_{\underline{x} \in B} (A + \underline{x}) \tag{6-86}$$

Thus, $A \, [-] \, B$ is the intersection, over all elements of $B$, of the translated points in $A + \underline{x}$. In addition the *reflection* of a set $A$, denoted $-A$, is given by

$$-A \equiv \{-\underline{a}_i | \underline{a}_i \in A\} \tag{6-87}$$

and the *complement* of a set is

$$A^c \equiv \{\underline{x} | \underline{x} \notin A\} \tag{6-88}$$

We define the union of two images denoted $A \cup B$ to be the union of the two sets representing $A$ and $B$. Finally, the *difference* operation (as opposed to the previously defined subtraction) is denoted $[/]$ and defined as

$$A \, [/] \, B \equiv \{\underline{x} | \underline{x} \in A \text{ XOR } B\}$$
$$= \{\underline{x} | (\underline{x} \in (A \cup B)) \cap (\underline{x} \notin (A \cap B))\} \tag{6-89}$$

These operations are shown in Figure 6.36. Readers should recall the important duality properties for the logical AND and OR functions in Boolean algebra. An interesting result that intuitively parallels De Morgan's theorem in the case of Minkowski addition and subtraction is

$$A \, [+] \, B = (A^c \, [-] \, B)^c \tag{6-90}$$

and

$$A \, [-] \, B = (A^c \, [+] \, B)^c \tag{6-91}$$

In addition, several proofs make use of the following

$$A \, [+] \, (B + \underline{x}) = (A \, [+] \, B) + \underline{x} \tag{6-92}$$

$$A \, [-] \, (B + \underline{x}) = (A \, [-] \, B) + \underline{x} \tag{6-93}$$

On the basis of these definitions, we are now ready to formally define the useful Minkowski operations of *dilation and erosion*.

*Erosion.* The erosion of image $A$ by structuring element $B$ is denoted as $A \, (--) \, B$ and defined as

$$\text{er} \, (A, B) \equiv A \, (--) \, B = \{\underline{x} | (B + \underline{x}) \subset A\} \tag{6-94}$$

which may be simply formulated using Minkowski subtraction and reflection as

$$A \, (--) \, B = A \, [-] \, (-B) \tag{6-95}$$

Note that the 180° rotation of the elements of $B$ (to form $-B$) for the erosion operator is analogous to the reflection about the coordinate axes of the convolution kernel in Chapter 3, Eq. 3-41. A template $(B_s)$ that is symmetric with respect to the $x_1$ and $x_2$ axes (invariant with respect to a 180° rotation) thus allows Eq. 6-95 to be written as

$$A \, (--) \, B_s = A \, [-] \, B_s \tag{6-96}$$

This operation is shown in Figure 6.37c. In erosion, the output or (eroded) image is a set containing all points in which the rotated structuring element, $B$, "matches"

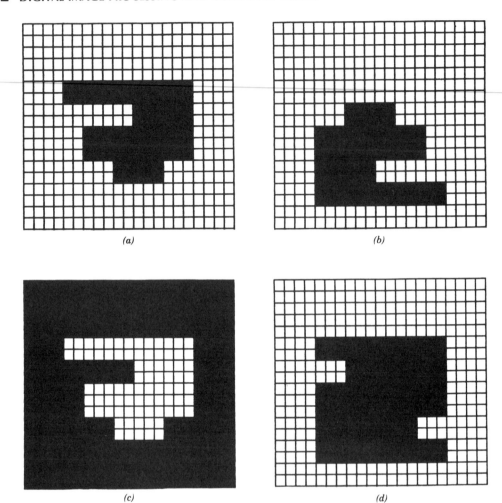

**FIGURE 6.36** Elementary operators

(a) Binary image, A

(b) Reflection of (a) $(-A)$

(c) $A^c$

(d) Union of (a) and (b) $(A \cup (-A))$

(e) Intersection of (a) and (b) $(A \cap (-A))$

(f) Difference of (a) and (b) $A [/] (-A)$

(g) Translation (Minkowski addition of $x = (2, 2)^T$ to (a), i.e., $A [+] (2, 2)^T$

(h) Structuring element, $B_T$, which yields (g), using $A [+] B_T$

the image points. This may be viewed as the template $B$ "fitting inside" the region in the image. *Erosion is thus based on containment.* Thus, unless $B$ is a single pixel of intensity "1," a region may be "eroded."

*Dilation.* The dilation of $A$ by structuring element $B$ is simply defined as

$$\text{dil} (A, B) \equiv A (++) B = A [+] B \tag{6-97}$$

Thus, the dilation operation is based on Minkowski addition, which in turn relies

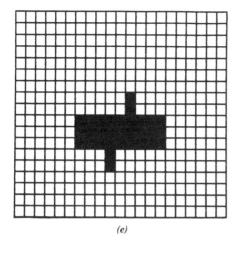

(e)

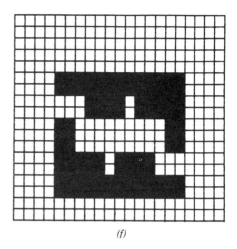

(f)

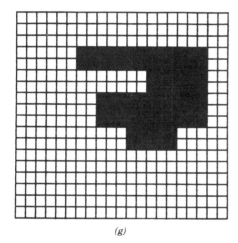

(g)

(h)

**FIGURE 6.36** *Continued.*

upon the OR-ing or the union operation. This is shown in Figure 6.37b. Therefore, both dilation and erosion are defined in terms of the primitive Minkowski addition and subtraction operators. In fact, Eqs. 6-96 and 6-97 show this direct relationship between Minkowski addition and dilation and Minkowski subtraction and erosion.

*Relation Between Dilation and Erosion.* A duality relationship holds for dilation and erosion. It is relatively easy to prove

$$A \ (+ +) \ B \ = \ [A^c \ (- -) \ (- B)]^c \tag{6-98}$$

and

$$A \ (- -) \ B \ = \ [A^c \ (+ +) \ (- B)]^c \tag{6-99}$$

This is shown graphically in Figure 6.38.

(a)

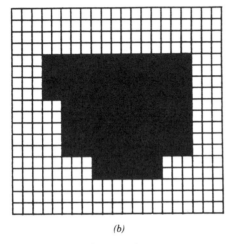

(b)

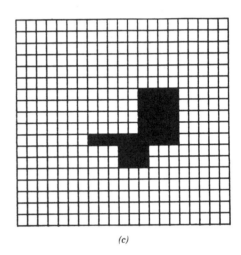

(c)

**FIGURE 6.37** Dilation and erosion
(a)  3 × 3 structuring element $B_3$
(b)  Dilation $A [+] B_3$
(c)  Erosion $A (- -) B_3$

*Opening and Closing Operators.* Two additional operations are opening and closing. In terms of dilation and erosion, opening is defined as

$$\text{open } (A, B) \equiv \text{dil (er } (A, B), B)$$

$$= (A (- -) B) (+ +) B \qquad (6\text{-}100)$$

$$= (A [-] (-B)) [+] B$$

Similarly, closing is defined as

$$\text{close } (A, B) \equiv \text{er (dil } (A, -B), -B)$$

$$= (A (+ +) (-B)) (- -) (-B) \qquad (6\text{-}101)$$

$$= (A [+] (-B)) [-] B$$

In the case of structuring elements invariant with respect to 180° rotations, simpler equations result. For example, given $B_s = -B_s$, we may write

$$\text{open } (A, B_s) = (A [-] B_s) [+] B_s \qquad (6\text{-}102)$$

and

$$\text{close } (A, B_s) = (A [+] B_s) [-] B_s \qquad (6\text{-}103)$$

Each of these operators is shown in Figure 6.39. Duality properties exist which are considered in the exercises.

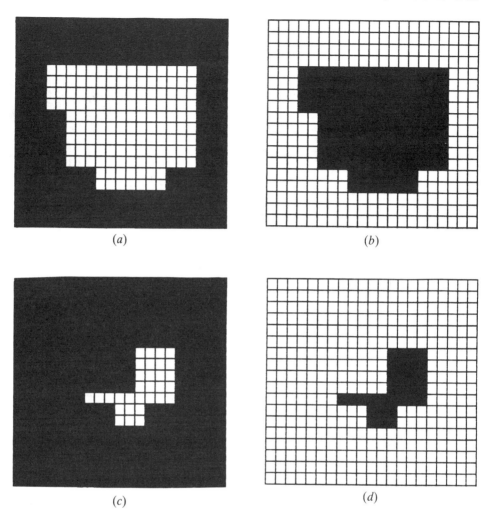

**FIGURE 6.38** Duality relationship between dilation and erosion
(a)  $A^c \, (--) \, (-B_3)$
(b)  Complement of (a), i.e., $[A^c \, (--) \, (-B_3)]^c \,=\, A \, (++) \, B_3$ from eq. (6-98)
(c)  $A^c \, (++) \, (-B_3)$
(d)  Complement of (c), i.e., $[A^c \, (++) \, (-B_3)]^c \,=\, A \, (--) \, B_3$ from eq. (6-99)

## ELEMENTARY APPLICATION OF MINKOWSKI OPERATORS TO IMAGE DATA

Recall that both the dilation and erosion operators are based on an input image and a template or structuring element, denoted $B$. Clearly, the choice of $B$ affects the outcome of these processes. Note that the definitions of the primitive Minkowski operators required a determination of all image points that satisfied a certain criteria. Basic implementation of these primitive operators, as we show below, is implemented by a "check" on computation over all image points, $\underline{x}$, using translation.

Therefore, the similarity of this operation with convolution, correlation, or template matching is apparent. In addition, note that preprocessing (e.g., thresholding) of grey-level image data is a prerequisite for application of the previously defined operators.

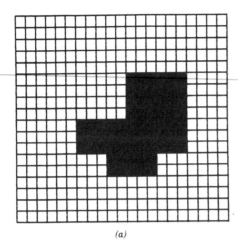

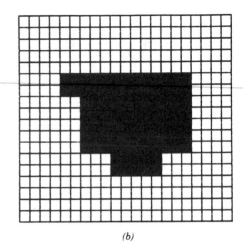

*(a)*    *(b)*

**FIGURE 6.39**  Opening and closing
(a)  Opening; open (A, B$_3$)
(b)  Closing; close (A, B$_3$)

*Binary Image Data Point Set Interpretation.* The application of Minkowski operators to binary image data follows directly if we adopt the convention that *point sets A and B (i.e., corresponding to the input image and structuring element, respectively) are defined to be the pixel locations whose intensities are "1" or ON.* With this convention, the primitive pixel set union, intersection, and complementing operations may be interpreted more intuitively. Assume a set of pixel locations, $A$, whose intensities are all ON (or 1), as shown in Figure 6.36$a$. The complement of set $A$, therefore, consists of all pixel locations whose intensity is OFF, or 0. This set, using our convention, may therefore be determined by simply forming the 1's complement of the entire image function. (We practically ignore the discrete nature of the problem as well as the finite image extent.)

*Digital Implementation of Minkowski Addition and Subtraction Via Template Matching.* The Minkowski addition and subtraction operators (and thus dilation and erosion) could be implemented by direct application of the set-based definitions in Eqs. 6-84, 6-85, and 6-86. This requires that nonzero pixel locations in the binary image and the structuring element be enumerated as sets and that operations such as union and intersection be implemented.

An alternative approach is to consider equivalent operations using the structuring element as a template. This requires, as we show below, a careful definition of template-image comparisons, in order to remain consistent with the Minkowski operators. A template-based matching approach is quite useful because of the variety of existing image processing architectures based on this operation.

*Minkowski Addition (Dilation) Via Templates.* We postulate the alternative formulation of Eq. 6-84 as

$$A \, [+] \, B = \{\underline{x} \mid [((-B) + \underline{x}) \cap A] \subset A\} \qquad (6\text{-}104)$$

In other words, the dilation of $A$ by $B$ is composed of all pixels where the reflected and shifted or translated structuring element and $A$ have at least one

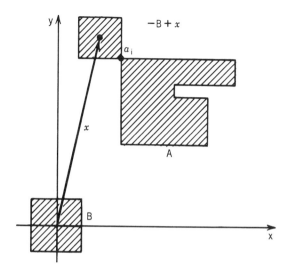

**FIGURE 6.40**  Example of dilation using templates

nonzero element (or pixel) in common. This more intuitive definition of addition (or dilation) is shown in Figure 6.40. We need, therefore, to prove the equality of Eqs. 6-104 and Eqs. 6-84 and 6-85. From Eqs. 6-84 and 6-85,

$$A\ [+]\ B = \bigcup_{\substack{\underline{a}_i \in A \\ \underline{y} \in B}} \{\underline{a}_i + \underline{y}\}$$

For implementation, we prove the equivalent of these below. From Eq. 6-104,

$$
\begin{aligned}
A\ [+]\ B &= \{\underline{x}\mid ((-B + \underline{x}) \cap A) \subset A\} \\
&= \{\underline{x}\mid \dashv\underline{a}_i \in A \text{ s.t. } \underline{a}_i \in (-B + \underline{x})\} \\
&= \{\underline{x}\mid \dashv\underline{a}_i \text{ s.t. } (\underline{a}_i - \underline{x}) \in -B\} \\
&= \{\underline{x}\mid \dashv\underline{a}_i \text{ s.t. } +\underline{x} \in B + \underline{a}_i\} \\
&= \{\underline{x}\mid \underline{x} \in (\bigcup_{\underline{a}_i \in A} B + \underline{a}_i)\} \\
&= A\ [+]\ B
\end{aligned}
\tag{6-105}
$$

Thus, the characterization allows implementation of addition (dilation) by viewing the rotated structuring element as a template and shifting the template throughout the image plane. The finite extent of the image plane requires that we consider matches outside of the image plane as "don't" cases. (This is explored in the problems.) Note in the case of addition (dilation) the comparison operation is union.

*Minkowski Subtraction as Template Matching.* Similarly, we may implement Minkowski subtraction using the alternative definition

$$A\ [-]\ B = \{\underline{x}\mid (B + \underline{x}) \subset A\} \tag{6-106}$$

Thus, with these interpretations, the digital implementation of the Minkowski operators is straightforward.

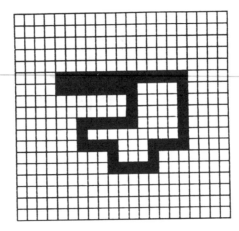

**FIGURE 6.41**  Isotropic border extraction example $A[/] (A (--) B_3)$

### SAMPLE APPLICATIONS

*Shifting of Image Data Using Asymmetrical Templates.* Consider the dilation operation with a structuring element as shown below:

$$B = \begin{bmatrix} 0 & 0 & 0 \\ 0 & 0 & 1 \\ 0 & 0 & 0 \end{bmatrix} \qquad (6\text{-}107)$$

Since, from the set-based viewpoint, with the coordinate system origin at the element $b_{22}$, the net effect of forming $A\,[+]\,B$ is the shifting of the image one pixel in the horizontal direction. We show later that this is useful in the determination of oriented edges. Figures 6.36g and h show this effect.

*Isotropic Border Extraction.* We have explored alternative edge detection and region boundary determination strategies. One approach to border extraction using Minkowski operators is to form the following

$$I_{border} = I_{in}\,[/]\,(I_{in}\,(--)\,B) \qquad (6\text{-}108)$$

This is shown in Figure 6.41.

*Oriented Edge Detection.* Figure 6.42 illustrates this application.

*Hole Filling, Connectivity, and Boundary Smoothing.* The closing operation may be used to preprocess a binary image. From the definition of closing Eq. 6-101, note that intuitively the primitive dilation operation "expands" a region, whereas the subsequent erosion operation "contracts" the expanded region. This expansion, as a function of the structuring element, $B$, will retain the rough shape of the region; however, small holes tend to be "filled." The subsequent shrinking operation, therefore, rescales the region, while retaining these smoothing results (e.g., holes do not reappear). This is shown in Figure 6.43.

*Elimination of Small Objects/Regions.* The opening operation, as defined by Eq. 6-100, consists of erosion, or shrinking, followed by dilation, or expansion. In this

*(a)*

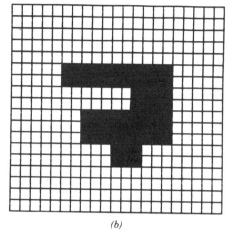

*(b)*

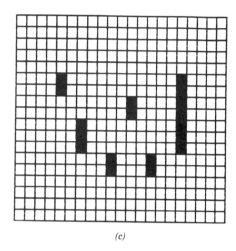

*(c)*

**FIGURE 6.42** Oriented edge extraction example
(a) Structuring element $B_v$, for oriented edge detection
(b) A $(--)$ $B_v$
(c) A $[/]$ $(A (--) B_v$

manner, regions smaller than the structuring element are eliminated, regions that almost touch are separated, and regional boundaries with high curvature are smoothed. This is shown in Figure 6.44. Note the similarity of this approach with that of thinning and median filtering.

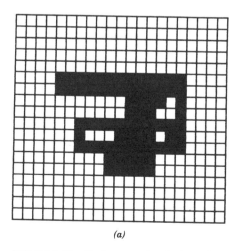

*(a)*

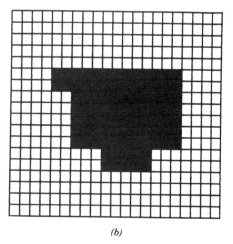

*(b)*

**FIGURE 6.43** Closing operation for boundary smoothing and hole filling
(a) Input binary image, $A_c$
(b) Close $(A_c, B_3)$

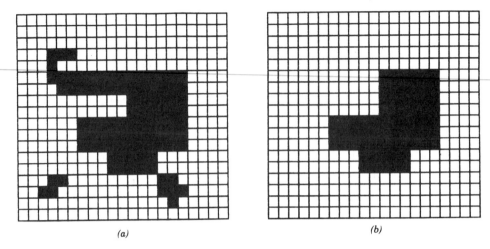

**FIGURE 6.44** Opening operation for contour smoothing and elimination of small objects
(a) Input binary image, $A_o$
(b) Open ($A_o$, $B_3$)

## IMPLEMENTATION OF MORPHOLOGICAL OPERATORS WITH COMPOSITE STRUCTURING ELEMENTS

Computer implementation of morphological operations favors a fixed size structuring element. In order to facilitate operations with an arbitrary dimensional structuring element, note that if

$$B_c = B_1 \cup B_2$$

then the following decompositions are possible

$$I_{in}\,(+\,+)\,B = (I_{in}\,(+\,+)\,B_1)\,\cup\,(I_{in}\,(+\,+)\,B_2)$$
$$I_{in}\,(-\,-)\,B = (I_{in}\,(-\,-)\,B_1)\,\cap\,(I_{in}\,(-\,-)\,B_2)$$

(6-109)

Proof of this property is left as an exercise.

## SKELETONIZING

Image skeletonizing, as indicated through the medial axis transform, is a significant geometric description approach. Skeletonizing via iterative application of Minkowski operators is shown here. For a structuring element $B$ and nonnegative integer $n$ we define

$$nB = \underbrace{B[+]B[+]\ldots[+]B}_{n \text{ times}}$$

The skeleton of image $A$, using $B$, denoted $S(A, B)$, and determined by a fairly complex iterative set of operations

$$S(A,B) = \bigcup_{n=0}^{N} S_n(A, B)$$

(6-110)

where

$$S_n = (A(-\,-)nB)\ \ [/]\ \ (\text{open }((A(-\,-)nB), B)$$

(6-111)

The value of $N$ is determined from

$$N = \max(j \,|\, A(--) \, jB \geq \{\emptyset\})$$ (6-112)

where $\{\emptyset\}$ denotes the null set.

An example of skeletonization is shown in Figure 6.45.

*(a)*

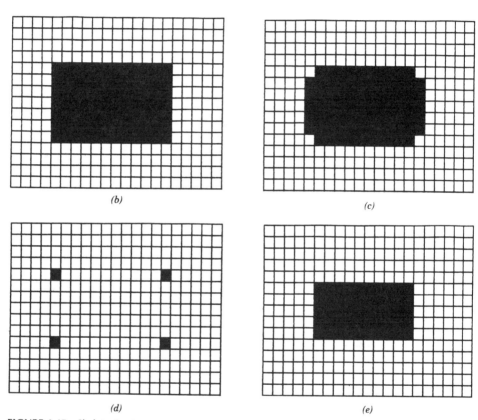

**FIGURE 6.45**  Skeletonization steps using (6-110) through (6-112) (iterative procedure)

(a)  $3 \times 3$ structuring element $B_s$, for skeletonization

(b)  Input binary image, $A_s$, for which skeleton is desired

(c)  Open $(A_s, B_s)$

(d)  $S_o = A_s \,[/]$ open $(A_s, B_s)$

(e)  $A_s \,(--)\, B_s$

(f)  Open $((A_s \,(--)\, B_s), B_s)$

(g)  $S_1 = (A_s \,(--)\, B_s) \,[/]$ open $((A_s \,(--)\, B_s), B_s)$

(h)  $I_2 = A_s \,(--)\, (B_s \,[+]\, B_s)$

(i)  $J_2 = $ open $(I_2, B_s)$

(j)  $S_2 = I_2 \,[/]\, J_2$

(k)  $I_3 = A_s \,(--)\, (B_s \,[+]\, B_s \,[+]\, B_s)$

(l)  $J_3 = $ open $(I_3, B_s)$ (note N = 3)

(m)  $S_3 = I_3 \,[/]\, J_3$

(n)  Result: $(\bigcup_{i=0}^{3} S_i)$

*Continued on next page*

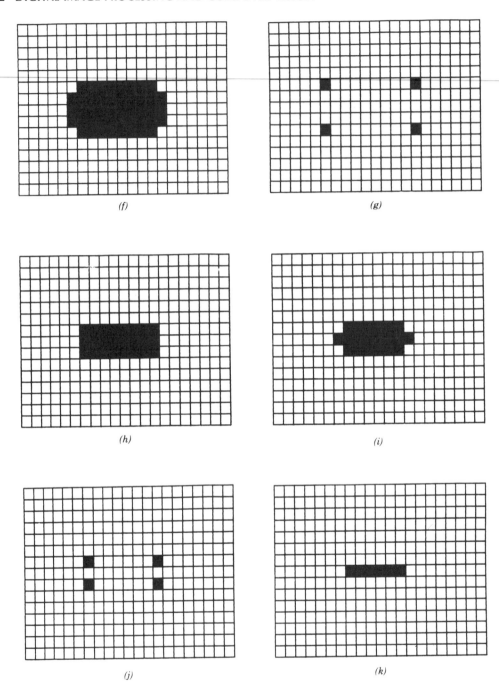

(f)

(g)

(h)

(i)

(j)

(k)

**FIGURE 6.45** *Continued.*

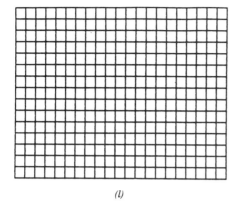

*(l)*

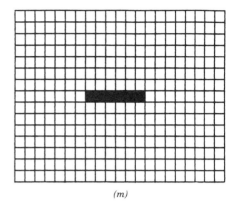

*(m)*

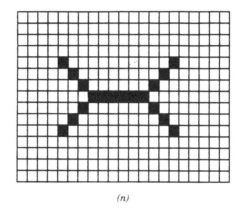

*(n)*

**FIGURE 6.45**   *Continued.*

## ■ SUMMARY

Analysis techniques for image data, as we have seen in this chapter, come from a variety of diverse sources, including statistical and syntactic pattern recognition, matching techniques, transforms, and morphology. Each of these sources yields a set of tools, or processing algorithms, each with its utility, limitations, and other characteristics (such as practical implementation concerns). The judicious choice of application, modification, or extension of these technical tools to particular image processing problems involves a great deal of engineering judgment. In the next chapter we explore a higher-level class of image analysis algorithms. These are based on the development of higher-level models that underlie the scenes, and employ higher-level constraint satisfaction formulations.

## ■ REFERENCES

Agin, G. J., and Binford, T. O. Computer description of curved objects. *IEEE Trans. Computers,* 1976, *25,* 439–440.

Andrews, H. C. Automatic interpretation and classification of images by use of the Fourier domain. In *Automatic interpretation and classification of images*. New York: Academic Press, 1969.

Ashkar, G. P., and Modestino, J. W. The contour extraction problem with biomedical applications. *Computer Graphics and Image Processing*, 1978, 7, 331–355.

Badi'i, F., and Majd, R. Parallel classification of 3-D moving objects. *Proc. 1985 IEEE Workshop on Computer Architecture for Pattern Analysis and Image Database Management*, Miami Beach, FL, November 1985, pp. 183–188.

Ballard, D. H. Generalizing the Hough transform to detect arbitrary shapes. *Pattern Recognition*, 1981, *13*(2), 111–122.

Blum, H. A transformation for extracting new descriptors of shape. In *Symposium on models for perception of speech and visual form*. (pp. 362–380). MIT Press, Cambridge, MA 1967.

Bolc, L. (Ed.). *Natural language communication with pictorial information systems*. New York: Springer-Verlag, 1984.

Brice, C. R., and Fenneman, C. L. Scene analysis using regions. *Artificial Intelligence*, 1970, *1*, 205–226.

Casasent, D. Position rotation and scale invariant optical correlation. *Applied Optics*, 1976, *15*(7), pp. 1795–1799.

Casasent, D., and Psaltis, D. New optical transforms for pattern recognition. *Proceedings of the IEEE*, 1977, *65*(1), 77–84.

Casasent, D., and Krishnapuram, R. Curved object location by Hough transformations and inversions. *Pattern Recognition*, 1987, *20*(2), 181–188.

Cooper, D. B., et al. Stochastic boundary estimation and object recognition. In A. Rosenfeld (Ed.), *Image modelling*. New York: Academic Press, 1981.

Dougherty, E. R., and Giardina, C. R. *Image processing-continuous to discrete*, Vol. I. Englewood Cliffs, NJ: Prentice Hall, 1987.

Duda, R. O., and Hart, P. E. *Pattern classification and scene analysis*. New York: Wiley, 1973.

Feivson, A. H. Classification by thresholding. *IEEE Trans. PAMI*, 1983, *5*(1), 48–54.

Fischler, M. A., and Elschlager, R. A. The representation and matching of pictorial structures. *IEEE Trans. Computers*, 1973, *C-22*(1), 67–92.

Freeman, H. Computer Processing of Line Drawing Images. *Computer Surveys*, Vol. 6, No. 1, March 1974, pp. 57–98.

Fu, K. S. Recent developments in pattern recognition. *IEEE Trans. on Computers*, 1980, *C-29*(10), 845–857.

Fu, K. S. *Syntactic pattern recognition and applications*. Englewood Cliffs, NJ: Prentice Hall, 1982.

Giuliano, V. E., et al. Automatic pattern recognition by a gestalt method. *Information and Control*, 1961, *4*, 332–345.

Granlund, G. H. Fourier preprocessing for hand print character recognition. *IEEE Transactions on Computers*, 1972, *C-22*, 195–201.

Haralick, R. M. Statistical and structural approaches to texture. *Proc. IEEE*, 1979, *67*(5), 786–804.

Haralick, R. M., Shanmugam, K., and Dinstein, I. Textural features for image classification. *IEEE Trans. on Systems, Man and Cybernetics*, 1973, *SMC-3*(6), 610–621.

Horowitz, S. L. and Pavlidis, T., Picture Segmentation by a Tree Traversal Algorithm. *Journal of the Assoc. Computing Machinery (ACM)*, Vol. 23, (1976), pp. 368–388.

Hu, M. K. Pattern recognition by moment invariants. *Proc. IRE*, 1961, *49*, 1428.

Hu, M. K. Visual pattern recognition by moment invariants. *Proc. IRE Trans. Information Theory*, 1962, *IT-8*, 179–187.

Kimme, C., Ballard, D., and Sklansky, J. Finding circles in an array of accumulators. *Communications of the ACM*, 1975, *18*(2) pp. 120–122.

Landgrebe, D. A. Analysis technology for land remote sensing. *Proc. IEEE*, 1981, *69*(5), 628–642.

Maragos, P. A., and Schafer, R. W. Application of morphological filtering to image analysis and processing. *Proceedings IEEE 1986 International Conference on Acoustics, Speech and Signal Processing*, Tokyo, Japan, pp. 2067–2071.

Mokhtarian, F., and Mackworth, A. Scale-based description and recognition of planar curves and two-dimensional shapes. *IEEE Trans. Pattern Analysis and Machine Intelligence*, 1986, *PAMI-8*(1), 34–43.

Montanari, U. A method for obtaining skeletons using a quasi-Euclidean distance. *Journal of the ACM*, 1968, *15*, 600–624.

Nahi, N. E., and Jahanshahi, M. H. Image boundary estimation. *IEEE Trans. Computers*, 1977, *C-26*(8), 772–781

Nevatia, R. *Machine perception*, Englewood Cliffs, NJ: Prentice-Hall, 1982.

Nevatia, R., and Babu, K. R. Linear feature extraction and description. *Computer Graphics and Image Processing*, 1980, *13*, 257–269.

Papoulis, A. *The Fourier integral and its applications*, New York: McGraw-Hill, 1962.

Peli, T., and Malah, D. A study of edge detection algorithms. *Computer Graphics and Image Processing*, 1982, *20*, 1–21.

Pratt, W. K., et al. Visual discrimination of stochastic texture fields. *IEEE Trans. Systems, Man and Cybernetics*, 1978, *SMC-8*(11), 796–804.

Robbins, G. M., and Huang, T. S. Inverse filtering for linear shift-variant systems. *Proc. IEEE*, 1972, *60*, 862–872.

Schalkoff, R. J. *Artifical intelligence: An engineering approach*. New York: McGraw-Hill, in press.

Serra, J. Introduction to mathematical morphology. *Computer Vision, Graphics and Image Processing*, 1986, *35*, 283–305.

Serra, J. *Image analysis and mathematical morphology*. New York: Academic Press, 1982.

Shaw, A. C. A formal picture description scheme as a basis for picture processing systems. *Information and Control*, 1969, *14*, 9–51.

Shaw, A. C. Parsing of graph-representable pictures. *Journal of the Association for Computing Machinery*, 1970, *17*(3), 453–481.

Swain, P. H., Siegel, H. J., and Smith, B. W. Contextual classification of multispectral remote sensing data using a multiprocessor system. *IEEE Trans. Geoscience and Remote Sensing*, 1980, *GE-18*(2), 197–203.

Teh, C. H., and Chin, R. T. On digital approximation of moment invariants. *Computer Vision, Graphics, and Image Processing*, 1986, *33*, 318–326.

Tenenbaum, J. M., Fischler, M. A., and Barrow, H. G. Scene modelling: a structural basis for image description. In A. Rosenfeld (Ed.), *Image modelling*. New York: Academic Press, 1981.

Trevedi, M. M., and Harlow, C. A. Identification of unique objects in high resolution aerial images. *Optical Engineering*, 1985, *24*(3), 502–506.

Weszka, J. S., Dyer, C. R., and Rosenfeld, A. A comparative study of texture measures for terrain classification. *IEEE Trans. Systems, Man, and Cybernetics*, 1976, *SMC-6*(4), 269–285.

Witkin, A. P. Recovering surface shape and orientation from texture. *Artificial Intelligence*, 1981, *17*, 17–45.

Wong, R. Y., and Hall, E. L. Sequential hierarchical scene matching. *IEEE Transactions on Computers*, 1977, *C-27*(4), 359–365.

Woods, J. W. Markov image modelling. *IEEE Trans. Automatic Control*, 1978, *AC-23*(5), pp. 846–849.

Zenzo, S. D. Advanced in image segmentation. *Image and Vision Computing*, 1983, *1*(4), 196–210.

Zucker, S. W., and Terzopoulos D. Finding structure in co-occurrence matrices for texture analysis. In A. Rosenfeld (Ed.), *Image modelling*. New York: Academic Press, 1981.

# ■ PROBLEMS

---

**1.** Show that, for any template, $g$, and image function, $f$, the measure of match

$$C_u(\alpha,\beta) = \frac{\sum\sum_{R'} g(x_1 + \alpha, x_2 + \beta)f(x_1,x_2)}{\{\sum\sum_{R'} g^2(x_1 + \alpha, x_2 + \beta)\}^{1/2}\{\sum\sum_{R'} g^2(x_1,x_2)\}^{1/2}}$$

yields a metric in the interval $[-1,1]$.

2. Derive the Mellin transform for the following functions:
   (i) $u_{-1}(x - 1)$ (unit step starting at $x = 1$)
   (ii) $x u_{-1}(x - 1)$ (ramp starting at $x = 1$)

3. (a) Prove that the intersection of the $p$-$\theta$ curves for any two (noncoincident) points determines the parameters of the line which is determined by these two points.
   (b) Extend this argument to the case of three colinear points.
   (c) Extend the solution in (b) to $n$ colinear points. In particular.
      (i) What is the largest number of intersections that will occur?
      (ii) How many intersections of less than that of (i) exist? Why?

4. Show how to convert a line description from slope intercept $(a,b)$ form to normal parameterization $(p,\theta)$ and vice-versa.

5. Given a set of $n$ points, $(x_i,y_i)$ $i = 1,2 \ldots n$ to which a single line is to be fitted, develop the least-squares estimation equations, using
   (a) the slope intercept form
   (b) normal form.
   In addition, discuss methods to determine the "goodness of fit" of the resulting line.

6. Consider the "misapplication" of a least-squares line fitting procedure to point sets which actually contain multiple lines of the following forms:

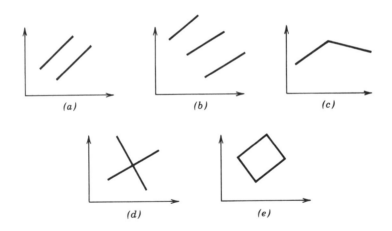

(a)     (b)     (c)

(d)     (e)

   In each case, state as quantitatively as possible, what the least squares procedure would return.

7. Verify (6-45); show how we may calculate curvature as:

$$k(s) = y''/(1 + (y')^2)^{3/2}$$

8. (i) Show that the curvature of a line is zero.
   (ii) Show that the curvature of a circle is constant.

9. For a square binary region of dimension $a \times a$, if the $x$ and $y$-dimension sampling intervals are such that

$$\Delta x = \Delta y = \frac{a}{5}$$

how much error is introduced in the moment-based future $\phi_1$?

10. Suppose we are given only the extracted medial axes for a geometric figure, and, for each point in these axes, the function $q(x, B)$, as given by Eq. 6-81. Is it possible to exactly reconstruct $B$ for this figure? Show a simple example that verified your answer.

11. Show for a square of dimensions $a$, with center arbitrary, that moment feature $\phi_1 = \frac{1}{6}$; that is, it is independent of $a$ and therefore scale invariant.

12. Prove $\mu_{10} = \mu_{01}$ and 0.

13. Prove, for a binary image region as shown in Figure 6.32 (symmetric about the line $y = x$) that all of the seven invariant moment features of Table 6.2 are zero except $\phi_1$.

14. Prove that

$$\frac{A_R}{(P_R)^2}$$

(a) is maximum for a figure that is a circle;

(b) is always less for a rectangle than a square; and

(c) (using an ellipse), decreases as the elongation (ratio of major to minor axis length) of the ellipse increases.

15. Given images of a triangle in 2 orientations formed by $5 \times 5$ arrays of black or white pixels:

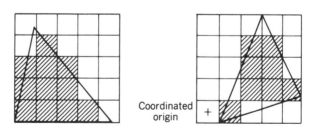

Find the moments $m_{00}$, $m_{10}$, and $m_{01}$, and explain their significance for each image. Find the "invariant" $\phi_1$ for each image. Is it invariant? Use an intensity of 1 for the shaded pixels and 0 for the unshaded and assume each pixel is of unit length. Note: It is convenient to define the coordinate system origin at the *center* of a pixel.

16. (a) Find the matrix representation for the moment transform in the form

$$M = [D^T] [f] [C]$$

where $p, q \; \varepsilon \; [0, N - 1]$. Test your results on the following two $4 \times 4$ "images":

(i) $[f]$ = 1 1 1 1
          1 1 1 1
          1 1 1 1
          1 1 1 1

(ii) $[f]$ = 1 0 0 0
           0 1 0 0
           0 0 1 0
           0 0 0 1

(b) Notice that these resulting transform matrices are considerably different from a Fourier or Hadamard transform, in particular "DC" images such as (i) return nonzero values for coefficients other than $m_{00}$. Comment on why.

17. (a) Given the following points:
(280,252), (233,249), (165,248), (325,254), (394,257)
(283,147), (281,212), (280,252), (278,290), (278,357)
use the Hough transform technique with

$$\Delta\rho = \frac{512\sqrt{2}}{200} \; ; \; \Delta\theta = \frac{2\pi}{200}$$

to determine
(i) the number of line segments these points comprise; and
(ii) the parameters of these lines.

(b) If a point $(x_p, y_p)$ represents the intersection of two line segments, it must contribute to two maxima $(\rho_1, \theta_1)$, $(\rho_2, \theta_2)$ in the Hough transform accumulator array. Show how to determine this point given $(\rho_1, \theta_1)$ and $(\rho_2, \theta_2)$.

18. Derive Eq. 6-74.

19. Suggest an operator based on the Fourier transform that is sensitive to *both* direction and coarseness of image texture.

20. Determine the effect of using $\delta_{20}$ and $\delta_{02}$ on the examples on page 274.

21. Discuss the implications, with respect to discrimination ability, when co-occurrence matrices are made symmetric; we use both $\delta_{01}$ and $\delta_{0(-1)}$ by only considering the magnitude of the separation distance.

22. Suppose, given a textured image, we use $H_\delta$ for discrimination based on texture direction. Discuss which $\delta$ to use and consequently which features to extract from $H_\delta$ to achieve this.

23. Show, by example, the operation of the entropy operator on the following $H_\delta$ matrices:

(a) 1 1 1 1
    1 1 1 1
    1 1 1 1
    1 1 1 1

(b) 1 2 1 2
    1 2 1 2
    1 2 1 2
    1 2 1 2

(c) 1 1 1 1
    2 2 2 2
    1 1 1 1
    2 2 2 2

(d) 1 5 1 5
    1 5 1 5
    1 5 1 5
    1 5 1 5

**24.** Apply the contrast and entropy operators of Eqs. 6-20 and 6-21 to Figure 6.10. Interpret the results.

**25.** (a) Let $(p,\theta)$ be a point in Hough space corresponding to a line segment in the input image centered at the origin. If the input image is rotated by an angle $\phi$, show that this line segment now maps into point $(p',\theta)$ in Hough space, where

$$p' = p$$

and

$$\theta' = \theta + \phi.$$

(b) Similarly, if the input image is translated by $(\Delta x, \Delta y)$, show that the point $(p,\theta)$ will map to $(p',\theta')$, where

$$p' = -p - t \cos(\theta - \alpha)$$
$$\theta' = \theta + \pi$$

if

$$p + t \cos(\theta - \alpha) < 0$$

or

$$p' = p + t \cos(\theta - \alpha)$$
$$\theta' = \theta$$

if

$$p + t \cos(\theta - \alpha) \geq 0$$

where

$$t = \sqrt{\Delta x^2 + \Delta y^2} \quad \alpha = \tan^{-1}(\Delta y/\Delta x)$$

**26.** Consider the application of the Hough transform to circle detection. Assume the circles to be detected are approximated by line segments which are tangential to the circle at various points, as shown by point $P$ in Fig. P.26-1. Also assume the circle is centered at the origin.

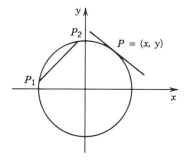

(a) Show, in this case, that the representation for the circle, in Hough transform space is a line described by $p = r$.

(b) Consider the effects of points $P_1$ and $P_2$, as shown in Figure P.26-1 on the Hough transform. How can false peaks due to the line segment joining these peaks be eliminated?

27. The Hough transform (for lines) maps points into sinusoids. More important, as described in the text, we may view this transform as mapping a continuous curve in image space to a continuous curve (after thresholding) in Hough space. Interestingly, no inverse appears to be defined for the Hough transform. It is the purpose of this problem to consider such an "inverse." Borrowing the projection concept from reconstruction problems:

(a) Show that the value of the accumulator bin at location $(p,\theta)$ represents the projection of image data along a line by $p$ and $\theta$.

(b) Using the results of (a), develop a method to "back project" $(p,\theta)$ accumulator values to reconstruct $f(\underline{x})$.

28. The purpose of this problem is to explore several consequences of the Brice–Fennema (BF) edge representation and its region-merging utility.

(a) Consider the $5 \times 5$ subimage shown below:

$$4\ 4\ 4\ 4\ 4$$
$$4\ 6\ 5\ 6\ 4$$
$$4\ 6\ 5\ 6\ 4$$
$$4\ 6\ 5\ 6\ 4$$
$$4\ 4\ 4\ 4\ 4$$

(i) Form the $(2n + 1) \times (2n + 1)$ BF array of edge vectors as in Figure 6.5 and show these graphically.

(ii) Show how the process of merging interim edges (due to texture) could be accomplished using "vector cancellation" of adjacent edges in the above example.

(b) Consider the application of the BF merging approach on the following 1-D sampled function:

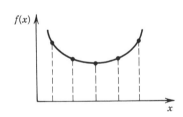

(i) Show the resulting 1-D B–F edge array. Does it make sense? (Hint: Consider the sampled signal representation.)

(ii) Suppose we merge adjacent edges, where possible. What does the result of (i) become? What input function would yield the same result? Does this suggest a frequency-domain equivalent to the edge vector merging process?

**29. (a)** Assume that the edge image segment of Figure 6.6 (reprinted below) represents a portion of the boundary of a single region. Draw all possible connected edge segments under the assumptions of:

(i) 4 connectedness; and

(ii) 8 connectedness.

**(b)** Repeat part (a) for the case of the alternate choice of seed pixel as shown. Comment on the differences and similarities in the four cases.

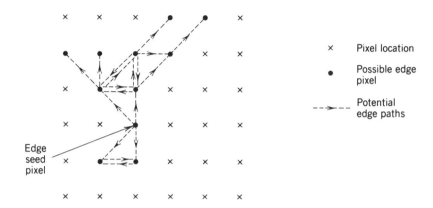

| | |
|---|---|
| × | Pixel location |
| ● | Possible edge pixel |
| ---->--- | Potential edge paths |

Edge seed pixel

**30.** Numerous versions of the split-and-merge algorithm are possible. Referring to the sample region splitting and merging algorithm on page 278, analyze the effects of the following two algorithm modifications:

(a) the $n \times n$ input image is initialized as $n^2$ individual regions (one per pixel).

(b) the merging occurs before the splitting.

Consider specifically the efficiency and the convergence properties of the algorithm. How do choices of the splitting geometry and $H(R)$ affect the modified algorithm.

**31.** Show graphically (using an example) the difference between Minkowski subtraction $[-]$ and the difference operator.

**32.** Prove: (a) $A [+] \{(0,0)\} = A$

(b) $A [+] [B + \underline{x}] = [A [+] B] + \underline{x}$

(c) $A [+] (B_1 \cup B_2) = (A [+] B_1) \cup (A [+] B_2)$ (structuring element decomposition)

(d) $(A \cap A_1) (- -) B = (A (- -) B) \cap (A_1 (- -) B)$ ("local knowledge property")

**33.** Another edge extraction approach, given an image $f$ and structing element $B$, using Minkowski operators is to form:

$$(f[++]nB) [/] (f[--]nB)$$

(a) Choose a suitable $B$ and compare this operator to that of Eq. 6-108. (In particular, comment on the "shifting" of region edges.)

    (b) Use the sample images in Figs. 6.36, 6.37, 6.43 and 6.44 for verification.

    (c) Explore the effect of $n$ on the edge "selectivity" of this operator.

**34.** Show Minkowski subtraction, defined by Eq. 6-86 is equivalent to:

$$A \, [-] \, B = \{\underline{x}|(-B) + \underline{x} \subset A\}$$

**35.** Is dilation, in some sense, the "inverse" of erosion? Is erosion, in some sense, the inverse of dilation? Justify your answers both analytically and with examples.

# 7

# IMAGE ANALYSIS, PART II

## ■ INTRODUCTION

As mentioned in the introduction to Chapter 6, the broad goal of high-level image analysis is to develop and use image and/or scene models and representations for interpretation of image information. This may involve hierarchical or multilevel image analysis, 3-D modeling and volumetric representations, and general procedures for image-based knowledge manipulation, including procedural or rule-based manipulation of image data. The highest level models typically employ a great amount of non-image-related knowledge underlying the scene representation, for example, knowledge about world physical constraints influencing imaged entities and their environment.

The overall image understanding system is comprised of an integrated set of algorithmic modules, as shown in Figure 7.1. A higher level algorithm, in conjunction with selected output from these modules, is used to guide the high-level image understanding.

We consider in detail the obtaining of an image or scene description consisting of labeled or identified objects. This is based on the use of high-level symbolic models composed of known a priori constraints and the achievement of a consistent representation satisfying these constraints. The concepts of labels and constraints have a strong AI link and lead to *relational* approaches.

Underlying image understanding research efforts is an implicit assumption that human-like image interpretation is a form of computation that may be identified and consequently automated. The two terms *identification* and *automation* often give rise to the two major impediments to success in image understanding, namely:

1. We are not able to identify or, more specifically, quantify this human capability in a form that lends itself to direct computer implementation (or, as

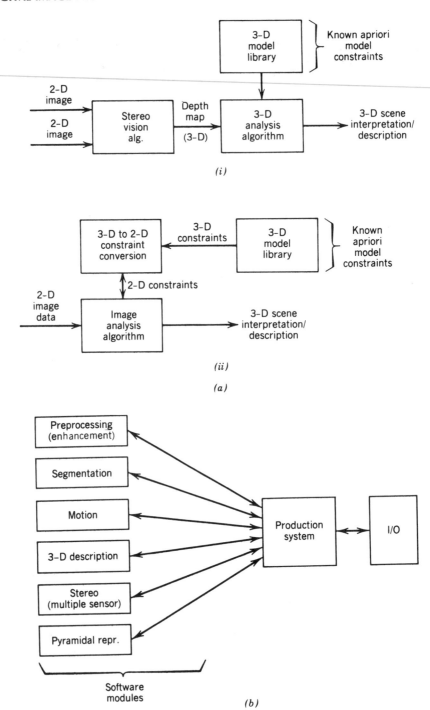

**FIGURE 7.1**  High level image understanding
(a)  3-D model-based image analysis approaches
    (i)  Via generation of 3-D data (active/multiple camera system)
    (ii)  Via prior conversion of 3-D constraints to 2-D
(b)  Image understanding system structure indicating cooperating modules

we will define later, a form that is symbolically tractable). In other words, a "knowledge calculus" does not presently exist. Another way to view this is to claim that what is lacking is a unified, versatile, high-level model from which algorithmic emulations may be developed.

2. Even with current computing resources, implementing even simple image understanding systems yields problems of tremendous complexity. We will see this remark amply verified in our exploration of algorithms that rely on *recursion* and *search*. Thus, languages and architectures that facilitate these operations are of fundamental interest.

Equivalently, it is assumed that there is another, higher level model to guide the extraction of higher level image concepts from these specific low-level primitives. For example, the extraction of simple edges via a low-level process may be used to provide input (primitives) to be manipulated or combined by a grammar-based model and corresponding algorithm. In the grammar-based model, basic primitives might consist of line segments. Using these primitives, higher level scene entities residing in the image (e.g., "house," "person," "airplane") are developed.

As we shall see, the task of image interpretation with these models often involves the manipulation and matching of extracted features and binding of model symbols (or named variables) to these extracted features, with the goal of obtaining a (model-) consistent structure to achieve "unification" of the model (feature structure and relationships) and the observed feature data.

# ■ HIERARCHICAL (PYRAMIDAL) OR MULTILEVEL IMAGE ANALYSIS

## CONCEPT AND APPLICATIONS

A hierarchical processing approach parallels the operation of the Human Visual System (HVS) in that processing proceeds from a coarse descriptive level to levels of increasing refinement. The hierarchical approach is applicable to the tasks of segmentation, feature extraction, description, and matching. One of the most significant benefits of this approach is the resultant computational savings.

### AN EXAMPLE OF SEQUENTIAL/HIERARCHICAL SEARCH AND MATCHING

Hierarchical search or matching is introduced using a simple example. The overall objective is to search the image data for potential matches as efficiently as possible. The sequentially extracted features are pixel grey levels at varying (increasing) spatial resolution levels. The matching process consists of a simple correlation of these features with a template. A simple 1-D example, with a linear array as the image, is used. Consider the following template and corresponding array:

*template*

1  2  3  4

*array*

7  6  3  4  1  2  4  3  1  2  3  4  5  6  5  4

Thirteen possible match locations are in the array (considering edge effects). Assuming that the computational expense of matching using correlation is primarily due to multiplications, each of these potential matches therefore costs four computations. This results in a computational expense of 52 operations to completely explore the full resolution array for matches. To reduce this cost, a reduced resolution template and array are formed by simple (2-pixel) neighborhood averaging. Thus, at the next lower resolution level the template and array become

*template*

3/2   7/2

*array*

13/2   7/2   3/2   7/2   3/2   7/2   11/2   9/2

The matching process now involves seven candidate locations, each with a computational expense of two multiplications. The total computational cost of correlation matching at this level is therefore 14. More important, regions that are not of interest (i.e., do not yield normalized correlation values above a threshold) in the reduced resolution representations may be eliminated from further consideration, thus restricting the scope of the match search.

## SCALE-SPACE FILTERING (GAUSSIAN KERNEL)

Multilevel or hierarchical image analysis involves the creation of a sequence of images at various spatial resolutions or scales. Too fine a scale may yield extraneous detail; too coarse a scale may cause significant features to be missed or distorted. Furthermore, multiscale image representations should be consistent, since features at different resolutions may be related. As resolution increases, significant features should not randomly appear and disappear. For example, suppose edge enhancement operators were applied to a sequence of multiresolution images. If edges appeared and disappeared as the resolution varied, it would be difficult to relate these edge descriptors at different scales.

A more quantitative basis for hierarchical processing is now developed. A *scale-space representation* of an image may be formed by convolving the input (highest resolution) image with a kernel containing a scale parameter.

We show the theory for a 1-D signal, $f(x)$, then extend the result to 2-D signals. The smoothing or scale-reduction parameter is denoted $y$, and the respective scaling kernel is $g(x,y)$, with $y$ being positive. An increase in $y$ denotes increased smoothing or scale reduction. Some works refer to the smoothing kernel in terms of a *bandwidth parameter*, $\hat{y}$; this parameter is inversely related to $y$. The output of the scale-space operation is the surface denoted $\phi(x,y)$, which is only defined over a half-plane in $(x,y)$ space. With this model, the scale-modified 1-D function is given by

$$\phi(x,y) = f(x) * g(x,y) \tag{7-1}$$

where the * denotes convolution, that is,

$$\phi(x,y) = \int_{-\infty}^{\infty} f(u) \, g(x-u,y) \, du \tag{7-2}$$

Note that Eq. 7-2 produces an ensemble of images as a function of the scale parameter $y$. As $y$ increases, the range of representational values of $x$ decreases.

A desirable property of Eq. 7-2 is that as $y$ approaches 0 (no smoothing), $\phi(x,y)$ approaches $f(x)$. This requires $g(x,y)$ to approach an impulse at $y = 0$. Assume that the features of significance in $f(x)$ are extrema, specifically, the zero crossings of $L(f)$, where $L$ is a linear differential operator. In the LOG operator, for example, zero crossings of the second derivative are often reliable indicators of the presence of an edge.

An analysis of the effect of the smoothing kernel on these zero crossings in $\phi(x,y)$ is required. These extrema are the values of $x$ that satisfy

$$f_{xx}(x,y) = 0 \qquad (7\text{-}3)$$

where the subscript $xx$ denotes the second derivative. Because the differential operator is linear, we may examine the behavior of the scale reduction operator via $\phi_{xx}(x,y)$, specifically, the behavior of

$$\phi_{xx}(x,y) = 0 \qquad (7\text{-}4)$$

A consistent scale-spaced kernel, $g(x,y)$, has the characteristic that an edge at a lower resolution remains as the resolution is increased. This means that from large values of $y$ to smaller values (i.e., $\phi(x,y)$ goes from low resolution to higher resolution), *new zero crossings may appear, but existing ones never disappear.* For visualization, the plot of $\phi_{xx}(x,y)$ is three-dimensional; however, only $(x,y)$ locations where this quantity is zero are of interest. The consistency constraint is equivalent to requiring that the plot of the contours of $\phi_{xx}(x,y) = 0$ versus $x$ and $y$ is closed above, but never below, as shown in Figure 7.2. Figure 7.3 (Baubaud, et al., 1986) indicates this characteristic using real data. A strict hierarchy of extrema detail is thus required. (Because the smoothing achieved by $g(x,y)$ compresses the range of values of $x$, the figures are corrected for display purposes.) In Figures 7.2

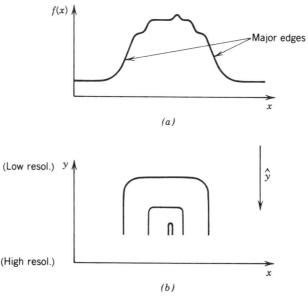

(a)

(b)

**FIGURE 7.2** Extrema consistency constraint for scale space filtering
(a)  Sample function (note "major" and "minor" edges)
(b)  Required behavior of contours $\phi_{xx} = 0$, as function of x and $\hat{y}$

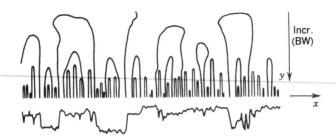

**FIGURE 7.3** A signal, and contours of $\phi_{xx} = 0$ in its scale-space image. The x-axis is horizontal; the coarsest scale is on top. The contours describe the behavior of inflections in the Gaussian-smoothed signal, as the standard deviation of the Gaussian is varied. (From [Bibaud, et al.] p. 26 Copyright © 1986 IEEE)

and 7.3, the initial appearance and the progress of extrema as $y$ decreases are significant. The characteristic "birth" of an extrema can be seen as the curve begins at a single point and spreads out into one or two approximately vertical lines, indicating the consistent appearance of an extrema with increasing resolution.

*Derivation of Constraints on $g(x,y)$.* The constraints on $g(x,y)$ that lead to the type of consistent hierarchy of extrema illustrated by Figure 7.3 are examined. Instead of using a scale parameter, $y$, we use the inverse of $y$, namely a bandwidth parameter, denoted by $\hat{y}$ to make the derivation consistent with Baubaud et al. (1986). Thus, low values of $\hat{y}$ correspond to significant reduction in resolution (or in the frequency domain, bandwidth), whereas as $\hat{y}$ approaches infinity, $\phi(x,\hat{y})$ approaches $f(x)$. The derivation is based on constraining $g(x,\hat{y})$ to achieve an output function $\phi(x,\hat{y})$, with the characteristic that as $\hat{y}$ increases, local maxima of $\phi(x,\hat{y})$ always increase and local minima decrease. Thus, the peaks and valleys of $\phi(x,\hat{y})$ become more pronounced, and the zero crossing contours of $\phi_{xx}(x,\hat{y}) = 0$ that appear at low bandwidth cannot vanish as $\hat{y}$ increases.

A scale-space filtering kernel $g(x,\hat{y})$ with these properties must satisfy the following:

**1.** $g(x,\hat{y}) = \hat{y}h(x,\hat{y})$             (7-5a)

This constraint intuitively defines a scale parameter.

**2.** $g(-x,\hat{y}) = g(x,\hat{y})$             (7-5b)

This requires $g$ to be symmetric.

**3.** $g(x,\hat{y})$, for all $\hat{y} > 0$, is normalized so that

$$\int_{-\infty}^{\infty} g(x,\hat{y}) \, dx = 1 \qquad (7-5c)$$

This requires the smoothing kernel to have unity area. It guarantees the desirable property that if $f(x) = a$, $\phi(x,\hat{y}) = a$, causing $\phi(x,\infty) = \delta(x)$. Verifying these properties is left for the problems at the end of this chapter.

As shown in Baubaud et al. (1986), a function that satisfies the above requirements is the Gaussian kernel, that is,

$$g(x,\hat{y}) = (1/\sqrt{2\pi}) \, \hat{y} \exp \left[ -(1/2)(x\hat{y})^2 \right] \qquad (7-6)$$

This result is not surprising, due to the properties of the Gaussian function and its preponderance in many other applications (e.g., the LOG operator, considered in Chapter 4). More important, however, Eq. 7-6 indicates an intuitively satisfying result, namely, that the smoothing kernel has low-pass frequency domain characteristics. Note that many of the popular scale-reduction methodologies, such as averaging, do not satisfy the above requirements; however, they are approximations to the ideal Gaussian kernel (explored in the problems).

*Application to Scale-Space Filtering.* In a manner similar to that used for the LOG approach in Chapter 4, the development of a multiresolution feature extraction operator is possible. For a linear differential operator, $L$,

$$L[\phi(x,\hat{y})] = L[f(x)] * g(x,\hat{y})$$
$$= f(x) * L[g(x,\hat{y})]$$

(7-7)

Thus, Eq. 7-7 (the proof is left as an exercise) indicates that we may develop a feature extracted or enhanced multiresolution image sequence by first enhancing the image (before scale reduction) and then smoothing this result. Alternately, we may derive an operator, $L[g(x,\hat{y})]$, which generates the sequence (as a function of values of $\hat{y}$) of enhanced images. Depending on the specific application, both results are useful. This approach may be easily generalized to 2-D spatial functions.

## IMPLEMENTATION EXAMPLES

### QuadTrees—A Data Structure for Multiresolution Image Representation

Efficient representational methods, that is, image data structures, are important in multiresolution image representations. The quadtree concept is an approach to hierarchical image representation based on successive subdivision of the image into quadrants. This concept is conceptually simple; each partitioned region of the image is further subdivided into four subregions, which are in turn subdivided into four others. The process ceases when the individual pixel level is reached; no further subdivision is possible. Figure 7.4 shows the overall concept for a $4 \times 4$ pixel image. This subdivision of the image spatial extent may be viewed graphically through a tree structure, where the whole image is represented by the topmost node or root of the tree and the finest level of detail (i.e., individual pixels) form

| 0 | 1 | 2 | 3 |
| 4 | 5 | 6 | 7 |
| 8 | 9 | 10 | 11 |
| 12 | 13 | 14 | 15 |

**FIGURE 7.4** $4 \times 4$ image for quadtree representation example (pixels numbered 0..15)

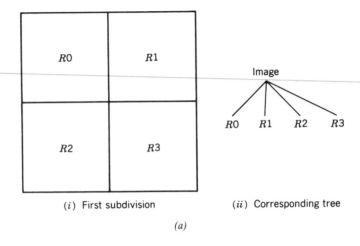

(i) First subdivision   (ii) Corresponding tree

(a)

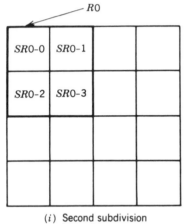

(i) Second subdivision
(R0 only)

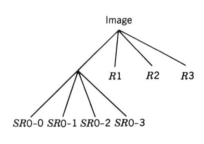

(ii) Corresponding tree
(R0 branch only)

(b)

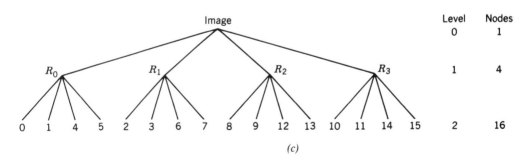

(c)

FIGURE 7.5
(a) Simple quadtree spatial image decomposition
  (i) First subdivision
  (ii) Corresponding tree
(b) Second decomposition level
  (i) Second subdivision ($R_\phi$ only)
  (ii) Corresponding tree ($R_\phi$ branch only)
(c) Resulting tree (pixel #'s from part (a) shown on leaves)

the leaves. Depicted graphically, this yields a *quadtree*, as shown in Figure 7.5. Assume a square image of spatial extent $2^n \times 2^n$ pixels. Thus, the total number of pixels is $2^{2n}$, or $4^n$. The outdegree of each node in the quadtree is 4, and the root node of the tree represents the entire image. Each level of the tree, excluding the root node, must contain four nodes. We number the root node as the $0^{th}$ level, thus, the $k^{th}$ level of the quadtree contains $4^k$ nodes. Since each leaf node represents a pixel, there must be $4^n$ leaf nodes in the quadtree. Therefore, the quadtree must have $n$ levels and the entire representation of $4^n$ pixel locations requires

$$\sum_{k=0}^{n} 4^k \approx \tfrac{4}{3} 4^n$$

nodes. Thus, without considering ways to efficiently represent quadtrees, the complete quadtree requires approximately $\frac{1}{3}$ of the storage required for the ordinary spatial representation of the image.

The structure inherent in the quadtree representation may be expressed with several numbering codes. This results in a label on each pixel, indicating membership in specific image subdivisions, as shown in Figure 7.6. Proceeding from left to right in each pixel code, each digit represents the node location in the respective level, where the $0^{th}$ level is not used (i.e., it is assumed the pixels are known to be in a specific image).

In the case of binary images, considerable economy in storage may be obtained by simply storing the coordinates of the nonzero pixels. For example, as shown in Figure 7.7, if few of the pixels in the image are ON or "1," the image may be efficiently stored and exactly reconstructed by using a list of the Cartesian coordinates corresponding to the ON pixels. A similar economy may be obtained in the quadtree representation by subdividing the image until the members of each subdivision are either all ON or all OFF, as shown in Figure 7.7b.

## PYRAMIDAL ANALYSIS

The quadtree concept has been introduced as a spatial decomposition technique, without regard to the representation of grey-level intensities at each level. Using a simple (quadrant) averaging approach (which is computationally simple, but does

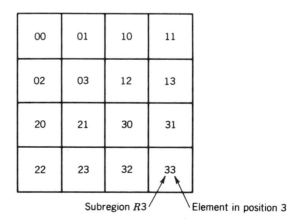

**FIGURE 7.6** Pixel locations using quadtree and quantic notation

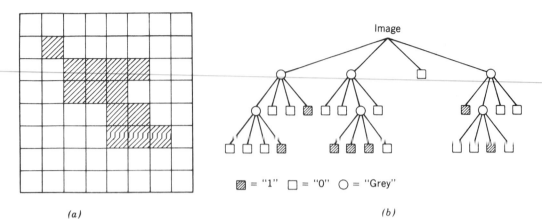

(a)

(b)

**FIGURE 7.7** Quadtree representation of binary image
(a)   8 × 8 image
(b)   Resulting quadtree

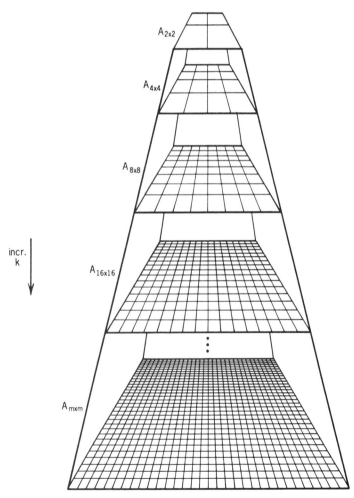

**FIGURE 7.8**   (Discrete) pyramid structure

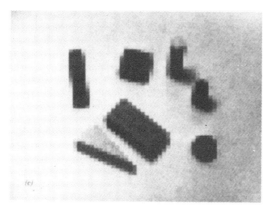
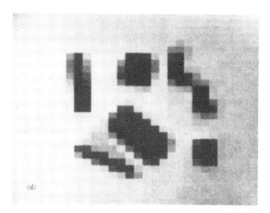
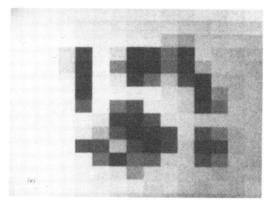

**FIGURE 7.9** Sequence of images with varying resolution (quadrant averaging used)
(a)  240 × 256 pixels (× 6 bits)
(b)  120 × 128 pixels
(c)  60 × 64 pixels
(d)  30 × 32 pixels
(e)  15 × 16 pixels

not guarantee that extrema are preserved), the objective is the creation of a sequence of 2-D arrays of varying (increasing or decreasing) resolution, as shown in Figure 7.8. A pyramid, $P$, is the set of images

$$P = \{ A_{1 \times 1}, A_{2 \times 2}, A_{4 \times 4}, \ldots, A_{256 \times 256}, A_{m \times m} \} \qquad (7\text{-}8)$$

where $m = 2^n$. In this pyramidal representation, $A_{m \times m}$ is the full or highest resolution image; $A_{1 \times 1}$ is a (probably useless) one-pixel representation of the reduced resolution image. The pyramid may be viewed as a 4-D entity where the intensity is a function of three arguments: a level designator and a set of indices with level-dependent support, that is, the pyramid is denoted $f(i, j, k)$, where $i$ and $j$ are spatial indices and $k$ is the level in the pyramid.

The creation of a quadtree or pyramid and image representation is straightforward. Quadruples of pixels in the input image are examined. A function to relate images at one resolution to another (perhaps recursively) is necessary. This is shown below via an averaging approach. Given the input image at level $n$ (the highest resolution), a pyramid is created via

$$f(i,j,k) = \left(\frac{1}{4}\right) \sum_{p=0}^{1} \sum_{q=0}^{1} f(2i+p, 2j+q, k+1) \qquad (7\text{-}9)$$

where for a $2^n \times 2^n$ image,

$$k \in [0, n]$$

and, at level $k$, the indices are restricted to

$$0 \le i, j \le 2^k - 1$$

The process in Eq. 7-9 is repeated until an image of the desired level (or consisting of a single pixel) is obtained. Figure 7.9 shows an example of a pyramid. Note that most of the information, or significant detail, exists in the images in the pyramid with significantly lower resolution.

# ■ HIGHER DIMENSIONAL MODELING (2-$\frac{1}{2}$ and 3-D)

In this section, we explore modeling methodologies for representing the information relative to underlying scene objects. This includes so-called *intrinsic* or 2-$\frac{1}{2}$-*D* images and 3-D volumetric representations. An intrinsic image is a subset of the class of *generalized images*, which are obtained as the output of lower level, model-based early vision processing algorithms. Generalized images are typically iconic (e.g., a relational graph of a segmented image in terms of regions).

## 2-$\frac{1}{2}$-D MODELS AND THE GAUSSIAN IMAGE

A good example of a 2-$\frac{1}{2}$-D model is the so-called *Extended Gaussian Image (EGI) model* (Horn, 1984). The EGI model records the variation of surface area with surface orientation. Examples of the use and theory of EGI models is found in Little (1985) and Horaud (1987). A simple example of the Gaussian Image concept is shown in Figure 7.10a. In polyhedron object models, the EGI representation involves a model consisting of visible areas and normals to these areas, as shown in Figure 7.10b. Recognition of objects with the EGI models proceeds by first determining the EGI of the visible object portion (using a photometric stereo model and point determination scheme). The EGI of the stored object that most closely matches the extracted EGI then determines the object identity, in a nearest-neighbor classification or matching scheme. The EGI object representation is sensitive to object rotations and thus the classification scheme is sensitive to orientation.

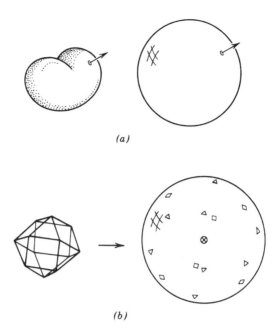

**FIGURE 7.10**

(a) The Gaussian image of an object is obtained by associating with each point on its surface the point on the Gaussian sphere which has the same surface orientation. The mapping is invertible if the object has positive Gaussian curvature everywhere.

(b) The extended Gaussian image of a polyhedron can be thought of as a collection of point masses on the Gaussian sphere. Each mass is proportional to the area of the corresponding face. Point masses on the visible hemisphere are shown as solid marks, the others as open marks. The center of mass (shown as the symbol ⊗) must be at the center of the sphere if the polyhedron is a closed subject. (Copyright © 1984 IEEE)

## *3-D MODELING ISSUES*

A major problem underlying model-based 3-D vision is the issue of 3-D modeling. This includes the search for

**1.** Tractable (manipulable) models.
**2.** Models conceptually related to visual appearance.
**3.** 3-D object representation and descriptive approaches.

The use of 3-D models is an attempt to bridge the gap between the 2-D image data and the 3-D scene. From the point of view of the perspective-projective (p-p) model of Chapter 2, it is not possible to exactly reconstruct 3-D scene structures with a single 2-D image, *in the absence of any additional information that leads to additional constraints*. Thus, the image analysis problem is numerically underconstrained using the p-p geometric model; however, a higher level of modeling involving symbolic constraints may lead to unique solutions.

### GENERALIZED CYLINDERS AND SWEPT VOLUMES

Generalized cylinders are one of the most popular and intuitively satisfying models for 3-D objects. The basis of the models is the concept of a "swept volume" of 2-D area along a 3-D trajectory. Specifically, a generalized cylinder (GC) is a solid whose axis is a 3-D space curve. Usually the axis is perpendicular to the cross section. For example, the typical cylinder, or "can," may be described by sweeping a circle along a line. A generalized cylinder representation is characterized by three parameters (Navatia & Binford, 1977):

1. A planar cross section.
2. A three-dimensional curve or "spine".
3. A sweeping rule.

The GC representation requires specification of the cross section, spine, and sweeping rule in quantitative (analytic) form. We show an extension of the GC modeling approach to qualitative object description (Biederman, 1985). In this approach, the object is specified using

1. A qualitative descriptor of the cross section edge curvature. This may be either straight (S) or curved (C).
2. The cross section degree of symmetry. Symmetry is defined as invariant under reflection and rotation (Symm + +), invariant under reflection only (Symm +) or asymmetric (Asymm).
3. The change of cross section as a function of sweep. This may be constant

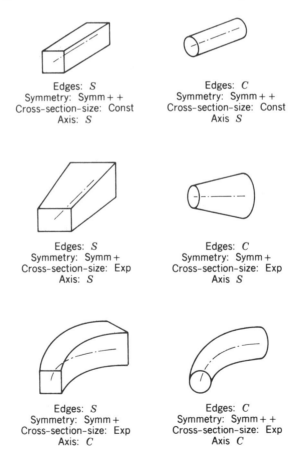

<table>
<tr><td>Edges: S<br>Symmetry: Symm + +<br>Cross-section-size: Const<br>Axis: S</td><td>Edges: C<br>Symmetry: Symm + +<br>Cross-section-size: Const<br>Axis S</td></tr>
<tr><td>Edges: S<br>Symmetry: Symm +<br>Cross-section-size: Exp<br>Axis: S</td><td>Edges: C<br>Symmetry: Symm +<br>Cross-section-size: Exp<br>Axis S</td></tr>
<tr><td>Edges: S<br>Symmetry: Symm +<br>Cross-section-size: Exp<br>Axis: C</td><td>Edges: C<br>Symmetry: Symm + +<br>Cross-section-size: Exp<br>Axis C</td></tr>
</table>

**FIGURE 7.11** Examples of generalized cylinders from |Topa|·and |Agin|

(Const), expanding (Exp), contracting (Contr), expanding then contracting (Exp-Contr), or contracting then expanding (Contr-Exp).

4. The degree of curvature of the spine. This may be straight (S) or curved (C).

An example of generalized cylinder representations, together with these qualitative features, is shown in Figure 7.11. The generalized cylinder approach may be used in a hierarchical scheme in which generalized cylinders are primitives and composition rules specify the relative orientations of the primitives (Agin, 1981).

VOLUMETRIC MODELS AND HIERARCHICAL REPRESENTATIONS

Techniques of constructive solid geometry may be used to develop representations based on 3-D spatial occupancy. For example, 3-D space may be quantized using a 3-D array of volume cells that are either "filled" (i.e., occupied by the object) or not. This reasoning leads to the concept of volume elements or *voxels*, which may be thought of as the 3-D counterparts of 2-D pixels. The voxel representation allows a hierarchical 3-D cell-based representation of space.

An example of a hierarchical representation in 3-D is the use of a related octree representation of 3-D scene views for next best view determination (Connolly, 1985). A 3-D object model viewed in a planetarium scenario is assumed, that is, enclosed by a sphere where the viewer may reside at any point on the sphere and view the object(s) in a direction radially inward. The representation of the enclosed 3-D space containing the object is based on the use of octrees to indicate, from a given viewing direction, whether the space is empty, occupied, or unseen.

Numerous ways to acquire 3-D information from images exist. In this and previous chapters, we have explored several of these techniques, including stereo, motion, and radiometric image formation models. Figure 7.12 (Nitzan, 1988) summarizes 3-D measurement techniques.

# ■ IMAGE-BASED KNOWLEDGE MANIPULATION

## *INTRODUCTION*

This section explores a significant research area in computer vision. To some extent, it may be viewed as an extension of the structured (syntactic) description approach in Chapter 6. In addition to the theoretical underpinnings, we explore the two emerging paradigms for image knowledge representation and manipulation, namely *rule-based systems* and *first-order predicate logic*. These approaches are fundamentally different in theory. Their implementations, however, rely on much common processing (unification).

Specifically, an image or scene description is desired. This is based on labeled or identified objects, and the use of a priori constraints to achieve a consistent interpretation. The concepts of labels and constraints have a strong AI link and lead to relational approaches. Often we have less confidence in the individual feature class, or label, but are easily able to discern, with a high degree of confidence, the relationships among "loosely" labeled features. Knowledge of these relationships and their constraints may be used to guide, in an iterative manner, the labeling of image entities. In some sense, we are modeling what cannot occur

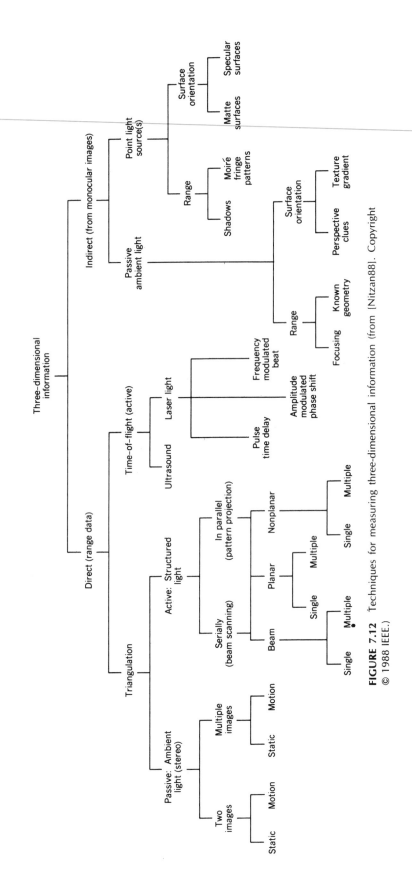

**FIGURE 7.12** Techniques for measuring three-dimensional information (from [Nitzan88]. Copyright © 1988 IEEE.)

and thereby systematically ruling out what is often a formidable amount of possibilities.

The search for consistency, given a set of constraints, may be achieved by a production system consisting of a set of allowable combinations of information at various levels. Low-level productions may be handled by a grammar-based approach; typically, rules or logical constraints are employed at higher levels. We will investigate these approaches using the symbolic manipulation languages PROLOG and LISP, which are summarized in Appendix 6. Elements of discrete mathematics that are applicable to image analysis models, representations, and approaches are summarized in Appendix 5.

## SYMBOLIC IMAGE AND SCENE MODELING

### MODELS AND ATTRIBUTES

In any attempt at modeling and implementing high-level vision processes, we identify three levels or development stages, as shown in Figure 7.13. These are the *conceptual*, *representational*, and *implementational* levels. Note also that Figure 7.13 indicates that a practical model is incomplete, that is, it is not possible to exhaustively model all aspects of a situation. The level of completencss for the model is a function of the available features and determines, to some extent, the range of applicability of the model.

*Declarative and Procedural Models and Representations.* Image-based knowledge models and representation approaches may be subdivided into *declarative* (meaning the representation of facts and assertions) and *procedural* (meaning the storing of actions or consequences). Research emphasis appears divided between these approaches. The specifics of an application may dictate a preference for a particular approach.

Declarative schemes include logic-based and relational approaches. Relational models may lead to representations in the form of trees, graphs, or semantic networks (see Appendix 5). Logical representation schemes include the use of propositional logic and, more important, predicate logic implementations (e.g., PROLOG). Procedural models and representational schemes, on the other hand, are characterized by formal grammars (as in Chapter 6) and are usually implemented via procedural or rule-based (production) systems.

## APPLICATION OF SYMBOLIC MODELING AND CONSTRAINT SATISFACTION TO IMAGE LABELING—AN EXTENDED EXAMPLE

### INTRODUCTION

In this section, we build on the mathematical formalism for high level image representation presented in the previous section and in Appendix 5. Specifically, we consider both the theoretical and practical aspects associated with image description or analysis. For example, we develop a relational model for the information in a segmented image, using constraints in the form of relations between regions. The image description then proceeds by labeling the image regions with labels consistent with the high-level constraints. We develop several alternative (but related) approaches to the problem. One alternative involving neural network computing is

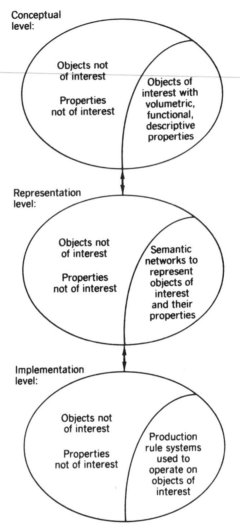

**FIGURE 7.13** Sample development stages for a high level computer vision system

detailed in Chapter 8. Although simplistic, this example exemplifies many of the significant theoretical and practical aspects of this type of image analysis problem.

### OVERALL PROBLEM FORMULATION

Region labeling serves as the basis for an image description, since after the identity of each image region is determined, the overall image contents may be described on the basis of the nature and interrelationships of labeled regions.

We assume that a preprocessing algorithm has produced a segmented image of the form shown in Figure 7.14. As the figure indicates, we consider the labeling of six regions, denoted as R1, R2, . . ., R6, with five possible labels: car, road, trees, grass, and sky. An exhaustive enumeration of the unconstrained labeling of these regions yields $5^6$ or 15,625 possibilities.

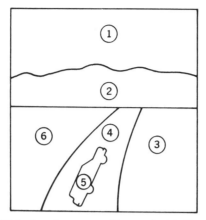

**FIGURE 7.14**  Sample segmented image (for labelling example)

CONSTRAINT DETERMINATION

Two types of sample constraints are used:

1. *Unary* constraints or properties.
2. *Binary* constraints or relations. "Next-to(a,b)" is an example of this type of constraint.

It is necessary to formulate the image-labeling problem constraints. For simplicity, we first consider a single binary constraint, namely that of region adjacency. Two regions that share a boundary are said to be adjacent. This is an easily extracted relation involving the image regions shown in Figure 7.14. Adjacency is a symmetric relation (see Appendix 5), which is easily depicted via an adjacency graph. The region adjacency graph (in terms of unlabeled regions $R_i$) for the sample segmented image in Figure 7.14 is shown in Figure 7.15. Although adjacency is a symmetric relation, it is not transitive, that is, *a* adjacent to *b* and *b* adjacent to *c* does not imply *a* adjacent to *c* (since we may have to go through region *b* to get to region *c* from region *a*). We indicate the symmetry of the adjacency relation by an undirected arc in the figure.

A set of constraints on allowable labels may be developed as a function of whether the regions are adjacent or not. For example, it makes sense to allow two adjacent regions to have the labels "car" and "road," that is, human intuition is not violated when viewing an image in which a car is adjacent to a road. On the other hand, a car adjacent to grass (the driver is driving off the road) is atypical. We therefore generate the set of compatible labels shown below and graphically in Figure 7.16.

**FIGURE 7.15**  Observed region adjacency graph

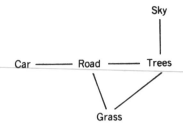

**FIGURE 7.16** Allowed (constrained) adjacent region labels

We do not enumerate the symmetric version of each allowable adjacency relation in the list below.

Allowable Labels on Adjacent Regions
"car" is adjacent to "road"
"road" is adjacent to "grass"
"grass" is adjacent to "trees"
"road" is adjacent to "trees"
"sky" is adjacent to "trees"
(symmetry of relation not enumerated)

PROLOG IMPLEMENTATION OF CONSTRAINT SATISFACTION

We now develop an appropriate solution and implementation to the constrained labeling problem formulated in the previous three sections. The list of allowed labels on adjacent regions is used to generate the following PROLOG database:

Sample PROLOG Problem Database (Adjacency Labeling Constraint)
adjacent_to(car,road).
adjacent_to(road,car).
adjacent_to(road,grass).
adjacent_to(grass,road).
adjacent_to(road,trees).
adjacent_to(trees,road).
adjacent_to(sky,trees).
adjacent_to(trees,sky).
adjacent_to(grass,trees).
adjacent_to(trees,grass).

This database of facts, based on the PROLOG predicate adjacent_to, incorporates the constraints shown in Figure 7.16. To formulate a processing goal, the observed region adjacency graph (incorporating the region variables) must be formulated as a conjunction of clauses involving the predicate adjacent_to. For example,

Goal for Sample Problem (Simplified)
adjacent_to(R1,R2),
adjacent_to(R2,R6),
adjacent_to(R2,R3),

adjacent_to(R3,R4),
adjacent_to(R2,R4),
adjacent_to(R4,R6),
adjacent_to(R4,R5).

The result of all possible unifications of this goal with the database (since the problem is still underconstrained) indicates 42 possible solutions. Lest the reader suspect these are erroneous solutions, we emphasize that each of these solutions satisfies the allowable adjacency graph. The fact that most of these solutions contradict human intuition results from the fact that the PROLOG system "sees" the PROLOG database, not the figure. Furthermore, the 42 solutions include the correct one, that is, the one a human observer would return.

Although we have considerably reduced the *solution space*, we have not reached our goal of a consistent labeling that would be produced by a human observer. To do this, additional constraints must be employed to further restrict the solution space. To accomplish this, two additional unary constraints are employed: "highest" and "moving." The revised goal and database are shown below.

Goal Modification
adjacent_to(R1,R2),
adjacent_to(R2,R6),
adjacent_to(R2,R3),
adjacent_to(R3,R4),
adjacent_to(R2,R4),
adjacent_to(R4,R6),
adjacent_to(R4,R5),
highest(R1),
moving(R5).

Database Modification
highest(sky).
moving(car).
adjacent_to(car,road).
adjacent_to(road,car).
adjacent_to(road,grass).
adjacent_to(grass,road).
adjacent_to(road,trees).
adjacent_to(trees,road).
adjacent_to(sky,trees).
adjacent_to(trees,sky).
adjacent_to(grass,trees).
adjacent_to(trees,grass).

This approach yields a single solution, the one a human observer would have produced, as shown in Figure 7.17. Note that the use of five symmetric adjacency constraints and two unary constraints eliminated all but 0.0064 percent of the possible (unconstrained) labelings. This indicates the value of high-level symbolic manipulation in the image analysis process.

We now consider alternate mathematical formulations of this problem.

region 1 is bound to   sky
region 2 is bound to   trees
region 3 is bound to   road
region 4 is bound to   grass
region 5 is bound to   road
region 6 is bound to   road

region 1 is bound to   sky
region 2 is bound to   trees
region 3 is bound to   grass
region 4 is bound to   road
region 5 is bound to   car
region 6 is bound to   grass

**(b)**

region 1 is bound to   sky
region 2 is bound to   trees
region 3 is bound to   road
region 4 is bound to   grass
region 5 is bound to   trees
region 6 is bound to   road

region 1 is bound to   sky
region 2 is bound to   trees
region 3 is bound to   grass ⎫
region 4 is bound to   road  ⎬  correct solution
region 5 is bound to   car   ⎭
region 6 is bound to   grass

region 1 is bound to   sky
region 2 is bound to   trees
region 3 is bound to   grass
region 4 is bound to   road
region 5 is bound to   grass
region 6 is bound to   grass

region 1 is bound to   sky
region 2 is bound to   trees
region 3 is bound to   grass
region 4 is bound to   road
region 5 is bound to   trees
region 6 is bound to   grass

**(a)**

**FIGURE 7.17**   PROLOG image labeling results
(a)   Results using a single unary constraint (highest)
(b)   Results with two unary constraints (highest, moving)

## ALTERNATE MATHEMATICAL FORMULATION OF LABELING

To introduce alternate formulations, recall the basic premise of the constraint satisfaction (labeling) problem:

*Given feature information extracted from a problem domain in terms of a set of (unlabeled or variable) entities and observed relations, use a set of a priori constraints (that labels of objects satisfying these relations must satisfy) to map labels to objects so that a valid, that is, globally consistent, labeling is obtained.*

When it is accomplished in an iterative fashion, the constraint satisfaction process involving labeling we are considering is referred to as *relaxation labeling*. The terminology and formulation is from Henderson (1984). The basis for this approach applied to image processing was developed by Rosenfeld, et al. (1976), and explored by Hummel and Zucker (1983).

We define the following quantities:

$$U = \{u_1, u_2, \ldots, u_n\} \text{ is the set of } n \text{ objects to be labeled.}$$

$$\Omega = \{\lambda_1, \lambda_2, \ldots, \lambda_m\} \text{ is the set of } m \text{ possible labels.}$$

and

$$\Omega_i = \{l_1, l_2, \ldots, l_m\}^T$$

is a binary column vector that indicates the applicable labels for object $u_i$, that is, the $j^{\text{th}}$ component of $\Omega_i$ is 1 if label $\lambda_j$ is compatible with $u_i$; otherwise, it is zero. This is necessary since some labels in $\Omega$ may be inappropriate for certain objects. Note that this vector only specifies the possible or allowable labels on a certain object; no concern is paid to the compatibility of adjacent (or otherwise related) object labels at this point. This vector therefore indicates a unary constraint on the allowable labels for each object. As indicated by the notation, all vectors are understood to be column vectors.

Along with the above binary vector, we define the corresponding set entities:

$\Gamma_i$ = the set of all $\lambda$ such that the corresponding element in $\Omega_i$ is 1.

$\Gamma_{ij}$ = the set of all label pairs corresponding to valid labels on adjacent objects $u_i$ and $u_j$ that is, labels that correspond to $c_{ij}$ (defined below) = 1. Note $\Gamma_{ij} \subseteq \Gamma_i \times \Gamma_j$.

We now address the determination of interlabel compatibility by defining an $m \times m$ compatibility matrix $C$ such that the $i,j^{\text{th}}$ element of $C$, denoted $c_{ij}$ is given by

$$c_{ij} = \begin{cases} 1 & \text{if } \lambda_i \text{ is compatible with } \lambda_j \\ 0 & \text{otherwise} \end{cases} \tag{7-10}$$

In other words, $C$ conveys the compatibility of all label pairs with regard to a relation among their corresponding objects. Clearly, all compatible label pairs $(\lambda_i, \lambda_j)$ for which $c_{ij} = 1$ are a subset of $\Gamma_i \times \Gamma_j$. We may then define an $m \times m$ label compatibility matrix for objects $u_i$ and $u_j$ as the matrix $\Omega_{ij}$. First, we consider the set of all possible label pairs on these two objects (without any constraints on the compatibility of the labels). This information may be written as an $m \times m$ matrix ($P_{ij}$, for "permissible") and is given by the outer product of the $\Omega_i$ and $\Omega_j$ vectors indicating applicable labels for each object. This constraint in terms of the binary matrix $P$ may be written

$$P_{ij} = \rangle \, \Omega_i, \Omega_j \, \langle$$

where the $\rangle \langle$ symbols indicate vector outer product, that is,

$$P_{ij} = (\Omega_i \times \Omega_j^T), \tag{7-11}$$

and the $\times$ indicates vector multiplication. The $P_{ij}$ matrix, therefore, only indicates the possible combinations of label pairs on $u_i$ and $u_j$. For example, if the $q,r^{\text{th}}$ element of $P_{ij}$ is 1, this indicates that label $\lambda_q$ is a permissible label for object $u_i$ and label $\lambda_r$ is a permissible label for $u_j$, but the $q,r^{\text{th}}$ element of $P_{ij}$ does not consider the interobject compatibility of the labels. Clearly, in determining a valid labeling, this is the first step. The next step is to introduce constraints between the labels on objects which satisfy a certain relation, e.g., adjacent objects. To do this, we introduce a function $Nei\ (i,j)$, which has the form

$$Nei\ (i,j) = \begin{cases} 1, & \text{if } u_i \text{ and } u_j \text{ are adjacent (i.e., neighbors)} \\ 0, & \text{otherwise} \end{cases} \tag{7-12}$$

Thus, the complement of the $Nei$ function (denoted $\neg\ Nei$) signifies the situation where $u_i$ and $u_j$ are not neighbors, and we may use this information to avoid invoking any interlabel compatibility constraints. Finally, we define a matrix $E$ that is a matrix of all 1's. With this, we are able to show the evolution of the $m \times m$ label compatibility matrix for objects $u_i$ and $u_j$, denoted $\Omega_{ij}$, as

$$\Omega_{ij} = P_{ij} * (\neg\ Nei\ (i,j)\ E\ +\ C) \tag{7-13}$$

where the $*$ and $+$ indicate element-by-element Boolean AND and OR operations, respectively. Thus, we see that the second term in Eq. 7-13 handles the case where the labels on adjacent or neighboring objects must be compatible.

For example, in the case where $u_i$ and $u_j$ are not neighbors, the binary label compatibility matrix for objects $u_i$ and $u_j$ is simply

$$\Omega_{ij} = \Omega_i \times \Omega_j^T \tag{7-14}$$

Conversely, if these objects are neighbors, then

$$\Omega_{ij} = (\Omega_i \times \Omega_j^T) * C \tag{7-15}$$

Note that Eq. 7-13 constrains labels on the adjacent objects to be both permissible (via the $\Omega_i$'s) and compatible (via $C$). There exists one matrix $\Omega_{ij}$ for each pair of objects.

*Relaxation-Based Solution Approach (Deterministic Approach).* Consider the problem representation as a digraph (note that the symmetry of the relation we are considering, i.e., adjacency, allows us to ignore the relation direction). The nodes, numbered $i = 1$ through $n$, correspond to the regions or objects to be labeled. The observed relation between nodes is indicated as arcs in the digraph. In addition, each node (e.g., node $i$) has an associated set of labels, denoted $\Gamma_i$, with a member in $\Gamma_i$ denoted by $t$. In the case where $\Omega_i = [1, 1, 1, \ldots, 1]^T$, (i.e., any label is possible on any object), $\Gamma_i = \Gamma\ \forall i$, where each $\Gamma$ has (initially) $m$ members.

Interobject label compatibility is represented by denoting $\Gamma_{ij}$ as the set of all label pairs $(t,t')$ *which correspond to* the $\Omega_{ij} = 1$. Thus, in this formulation, the local processing objective is the following:

*Given pairs of nodes i and j, determine what should be discarded from $\Gamma_i$ and $\Gamma_j$ using $\Gamma_{ij}$.*

This yields the *label discarding rule* (Hummel and Zucker, 1983), where we adopt the following processing paradigm:

*Discard label $t \in \Gamma_i$ at node i, if $\exists$ a neighbor j of i such that every label $t' \in \Gamma_j$ is incompatible with t, i.e., $(t,t') \notin \Gamma_{ij}\ \forall t'$ in $\Gamma_j$.*

This rule may be applied iteratively at each node until there is no further change in the $\Gamma_i$, in a manner analogous to the numerical relaxation process examined above. This yields the *limiting label sets*, or simply *limit sets*. Notice we employ a local test for each $(t, t')$ pair, seeking support for the hypothesis that the assigned label is valid in the local labeling context. In the case where one or more $\Gamma_i$ are empty, there is no globally consistent labeling. Conversely, the case of one or more $\Gamma_i$ in the limit set with several elements indicates a nonunique globally consistent solution.

The reader may also want to consider a positive formulation (i.e., a "label retention rule") of the above approach. It is left as an exercise to determine the validity of the following alternative approach:

*Retain* $t \in \Gamma_i$ *at node* i *if* $\nexists$ *a* t' *s.t* $(t, t') \in \Gamma_{ij}$ $\forall$ *neighbors of* i.

*Example Using the Image Labeling Problem.* In terms of the constraint formulation in our previous example, we develop the $C$ matrix as follows:

### Adjacency-based label compatibility matrix

|  | $\lambda_1$ (car) | $\lambda_2$ (grass) | $\lambda_3$ (road) | $\lambda_4$ (trees) | $\lambda_5$ (sky) |
|---|---|---|---|---|---|
| $\lambda_1$ (car) | 0 | 0 | 1 | 0 | 0 |
| $\lambda_2$ (grass) | 0 | 0 | 1 | 1 | 0 |
| $\lambda_3$ (road) | 1 | 1 | 0 | 1 | 0 |
| $\lambda_4$ (trees) | 0 | 1 | 1 | 0 | 1 |
| $\lambda_5$ (sky) | 0 | 0 | 0 | 1 | 0 |

We form the graphical abstraction shown in Figure 7.18a. For simplicity, let us assume that we enter the node-serial iterative process at a point somewhere before the convergence of the algorithm and that the highest and moving constraints are also employed to yield a unique solution. The starting state of our example is therefore shown in Figure 7.18b. The solution process using the label discarding rule is shown in Figure 7.18c.

### EXTENSION TO CONTINUOUS/PROBABILISTIC FORMULATIONS

In the discrete relaxation approach discussed in the preceding section, pairs of labels are either compatible or (meaning "exclusive or") completely incompatible, that is, only one of two logical assertions regarding the satisfaction of a local constraint is possible. An extension to this approach, which yields continuous relaxation, is to allow compatibilities to be described in terms of relative preferences (or probabilities) via weighted values from a continuous interval. Since, in our previous example, membership in $\Gamma_{ij}$ is a binary function (i.e., an element is either a member of the set or not), this extension formally proceeds on the basis of fuzzy set theory (Zadeh, 1975).

The continuous formulation allows encoding of relational information in a more flexible fashion and may lead to more efficient solutions (i.e., quicker algorithm convergence). For example, in our previous example, the labels "grass" and "road" on adjacent objects (regions) were as equally allowable as the labels "road" and "trees."

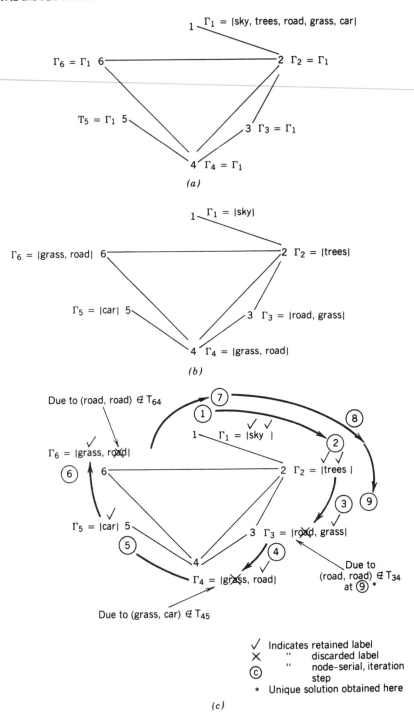

**FIGURE 7.18** Example of constraint satisfaction using "label discarding rule"
(a) Initial state
(b) Starting state for solution illustration
(c) Steps leading to unique solution

The revised constraint satisfaction formulation is based on the determination of local support for compatible labels. Labels are no longer thought of as just being compatible, but rather certain adjacent label combinations are viewed as positively, negatively or neutrally supporting a hypothesis concerning the true state of the object label. For example, the hypothesis "the label on object $i$ is sky" is positively supported if it is observed that a label on an adjacent object is "trees," but the hypothesis is negatively supported if the label on an adjacent object is "car." This is akin to a reward and punishment strategy.

Initially, a label suitability or confidence measure for label $t$ denoted $P_i(t)$ is defined.

$$P_i(t) = \begin{cases} 1, & \text{if } t \text{ is associated with object } i \text{ in the limit set} \\ 0, & \text{if } t \text{ is not associated with object } i \text{ in the limit set} \end{cases}$$

Furthermore, the strength of a constraint will be denoted using the variable $r_{ij}(t,t')$, where

$$r_{ij}(t,t') = \begin{cases} 1, & \text{if } (t,t') \in \Gamma_{ij} \\ 0, & \text{otherwise} \end{cases} \tag{7-16}$$

Note that $r_{ij}(t,t')$ contains information equivalent to the $(p,q)^{\text{th}}$ component of $\Omega_{ij}$ above, where the $p^{\text{th}}$ row corresponds to $t$ and the $q^{\text{th}}$ column corresponds to $t'$.

A more flexible formulation allows the compatibility measures $P$ and $r$ to take on values over a continuous range, which spawns a continuous (as opposed to discrete) constraint satisfaction problem. $P_i(t)$ thus denotes confidence in the assignment of label $t$ with object $i$. Normalizing

$$0 \le P_i(t) \le 1 \qquad \forall\ i,t$$

and

$$\sum_\tau P_i(\tau) = 1 \qquad \forall\ i = 1,2\ldots, n \tag{7-17}$$

allows $P_i$ to be interpreted as a probability. Furthermore, we adopt the following interpretation for $r_{ij}(t,t')$:

$$r_{ij}(t,t') = \begin{cases} 1.0 \text{ if label } t \text{ on object } i \text{ supports label } t' \text{ on object } j \\ 0.0 \text{ if there is no supportive interaction between labels } t \text{ and} \\ \quad t' \text{ (e.g., objects } i \text{ and } j \text{ are not related—the "neutral} \\ \quad \text{case)} \\ -1.0 \text{ if labels } t \text{ and } t' \text{ on the respective objects are} \\ \quad \text{inconsistent} \end{cases} \tag{7-18}$$

In terms of the above measures, the support for label $t$ at object $i$, denoted $s_i(t)$, is

$$s_i(t) = \sum_{j \ne i} \sum_{t'} r_{ij}(t,t')\, P_j(t') \tag{7-19}$$

It is often necessary to normalize $s_i(t)$, that is,

$$s_i(t) = c\sum_{j \ne i} \sum_{t'} r_{ij}(t,t')\, P_j(t') \tag{7-20}$$

where, for example, $c = 1/n$. In the limit set, a label, $t$, that has positive support from many neighbors will thus have a large value of $s_i(t)$. The only remaining step is to form a reasonable iterative procedure that allows modification of the $P_i(t)$ values $\forall\ i,t$, using $s_i(t)$.

An interactive solution procedure modified from Rosenfeld, Hummel, and Zucker (1976) is

Iterative Stochastic Labeling Algorithm

**1.** Initialize $P_i(t)^{(k)}$ for $k = 0$.

**2.** Form

$$s_i(t)^{(k)}, \text{ using } P_i(t)^{(k)}$$

Normalize or modify $s_i(t)^{(k)}$ so that $[1 + s_i(t)^{(k)}]$ is nonnegative.

**3.** Form

$$P_i(t)^{(k+1)} = \frac{\{P_i(t)^{(k)}\,[1 + s_i(t)^{(k)}]\}}{D^{(k)}} \qquad (7\text{-}21)$$

where

$$D^{(k)} = \sum_t P_i(t)^{(k)}\,[1 + s_i(t)^{(k)}]$$

**4.** Stop when values of $P_i(t)^{(k)}$ converge.

Of course, other formulations are possible.

We now consider an example of the previous approach to image region labeling, using two examples. First, we must choose a set of compatibility coefficients. Notice that with five possible values for $t$ and $t'$, for fixed $ij$ the matrices are of dimension $5 \times 5$. Furthermore, given six regions to label, the pairwise consideration of six items yields thirty $5 \times 5$ matrices. Recall, for each value of $ij$, the matrix column values that correspond to the label

$$t' \rightarrow$$

(car)    (grass)    (road)    (trees)    (sky)

and row values correspond to the labels

(car)

(grass)            $t$

(road)              $\downarrow$

(trees)

(sky)

We consider the following cases:

*Case 1: Regions* i *and* j *are adjacent.*

In this case, we have considerable freedom in the selection of $r_{ij}(t,t')$ parameters. For example, simply using the label comparability matrix for adjacent objects (i.e., $\Omega_{ij}$) yields a matrix:

$$\begin{bmatrix} 0 & 0 & 1 & 0 & 0 \\ 0 & 0 & 1 & 1 & 0 \\ 1 & 1 & 0 & 1 & 0 \\ 0 & 1 & 1 & 0 & 1 \\ 0 & 0 & 0 & 1 & 0 \end{bmatrix}$$

Because there is considerable freedom in choosing the $r_{ij}(t,t')$ parameters, other a priori information may be incorporated. For example, $r_{ij}$ may reflect the number of neighbors of a particular region. For example, one possible formulation is

$$r_{ij}(t,t') = 1 \text{ IF}$$

**a.** Region $i$ is observed adjacent to region $j$.

**b.** Label $t$ and $t'$ are compatible under adjacency.

**c.** The number of regions that region $i$ is observed to be adjacent to is greater than or equal to the number of labels that label $t$ is allowed to be adjacent to.

This constraint formulation is shown in Figure 7.19.

```
       i
   ┌──────▶
   │  00000   00100   00000   00000   00000   00000
   ▼  00000   00000   00000   00000   00000   00000
 j    00000   00000   00000   00000   00000   00000
      00000   00000   00000   00000   00000   00000
      00000   00010   00000   00000   00000   00000

      00100   00000   00100   00100   00000   00100
      00110   00000   00110   00110   00000   00110
      11010   00000   11010   11010   00000   11010
      01101   00000   01101   01101   00000   01101
      00010   00000   00010   00010   00000   00010

      00000   00100   00000   00100   00000   00000
      00000   00110   00000   00110   00000   00000
      00000   00000   00000   00000   00000   00000
      00000   00000   00000   00000   00000   00000
      00000   00010   00000   00010   00000   00000

      00000   00100   00100   00000   00100   00100
      00000   00110   00110   00000   00110   00110
      00000   11010   11010   00000   11010   11010
      00000   01101   01101   00000   01101   01101
      00000   00010   00010   00000   00010   00010

      00000   00000   00000   00100   00000   00000
      00000   00000   00000   00000   00000   00000
      00000   00000   00000   00000   00000   00000
      00000   00000   00000   00000   00000   00000
      00000   00000   00000   00010   00000   00000

      00000   00100   00000   00100   00000   00000
      00000   00110   00000   00110   00000   00000
      00000   00000   00000   00000   00000   00000
      00000   00000   00000   00000   00000   00000
      00000   00010   00000   00010   00000   00000
```

**FIGURE 7.19**  One choice of label compatibility coefficients $r_{ij}(t,t')$ (see text)

*Case 2: Regions* i *and* j *are not adjacent.*

A simplistic interpretation for this case is that because no positive or negative supporting (conflicting) information is possible, the zero matrix is appropriate. This was chosen in Figure 7.19.

*Case 3:* i = j.

Here, the suitability of assigning any nonzero weight to the $r_{ij}(t,t')$ parameters makes little sense, since for $t \neq t'$ the weights should be zero, and for $t = t'$ the only effect of a positive weight would be a false reinforcement of our choice of label $t$. Thus, we set all matrices in this case equal to the zero matrix.

Note that the choices of label compatibility coefficients, $r_{ij}(t,t')$ shown in Figure 7.19 are neither unique nor optimal.

*Sample Results.* Initial label probabilities are shown to be equal in the following:

|          | car    | grass  | road   | trees  | sky    |
|----------|--------|--------|--------|--------|--------|
| Region 1 | 0.2000 | 0.2000 | 0.2000 | 0.2000 | 0.2000 |
| Region 2 | 0.2000 | 0.2000 | 0.2000 | 0.2000 | 0.2000 |
| Region 3 | 0.2000 | 0.2000 | 0.2000 | 0.2000 | 0.2000 |
| Region 4 | 0.2000 | 0.2000 | 0.2000 | 0.2000 | 0.2000 |
| Region 5 | 0.2000 | 0.2000 | 0.2000 | 0.2000 | 0.2000 |
| Region 6 | 0.2000 | 0.2000 | 0.2000 | 0.2000 | 0.2000 |

Sample results using these values and the $r_{ij}$ coefficients derived above are shown in Figure 7.20a. Note that the converged solution is ambiguous. In Case 2, we use the same constraint matrices; however, the initial condition in region 1 is forced to indicate that certainty of the correct label is "sky" (analogous to the use of the unary "highest" constraint in the PROLOG formulation) and region 5 is "car". Thus, the initial probability assignments (Case 2) are

|          | car    | grass  | road   | trees  | sky    |
|----------|--------|--------|--------|--------|--------|
| Region 1 | 0.0000 | 0.0000 | 0.0000 | 0.0000 | 1.0000 |
| Region 2 | 0.2000 | 0.2000 | 0.2000 | 0.2000 | 0.2000 |
| Region 3 | 0.2000 | 0.2000 | 0.2000 | 0.2000 | 0.2000 |
| Region 4 | 0.2000 | 0.2000 | 0.2000 | 0.2000 | 0.2000 |
| Region 5 | 1.0000 | 0.0000 | 0.0000 | 0.0000 | 0.0000 |
| Region 6 | 0.2000 | 0.2000 | 0.2000 | 0.2000 | 0.2000 |

Figure 7.20b shows sample results, which are observed to correspond with our previous solution.

The symbolic and numerical manipulation methods presented above all share a common characteristic in that they involve a search for a consistent global solution problem. This leads to computationally expensive solutions in problems of larger dimensionality and suggests the utility of developing additional constraints (or heuristics) to be used to limit the search. The evaluation of relaxation labeling convergence is shown in Fekete, Eklundh, and Rosenfeld (1981). The possibility of implementing constraint satisfaction solutions using the connectionist or neural network computational paradigm is shown in Chapter 8.

The probabilities at iteration   3:

|  | car | grass | road | trees | sky |
|---|---|---|---|---|---|
| region1 | 0.2860 | 0.1427 | 0.1427 | 0.1427 | 0.2860 |
| region2 | 0.0486 | 0.1412 | 0.3808 | 0.3808 | 0.0486 |
| region3 | 0.2010 | 0.4837 | 0.0572 | 0.0572 | 0.2010 |
| region4 | 0.0486 | 0.1412 | 0.3808 | 0.3808 | 0.0486 |
| region5 | 0.2860 | 0.1427 | 0.1427 | 0.1427 | 0.2860 |
| region6 | 0.2010 | 0.4837 | 0.0572 | 0.0572 | 0.2010 |

The probabilities at iteration   6:

|  | car | grass | road | trees | sky |
|---|---|---|---|---|---|
| region1 | 0.3966 | 0.0690 | 0.0690 | 0.0690 | 0.3966 |
| region2 | 0.0049 | 0.0374 | 0.4764 | 0.4764 | 0.0049 |
| region3 | 0.1050 | 0.7805 | 0.0048 | 0.0048 | 0.1050 |
| region4 | 0.0049 | 0.0374 | 0.4764 | 0.4764 | 0.0049 |
| region5 | 0.3966 | 0.0690 | 0.0690 | 0.0690 | 0.3966 |
| region6 | 0.1050 | 0.7805 | 0.0048 | 0.0048 | 0.1050 |

The probabilities at iteration   9:

|  | car | grass | road | trees | sky |
|---|---|---|---|---|---|
| region1 | 0.4632 | 0.0246 | 0.0246 | 0.0246 | 0.4632 |
| region2 | 0.0003 | 0.0061 | 0.4966 | 0.4966 | 0.0003 |
| region3 | 0.0374 | 0.9248 | 0.0002 | 0.0002 | 0.0374 |
| region4 | 0.0003 | 0.0061 | 0.4966 | 0.4966 | 0.0003 |
| region5 | 0.4632 | 0.0246 | 0.0246 | 0.0246 | 0.4632 |
| region6 | 0.0374 | 0.9248 | 0.0002 | 0.0002 | 0.0374 |

The probabilities at iteration   12:

|  | car | grass | road | trees | sky |
|---|---|---|---|---|---|
| region1 | 0.4884 | 0.0077 | 0.0007 | 0.0077 | 0.4884 |
| region2 | 0.0000 | 0.0008 | 0.4996 | 0.4996 | 0.0000 |
| region3 | 0.0117 | 0.9765 | 0.0000 | 0.0000 | 0.0117 |
| region4 | 0.0000 | 0.0008 | 0.4996 | 0.4996 | 0.0000 |
| region5 | 0.4884 | 0.0077 | 0.0077 | 0.0077 | 0.4884 |
| region6 | 0.0117 | 0.9765 | 0.0000 | 0.0000 | 0.0117 |

The probabilities at iteration   15:

|  | car | grass | road | trees | sky |
|---|---|---|---|---|---|
| region1 | 0.4965 | 0.0023 | 0.0023 | 0.0023 | 0.4965 |
| region2 | 0.0000 | 0.0001 | 0.4999 | 0.4999 | 0.0000 |
| region3 | 0.0035 | 0.9929 | 0.0000 | 0.0000 | 0.0035 |
| region4 | 0.0000 | 0.0001 | 0.4999 | 0.4999 | 0.0000 |
| region5 | 0.4965 | 0.0023 | 0.0023 | 0.0023 | 0.4965 |
| region6 | 0.0035 | 0.9929 | 0.0000 | 0.0000 | 0.0035 |

The probabilities at iteration   18:

|  | car | grass | road | trees | sky |
|---|---|---|---|---|---|
| region1 | 0.4990 | 0.0007 | 0.0007 | 0.0007 | 0.4990 |
| region2 | 0.0000 | 0.0000 | 0.5000 | 0.5000 | 0.0000 |
| region3 | 0.0011 | 0.9979 | 0.0000 | 0.0000 | 0.0011 |
| region4 | 0.0000 | 0.0000 | 0.5000 | 0.5000 | 0.0000 |
| region5 | 0.4990 | 0.0007 | 0.0007 | 0.0007 | 0.4990 |
| region6 | 0.0011 | 0.9979 | 0.0000 | 0.0000 | 0.0011 |

The number of iterations  =  19

The converged probabilities:

|  | car | grass | road | trees | sky |
|---|---|---|---|---|---|
| region1 | 0.4993 | 0.0005 | 0.0005 | 0.0005 | 0.4993 |
| region2 | 0.0000 | 0.0000 | 0.5000 | 0.5000 | 0.0000 |
| region3 | 0.0007 | 0.9986 | 0.0000 | 0.0000 | 0.0007 |
| region4 | 0.0000 | 0.0000 | 0.5000 | 0.5000 | 0.0000 |
| region5 | 0.4993 | 0.0005 | 0.0005 | 0.0005 | 0.4993 |
| region6 | 0.0007 | 0.9986 | 0.0000 | 0.0000 | 0.0007 |

**FIGURE 7.20(a)**   Continuous probabilistic relaxation labeling solution (case 1: Initial probabilities equal)

Continued on next page

The probabilities at iteration 12 (continued):

|  | car | grass | road | trees | sky |
|---|---|---|---|---|---|
| region4 | 0.0000 | 0.0001 | 0.9949 | 0.0050 | 0.0000 |
| region5 | 1.0000 | 0.0000 | 0.0000 | 0.0000 | 0.0000 |
| region6 | 0.0110 | 0.9780 | 0.0000 | 0.0000 | 0.0110 |

The probabilities at iteration   15:

|  | car | grass | road | trees | sky |
|---|---|---|---|---|---|
| region1 | 0.0000 | 0.0000 | 0.0000 | 0.0000 | 1.0000 |
| region2 | 0.0000 | 0.0000 | 0.0011 | 0.9989 | 0.0000 |
| region3 | 0.0033 | 0.9934 | 0.0000 | 0.0000 | 0.0033 |
| region4 | 0.0000 | 0.0000 | 0.9989 | 0.0011 | 0.0000 |
| region5 | 1.0000 | 0.0000 | 0.0000 | 0.0000 | 0.0000 |
| region6 | 0.0033 | 0.9934 | 0.0000 | 0.0000 | 0.0033 |

The probabilities at iteration   18:

|  | car | grass | road | trees | sky |
|---|---|---|---|---|---|
| region1 | 0.0000 | 0.0000 | 0.0000 | 0.0000 | 1.0000 |
| region2 | 0.0000 | 0.0000 | 0.0002 | 0.9998 | 0.0000 |
| region3 | 0.0010 | 0.9980 | 0.0000 | 0.0000 | 0.0010 |
| region4 | 0.0000 | 0.0000 | 0.9998 | 0.0002 | 0.0000 |
| region5 | 1.0000 | 0.0000 | 0.0000 | 0.0000 | 0.0000 |
| region6 | 0.0010 | 0.9980 | 0.0000 | 0.0000 | 0.0010 |

The number of iterations = 18

The converged probabilities:

|  | car | grass | road | trees | sky |
|---|---|---|---|---|---|
| region1 | 0.0000 | 0.0000 | 0.0000 | 0.0000 | 1.0000 |
| region2 | 0.0000 | 0.0000 | 0.0002 | 0.9998 | 0.0000 |
| region3 | 0.0010 | 0.9980 | 0.0000 | 0.0000 | 0.0010 |
| region4 | 0.0000 | 0.0000 | 0.9998 | 0.0002 | 0.0000 |
| region5 | 1.0000 | 0.0000 | 0.0000 | 0.0000 | 0.0000 |
| region6 | 0.0010 | 0.9980 | 0.0000 | 0.0000 | 0.0010 |

The probabilities at iteration    3:

|  | car | grass | road | trees | sky |
|---|---|---|---|---|---|
| region1 | 0.0000 | 0.0000 | 0.0000 | 0.0000 | 1.0000 |
| region2 | 0.0427 | 0.0990 | 0.2234 | 0.5996 | 0.0353 |
| region3 | 0.2000 | 0.4916 | 0.0542 | 0.0542 | 0.2000 |
| region4 | 0.0353 | 0.0990 | 0.5996 | 0.2234 | 0.0427 |
| region5 | 1.0000 | 0.0000 | 0.0000 | 0.0000 | 0.0000 |
| region6 | 0.2000 | 0.4916 | 0.0542 | 0.0542 | 0.2000 |

The probabilities at iteration    6:

|  | car | grass | road | trees | sky |
|---|---|---|---|---|---|
| region1 | 0.0000 | 0.0000 | 0.0000 | 0.0000 | 1.0000 |
| region2 | 0.0041 | 0.0141 | 0.0911 | 0.8895 | 0.0012 |
| region3 | 0.1008 | 0.7904 | 0.0040 | 0.0040 | 0.1008 |
| region4 | 0.0012 | 0.0141 | 0.8895 | 0.0911 | 0.0041 |
| region5 | 1.0000 | 0.0000 | 0.0000 | 0.0000 | 0.0000 |
| region6 | 0.1008 | 0.7904 | 0.0040 | 0.0040 | 0.1008 |

The probabilities at iteration    9:

|  | car | grass | road | trees | sky |
|---|---|---|---|---|---|
| region1 | 0.0000 | 0.0000 | 0.0000 | 0.0000 | 1.0000 |
| region2 | 0.0003 | 0.0011 | 0.0227 | 0.9759 | 0.0000 |
| region3 | 0.0353 | 0.9291 | 0.0002 | 0.0227 | 0.0353 |
| region4 | 0.0000 | 0.0011 | 0.9759 | 0.0227 | 0.0003 |
| region5 | 1.0000 | 0.0000 | 0.0000 | 0.0000 | 0.0000 |
| region6 | 0.0353 | 0.9291 | 0.0002 | 0.0002 | 0.0353 |

The probabilities at iteration   12:

|  | car | grass | road | trees | sky |
|---|---|---|---|---|---|
| region1 | 0.0000 | 0.0000 | 0.0000 | 0.0000 | 1.0000 |
| region2 | 0.0000 | 0.0001 | 0.0050 | 0.9949 | 0.0000 |
| region3 | 0.0110 | 0.9780 | 0.0000 | 0.0000 | 0.0110 |

FIGURE 7.20(b)  Continuous probabilistic relaxation labeling solution (Case 2: Unequal initial probabilities)

## PROCEDURAL OR RULE-BASED IMAGE ANALYSIS

In this section, we introduce the formalism of a rule-based systems approach to image analysis and show several examples of applications. We concentrate on the fundamentals of the approach, since specifics will probably change over time. Readers may wish to refer to Appendix 6 for an overview of LISP.

### RULE-BASED SYSTEMS

*Production Systems.* One of the most widely used models of knowledge representation and manipulation is the *production system* (Nilsson, 1980). An example is OPS5, a development environment for rule-based systems. Production system features vary among implementations. The term *expert system* (Davis & Lenat, 1982; Hayes-Roth & King, 1983 Waterman, 1986) is used to indicate a subset of production systems restricted to specific task domains.

A *production system* consists of

1. A set of rules or productions that allow the production of new information or actions on the basis of (currently) known facts
2. A database of information or facts
3. A control mechanism/rule interpreter that determines the applicability of the rules in the context of the current database, the selection of appropriate rules, and the resolution of any conflicts that may arise.

This triad constituting a production system is shown in Figure 7.21(*a*). Of considerable importance in rule-based design is the *control algorithm* or *inference engine* (IE), which implements the control mechanism. Figure 7.21(*b*) shows a simple production system operation.

For practical reasons, the IF-THEN, or implication, (Appendix 5) form is often chosen to represent rules. Image analysis takes place in a *forward-chaining system* by linking initial facts and/or the THEN parts of applicable rules (i.e., those which may be "fired") to the IF parts of others and proceeding until a goal statement is verified. Appendix 5 shows a simple example of forward chaining in a rule-based system.

In reasonable rule-based applications, it is common for the rule base to have 500 to 1000 rules, with each being of considerable complexity. This significantly affects the ability of the system to efficiently search the rule and fact bases, chaining toward an image description. In considering efficient chaining strategies, the incorporation of "metarules" (rules about rules) is used to guide the production of new facts.

*OPS5 Production System Programming Language.* This section introduces the reader to the rudiments of the Official Production System, Version 5 (OPS5) production system programming language. OPS5 typifies a "canned" rule-based implementation and serves to facilitate exploration of the rule-based motion and structural identification example. OPS5 is a production system language that is normally implemented as an extension to LISP. It represents an attempt to develop a standardized approach to rule-based inference. The initial version was written at Carnegie-Mellon University in the mid 1970s (Brownston et al., 1986).

From a programming viewpoint, an OPS5 implementation consists of a set of

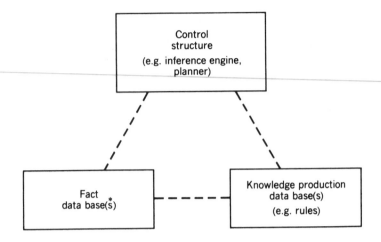

*given or derived
facts

(a)

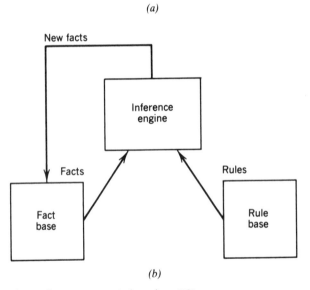

(b)

**FIGURE 7.21 (a)** The production sysem triad (neglects I/O)
(b) Elementary rule-based system operation

suitably coded facts in *working memory* and a set of rules in *production memory*. Rules are of the IF-THEN form. In the simplest form, the LHS of a rule is a set of condition elements that specify patterns to be matched against facts in working memory. The RHS of the rule is a sequence of actions. For example, a sample rule for finding the line segment in the image whose endpoints are the values of the variables $(\langle x0\rangle,\langle y0\rangle)$, $(\langle x1\rangle,\langle y1\rangle)$ in OPS5 is

```
(p find-segment
   (goal ˆtype find-segment   ˆx0 ⟨x0⟩ ˆy0 ⟨y0⟩)
   (segment   ˆx0 ⟨x0⟩ ˆy0 ⟨y0⟩ ˆx1 ⟨x1⟩ ˆy1 ⟨y1⟩)
——⟩
   (write a segment has been found with coordinates
      (⟨x0⟩, ⟨y0⟩, ⟨x1⟩, ⟨y1⟩)))
```

This rule may be paraphrased as:

IF the goal is to find a segment with beginning coordinates ($\langle x0 \rangle$, $\langle y0 \rangle$) in working memory

THEN print an indication of success and the segment endpoint locations

In OPS5, facts are stored in working memory in attribute-value elements. Each element consists of a class name and a list of attribute-value pairs. For example, a line segment with endpoint coordinates (100, 100) and (200, 300) could be represented as an OPS5 fact in the form of an attribute-value element:

(segment    ^x0 100 ^y0 100 ^x1 200 ^y1 300)

The OPS5 IE loops through a recognize-act cycle, where rule antecedents are examined, a set of rules eligible for firing (the conflict set) is identified, and one rule is chosen for firing. Additional OPS5 coding examples are shown in Figs. 7.32 and 7.36.

EXAMPLES OF RULE-BASED DESIGN

In this section, three examples of the application of rule-based systems to image analysis are explored. In the following application-dependent examples, data structures, extracted features, and control strategies differ. The reader should note, however, the structural similarity of the different examples cited as well as the similarity to the generic production system described previously.

*Segmentation Example.* A classic example of the application of rule-based system design applied to the problem of image segmentation is found in Nazif and Levine (1984). The system is structured as shown in Figure 7.22. The IE is itself rule-based, that is, consisting of metarules that, among other actions, guide the system focus of attention and thus rule selection. Rules are in IF-THEN form, with rule antecedents in conjunctive (AND) form. Figure 7.23 shows the features that may appear in the antecedents of a rule. Figure 7.24 shows sample rules to

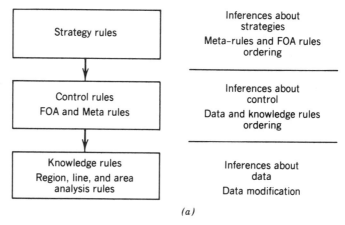

*(a)*

FIGURE 7.22   Segmentation system structure and rule actions. Copyright © 1984 IEEE
(a)   Three levels of rules
(b)   Rule actions (or consequents)

*Continued on next page*

TABLE III
THE RULE ACTIONS

## AREA ANALYZER ACTIONS

| Create Smooth Area | Add to Smooth Area | Save Smooth Area |
| Create Texture Area | Add to Texture Area | Save Texture Area |
| Create Bounded Area | Add to Bounded Area | Save Bounded Area |

| Relabel Area to Smooth | Relabel Area to Texture |
| Relabel Area to Bounded | Delete Area |

## REGION ANALYZER ACTIONS

| Split a Region by Histogram | Merge Two Regions |
| Split Region at Lines | |

## LINE ANALYZER ACTIONS

| Extend Line Forward | Extend Line Backward |
| Join Lines Forward | Join Lines Backward |
| Insert Line Forward | Insert Line Backward |
| Merge Lines Forward | Merge Lines Backward |
| Delete Line | |

## FOCUS OF ATTENTION ACTIONS

| Region with Highest Adjacency | Largest ADJACENT Region |
| Region with Lowest Adjacency | Smallest ADJACENT Region |
| Region with Higher Label | Next Scanned Region |
| Region to the LEFT OF Line | Region to the RIGHT OF Line |

| Closest Line IN FRONT | Closest Line BEHIND |
| Closest PARALLEL Line | Shortest Line that is near |
| Longest Line that is Near | Strongest Line that is near |
| Weakest Line that is Near | Line with Higher Label |
| Next Scanned Line | Line INTERSECTING Region |

| Defocus (Focus on Whole Image) | Focus on Areas |
| Clear Region List | Clear Line List |
| Freeze Area | Next Area (any) |
| Next Smooth Area | Next Texture Area |
| Next Bounded Area | |

## SUPERVISOR ACTIONS

| Initialize Regions | Initialize Lines | Generate Areas |
| Match Region Rules | Match Line Rules | Match Area Rules |
| Match Focus Rules | Start | Stop |

(b) Rule Actions (or Consequents)

**FIGURE 7.22** *Continued*

TABLE I
POSSIBLE DATA ENTRIES

| DATA ENTRY | SYMBOL |
|---|---|
| Current Region | REG |
| Current Line | LINE |
| Current Area | AREA |
| Region ADJACENT to current region | REGA |
| Region to the LEFT OF current line | REGL |
| Region to the RIGHT OF current line | REGR |
| Line NEAR current line | LINEN |
| Line IN FRONT OF current line | LINEE |
| Line BEHIND current line | LINEB |
| Line PARALLEL TO current line | LINEP |
| Line INTERSECTING current region | LINEI |

TABLE II
THE FEATURES IN A CONDITION

### NUMERICAL DESCRIPTIVE FEATURES

| | | |
|---|---|---|
| Feature 1 | Feature 2 | Feature 3 |
| Variance 1 | Variance 2 | Variance 3 |
| Intensity | Intensity Variance | Gradient |
| Gradient Variance | X-Centroid | Y-Centroid |
| Minimum X | Minimum Y | Maximum X |
| Maximum Y | Starting X | Starting Y |
| Ending X | Ending Y | Starting Direction |
| Ending Direction | Average Direction | Length |
| Start-End Distance | Size | Perimeter |
| Histogram Bimodality | Circularity | Aspect Ratio |
| Uniformity 1 | Uniformity 2 | Uniformity 3 |
| Region Contrast 1 | Region Contrast 2 | Region Contrast 3 |
| Line Contrast 1 | Line Contrast 2 | Line Contrast 3 |
| Line Connectivity | Number of Regions | Number of Lines |
| Number of Areas | | |

### NUMERICAL SPATIAL FEATURES

| | |
|---|---|
| Number of ADJACENT Regions | Adjacency Values |
| Number of INTERSECTING Lines | Line Content between Regions |
| Distance to Line IN FRONT | Nearest Point on Line IN FRONT |
| Distance to Line BEHIND | Nearest Point on Line BEHIND |
| Distance to PARALLEL Line | Number of PARALLEL Points |
| Adjacency of LEFT Region | Adjacency of RIGHT Region |
| Number of Lines IN FRONT | Number of Lines BEHIND |
| Number of PARALLEL Lines | Number of Regions to the LEFT |
| Number of Regions to the RIGHT | |

**FIGURE 7.23** Segmentation system possible rule antecedants. Copyright © 1984 IEEE
Table I. Possible data entries
Table II. The features in a condition.

Continued on next page

LOGICAL FEATURES

| | |
|---|---|
| Histogram is bimodal | Region is bisected by line |
| Line is open | Line is closed |
| Line is loop | Line end is open |
| Line start is open | Line is clockwise |
| Area is smooth | Area is textured |
| Area is bounded | Area is new |
| One region to the LEFT | One region to the RIGHT |

Same region to the LEFT and RIGHT OF line
Same region LEFT OF line 1 and line 2
Same region RIGHT OF line 1 and line 2
Same region to the LEFT OF line 1 and RIGHT OF line 2
Same region to the RIGHT OF line 1 and LEFT OF line 2
Two lines are touching (8 connected)

| | |
|---|---|
| Areas are absent | Regions are absent |
| Lines are absent | System is starting |
| Process was Regions | Process was Lines |
| Process was Areas | Process was Focus |
| Process was Generate Areas | Process was active |

**FIGURE 7.23**  *Continued*

facilitate region merging and region splitting. Results using this system are shown in Figure 7.25.

*Image Analysis Example.* A sophisticated, frame-based implementation of an image understanding system is typified by the SIGMA system of Hwang, Davis, and Matusuyama (1986). The SIGMA system provides an interpretation of a static image based on an underlying scene model, as shown in Figure 7.26a. The structure of the system is shown in Figure 7.27b. The system model representation and implementation is frame based (Schalkoff, to be published), with entities being described by frames composed of slots. Slots allow different objects to be related through the AKO ("a kind of"; also known as ISA) relation. Frame representations facilitate the inheritance of properties and values for an entity via ISA. Figure 7.27 shows an example of this representation. The frame concept is a data structure, not an inference mechanism. Frames may contain slots indicating applicable rules, or rules whose application yields values of properties of the entity. Figure 7.28 shows a model for houses in the form of entity frames and links.

The SIGMA system employs both bottom-up (data driven) and topdown (model-driven) inference. The overall objective is the formation of a maximally consistent unification of the observed (perhaps preprocessed) image contents and an underlying scene model (Figure 7.26a). Consistency is achieved by formulating a set of rules based on relational constraints between entities (similar to the use of the adjacency relation).

The SIGMA IE is based on the formation and confirmation of hypotheses and guides image interpretation by determining, among other things, what to look for, where to look, and when (at what processing stage) to look. The overall unification strategy employed in SIGMA is shown in Figure 7.29.

RULE (801):

IF: (1) There is a LOW DIFFERENCE in
REGION FEATURE 1
(2) There is a LOW DIFFERENCE in
REGION FEATURE 2
(3) There is a LOW DIFFERENCE in
REGION FEATURE 3

THEN:(1) MERGE the two REGIONS

RULE (802):

IF: (1) The REGION SIZE is VERY LOW
(2) The ADJACENCY with another REGION is HIGH
(3) The DIFFERENCE in REGION FEATURE 1 is
NOT HIGH
(4) The DIFFERENCE in REGION FEATURE 2 is
NOT HIGH
(5) The DIFFERENCE in REGION FEATURE 3 is
NOT HIGH

THEN:(1) MERGE the two REGIONS

(a) Region merging

RULE (901):

IF: (1) The REGION HISTOGRAM is BIMODAL

THEN:(1) SPLIT the REGION according to the
HISTOGRAM

RULE (902):

IF: (1) The REGION HISTOGRAM BIMODALITY is
NOT LOW
THEN:(1) SPLIT the REGION according to the
HISTOGRAM

RULE (908):

IF: (1) The REGION SIZE is NOT LOW
(2) REGION is BISECTED BY LINE
(3) The LINE LENGTH is NOT LOW
(4) The LINE AVERAGE GRADIENT is HIGH

THEN:(1) SPLIT the REGION at LINES

(b) Region splitting

**FIGURE 7.24** Samples of "knowledge rules". Copyright © 1984 IEEE
(a) Region merging
(b) Region splitting

**FIGURE 7.25** Rule-based segmentation vs. alternate approaches (blocks world). Copyright © 1984 IEEE.
(a)   The original image
(b)   Rule-based segmentation
(c)   Histogram splitting
(d)   Split-and-merge

*Motion and Structural Identification.* The rule-based system discussed here employs a modeling and computational paradigm to determine object structure and motion from a sequence of images (Topa & Schalkoff, 1987). An overall diagram of the system is shown in Figure 7.30. As shown, this data-directed system employs a spatiotemporal feature extraction module that provides low-level, edge-based feature information as input to the rule-based processing module. Rules are used for both low-level preprocessing of the edge data (similar to the segmentation example) and for the structural unification of the processed data at a higher level. The system rules are written primarily in the OPS5 programming language.

A set of spatiotemporal templates is used to obtain edge-based feature information, including static edge orientation and edge motion direction. A low-level

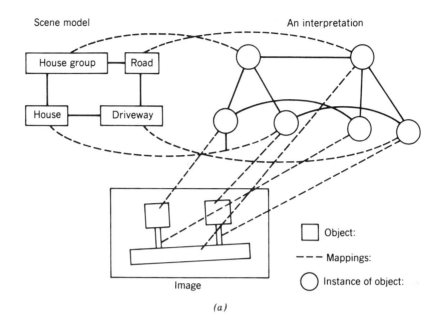

*(a)*

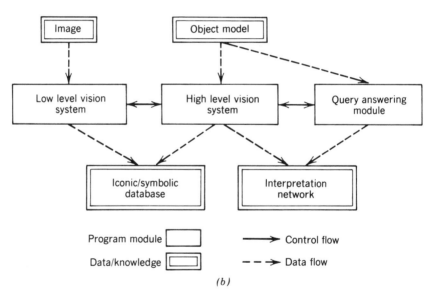

*(b)*

**FIGURE 7.26** Rule-based system of [Hwang/Davis]. Copyright © 1986 Academic Press, Inc.

(a) Mappings between the scene and the image (system conceptual basis)

(b) System architecture for the SIGMA image understanding system

preprocessing module outputs a list of spatiotemporal edges, with attributes indicating endpoint coordinates, segment length, spatial orientation, and motion direction. This input is used by the low-level, rule-based processing module to group, merge, or link segments based on a set of similarity measures formulated as rules. Examples of these are shown graphically in Figure 7.31, and sample OPS5 code for the merging of line segments is shown in Figure 7.32.

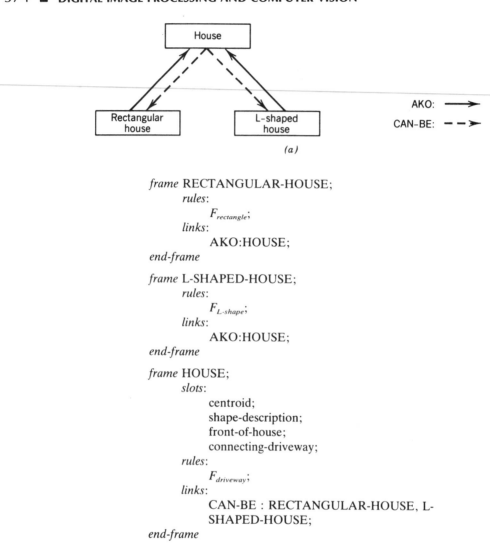

*(a)*

*frame* RECTANGULAR-HOUSE;
    *rules*:
        $F_{rectangle}$;
    *links*:
        AKO:HOUSE;
*end-frame*

*frame* L-SHAPED-HOUSE;
    *rules*:
        $F_{L\text{-}shape}$;
    *links*:
        AKO:HOUSE;
*end-frame*

*frame* HOUSE;
    *slots*:
        centroid;
        shape-description;
        front-of-house;
        connecting-driveway;
    *rules*:
        $F_{driveway}$;
    *links*:
        CAN-BE : RECTANGULAR-HOUSE, L-
        SHAPED-HOUSE;
*end-frame*

*(b)*

**FIGURE 7.27** Sample frame-based representation. © 1986 Academic Press, Inc.
(a) Links between HOUSE, RECTANGULAR-HOUSE, and L-SHAPED HOUSE frames
(b) Frame definitions for HOUSE, RECTANGULAR-HOUSE, and L-SHAPED HOUSE

More important, the preprocessing module also identifies related segments and their medial axes (or "spines"), which are assumed to represent the visible projection of a generalized cylinder in the image plane. These projections are referred to as "ribbons," as shown in Figure 7.33. Ribbons therefore form the basis of the hypothesized generalized cylinder model. Ribbons may be merged using rules analogous to those for linking line segments. Once a set of ribbons has been extracted, unification with a generalized cylinder model from a particular 3-D model library proceeds.

Objects in the system are modeled using a tree-structured description in terms

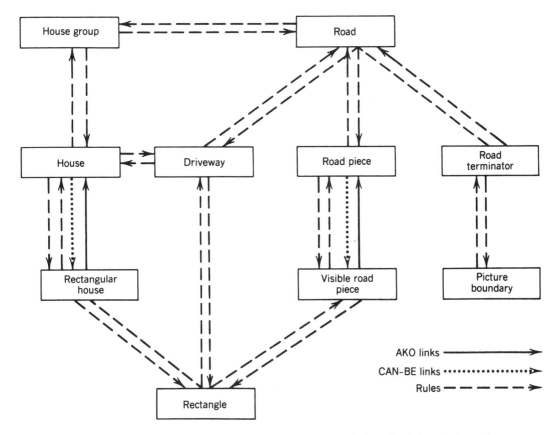

**FIGURE 7.28** Sample SIGMA frame-based model showing links and rule-based relational constraints (A model of a suburban housing development). Copyright © 1986 Academic Press, Inc.

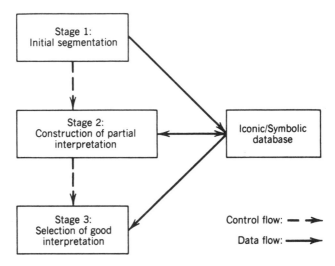

**FIGURE 7.29** SIGMA IE sequence (the stages of the control of SIGMA). Copyright © 1986 Academic Press, Inc.

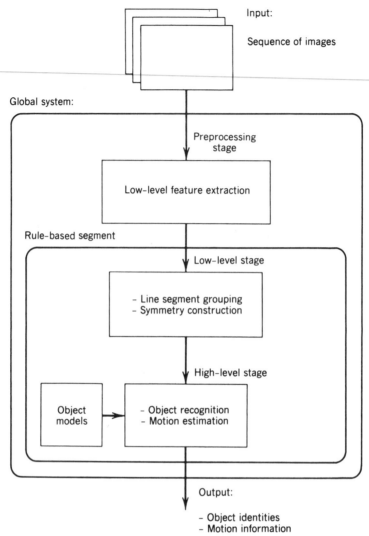

**FIGURE 7.30** System computational architecture

of component subparts. The higher level description employs the use of generalized cylinders and their qualitative features (such as symmetry), as detailed in the section on 3-D modeling issues.

The grammar for object description is shown in Backus-Naur form in Figure 7.34. Nonterminals are indicated by lowercase alphanumeric strings; terminals are capitalized. Disjunction (OR) is indicated by a vertical bar and conjunction (AND) is denoted using a space. The symbol ::= indicates replacement. As shown in the figure, each part is specified by a primitive part (a root), a symbolic name, a generalized cylinder description, and a list of attached subparts. The description also constrains the possible subpart attachment, using where, how, and by-what descriptors. Figure 7.35 shows two examples of values for these descriptors. Implementation of this object model grammar in OPS5 is shown in Figure 7.36a; an OPS5 description for the case of an airplane is shown in Figure 7.36b.

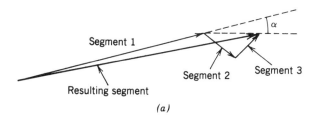

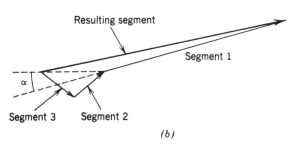

**FIGURE 7.31** Merging segment rules
(a) Extending segments from the head
(b) Extending segments from the tail

```
(p geometric::link-segments:head-to-tail
    (goal ^status active ^type link-segments ^value ⟨length⟩)
    (segment ^length > ⟨length⟩ ^id ⟨id1⟩ ^x2 ⟨x⟩ ^y2 ⟨y⟩)
    (segment ^id ⟨id2⟩ ^x1 ⟨x⟩ ^y1 ⟨y⟩)
  - (geometric-relation ^type linked-to ^segm1 ⟨id1⟩ ^segm2 ⟨id2⟩)
  - (geometric-relation ^type linked-to ^segm1 ⟨id2⟩ ^segm2 ⟨id1⟩)
  →
    (write (crlf) segment ⟨id1⟩ is linked to segment ⟨id2⟩)
    (make geometric-relation ^type linked-to
       ^segm1 ⟨id1⟩ ^segm2 ⟨id2⟩)
    (make geometric-relation ^type linked-to
       ^segm1 ⟨id2⟩ ^segm2 ⟨id1⟩))
```

(a) Segment linking

```
(p geometric::longest-shortest:longest-segment
    (goal ^status active ^type longest-shortest)
    (segment ^id ⟨id⟩ ^time ⟨time⟩ ^length ⟨length⟩)
  - (segment ^length > ⟨length⟩ ^id {⟨id1⟩ ⟨⟩ ⟨id⟩})
  - (geometric-relation ^type longest-segm)
  →
    (write (crlf) segment ⟨id⟩ is the longest: length is ⟨length⟩)
    (make geometric-relation ^type longest-segm ^segm1 ⟨id⟩))
```

(b) Finding longest segment

**FIGURE 7.32** Sample OPS5 production rules for motion/structural description system
(a) Segment linking
(b) Finding longest segment

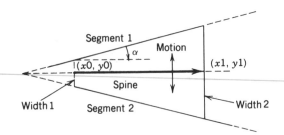

Ribbon parameters:

- Identification number
- Tail coordinates ($x0$, $y0$)
- Head coordinates ($x1$, $y1$)
- Spine length
- Spine slope (angle from the $x$-axis)
- Width 1
- Width2
- $\alpha$
- Motion (no–motion, left, right)

**FIGURE 7.33**   Spine and ribbon definition

Unification of the extracted and processed descriptors with a model is analogous to searching AND-OR goal trees. AND nodes represent the recognition and identification of attached object subparts that must all be present. OR nodes represent possible different generalized cylinders in the ribbon input data that may correspond to model components. For example, starting from the root, the system chooses some extracted data part to be matched to model part A (part (a)) and then must find a match for parts B and C. Figure 7.37(*b*) shows the AND-OR tree for the simplified object model shown in Figure 7.37*a*, and illustrates a depth-first search technique. Sample results of the system input and various processing stages are shown in Figure 7.38.

### OTHER APPROACHES BASED ON MODEL UNIFICATION

The previous examples of high-level image analysis illustrate typical approaches. A multitude of other examples, based on the overriding concept of model unification, exist. In many cases (as we have seen), the algorithms rely on successive refinement of a hypothesis for model unification. This often involves a succession of feature extraction/model unification cycles, as shown in Figure 7.39. Efficient search is an integral part of the algorithm.

Many challenges in model unification-based image analysis exist. Several conceptual concerns are

1. Relating 2-D image data to the model representation to constrain the selection of a 3-D model. This depends on an assumed viewing direction (or viewpoint) and requires the confirmation of correspondence between image features and the projection of the 3-D model onto the image plane. Lowe (1987) refers to this as the *viewpoint consistency constraint*. Thus, we are relating, or more specifically unifying, image measurements and an object or scene model. In addition, other 3-D constraints (e.g., object rigidity) must be enforced.

object :: = object-name root

root :: = part

part :: = part-name cylinder carries

cylinder :: = cyl-name edges symmetry cross-section-size
              axis aspect-ratio

carries :: = NIL | (subpart carries)

subpart :: = subpart-name attachment part

attachment :: = where how by-what

object-name :: = identifier

part-name :: = identifier

subpart-name :: = identifier

cyl-name :: = identifier

edges :: = S | C

symmetry :: = Symm+ + | Symm+ | Asymm

cross-section-size :: = Const | Exp | Exp-Contr

axis :: = S | C

aspect-ratio :: = Long | Normal | Short

where :: = Same-axis-top | Same-axis-bottom
         | Right-side-top | Right-side-middle | Right-side-bottom
         | Left-side-top | Left-side-middle | Left-side-bottom

how :: = Perpendicular | Acute-angle | Obtuse-angle

by-what :: = By-the-top | By-the-bottom

**FIGURE 7.34** Object model grammar

2. The identification and grouping of observed or extracted structures in the image that are invariant over some range of viewpoints and are model-specific. This is a somewhat conflicting objective, since although we desire a set of model-specific features that allow some viewing flexibility, this flexibility may yield intermodel ambiguity. Furthermore, the extraction of these features and structures must be practical, which usually implies the use of edges, regionally segmented images, surface orientation, and the like. The grouping or organization of these features may parallel that of HVS perceptual or-

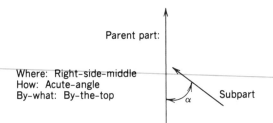

**FIGURE 7.35**  Attachment of object subparts

```
(literalize object)
    name        ; object name
    root        ; name of object part used as root for description
)
(vector-attribute carries)
(literalize part
    name        ; part name
    cylinder    ; name of generalized cylinder describing the part
    carries     ; names of subparts attached to the part (nil if none)
)
(literalize gen-cylinder
    name        ; generalized cylinder name
    edges       ; straight | curved
    symmetry    ; symm + + | symm + | asymm
    cross-sect  ; constant | expanded | expanded-contracted
    axis        ; straight | curved
    aspect      ; aspect ratio: long | normal | short
)
(literalize attachment
    subject     ; name of the part carrying the subpart
    object      ; name of carried part
    where       ; same-axis-head | same-axis-tail
                ; right-side-head | right-side-middle | right-side-tail
                ; left-side-head | left-side-middle | left-side-tail
    how         ; perpendicular | acute-angle | obtuse-angle
    by-what     ; by-the-head | by-the-tail
)
```

**FIGURE 7.36**
(a)  Object model grammar implementation in OPS5
(b)  Airplane model in OPS5

```
(make object
    ^name airplane
    ^root fuselage
)
(make part
    ^name        fuselage
    ^cylinder    cyl1
    ^carries     right-wing left-wing
                 right-stabilizer left-stabilizer
)
(make part
    ^name        right-wing
    ^cylinder    cyl2
    ^carries     nil
)
(make part
    ^name        left-wing
    ^cylinder    cyl2
    ^carries     nil
)
(make part
    ^name        right-stabilizer
    ^cylinder    cyl3
    ^carries     nil

)
(make part
    ^name        left-stabilizer
    ^cylinder    cyl3
    ^carries     nil
)

(make attachment ;; dummy attachment for
                    the root
    ^subject     airplane
    ^object      fuselage
)
(make attachment
    ^subject     fuselage
    ^object      right-wing
    ^where       right-side-middle
    ^how         acute-angle
    ^by-what     by-the-head
)
(make attachment
    ^subject     fuselage
    ^object      left-wing
    ^where       left-side-middle
    ^how         acute-angle
    ^by-what     by-the-head
)
```

```
(make attachment
    ^subject     fuselage
    ^object      right-stabilizer
    ^where       right-side-tail
    ^how         acute-angle
    ^by-what     by-the-head
)
(make attachment
    ^subject     fuselage
    ^object      left-stabilizer
    ^where       left-side-tail
    ^how         acute-angle
    ^by-what     by-the-head
)

(make gen-cyl-
inder
    ^name        cyl1
    ^edges       curved
    ^symmetry    symm + +
    ^cross-sect  expanded-contracted
    ^axis        straight
    ^aspect      long
)
(make gen-cylinder
    ^name        cyl2
    ^edges       straight
    ^symmetry    symm +
    ^cross-sect  expanded
    ^axis        straight
    ^aspect      long
)
(make gen-cylinder
    ^name        cyl3
    ^edges       straight
    ^symmetry    symm +
    ^cross-sect  expanded
    ^axis        straight
    ^aspect      normal
)
```

**FIGURE 7.36** *Continued*

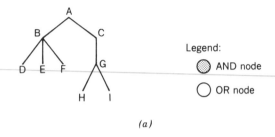

*(a)*

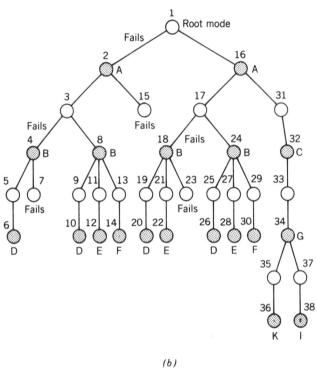

*(b)*

**FIGURE 7.37** Searching process for model unification (identification)
(a) Object model
(b) Possible search tree for model unification

ganization and therefore may rely on similarity measures such as proximity, parallelism, and other feature attributes. A good example of the model unification process using this approach is Lowe's (1987) SCERPO system implementation.

Lowe and Binford (1985) suggest a few heuristics to aid in this process, as shown in Figure 7.39. The reader is encouraged to verify the plausibility of the 10 inference procedures suggested in the figure in the context of the geometric model for imaging studied in Chapter 2. For example, recall that parallel lines in 3-D (under the p-p transformation) do not map into parallel

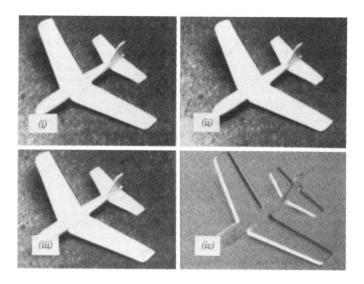

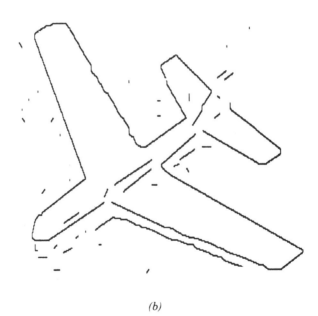

*(b)*

**FIGURE 7.38** Airplane example
(a)  Grey-level image sequence for an airplane
    *(i)* $f(\underline{x},t_1)$   *(ii)* $f(\underline{x},t_2)$   *(iii)* $f(\underline{x},t_3)$   *(iv)* $f_d(\underline{x},t_1,t_3)$
(b)  Output of the low-level processing stage with an airplance
(c)  Output of the edge linking step withan airplane
(d)  Output of the ribbon finding step with an airplane

*Continued on next page*

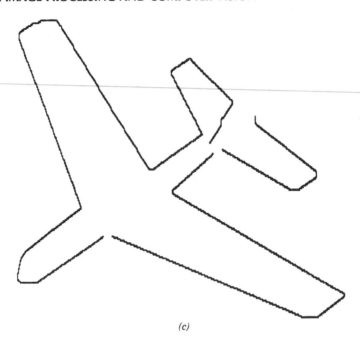

(c)

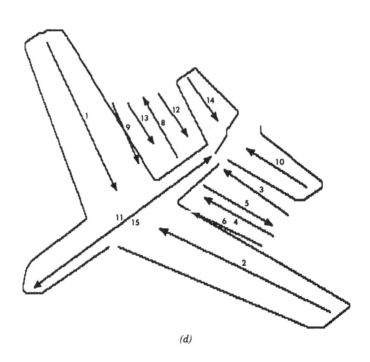

(d)

**FIGURE 7.38** *Continued*

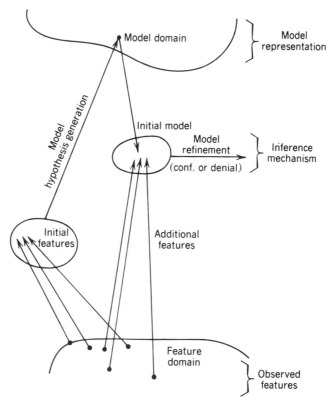

**FIGURE 7.39** A paradigm for model unification

lines in the image plane. Figure 7.40 (relation 6), however, postulates that the converse is true.

3. Determining a plausible viewpoint on the basis of the hypothesized model and the features noted in 2 above. "Trigger features" (Lowe, 1987) are often employed.

4. Incorporation of other available information in the form of depth measurements; stereo image pairs (Hwang & Hall, 1982 is an excellent example of this), motion information (as in the motion example above), and other a priori information such as time of day, likely object classes to be encountered, etc.

Many early algorithmic approaches were based on the above design paradigm. Waltz (1975) developed one of the first image understanding paradigms for the analysis of "blocks world" images by using a line segment labeling approach based on junctions and viewing constraints that governed the local interconnection of junctions. This yielded, as in our labeling problem, a globally consistent solution. This work is very similar to the early work of Roberts (1965) who explored similar constraint-based labeling schemes for the recognition of polyhedra. A system similar to that of Nazif and Levine (1984) but applied to the segmentation of angiogram images, is that of Stansfield (1986). Similarly, Whitaker and Huhns (1986) implemented a rule-based system with the ability to infer hidden information in viewing scenes of polyhedral objects. Perhaps one of the best-known systems is the AC-

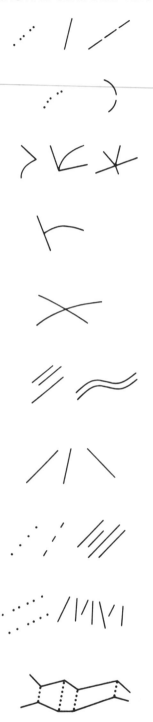

**FIGURE 7.40** Sample image-scene inferences using extracted image curves (from [Lowe/Bin85] Copyright © 1985 IEEE).

RONYM system of Brooks (1981). ACRONYM stores object models in terms of component parts, which are themselves modeled as generalized cylinders. The system uses geometric reasoning, with an assumption as to viewpoint, to predict object features that are visible in order to unify observed data with a stored model. ACRONYM uses hypothesis generation and a backward chaining algorithm for model confirmation.

## ■ SUMMARY

In this chapter, we have investigated the second or higher level of image analysis algorithms. These algorithms attempt to mimic the ability of the human visual system to synthesize a global conclusion (or set of conclusions) by considering the relationships and features of a set of extracted image primitives. Models are used to make high-level inferences regarding scene content. The modeling limitations in image analysis parallel those in other AI application areas. For example, it is not clear how to effect the representation and manipulation of "deep knowledge" or common sense in these models. In addition, the representation and the control necessary to achieve learning have not been addressed. These are fundamental obstacles in the achievement of systems that emulate human capability and are consequently the subject of much present and future computer vision and associated AI research.

## ■ REFERENCES

Agin, G. J. "Hierarchical Representation of Three-Dimensional Objects Using Verbal Models," *IEEE Trans. Pattern Analysis and Machine Intelligence*, Vol. PAMI-3, No. 2, March 1981, pp. 197–204.

Baubaud, J., Witkin, A., Baudin, M., and Duda, R. O. "Uniqueness of the Gaussian Kernel for Scale-Space Filtering," *IEEE Trans. Pattern Analysis and Machine Intelligence*, Vol. PAMI-8, No. 1, Jan. 1986, pp. 26–33.

Biederman, I. "Human Image Understanding: Recent Research and a Theory," *Computer Vision, Graphics and Image Processing*, Vol. 32, 1985, pp. 29–73.

Brooks, R. A. "Symbolic Reasoning Among 3-D Models and 2-D Images," *Artificial Intelligence*, Vol. 17, 1981, pp. 285–348.

Brownston, L., Farrel, R., Kant, E., and Martin, N. *Programming Expert Systems in OPS5*. Reading, MA: Addison Wesley, 1986.

Connolly, C. J. "The Determination of Next Best Views," in *Proc. 1985 IEEE Conf. on Robotics and Automation*, March 1985, St. Louis, MO, pp. 432–434.

Davis, R., and Lenat, D. *Knowledge-Based Systems in Artificial Intelligence*. New York: McGraw-Hill, 1982.

Fekete, G., Eklundh, J. O., and Rosenfeld, A. "Relaxation: Evaluation and Applications," *IEEE Trans. Pattern Analysis and Machine Intelligence*, Vol. PAMI-3, No. 4, July 1981, pp. 459–469.

Hayes-Roth, F., and King, D. *Building Expert Systems*. Reading, MA: Addison Wesley, 1983.

Henderson, T. C. "A Note on Discrete Relaxation," *Computer Vision, Graphics, and Image Processing*, No. 28, 1984, pp. 384–388.

Horaud, R. "New Methods of Matching 3-D Objects with Single Perspective Views," *IEEE Trans. Pattern Analysis and Machine Intelligence*, Vol. PAMI-9, No. 3, May 1987, pp. 401–412.

Horn, B. K. P. "Extended Gaussian Images," *Proc. of the IEEE*, Vol. 72, No. 12, Dec. 1984, pp. 1671–1686.

Hummel, R. A., and Zucker, S. W. "On the Foundations of Relaxation Labelling Processes," *IEEE Trans. Pattern Analysis and Machine Intelligence*, Vol. PAMI-5, No. 3, May 1983, pp. 267–287.

Hwang, J. J., and Hall, E. L. "Matching of Featured Objects Using Relational Tables from Stereo Images," *Computer Graphics and Image Processing*, No. 20, 1982, pp. 22–42.

Hwang, V. S., Davis, L. S., and Matusuyama, T. "Hypothesis Integration in Image Understanding Systems," *Computer Vision, Graphics and Image Processing*, Vol. 36, 1986, pp. 321–371.

Little, J. J. "Extended Gaussian Images, Mixed Volumes, and Shape Reconstruction," in *Proc. of the Symposium on Computational Geometry*, Baltimore, MD, June, 1985, pp. 15–23.

Lowe, D. G. "Three-Dimensional Object Recognition form Single Two-Dimensional Images," *Artificial Intelligence*, Vol. 31, 1987, pp. 335–395.

Lowe, D. G., and Binford, T. O. "The Recovery of Three-Dimensional Structure from Image Curves," *IEEE Trans. Pattern Analysis and Machine Intelligence*, Vol. PAMI-7, May 1985, pp. 320–326.

Nazif, A. M., and Levine, M. D. "Low Level Image Segmentation: An Expert System," *IEEE Trans. Pattern Analysis and Machine Intelligence*, Vol. PAMI-6, No. 5, September 1984, pp. 555–577.

Nevatia, R., and Binford, T. O. "Description and Recognition of Curved Objects," *Artificial Intelligence*, Vol. 8, 1977, pp. 77–98.

Nilsson, N. J. *Principles of Artificial Intelligence*, Palo Alto, CA: Tioga Publications, 1980.

Nitzan, D. "Three-Dimensional Structure for Robot Applications," *IEEE Trans. Pattern Analysis and Machine Intelligence*, Vol. PAMI-10, No. 3, May 1988, pp. 291–309.

Roberts, L. G. "Machine Perception of Three-Dimensional Solids," in *Optical and Electro-Optical Information Processing* (J. T. Tippett et al. eds.), Cambridge, MA: MIT Press, 1965.

Rosenfeld, A., Hummel, R. A., and Zucker, S. W. "Scene Labelling by Relaxation Operations," *IEEE Trans. Systems Man and Cybernetics*, Vol. SMC-6, No. 6, June 1976, pp. 420–433.

Schalkoff, R. J. *Artificial Intelligence: An Engineering Approach*, to be published. New York: McGraw-Hill.

Stansfield, S. A. "ANGY: A Rule-Based Expert System for Automatic Segmentation of Coronary Vessels form Digital Subtracted Angiograms," *IEEE Trans. Pattern Analysis and Machine Intelligence*, Vol. PAMI-8, No. 2, March 1986, pp. 188–199.

Topa, L. C., and Schalkoff, R. J. "A Rule Based Expert System for the Determination of Object Structure and Motion Information from a Sequence of Digital Images," submitted to *Computer Vision, Graphics and Image Processing*, Sept. 1987. (Also available as L. C. Topa, PhD Dissertation, Dept. of Electrical and Computer Engineering, Clemson University, December 1987.)

Waterman, D. A. *A Guide to Expert Systems*. Reading, MA: Wesley, 1986.

Whitaker, E. T., and Huhns, M. N. "Rule-Based Geometrical Reasoning for the Interpretation of Line Drawing," MCC Technical Report No. AI-013-86. Austin, TX: Microelectronics and Computer Technology Corporation, Jan. 1986.

Zadeh, L, et al. *Fuzzy Sets and Their Applications to Cognitive and Decision Processes*. New York: Academic Press, 1975.

# ■ BIBLIOGRAPHY

Barrow, H. G., and Tenenbaum, J. M. "Interpreting Line Drawings as Three-Dimensional Surfaces," *Artificial Intelligence*, Vol. 17, 1981, pp. 75–116.

Binford, T. O. "Inferring Surfaces from Images," *Artificial Intelligence*, Vol. 17, 1981, pp. 205–244.

Binford, T. O. "Survey of Model-Based Image Analysis Systems," *Int'l. J. of Robotics Research*, Vol. 1, No. 1, 1982.

Brady, M. "Computational Approaches to Image Understanding," *Computing Surveys*, Vol. 14, No. 1, 1982.

Chin, R. T., and Dyer, C. R. "Model-Based Recognition in Robot Vision," *Computing Surveys*, Vol. 14, No. 1, March 1986, pp. 67–108.

Feldman, J. A., and Ballard, D. H. "Connectionist Models and Their Properties," *Cognitive Science*, Vol. 6, No. 3, 1982.

Herman, Kanade, and Kuroe "3-D Scene Modelling from Images," *IEEE Trans. Pattern Analysis and Machine Intelligence*, Vol. PAMI-6, No. 3, May 1984, p. 331.

Kanade, T. "Recovering of the Three-Dimensional Shape of an Object from a Single View," *Artificial Intelligence*, Vol. 17, 1981, pp. 409–460.

Klinger, A., and Rhodes, M. L. "Organization and Access of Image Data by Areas," *IEEE Trans. Pattern Analysis and Machine Intelligence*, Vol. PAMI-1, Jan. 1979, pp. 50–60.

Lin, W. C., and Fu, K. S. "A Syntactic Approach to 3-D Object Representation," *IEEE Trans. Pattern Analysis and Machine Intelligence*, Vol. PAMI-6, No. 3, May 1984, pp. 351–364.

Mackworth, A. K. "Consistency in Networks of Relations," *Artificial Intelligence*, Vol. 8, 1977, pp. 99–118.

Marr, D., and Nishihara, H. K. "Representation and Recognition of the Spatial Organization of Three Dimensional Shapes," *Proc. Royal Soc. of London B*, Vol. 200, No. 1140, 1978, pp. 269–294.

Martin, W. N., and Aggarwal, J. K. "Volumetric Descriptions of Objects from Multiple Views," *IEEE Trans. Pattern Analysis and Machine Intelligence*, Vol. PAMI-5, No. 2, March 1983.

Pavlidis, T. *Algorithms for Graphics and Image Processing*, Rockville, MD: Computer Science Press, 1982.

Peleg, S. "A New Probabilistic Relaxation Scheme," *IEEE Trans. Pattern Analysis and Machine Intelligence*, Vol. PAMI-2, No. 4, 1980, pp. 362–369.

Ramapriyan, H. K. "A Multilevel Approach to Sequential Detection of Pictorial Features," *IEEE Trans. Computers*, Vol. C-25, No. 1, Jan. 1976, pp. 66–78.

Rutkowski, W. S., Peleg, S., and Rosenfeld, A. "Shape Segmentation Using Relaxation," *IEEE Trans. Pattern Analysis and Machine Intelligence*, Vol. PAMI-3, No. 4, July 1981, pp. 368–375.

Samet, H. "An Algorithm for Converting Images into Quadtrees," *IEEE Trans. Pattern Analysis and Machine Intelligence*, Vol. PAMI-3, No. 1, Jan. 1981, pp. 93–95.

Shirai, Y., and Tsujii, J. *Artificial Intelligence: Concepts, Techniques, and Applications*, New York: Wiley, 1984.

Tan, C. L., and Martin, W. N. "A Distributed System for Analyzing Time-Varying Multiresolution Imagery," *Computer Vision, Graphics and Image Processing*, Vol. 36, 1986, pp. 162–174.

Tanimoto, S., and Pavlidis, T. "A Hierarchical Data Structure for Picture Processing," *Computer Graphics and Image Processing*, Vol. 4, No. 2, June 1975, pp. 104–119.

Waltz, D. "Understanding Line Drawings of Scenes with Shadows," in *The Psychology of Computer Vision* Chap. 3 (P. H. Winston, ed, McGraw-Hill, NY, 1975, pp. 19–91.

Zeno, S. D. "Advances in Image Segmentation," *Image and Vision Computing*, Vol. 1, No. 4, Nov. 1984, pp. 196–200.

## ■ PROBLEMS

1. Prove that if $g(x,\hat{y})$ satisfies Eq. 7-5c, the convolution of Eq. 7-2 has the property that if $f(x) = a$, $\phi(x,\hat{y}) = a$.

2. Show that the Gaussian kernel used for scale-space filtering defined in Eq. 7-6 approaches a Dirac delta function as $\hat{y} \to \infty$.

3. Using the result of Eq. 7-6, what is the function $h(x\hat{y})$ in Eq. 7-5a? (Note: this result may make the succeeding properties easier.)

4. Show the frequency domain characteristics of

$$F\left[g(x,\hat{y})\right] = G(w)|_{\hat{y}}$$

for $\hat{y} > 0$. Specifically, (1) show that it has a low-pass characteristic and (2) relate $G(w)$ for various values of $\hat{y}$. The result in Eq. 7-6 indicated that the Gaussian kernel is the only smoothing kernel for which hierarchical feature consistency is obtained. This apparently presents significant problems, since most multiresolution (pyramidal) approaches employ simple averaging (e.g., over quadrants) to produce the sequence. Compare simple averaging with the use of the Gaussian kernel.

5. Prove that the Gaussian kernel satisfies Eq. 7-5c.

6. Given a linear differential operator (e.g. the Laplacian), $L$, and using the definition of convolution, prove

$$L\,[\phi(x,\hat{y})] = L\,[f(x)] * g(x,\hat{y})]$$

$$= f(x) * L\,[g(x,\hat{y})]$$

7. Derive

$$L\,[g(x,\hat{y})]$$

for the case where $g$ is the Gaussian kernel defined in Eq. 7-6.

8. Prove that if we store $f(i,j,k)$ and the three quantities

$$f(2i,\ 2j+i,\ k+1)\ -\ f(i,j,k)$$

$$f(2i+1,\ 2j,\ k+1)\ -\ f(i,j,k)$$

$$f(2i+1,\ 2j+1,\ k+1)\ -\ f(i,j,k)$$

at each level $k$ we can uniquely reconstruct the input image from $f(i,j,1)$.

9. Discuss the application of pyramidal representations to the problems of
   a. Stereo vision, specifically the successive refinement of a surface map.
   b. Motion detection and estimation, with specific emphasis on optical flow determination.

10. Is it possible to relate the Fourier transforms of different resolution images in a pyramidal sequence? Show, with as much detail as possible. Consider using a 4-pixel average and the Gaussian kernel.

11. Compare the overall number of bits required to represent all the spatial locations of (a) a $256 \times 256$ pixel image, (b) a $512 \times 512$ pixel image, and (c) a $1024 \times 1024$ pixel image using Cartesian coordinates and a quadtree. Assume that the minimum number of bits is used for any binary representation of a nonbinary digit.

12. In a hierarchical quadtree representation, with the ordering shown in Figure 7-5, the descendants of a node may be described by labeling the arc "a part of" (e.g., pixels 0 and 1 are "a part of" region R$\phi$). Furthermore (although we do not draw labeled arcs to indicate this), subdivisions (including pixels) possess other relationships, such as "left-of" (e.g., pixels 0-1 and 4-5) and "other diagonal" (e.g., pixels 1-4).
   a. Convert the quadtree in Figure 7-5 to a more complete semantic set for this representation by forming a digraph with labeled arcs to indicate all practical relations.
   b. Describe the inheritance of node properties due to the transitivity of relations such as "left-of" and "contained-in."

13. Explore the possibility of a hierarchical image decomposition similar to the quadtree approach where
    a. The decomposition is in one spatial direction only, that is, the image is hierarchically decomposed using lines or columns.
    b. The decomposition occurs first in one spatial extent, then the other.

    In each case, examine the potential properties and implementation ramifications.

14. This problem investigates the properties of a particular data structure for representation of an image in quadtree form. A quadcode of length $n$ is a quaternary (base-4) code of the form

$$Q = q_1 q_2, \ldots, q_n$$

    where

$$q_i \in \{0,1,2,3\} \text{ for } i = 1,2, \ldots, n$$

    Each character of the quadcode represents one operation of subdividing the image or its subimage into quadrants with the convention shown in Figure P-1 for the case of $n = 1$.

    Using the quadcode, an image is subdivided into much smaller units, so the subdividing operation can be repeated recursively many times, until there is no further subdividing possible.
      Show the quadcode representation for
    (i) a 4 × 4 image; and
    (ii) an 8 × 8 image.

15. Referring to Problem 14, verify the following properties of the quadcode:
    a. The quadcode length of individual pixels in a $2'' \times 2''$ image is $n$.
    b. The side length of a subimage with quadcode length $m$ in a $2'' \times 2''$ image is $2^{n-m}$.
    c. The area of a subimage with quadcode length $m$ in an image of area $A_0$ is $4^{-m}A_0$.
    d. Adding one character to a given quadcode subdivides the given subimage into its quadrants.
    e. If four quadcodes of length $i$ have the first $i - 1$ positions the same, they represent the four quadrants of the same subimage, represented by the $(i-1)$-position quadcode.

16. This problem considers the behavior of scale-space filtering techniques with just distinguishable extrema. Referring to the plots of $\phi_{xx}(x,y) = 0$ for the scale-space filtering examples of Figures 7.2 and 7.3, discuss the behavior of

the nearly vertical sections of these curves, that is, the regions where an extrema just appears at some resolution. These indicate the birth (via spreading out with respect to $x$) or disappearance (via collapse) of an extrema depending on a small change in resolution. Explain with as much analytical justification as possible, the origin of these curves, particularly with respect to their shape.

17. Referring to the four segmented images shown below, apply the label discarding rule to each of these images (with appropriate unary constraints).

18. Formulate a "label retention rule" and show its application to the labeling problem using the examples in Problem 17. Consider the application of unary constraints to limit the initial $\Gamma_i$.

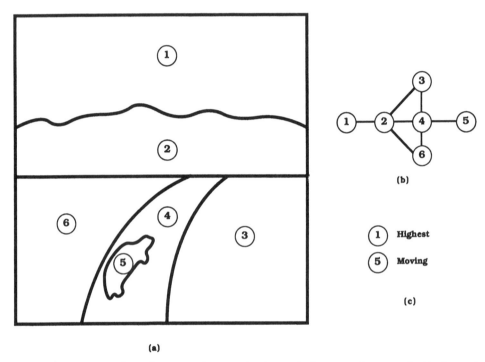

FIGURE P.17-1  Example 1 (a) segmented image; (b) observed adjacency relation graph; (c) observed unary relations

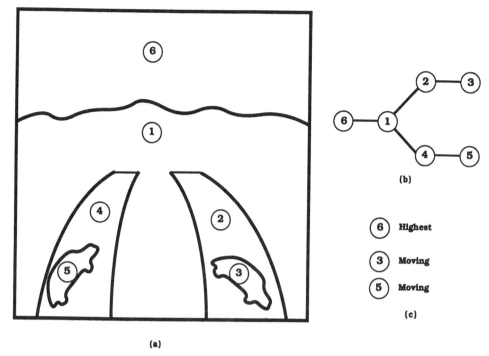

**FIGURE P.17-2** Example 2 (a) segmented image; (b) observed adjacency relation graph; (c) observed unary relations

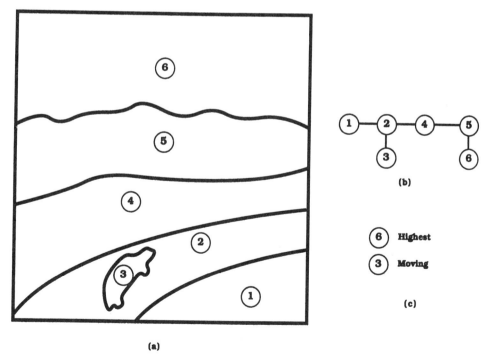

**FIGURE P.17-3** Example 3 (a) segmented image; (b) observed adjacency relation graph; (c) observed unary relations

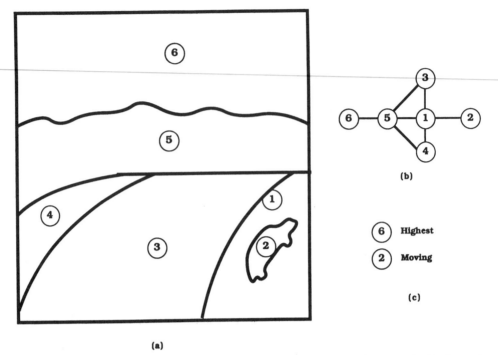

**(a)**

**(b)**

**(c)**

**FIGURE P17-4**  Example 4 (a) segmented image; (b) observed adjacency relation graph; (c) observed unary relations

# 8

# PRACTICAL IMAGE PROCESSING CONCERNS

## ■ INTRODUCTION

The previous seven chapters have concentrated on the modeling and algorithmic aspects of digital image processing and computer vision. In this chapter, we consider practical ramifications, particularly sensing and computational aspects. This includes

1. **Acquiring image data**. We examine the solid state imaging devices, serial formats for image data transmission, and constraints on spatial resolution.
2. **Processing of image data**. We examine the computational complexity of this task and the difficulty of achieving this processing in real time. We consider the characterization of computer architectural features necessitated by certain classes of image processing and computer vision algorithms. We explore the potential application of new or emerging computer architectures (e.g., systolic arrays and dataflow machines) to image processing and computer vision problems.

## ■ ELECTRONIC FORMATION OF IMAGES

The basic mechanism for generating raw image data is the conversion of incident light intensity into spatially distributed electrical signals. These signals are in turn converted into digital representations suitable for processing. Several mechanisms are available and are discussed in the following sections.

## *VIDICON IMAGERS AND SERIAL IMAGE TRANSMISSION STANDARDS*

The operation of the vidicon imager (Deutsch, 1951) (i.e., television cameras) is based on scanning a photosensitive tube and is likely to become less significant as alternative (e.g., solid state) sensors emerge. However, the scanning of the vidicon tube to convert a 2-D image into a 1-D time-varying signal has yielded a raster scan format and associated serial transmission (broadcast) standards that may continue to be significant. These serial standards allow the transmission of image data from one medium to another, for example, from a camera to a monitor. Of more interest in digital image processing is moving the image data from a sensor to a computer interface. Solid-state sensors emulate these serial standards for compatibility reasons. The existence of serial standards for image transmission does not preclude other formats. Indeed, it might be desirable to develop mechanisms that transmit entire images in parallel.

### NTSC AND RS-170 (AND DERIVATIVES)

The predominant serial standard in the United States was developed by the National Television System Committee (NTSC) in the 1940s. Typical of this standard are the RS-170, CCIR, and RS-343 specifications. Here we focus on the RS-170. Like most RS serial standards (e.g., RS-232), the standard defines both a signal format and electrical specifications (voltage polarities and levels). Our concern is primarily with the signal format.

As shown in Figure 8.1, the objective is to convert a 2-D intensity array into a 1-D signal. In this figure, sampling along (approximately) horizontal lines is used.

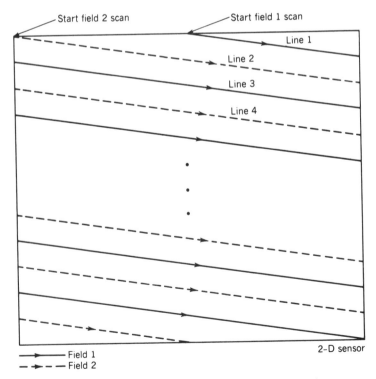

**FIGURE 8.1** Image scanning process derived from Vidicon, with 2:1 interlace (retrace not shown)

The spectrum of the output sampled signal reflects the effect of this sampling, and thus aliasing (Chapter 3) in the vertical direction is possible. Of course, many other spatial sampling possibilities, such as spiral sampling, exist. Historically, the signal intensity was analog, and therefore amplitude quantization error was not a factor.

RS-170 specifications govern both the spatial and temporal sampling of the sensor. One frame, or image temporal sample, consists of 525 lines and is acquired in 1/30 sec. Moreover, the frame is subdivided into odd and even fields, each representing one-half the image samples. Each field represents a sampling of the image with twice the line spacing (one-half the line sampling frequency). This yields 262.5 lines per field. The fields are thus *interlaced*, as shown in Figure 8.1. Interlacing reduces the appearance of *flicker* in the display. Thus, each field samples half of the image extent somewhat coarsely in one-half of the frame rate. A 1/60 sec field sampling rate allows the commercial power line fundamental frequency (available in the U.S., excepting Hawaii) to be used as a synchronization signal. The 30-Hz frame rate is also significant in that it differs from the 25 (or 24) frames per second sampling rate used in the production of film-based motion pictures. Adoption of a film frame rate of 30 frames per second increases both the quality and, more important, the compatibility of motion picture film with television media (Adam, 1986).

Furthermore, not all the sampled lines in a frame, nor all portions of sampled lines, are visible. To allow for line and field retrace of either the sampling or display beam using vidicon technology, vertical and horizontal *retrace intervals* are provided to turn off the display while the beam moves (in the case of a new frame) from the lower righthand position of the device to the upper lefthand corner (vertical retrace). Approximately twenty lines in each field are blanked for the vertical retrace interval. This yields an effective resolution of 484 visible lines. Furthermore, 16 percent of the time allocated to a line is allocated to horizontal retrace.

In converting the 2-D image data to serial format, it is necessary to encode information (other than the video data) regarding the start of frames, fields, and lines. This is done via the introduction of *sync pulses*, whose intensities are in the ultra black. Once converted to a serial format, the data for an entire image may be displayed as a function of (sampling) time. This is shown in Figure 8.2, parts (a), the composite image and (b), a single line with sync pulses. The intensity levels shown in Figure 8.2b are in IRE units, ranging from $-40$ to $+100$. One hundred IRE units equal a peak-to-peak voltage of 0.714 volts, and we note the following:

$$+100 \text{ IRE units } = \text{ white video level}$$

$$+7.5 \text{ IRE units } = \text{ black video level}$$

We defer a detailed analysis of the timing considerations involved in acquiring images transmitted in this format to the discussion of speed and memory problems. Note, however, that the serial standard we have investigated is but one of a number of existing standards (e.g., PAL and Secam). Furthermore, two additional factors are likely to become more important in the future:

1. The development, or modification, of standards to facilitate high-resolution (e.g., 1125 or more visible lines) television (HDTV). Currently, there is no shortage of proposed high-resolution TV systems, with a plethora of variable line specifications, frame rates, and interlacing strategies. It is reasonable to expect that some standardization must precede any commercialization attempts (Roizen, 1986).

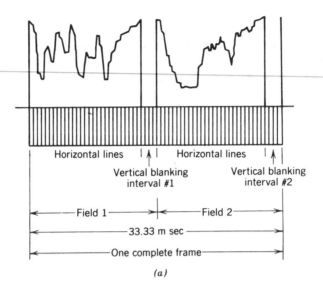

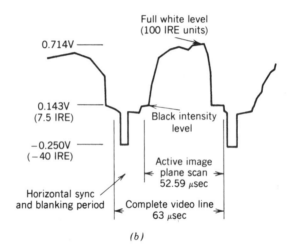

**FIGURE 8.2** The image as a serial signal

(a) One complete frame

(b) One complete line

2. Interface standards for non-RS-170 devices. These are typically line-scan arrays. The devices are often operated in an asynchronous mode and begin acquisition on receipt of a start pulse. The utility of this latter characteristic enables the matching of the video acquisition process, particularly the temporal sampling rate, with the application.

## SOLID-STATE SENSORS (LINE AND AREA)

There exist several solid state approaches to the conversion of incident illumination into electronically manipulable images. Foremost among these approaches are *photodiode arrays*, *charge injection devices* (CIDs), and *charge coupled devices* (CCDs) Our analysis is concentrated on CCD technology. Buss and Melen (1977) present a comprehensive review of CCD technology and imaging applications.

### CHARGE COUPLED TECHNOLOGY

Inherent in CCD technology are a discrete number of charge storage sites and a charge transfer mechanism. The stored charge (neglecting quantum theory) could represent an analog signal with practically infinite resolution. Thus, quantization errors are almost nonexistent. CCDs and CIDs exhibit similar characteristics in the conversion of incident energy into electrical charge; however, the mechanism for moving and sensing this charge is substantially different in each device.

Imaging techniques frequently involve 2-D area sensors such as CCD or CID area arrays. However, an equally important approach, particularly for current high-resolution applications, is the linear or line-scan array, consisting of a high-resolution 1-D sensing array with sensing elements arranged in a single row. Incident illumination from a 2-D source is then converted into a 2-D signal array by scanning (electronically and/or optically) the scene, or, alternately, by moving the scene past the sensor. The former is the technique typically employed in high-resolution satellite sensors; the latter is the predominant technique in line-scanner-based optical character readers (OCRs) for document conversion.

Typical solid-state area imagers employ a rectangular grid of $n \times m$ elements. This regular structure facilitates the fabrication of the device and compatibility with existing serial standards such as RS-170. Although this structure is reasonable, it is not apparent that it is optimal. For example, the distribution of optically sensitive nerve endings in the retina of high-level biological systems is not uniform. In fact, it has been suggested (Levine, 1985; Hoffman, 1968) that the nonuniform distribution of these nerves may aid in feature extraction, focus-of-attention, and hierarchical processing.

*Charge Transfer Device Basics.* Charge transfer devices (CTDs) are easily visualized as a "bucket brigade" of transferred charge, where, during transfer, the charge in one bucket (CTD cell) is poured or moved into the adjacent bucket. More precisely, as shown in Figure 8.3$a$–$d$ the basic CCD cell is an enhancement-model MOS device that behaves like a capacitor. The device is formed by diffusing an impurity (either a group III or V element) into pure silicon (a group IV element). This creates a semiconductor device upon which an insulator (typically, silicon dioxide) is formed. Finally, electrodes are deposited on top of the insulator to facilitate charge transfer. The minority carriers (holes or positive charge regions in $n$-type semiconductors and electrons in $p$-type semiconductors) are then moved

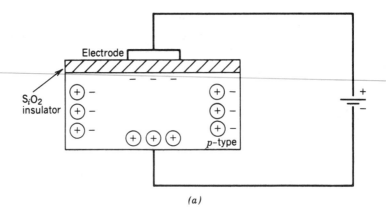

(a)

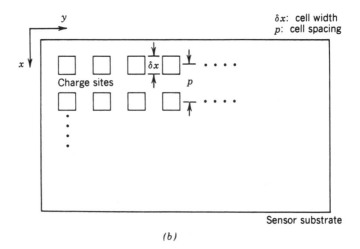

$\delta x$: cell width
$p$: cell spacing

(b)

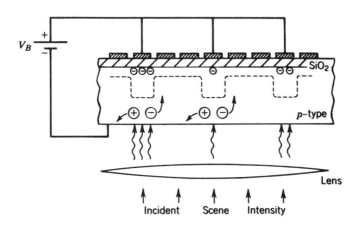

**FIGURE 8.3** CCD structure (p-type)
(a) Structure for p-type CCD (1-D "slice")
(b) Array structure
(c) Generation of minority carrier charge packet from incident illumination (1-D "slice")

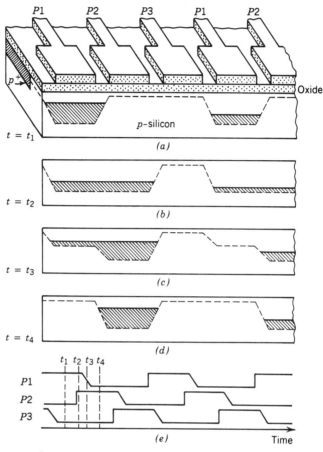

**FIGURE 8.4** Moving charge in a CCD device. Copyright © 1970 Academic Press, Inc.

by applying suitable voltages to the transfer conductors. In Figure 8.3*a* a *p*-type semiconductor is used for illustration. The charge of interest (negatively charged electrons) is attracted to the electrodes when a positive voltage is applied to them (with respect to the substrate). This creates charge packets stored in potential wells under the electrode.

As shown in Figure 8.4, charge is moved by properly sequencing the cell electrode voltages. Figure 8.4(*d*) shows a three-phase sequencing. Although significant silicon area is necessary for the three electrodes, two symmetric electrodes would be insufficient to force the charge to move in the desired direction. Designs employing as many as four phases and as few as two asymmetrical electrodes are in use.

GENERATING CHARGE FROM INCIDENT ILLUMINATION

Having determined how charge is moved in a CCD device, we now turn our attention to the mechanics of converting scene illumination into minority carrier charge. As shown in Figure 8.3(*b*) the CCD imaging sensor consists of an area array of the CCD cells studied above. This discrete sensing array involves a finite sensing area under each potential well that converts incident illumination in this area to minority carriers. The fact that this area has finite extent causes our analysis of the sampling properties of the sensor to be modified from that of Chapter 3. Nominal dimensions for these sensing sites are on the order of $10\mu m \times 10\mu m$ for a medium-resolution sensor.

The incident scene illumination generating the image is represented as a spatially distributed array of photons. Consider a 1-D horizontal or vertical slice of the array, as shown in Figure 8.3c. The conversion of incident scene illumination into sensed charge is presented in detail in Buss and Mellen, 1977. Basically, scene luminance energy (after appropriate lensing) impinges on the face of the CCD sensor. Incident photon energy at each sensing site is absorbed in the silicon substrate and frees a number of electron-hole pairs from one another. The minority carriers (electrons in our example) then agglomerate under the appropriate electrode, thus forming a charge packet whose size is dependent upon the incident illumination at this site. The amount of charge thus generated at each sensing site is also a function of the dimensions (area) of the site and the time during which this accumulation is allowed. This time is determined by the frame rate of the system and is typically 1/30 of a second. Thus, both temporal and spatial integration of incident illumination is involved.

### Sampling the CCD Array (Output of Charge-Based Image)

Once the charge packets have been collected at each of the sensing sites, the CCD transfer mechanism (phased electrode voltages), in conjunction with a set of ancillary transfer arrays, is used to generate the output serial signal. The transfer arrays are shielded from the incident illumination so that charge does not accumulate, but is only moved under these electrodes. The existence of a vidicon-based serial standard necessitates, in most applications, mimicking this format using the charge transfer array. We note in passing that one of the more ambitious sampling strategies envisioned is one in which the charge (or image data), instead of being moved in a 2-D fashion out of the sensor array, is moved in parallel to another level or processing plane, thus effecting a 3-D processing structure.

We show an example of this process using the Fairchild CCD222 device. Excerpts from the specification sheet for this device are shown in Figure 8.5. Other CCD imaging devices are similar in nature. Only one of the two interlaced fields is shown in the figure. The other field has a similar readout.

Referring to Figure 8.5, assume that incident illumination at the charge sites has generated a 2-D array of charges comprising the image via the mechanism cited above. At the end of the temporal integration period for the field, charge packets from sensor sites in the field are all transferred horizontally (in parallel) to their respective adjacent vertical transport registers. Note from the figure that the vertical transport registers feed into the horizontal transport array, which generates the serial sensor output. The charge packets residing in the (illumination-shielded) vertical transport arrays are then shifted (in parallel) vertically one element into the horizontal transport array. Thus, one image sensor line now resides in the horizontal transport array; this line is the top line of the sensed image. It is then shifted horizontally out of the sensing chip until all elements have been converted to an appropriate voltage, thus forming the first serial line output.

Following this, the second element of each sensor row, which is now the topmost element of the vertical transfer array, is in turn shifted into the horizontal transport array. This data is then serially shifted out of the sensor array and represents the second image line. The remaining data in this field is moved similarly. The accu-

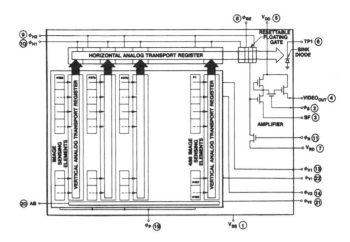

**FIGURE 8.5** CCD 222 488 × 380-element area image sensor (Fairchild semiconductor). (Copyright © 1983 Fairchild Weston Systems, Inc. CCD Imaging Division)

mulated charge residing in the alternate field sensing sites is then converted in the same fashion. The actual signal produced by the CCD sensor is a time-varying (due to the scanning approach) voltage. Conversion of the sensed charge into a voltage is accomplished by a "floating gate" amplifier shown in Figure 8.5.

## DISCRETE SENSOR CHARACTERIZATIONS

CCDs have numerous advantages over conventional vidicon sensors:

1. **Minimal impacts of blooming**. Blooming is the spreading of incident illumination from an intensely illuminated pixel location to adjacent pixel locations, which produces an imaged spot whose apparent size is (perhaps considerably) larger than its true size. Phosphor-based vidicon imagers are particularly prone to blooming; the physical separation of charge sensing sites in the CCD sensor tend to limit this effect.

2. **Faster response to changes in incident illumination**. The resultant bright streaks that occur (e.g., when a vidicon television camera is panned through bright lights) are due to the persistence of the vidicon phosphor. CCD (or CID) response time is governed primarily by the rate at which minority carriers may recombine in the substrate.

3. **Smaller size and lower power**. The compact size of solid-state cameras in general results because there is no need for an elongated vidicon tube.

4. **Good low-level light performance.**

## RESOLUTION

In this section we are concerned with investigating the resolution of electronic sensors. The term "resolution" connotes many varied meanings. For example, we may be interested in the minimum feature resolution of a sensor, that is, the smallest angular difference in which two different intensities may be discerned. Note that resolution is a property of the overall imaging and computer interface system and includes such effects as lenses, analog/digital conversion rate, and so on.

The HVS possesses about 1/60 degree of spatial resolution. Given a total field of view (FOV), this would allow estimation of the total number of image samples needed to achieve HVS resolution. Another point of reference is the resolution of film-based (e.g., silver halide processes) imaging. For reference, a 35-mm Koda-chrome transparency has a resolution of approximately 18 million pixels, which, assuming a square image (it is not), yields image dimensions of 4,243 × 4,243 pixels. Film is therefore liable to be the predominant reference for achievable high-resolution imaging for some years to come.

Image engineers must be aware of the possibility that resolution and representation dimension may be different and may not be preserved after conversion to computer-manipulable form. RS-170, for example, specifies the total number of lines in an image, not the sensor resolution. It is possible to convert the output of a sensor with 100 lines of resolution to RS-170 and to subsequently convert this signal into a 512 × 512 sampled version. It is incorrect, however, to infer that the resulting stored image has 512 × 512 resolution.

### SENSOR MODULATION TRANSFER FUNCTION (MTF)

We noted that the sensor is a discrete and periodic array of charge sites with finite area, as shown in Figure 8.3b. Here, for simplicity, we consider only the vertical direction, indexed by $x$. In contrast with the ideal sampling in Chapter 3, the CID or CCD sensor integrates the incident illumination over an extent of $\delta x$ in each direction. This spatial integration gives rise to nonideal sensing or sampling characteristics. Intuitively, one would suspect that this integration gives rise to smoothing (or perhaps "smearing") of the incident image data, due to the low-pass nature of the integration process. For example, line-like features with dimensions of less than $\delta x$ will be spread throughout the cells with dimension $\delta x$ across which they appear.

In addition to this integration, two other nonideal characteristics of the sensor that contribute to decreased response that have not been modeled previously are the effect of nonideal charge transfer and the diffusion of photon-generated minority carriers into regions other than the potential wells. A characterization for each of these effects in the frequency domain is possible (Barbe, 1975). This yields a frequency domain characterization of the sensor in terms of an MTF. Assume that an interlaced sampling scheme is used with the sensor shown in Figure 8.3b. The distance between spatially adjacent sampling sites in the interlaced image is denoted $p$.

As shown in Chapter 3, the sensor MTF is defined as the modulus of the Fourier transform due to the sensor. Recall that the assumption of impulse sampling (Chapter 3) yields an MTF of unity. Furthermore, the resolution of the sensor may be characterized in units of cycles per spatial image measure (e.g., cycles per image or cycles per pixel unit). Given a sensor cell that integrates incident illumination over a cell of width $\delta x$, with an intercell distance of $p$ (shown in Figure 8.3b), a straightforward (see the problems) derivation of the MTF due to this cell is

$$\text{MTF} = \frac{\sin[(\pi/2) \ (f/f_{\max}) \ (\delta x/p)]}{(\pi/2) \ (f/f_{\max}) \ (\delta x/p)} \tag{8-1}$$

where $f_{\max} = \dfrac{1}{2p}$.

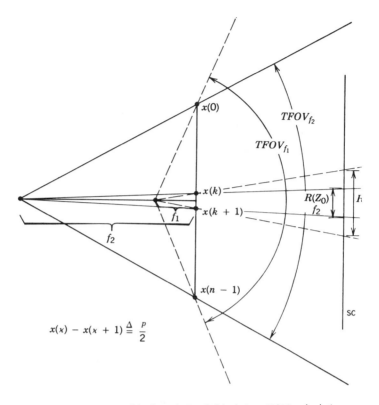

**FIGURE 8.6** Simplified resolution/field of view (FOV) calculation

The sinc-form of the MTF thus indicates loss (or "rolloff") of sensor frequency response due to the spatial integration. As $\delta x$ approaches 0, the MTF approaches unity, as expected. The MTF is developed further in the problems. The effects of nonideal optical processing (such as the point spread function induced by lenses) can also be described in the Fourier domain.

One resolution-related aspect of significance in computer vision applications is the relationship between (chip-level) sensor resolution and the achievable measurement resolution. A primary measure of this capability is that of resolution in the scene, that is, discernable differences of 3-D object points (at some perpendicular distance from the image plane). For example, given a specific sensor, it is relatively easy to choose a suitable lensing arrangement (i.e., choose a focal length) to achieve measurement accuracies on the order of .001 inch. The problem, however, is that the restricted FOV of this arrangement may prevent the acquisition of enough scene features to make the processing valuable.

Figure 8.6 quantifies this characteristic. For fixed interpixel (sensing sites) distance and sensor extent, the relationships between total FOV (TFOV), instantaneous FOV (IFOV), and scene resolution at a fixed magnification ratio are shown graphically. The spacing between adjacent sensor pixel sites is only used to illustrate the relative resolution concept; this spacing alone may not quantify the practical resolution of the overall imaging system because the image plane MTF, optical transfer function of the lensing system, and the frequency characteristics of the input image all contribute to this specification.

We illustrate the principle using a sensor modeled as a pinhole camera with the optical system effects (change of optical system focal length) modeled solely as a change in focal length. As shown in Figure 8.6, the smaller focal length, $f_1$, yields a larger TFOV, but a correspondingly lower IFOV. From Figure 8.6 the relationship between scene resolution, object distance, focal length, and interpixel spacing at the sensor central region may be simply quantified by

$$R_f(z_o) = (z_o/f)\,(p/2) \tag{8-2}$$

where $R_f$ is the discernable scene dimension, $z_o/f$ is the magnification ratio, and $p/2$ is the interpixel spacing.

For example, given the following parameters for a sensor for a satellite-based remote sensing system:

Typical perigee of satellite = 275 km (170 miles).
(equivalent) focal length of imaging system = 1 meter (m).
Minimum required ground resolution = 2m.

The required CCD sensor interpixel spacing is determined using Eq. 8-2, to be 7.3 μm. From this specification, the sensor might discern the presence of individuals, but objects they might be holding or their faces would not be discernable.

## ■ SPEED/MEMORY PROBLEMS

"A picture is worth a thousand words." In this section, we explicitly determine the number of computer memory words (or bytes) that storage of an image necessitates. As we will discover, 1000 bytes or words is inadequate to store even a small image.

### DATA TIMING AND VOLUME REQUIREMENTS (RS-170)

As a preliminary step, the data timing and volume requirements for typical data from a medium-resolution sensor outputting in RS-170 format are calculated. Assume that the sampled image has a spatial resolution of $512 \times 512$ pixels. The visible portion of a line (512 lines of 512 pixels each) is thus generated in $\frac{1}{525}$ of a frame period or 63.5 μsec. Sixteen percent of a line or 10.2 μsec of this interval are used for horizontal blanking. Thus, each pixel intensity must be sampled and discretized in less than

53.3 (μsec/line)/512 (samples/line) = 0.104 μsec/sample

or approximately 100 nanoseconds (nsec). Consequently, image acquisition systems tend to use high-speed flash analog/digital converters in the acquisition process.

Another related problem is that this conversion yields a formidable data rate for continuous processing (by 1989 standards). 512 samples (which we assume are stored as bytes) per line and 512 lines per frame yields 256 kilobytes (KByte) per frame. In 1 second, at RS-170 rates

256 KB/image × 30 images/sec = 7.5 megabytes (MByte)/sec

need to be processed. Furthermore, a $1024 \times 1024 \times 8$-bit (1 byte) image requires 1 MByte for storage. Thus, a few seconds of image data are likely to consume major storage resources. Consider that a standard $8\frac{1}{2} \times 11$ inch page of single-spaced text (with reasonable margins) is stored in approximately 2KByte of computer memory. Thus, 500 pages of text (approximately the contents of this book) have the same storage requirements as a single 1024 × 1024 pixel image. Furthermore, assuming that, on average in processing a single image, 10 floating-point operations per second (FLOPS) per pixel are required (which would be the case, for example, in a simple edge enhancement operation), this data rate requires a computer capable of processing rates of approximately 75 millions of FLOPS (MFLOPS). These computational and storage requirements exceed those of most reasonably sized comptuers.

# ■ ARCHITECTURES, DECOMPOSITIONS, AND ALGORITHMS

## INTRODUCTION

The computational resources needed to implement computer vision algorithms as shown in the previous section exceed the capability of most current uniprocessor computer architectures. Computing capability continues to evolve at an astonishing rate, and there are reasons to expect that image processing requirements will be met with more than simply a faster processor. Rather, radically different hardware and software architectures are likely to emerge.

For example, it may no longer be possible to speed up a particular processor by simply increasing clock speed, because the propagation delays of integrated circuit gates are approaching the speed of electricity through a wire (a theoretical limit). If we are unable to make one processor work faster, we can distribute the work over an ensemble of processors and achieve speedup as a result of concurrent implementation. This is the subject of this section.

There are numerous books on parallel processing in general (e.g., Hwang and Briggs, 1984) and parallel architectures and algorithms for image processing specifically (e.g., Duff and Levialdi, 1981). One source of practical reference concerning a variety of approaches is (IEEE Computer Society, 1985). Every aspect of parallel processing cannot be covered in this section. We focus on a fundamental concept at the heart of the parallelization of computer vision, namely, the identification of potential concurrency for the algorithm implementation. This concept is far more important than studying the implementation of a particular algorithm on a particular machine (which is likely to be obsolete in a year or two). Just as the development of a suitable model precedes the design of a computer vision algorithm, the development of one or more algorithm decompositions precedes the design of a parallel architecture for implementation.

Although, in this chapter, several of the emerging parallel computing techniques are highlighted for image processing applications, we are not concerned with the development of any single super (image processing) computer to meet all tasks. Rather, we concentrate on a modular approach, where future image processing and analysis systems are composed of a number of cooperating modules (e.g., feature extraction, motion estimation, surface mapping, rule-based content inference). Each of these modules is characterized by both dedicated software and hardware, which necessarily must interface with other modules to accomplish the overall processing objective.

## PARALLELISM AND COMPUTER ARCHITECTURES

A guiding principle in solving the computational aspects of computer vision algorithms is that if a particular image processing problem suggests a certain structure for its solution, an efficient computer implementation may be one that reflects that structure. For example, if the processing algorithm is based on the calculation of local image properties in all possible neighborhoods of the image, a logical problem decomposition and associated architecture might be a parallel computer in which each processing element independently processes neighborhood pixel data.

In exploring the parallel processing of digital image data, it is useful to view the (static) image as a 3-D discrete entity, with two spatially discretized indices and a discretized intensity value, as shown below:

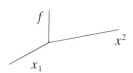

Parallel processing of image data (at the lowest level) may be conceptualized as the development of a minimum time-space hardware realization through which the above image data structure flows. Parallel decomposition concerns how the above data structure is partitioned, or "sliced," for processing.

### MEASURES OF PROCESSING CAPABILITY

For many tasks, MFLOPS (see the section on "Speed and Memory Problems") are an adequate measure. For others, particularly image analysis and AI-related operations, floating-point operations are insignificant. A better measure might be either millions of instructions executed per second (MIPS) or logical inferences per second (LIPS). A more suitable and independent measure of process or performance might be images per second.

### AREA/TIME TRADEOFFS AND DECOMPOSITIONS

A measure of the performance of a parallel computing architecture is of fundamental importance to its intelligent development and application. Intuitively, one might hope that an $n$ processor implementation of an algorithm will achieve the result in $1/n$ the time of a single processor. Unfortunately, this is at best an upper bound on processor speedup; actual performance increase is less impressive. This result is due in large measure to the processing time necessary for communication (e.g., sharing of data or results) between processors, the fact that some processors may have to wait for the results of other processors (i.e., the process was not fully decomposed into a parallel algorithm), and the fact that some area of data memory may need to be shared by several processors. For an $n$ processor implementation, we define speedup as the following ratio:

$$\text{Speedup} = \frac{\text{processing time with single processor}}{\text{processing time with } n \text{ processors}}$$

One significant result (Minsky's conjecture; Minsky and Papert, 1969) predicts that the actual speedup for $n$ processors is $\log_2(n)$. This, and other speedup predictors are shown in Table 8.1 and Figure 8.7.

■ **TABLE 8.1**
**Speedup comparisons**

| n (# processors)<br>(Ideal Speedup) | Minsky<br>($\log_2(n)$) | Optomistic<br>[Hwang/Briggs]<br>($n/\ln(n)$) | Amdahl's Law<br>[Amdahl]<br>($1/(s + p/n)$)<br>S = 0.05 | S = 0.20 |
|---|---|---|---|---|
| 4 | 2.0 | 2.9 | 3.5 | 2.5 |
| 10 | 3.3 | 4.3 | 6.9 | 3.6 |
| 100 | 6.6 | 21.7 | 16.8 | 4.8 |
| 1000 | 10.0 | 144.8 | 19.6 | 5.0 |
| 10,000 | 13.3 | 1,086.0 | 20.0 | 5.0 |

## CLASSES OF PARALLELISM AND ARCHITECTURAL PARTITIONS

Following the terminology of Yalamanchili and Aggarwal (1985), parallelism is defined in several ways. *Algorithmic parallelism* (AP) involves decomposition of an operation or algorithm into component operations, which in turn may be executed in parallel. *Data parallelism* (DP) involves decomposing the input data into partitions over which the operation may be carried out independently and in parallel. A similar taxonomy attributed to Flynn (1972) is that of partitioning the process into instructions (I) and data (D). By considering the manner in which a given architecture treats these entities to achieve concurrency, several classes of processors result. A processor architecture that executes a single instruction on a single datum is a *single instruction/single data stream* (SISD) computer. This architecture is typified by the familiar uniprocessor or Von Neumann's paradigm. An architecture in which a single instruction is executed on more than one datum

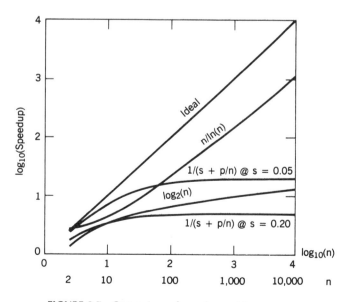

**FIGURE 8.7** Comparison of speedup metrics

is referred to as a *single instruction/multiple data stream* (SIMD) computer. An architecture in which independent instructions may be applied to a multiple data stream is termed a *multiple instruction/multiple data stream* (MIMD) computer.

Another architecture classification has resulted from the emergence of the data-driven or *data-flow computation paradigm.* In this architecture, instructions are not sequenced in the conventional manner (using an instruction pointer). Instead, computation proceeds when the operands for a given instruction become available. Depending on the specific algorithm, a data flow computer at any given time may operate as SISD, SIMD, or MIMD.

### PROCESSOR INTERCONNECTION STRATEGIES

Given $n$ processors, each of which is capable of independently carrying out some processing task on a set of input data, there exists a broad spectrum of interconnection strategies, as shown in Figure 8.8. Several of these interconnection strategies are useful for wide classes of algorithmic decompositions, discussed in the following sections.

## ALGORITHM DECOMPOSITION APPROACHES

### DATA FLOW GRAPHS

The data flow graph (DFG) for an algorithm (or subset of algorithm operations) is a useful graphical mechanism to identify potential algorithmic parallelism and, to a limited extent, data dependency. Consider the implementation of the following sample image processing operation, which approximates the magnitude of the smoothed spatial gradients of an image function $f(x_1,x_2)$:

$$f_{out}(x_1,x_2) = \text{sqrt}(f_{x1}^2(x_1,x_2) + f_{x2}^2(x_1,x_2)) \tag{8-3}$$

where

$$
\begin{aligned}
f_{x1}(x_1,x_2) = 1/3 \{ & [f(x_1 + 1,x_2 - 1) \\
& + f(x_1 + 1,x_2) + f(x_1 + 1,x_2 + 1)] \\
& - [f(x_1 - 1,x_2 - 1) \\
& + f(x_1 - 1,x_2) + f(x_1 - 1,x_2 + 1)] \}
\end{aligned}
$$

and

$$
\begin{aligned}
f_{x2}(x_1,x_2) = 1/3 \{ & [f(x_1 - 1,x_2 + 1) \\
& + f(x_1,x_2 + 1) + f(x_1 + 1,x_2 + 1)] \\
& - [f(x_1 - 1,x_2 - 1) \\
& + f(x_1,x_2 - 1) + f(x_1 + 1,x_2 - 1)] \}
\end{aligned}
$$

This operation, in terms of pixel locations in the image plane, is shown graphically in Figure 8.9. The local nature of the operation is noteworthy. We first seek to identify concurrency in the computation of a single pixel result, that is, $f_{out}(x_1,x_2)$. Since the operation needs to be performed for all desired pixel locations in $f_{out}$, a second level of parallel decomposition is possible. Assuming that all input image

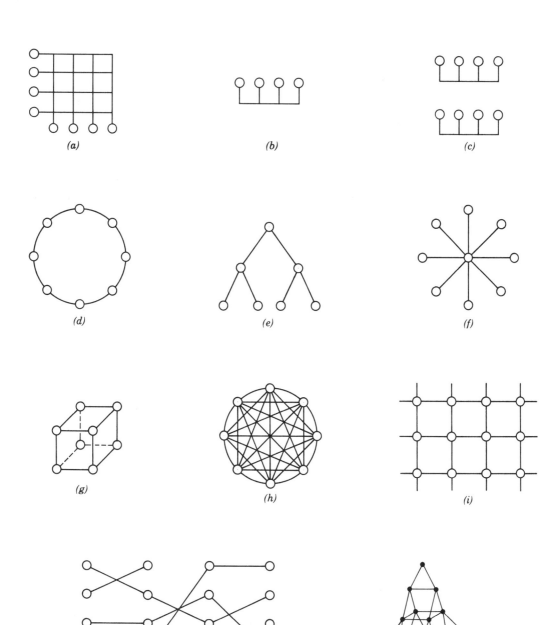

**FIGURE 8.8** Sample processor interconnection strategies (may be implemented by a combination of hardware and software protocols)

(a)   Crossbar switch (dynamic)
(b)   Single bus
(c)   Multiple bus
(d)   Ring
(e)   Tree
(f)   Star
(g)   Cube n = 3
(h)   All connected (same as (a))
(i)   Systolic array
(j)   Shuffle network (dynamic)
(k)   Pyramid (2-pyramid)

operands are available simultaneously, the DFG for this operation indicates the necessary computational modules (arithmetic operators in this case) and the relationship of the input and output of these modules. This is shown in Figure 8.9. *Note that the DFG for a particular algorithm is not unique.* Rearrangement of Eq. 8-3 yields alternate graph representations.

At this point we have decomposed the local operation into one that embodies parallelism. The final step is to consider the overall computation for all pixels in the output image. This yields significant additional parallelism, since, for example, the (global) DFG may indicate common intermediate results for different output pixels. In any case, a set of computational modules, as shown in Figure 8.9, that could be replicated in Very Large Scale Integration (VLSI), results in a parallel implementation and architecture for the computation.

Numerous examples of data dependency, which inhibits or considerably complicates parallel decomposition, arise. This is due to subtle ramifications of the assignment operator (e.g., the := operator in Pascal) in sequential programs. We briefly show an example.

Consider the following program fragment:

$$
\begin{array}{lll}
a := b + c & \text{(i)} & \\
d := a + c & \text{(ii)} & \text{(8-4)} \\
e := 5d + a & \text{(iii)} & \\
a := d + e & \text{(iv)} &
\end{array}
$$

As the DFG shows, the algorithm portion defined by statements (i) and (ii) (as written) cannot be executed in parallel because of data dependency. Specifically, the value of variable *a* must be computed before its use in (ii). Similarly, (iii) is data dependent on (i) and (ii). Another common type of data dependence is shown in (i) and (iv); here, a parallel decomposition would attempt to assign potentially conflicting values to *a*.

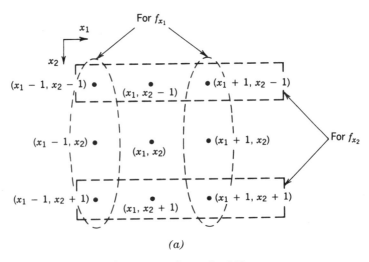

*(a)*

**FIGURE 8.9** Data flow graph example (corresponding to Eq. 8-3)
(a) Image plane local data dependence (8 neighbors of $(x_1, x_2)$) (note memory contention at "corners")
(b) Data flow graph (not unique)

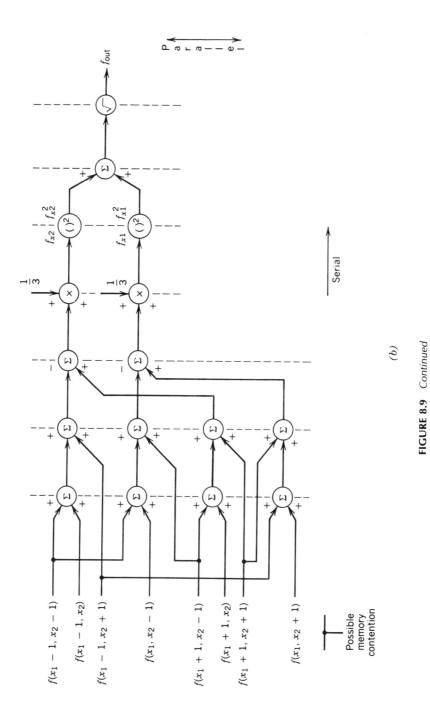

**FIGURE 8.9** *Continued*

413

Another problem area is the parallel decomposition of programs with control flow (e.g., conditional branches). Branches may represent a significant fraction (up to 25 percent) of the computation and may seriously limit practical parallel decomposition possibilities. One useful alternative is to attempt rewriting the program to eliminate the branch statement, as shown below.

$$\text{IF } a > 0$$

$$\text{THEN } b := d/f + g$$

$$\text{ELSE } b := d/f - g$$

could be rewritten as

$$b := d/f + \text{sgn}(a)\, g$$

This is one of the more active research areas in parallel computing (Hwang and Briggs, 1984).

## LOCALIZED DATA DECOMPOSITIONS

We have seen the attractiveness of algorithmic decompositions where the need for image data is kept local. "Local" may signify in a region of small pixel extent, or perhaps within a row or column of the image. The significance of the latter is that vector-type processing operations may be employed. This allows mapping of the algorithm onto a multiprocessor architecture with regular and, more important, local interprocessor communications. Several examples of this decomposition are

1. The separable implementation of the LOG operator in Chapter 4. In this chapter, the operation was decomposed into row and column operations.
2. Edge detection using $2 \times 2$ or $3 \times 3$ masks.
3. Computing geometric transforms iteratively so that the flow of data is restricted to local regions.

For example, an attempt might be made to decompose a geometric transformation (assuming this is possible) into a series of transformations that are more local in nature and thus only move data successively through local neighborhoods of a processor array. For example, in the implementation of a 45-degree rotation, that is, when

$$f_o(\underline{x}) = f_i[A_{45°}\underline{x}] \tag{8-5}$$

Neglecting interpolation, it is possible to achieve the same overall rotation by successively transforming $f_i$ in Eq. 8-5 with a matrix that only implements a portion of the transform (e.g., a 5-degree rotation) nine times. Alternately, for a translation

$$f_o(\underline{x}) = f_i[\underline{x} + \underline{b}] \tag{8-6}$$

the same result could (theoretically) be achieved by performing a sequence of 10 image transformations using $\underline{b}' = \underline{b}/10$. Practical concerns, however, limit the utility of this approach.

In both Eq. 8-5 and Eq. 8-6 above it is apparent that the flow of data in the intermediate transforms is kept local; thus, the processor interconnection network remains reasonable. Despite its appeal, several drawbacks to this approach exist:

1. The number of decompositions necessary to achieve local image plane operations (e.g., data flow within a $3 \times 3$ neighborhood) may be excessive.

2. The cumulative effects of roundoff encountered in each stage may overshadow the actual global transform, or otherwise require higher precision arithmetic, principally interpolation.

3. The ability to decompose an arbitrary geometric transform into a succession of local transforms is not, in general, guaranteed.

## PARALLEL PROCESSING SOFTWARE

The multiprocessor systems noted in "Speed/Memory Problems" are of limited practical utility unless suitable language support exists. Paramount in the capabilities of parallel processing software is the production of machine-level (or more correctly, multiprocessor system-level) instructions that enable parallel processing. In some cases, this is done by extending an existing language to allow parallel constructs. Currently, it is usual for the programmer to identify any parallelism in the computation. Ultimately, high-level parallelizing compilers that automatically determine parallelism may become available.

We may think of individual code segments as a set of computing processes. Three entities are fundamental to any consideration of parallel (declarative) programming languages:

1. A means to distinguish or delineate a process or code segment and denote the process as PARALLEL, SERIAL, or some combination (see the ALT construct in OCCAM).

2. A means to indicate a block of data that should be processed in parallel.

3. A means to allow synchronization or communication between processes (particularly when the run times of independent processes are not constant and are unknown a priori as well as overall input/output (I/O)). In the case of languages designed for some architectures (e.g., a systolic array), this includes implementation of instructions for both local (e.g., interprocessor) and global (see the GAPP architecture below) output.

Not all of the above are necessary for a specific architecture. For example, in the case of a SIMD machine, such as a systolic array, item 2 is of major importance because the single-instruction format implies a serial execution of the algorithm. In general, a language designed for an MIMD machine (e.g., a hypercube network of processors) must include all three.

The familiar serial version of Pascal has been extended to allow for the development of programs on SIMD and MIMD machines (Maggiollo-Schettini, 1981). This modification of Pascal has yielded OCCAM (Taylor and Wilson, 1982), a language designed to complement the Transputer (a parallel processing element designed by INMOS). The syntax of OCCAM is described in Figure 8.10. The use of the keywords SEQ, PAR, ALT, and CHAN reflect the three fundamental entities listed above.

Parallel symbolic languages for high-level image analysis implementation are available. For example, concurrent PROLOG (Shapiro, 1986) is an implementation of PROLOG that allows unification in parallel. Similarly, MultiLISP (Halstead,

| Keyword | Sample Use | Remarks |
|---|---|---|
| SEQ | SEQ<br>  get-char<br>  output-char | define a sequential block of processes<br>this first<br>then this |
| PAR | PAR<br>  in1 ? al<br>  in2 ? a2<br>  out1 ? x1<br>  out2 ? x2 | define a parallel block of processes<br>do this currently<br>with this . . . |
| ALT | ALT<br>  in1 ? char<br>    out ! char<br>  in2 ? char<br>    out ! char | alternate blocks as follows:<br>get character from<br>either in1 and output it<br>or in2 and output it |
| CHAN | CHAN in | declare a channel named "in"<br>used for both I/O and<br>interprocess communication) |
| PROC | PROC LeftEnd (CHAN ctr, in, out) =<br>  VAR x:<br>  SEQ<br>    x : = 0<br>    SEQ i = [0 FOR N]<br>      ctrl ! EndBuffer<br>      PAR<br>        in2 ANY<br>        out ! x | define a process called<br>"LeftEnd" with I/O channels ctrl, in<br>and out<br>declare a variable<br>execute sequence |

**FIGURE 8.10** OCCAM syntax

1986) is an example of LISP with parallel processing capability. Both of these are described in detail in Schalkoff (to be published).

One of the major advantages of standardization on a parallel language is that the user is not required to understand the details of the underlying parallel architecture. Therefore, the parallel machine is abstracted into a programming model. This allows access to a much larger audience of programmers and enables some portability of code from one parallel machine to another (or its successor).

## ■ COMPUTER IMPLEMENTATIONS FOR IMAGE PROCESSING TASKS

In this section, we explore some examples of existing and commercially available parallel computers for image processing.

### SYSTOLIC ARRAYS AND APPLICATIONS

The structure of the systolic array was considered in the "Classes of Parallelism" section and in Figure 8.8(i). We investigate the potential for implementing image processing algorithms using this multiprocessor interconnection paradigm, restricting our discussion to systolic arrays that are SIMD machines.

### A FICTITIOUS SYSTOLIC PROCESSOR (IP8650)

The heart of any systolic array is the component processor. We begin our examination of systolic array implementation by creating a fictitious processor, similar (but more advanced and user-friendly) than the commercially available counterpart explored below. Denoted the IP8650, the architecture of these fictional individual processors is similar to that of a reduced instruction set 8-bit processor. For ease of visualization, a 5 × 5 array of processors, interconnected as shown in Figure 8.11a, is used. Individual processor architecture is shown in Figure 8.11b. Each processing element (PE) has a 16-bit accumulator (AH, AL), an 8-bit communication register (CM), a status word (SW), and 16 bytes of random access memory (RAM) (MO-MF) for data storage. Each PE communicates with its four (N, S, E, W) neighbors via the communication register (CM). The fundamental data type is an unsigned 8-bit integer, although the accumulator can store a 16-bit signed integer. The status word is used to indicate the property of the result in the accumulator. Bit 0 is set if the data is equal to zero. Bit 1 is set if the data is negative. Bit 2 is set if the data is an 8-bit unsigned integer.

The IP8650 instruction set is described below. All numbers are represented in hexidecimal.

### LOAD M# filename

This (pseudo) instruction is used to load or initialize the processor array memories with image data. Image data is loaded in parallel into memory byte # of each PE. (# = 0, 1, . . 9, A, . ., F, since there are 16 bytes). filename is the data file assumed in text form. Processor data for byte # is entered by placing each data byte (an integer in the range 0 to 255) on one line of the file in the order (0,0), (0,1), (0,2), . . (0,4), (1,0), (1,1), . . . (4,4), where $(i,j)$ is the index of the $i,j$th element.

### ADD M#

This instruction adds two 16-bit sign integers together and stores the sum in the accumulator. One operand is assumed in the accumulator, another is stored in M# for lower byte and M(# + 1) for higher byte, where # = 0, . . 9, A, . . E.

### ADDB source

This instruction adds a 1-byte unsigned integer to the accumulator. The source can be M# (# = 0, . . 9, A, . . F) or CM.

### SUB M#

This instruction subtracts a 16-bit signed integer from the $n$ accumulator. The lower byte of that integer is stored in M#, and the higher byte is stored in M(# + 1).

### SUBB source

This instruction subtracts a byte unsigned integer from the accumulator. The source can be M# or CM.

### MULB source

This instruction multiplies a byte unsigned integer with the accumulator and stores the result in the accumulator. The source can be M# or CM.

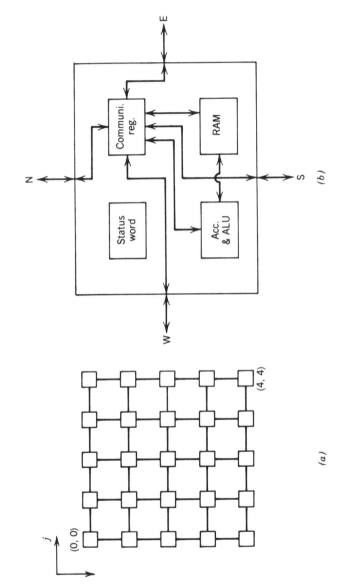

**FIGURE 8.11** IP8650 5 × 5 systolic array processor (used for illustration)
(a) Array configuration
(b) Processing element structure

### DIVB source

This instruction divides the data in the accumulator by a byte unsigned integer and stores the result in the accumulator. The source can be M# or CM.

### UP, DOWN, LEFT, RIGHT

These four instructions are used to facilitate the communication of data between each element and its four neighbors via CM. Note that data values that are not available at the edges of the array are assumed to be 0. (An alternative to this strategy is to allow wraparound of the array data, e.g., the value received by processor (0,0) following a DOWN instruction comes from processor (4,0).)

### MVIB $##

This instruction loads a byte unsigned integer into the lower byte of the accumulator.

### MOV destination source

This instruction transfers a 16-bit unsigned integer from source to destination. The destination and source can be M$n$ or AL where $\# = 0, . . 9, A, . . E$, and AL is the lower byte of the accumulator.

### MOVB destination source

This instruction transfers a byte unsigned integer from source to destination. The destination and the source can be M#, CM, and AL.

### SCL

This instruction scales a 16-bit signed integer into an 8-bit unsigned integer. The input 16-bit signed integer is stored in the accumulator and the result is stored in the lower byte of the accumulator.

### THR $##

This instruction thresholds the 8-bit unsigned integers, which are stored in the lower byte of the accumulator, where ## is the threshold. If the integer is less than ## H, AL = 00. If the integer is larger than or equal to ##H, AL = FF.

A program is run using the IP8650 simulator by creating a text file that loads the initial 5 × 5 image into the array and then mimics an instruction sequencer. Each instruction occupies one line. We show the implementation of an edge detection algorithm on a 5 × 5 image, where pixel intensity $(i,j)$ of the image is stored as 1 byte of the corresponding $(i,j)^{th}$ processor in the systolic array. The input image, with each 8-bit pixel stored in RAM byte M0 of the corresponding processor, is shown in Figure 8.12a. The edge detection algorithm used for illustration is a variant of the unsharp masking operator (Chapter 4). Figure 8.13 shows the mask values used.

Since the result for pixel $(i,j)$ requires image data values at location $(i,j)$ as well as the NSEW neighbors of $(i,j)$, the systolic array interprocessor data communications capability is used to shift these values down, left, up, and right (relative to processor $(i,j)$) to enable the computation. This action is shown in Figure 8.13. Figure 8.12b shows the contents of the M0 byte of each processor in the array after specific instruction executions. Note, from Figure 8.12c, that the desired result has been achieved.

| 00 | 00 | 00 | 00 | 3F |
|----|----|----|----|----|
| 00 | 00 | 00 | 3F | 3F |
| 00 | 00 | 3F | 3F | 3F |
| 00 | 3F | 3F | 3F | 3F |
| 3F | 3F | 3F | 3F | 3F |

(a)

| 5E | 5E | 5E | 9D | 00 |
|----|----|----|----|----|
| 5E | 5E | 9D | 1F | 3F |
| 5E | 9D | 1F | 5E | 3F |
| 9D | 1F | 5E | 5E | 3F |
| 00 | 3F | 3F | 3F | 1F |

(b)

| 00 | 00 | 00 | FF | 00 |
|----|----|----|----|----|
| 00 | 00 | FF | 00 | 00 |
| 00 | FF | 00 | 00 | 00 |
| FF | 00 | 00 | 00 | 00 |
| 00 | 00 | 00 | 00 | 00 |

(c)

**FIGURE 8.12** Sample execution of parallel edge extraction on IP8650 (data in hexadecimal)
(a)  Input 5 × 5 image data stored in individual processor RAM (M0)
(b)  Processor array RAM contents after instruction 19 (edge enhanced/rescaled) (M0)
(c)  Processor array RAM contents after thresholding (instruction 20) (M0)

The reader is encouraged to compute the speedup for this SIMD operation vis-à-vis a serial implementation. The problems explore using this SIMD architecture for alternative implementations.

THE NCR45CG72 (GAPP) 6 × 12 PROCESSOR ARRAY CHIP

We now briefly explore some of the ramifications of a commercially available processor array, notably the NCR45CG72 device, which is a single-chip unit con-

| Instruction Number | Instruction | Comment |
|----|----|----|
| 1 | LOAD M0 p86501.dat | ;LOAD IMAGE DATA INTO M0 |
| 2 | MVIB $4 | ;A = 4 |
| 3 | MOVB M1 AL | ;M1 = 4 |
| 4 | MVIB $0 | ;A = 0 |
| 5 | SUBB M0 | ;A = −P(I,J) |
| 6 | MULB M1 | ;A = −4*P(I,J) |
| 7 | MOVB CM M0 | ;CM = P(I,J) |
| 8 | DOWN | ;CM = P(I−1,J) |
| 9 | ADDB CM | ;A = A + P(I−1,J) |
| 10 | MOVB CM M0 | ;CM = P(I,J) |
| 11 | LEFT | ;CM = P(I,J+1) |
| 12 | ADDB CM | ;A = A + P(I,J+1) |
| 13 | MOVB CM M0 | ;CM = P(I,J) |
| 14 | UP | ;CM = P(I+1,J) |
| 15 | ADDB CM | ;A = A + P(I+1,J) |
| 16 | MOVB CM M0 | ;CM = P(I,J) |
| 17 | RIGHT | ;CM = P(I,J−1) |
| 18 | ADDB CM | ;A = A + P(I,J−1) |
| 19 | SCL | ;RESCALE THE DATA |
| 20 | THR $90 | ;THRESHOLD THE IMAGE |

(a)

**FIGURE 8.13** IP8650 processing strategy and programming for parallel edge extraction
(a)  Program to achieve parallel edge extraction
(b)  Processing strategy
  (i)   Mask used for 3 × 3 region centered at (i,j)
  (ii)  Array data movement for processor (i,j) (instruction number in ()   )

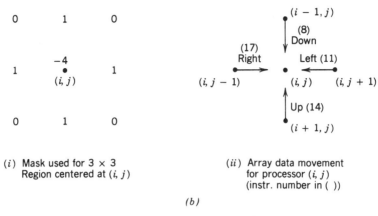

(i) Mask used for 3 × 3
Region centered at (i, j)

(ii) Array data movement
for processor (i, j)
(instr. number in ( ))

(b)

FIGURE 8.13 *Continued*

taining 6 × 12 or 72 simple processors. The GAPP architecture is essentially a 1-bit version of the fictitious IP8650 model studied above. The local interconnection details of the GAPP chip are shown in Figure 8.14. Figure 8.15 describes the architecture of a single processor. The internal flow of 1-bit data is controlled by a series of latches, whose control signals are common to all processors in the array. The processors receive instructions via an instruction sequencer, the details of which we omit here. The 6 × 12 processor array provided on a single chip may easily be extended to higher dimensions by simply cascading chips in 2-D.

## DATA FLOW MACHINES

The DFG introduced in the "Algorithm Decomposition Approaches" section served as a useful vehicle for the identification of algorithmic parallelism. Therefore, it is reasonable to expect that an architecture that could be configured to represent this DFG might be, in itself, a means of parallel processing. This is the concept behind data flow machines. The reconfigurable data flow machine hardware consists of modules or processing units that mimic the DFG.

Data flow machines depart somewhat more radically from the SISD (Von Neumann) architecture than does the SIMD systolic array explored above. Since the intermediate computations in a DFG may occur when the inputs to the processing elements are available, data flow machines theoretically have no central clock to synchronize processing. Thus, the data literally determines its own speed of flow through the machine, and the programmer does not need to specify the order in which computations are to occur. Rather, the programmer must specify the operations, operands and results of the intermediate computations and their relationship. A survey of the history and current trends in data flow languages and computing is found in Dennis (1980).

### THE NEC μPD7281 IMAGE PIPELINED PROCESSOR (IPP) CHIP

One example of an achievable data flow processor is produced by NEC (NEC Electronics, 1986). It represents a *token-based* architecture with multiple computational units in a circular pipelined architecture. The details of IPP architecture

**Block Diagram of Connections Between Four Processor Elements**

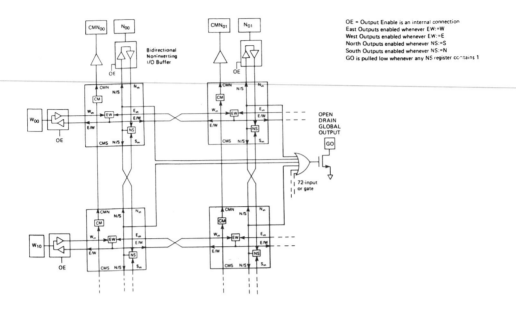

FIGURE 8.14   Detailed GAPP systolic interconnection strategy

**Schematic Diagram of One Processor Element**

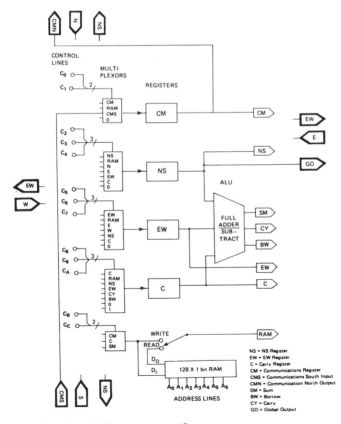

**FIGURE 8.15**   GAPP processor specifics
(a)   The layout of a single processor cell mirrors the simplicity of the overall array design. Each of the four registers, CM, NS, EW, and C accepts data from up to eight sources. The control lines select which information is sent to each register.

**Instruction Set**

| Register Operation | Mnemonic | $C_C$ | $C_B$ | $C_A$ | $C_9$ | $C_8$ | $C_7$ | $C_6$ | $C_5$ | $C_4$ | $C_3$ | $C_2$ | $C_1$ | $C_0$ | Description |
|---|---|---|---|---|---|---|---|---|---|---|---|---|---|---|---|
| CM | CM: = CM | X | X | X | X | X | X | X | X | X | X | X | 0 | 0 | MICRO-NOP |
|  | CM: = RAM | X | X | X | X | X | X | X | X | X | X | X | 0 | 1 | LOAD CM FROM RAM |
|  | CM: = CMS | X | X | X | X | X | X | X | X | X | X | X | 1 | 0 | MOVE FROM CMS INTO CM |
|  | CM: = 0 | X | X | X | X | X | X | X | X | X | X | X | 1 | 1 | LOAD 0 INTO CM |
| NS | NS: = NS | X | X | X | X | X | X | X | X | 0 | 0 | 0 | X | X | MICRO-NOP |
|  | NS: = RAM | X | X | X | X | X | X | X | X | 0 | 0 | 1 | X | X | LOAD NS FROM RAM |
|  | NS: = N | X | X | X | X | X | X | X | X | 0 | 1 | 0 | X | X | MOVE FROM N INTO NS |
|  | NS: = S | X | X | X | X | X | X | X | X | 0 | 1 | 1 | X | X | MOVE FROM S INTO NS |
|  | NS: = EW | X | X | X | X | X | X | X | X | 1 | 0 | 0 | X | X | MOVE FROM EW INTO NS |
|  | NS: = C | X | X | X | X | X | X | X | X | 1 | 0 | 1 | X | X | MOVE FROM C INTO NS |
|  | NS: = 0 | X | X | X | X | X | X | X | X | 1 | 1 | 0 | X | X | LOAD 0 INTO NS |
| EW | EW: = EW | X | X | X | X | X | 0 | 0 | 0 | X | X | X | X | X | MICRO-NOP |
|  | EW: = RAM | X | X | X | X | X | 0 | 0 | 1 | X | X | X | X | X | LOAD EW FROM RAM |
|  | EW: = E | X | X | X | X | X | 0 | 1 | 0 | X | X | X | X | X | MOVE FROM E INTO EW |
|  | EW: = W | X | X | X | X | X | 0 | 1 | 1 | X | X | X | X | X | MOVE FROM W INTO EW |
|  | EW: = NS | X | X | X | X | X | 1 | 0 | 0 | X | X | X | X | X | MOVE FROM NS INTO EW |
|  | EW: = C | X | X | X | X | X | 1 | 0 | 1 | X | X | X | X | X | MOVE FROM C INTO EW |
|  | EW: = 0 | X | X | X | X | X | 1 | 1 | 0 | X | X | X | X | X | LOAD 0 INTO EW |
| C | C: = C | X | X | 0 | 0 | 0 | X | X | X | X | X | X | X | X | MICRO-NOP |
|  | C: = RAM | X | X | 0 | 0 | 1 | X | X | X | X | X | X | X | X | LOAD C FROM RAM |
|  | C: = NS | X | X | 0 | 1 | 0 | X | X | X | X | X | X | X | X | MOVE FROM NS INTO C |
|  | C: = EW | X | X | 0 | 1 | 1 | X | X | X | X | X | X | X | X | MOVE FROM EW INTO C |
|  | C: = CY | X | X | 1 | 0 | 0 | X | X | X | X | X | X | X | X | LOAD C FROM CARRY |
|  | C: = BW | X | X | 1 | 0 | 1 | X | X | X | X | X | X | X | X | LOAD C FROM BORROW |
|  | C: = 0 | X | X | 1 | 1 | 0 | X | X | X | X | X | X | X | X | LOAD 0 INTO C |
|  | C: = 1 | X | X | 1 | 1 | 1 | X | X | X | X | X | X | X | X | LOAD 1 INTO C |
| RAM | READ | 0 | 0 | X | X | X | X | X | X | X | X | X | X | X | READ FROM RAM |
|  | RAM: = CM | 0 | 1 | X | X | X | X | X | X | X | X | X | X | X | LOAD RAM FROM CM |
|  | RAM: = C | 1 | 0 | X | X | X | X | X | X | X | X | X | X | X | LOAD RAM FROM C |
|  | RAM: = SM | 1 | 1 | X | X | X | X | X | X | X | X | X | X | X | LOAD RAM FROM SUM |

**Arithmetic Operations**

Adder/Subtracter Operations

| INPUT | | | OUTPUT | | |
|---|---|---|---|---|---|
| NS | EW | C | SM | CY | BW |
| 0 | 0 | 0 | 0 | 0 | 0 |
| 0 | 0 | 1 | 1 | 0 | 1 |
| 1 | 0 | 0 | 1 | 0 | 0 |
| 1 | 1 | 0 | 0 | 1 | 0 |
| 0 | 0 | 1 | 1 | 0 | 1 |
| 0 | 1 | 1 | 0 | 1 | 1 |
| 1 | 0 | 1 | 0 | 1 | 0 |
| 1 | 1 | 1 | 1 | 1 | 1 |

**Logic Operations**

| LOGICAL OPERATION | DESCRIPTION | CONDITIONS |
|---|---|---|
| INV | $SM = \overline{NS}$ | EW = 0, C = 1 |
|  | $SM = \overline{EW}$ | NS = 0, C = 1 |
|  | $SM = \overline{C}$ | NS = 0, EW = 1 |
| AND | $CY = NS \bullet EW$ | C = 0 |
|  | $CY = EW \bullet C$ | NS = 0 |
|  | $CY = NS \bullet C$ | EW = 0 |
|  | $BW = \overline{NS} \bullet EW$ | C = 0 |
| OR | $CY = NS + EW$ | C = 1 |
|  | $BW = \overline{NS} + EW$ | C = 1 |
|  | $BW = EW + C$ | NS = 0 |
| XOR | $SM = NS \oplus C$ | EW = 0 |
|  | $SM = NS \oplus EW$ | C = 0 |
|  | $SM = EW \oplus C$ | NS = 0 |
| XNOR | $SM = \overline{NS} \oplus \overline{EW}$ | C = 1 |

**FIGURE 8.15** Continued

(b) Table 8-1. GAPP instruction set
(c) Arithmetic and logic operations performed by a PE

and programming are complex; we present a summary here. Figure 8.16 illustrates the nine major blocks that constitute the IPP architecture. In the IPP, tokens (which may be viewed as additional bytes) are appended to the data as it proceeds into and through the pipeline. Fields of the token are used to indicate, among other things, the calculation or operation the data is to be involved in. Special tokens are used to indicate that the data is to be interpreted as program information and stored in various lookup tables in the pipeline. Thus, tokens are used by the IPP to indicate the flow of data between computational nodes in the DFG.

## OTHER PARALLEL MACHINES

The past decade has yielded many designs for large parallel machines applicable to image processing, but they are prohibitively expensive for individual laboratory use. Duff and Levialdi (1981) and Danielsson and Levialdi (1981) summarize these designs. Two examples are considered.

### MASSIVELY PARALLEL PROCESSOR (MPP)

The MPP was developed by Goodyear under contract to NASA. It contains 128 × 128 (16 K) one-bit processors. The overall architecture is shown in Figure 8.17. The array unit (AU) constitutes the heart of the MPP and represents a reconfigurable systolic array. For example, the AU interconnection may be programmed to represent a systolic array with NSEW interconnection of processors. Alternately, a "spiral" interconnection allows the 16 K processing elements to be connected together to form a single (long) linear array. Furthermore, staging memory (shown in Figure 8.17) provides a means of reordering the input data (similar to a shuffle network) before processing.

### CLIP4

A multiprocessor development effort similar to the MPP is ongoing at the University College of London. The latest in a sequence of evolutionary designs is the CLIP4. Figure 8.18 shows the overall architecture of the CLIP4. Note that the heart of the CLIP4 is a systolic interconnection of 96 × 96 (9216) 1-bit processors. This array may be configured for either square (NSEW) or hexagonal interconnection. The I/O shift registers that interface to the processor array are used, in a manner similar to the MPP, to rearrange data before processing or output. Fountain (1981) presents a state-of-the-art report on the CLIP4.

## NEURAL NETWORKS

This section presents an introduction to the exciting, emerging application of neural networks to low- and high-level image processing tasks. Neural networks are also referred to under the headings of parallel-distributed computation and connectionist computing.

Researchers from such diverse areas as neuroscience, mathematics, psychology, and computer science are beginning to see connections between underlying models for visual perception, the computation desired, parallelism that naturally (and fortunately) may be achieved, and the operation of related biological systems. An emerging nonalgorithmic computational paradigm involves large interconnected

**Block Diagram**

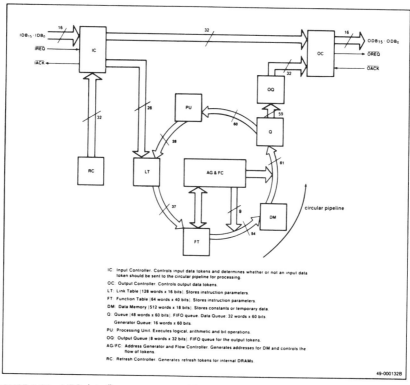

IC: Input Controller. Controls input data tokens and determines whether or not an input data token should be sent to the circular pipeline for processing.

OC: Output Controller. Controls output data tokens.

LT: Link Table (128 words x 16 bits). Stores instruction parameters.

FT: Function Table (64 words x 40 bits). Stores instruction parameters.

DM: Data Memory (512 words x 18 bits). Stores constants or temporary data.

Q: Queue (48 words x 60 bits). FIFO queue. Data Queue: 32 words x 60 bits. Generator Queue: 16 words x 60 bits.

PU: Processing Unit. Executes logical, arithmetic and bit operations.

OQ: Output Queue (8 words x 32 bits). FIFO queue for the output tokens.

AG/FC: Address Generator and Flow Controller. Generates addresses for DM and controls the flow of tokens.

RC: Refresh Controller. Generates refresh tokens for internal DRAMs.

49-000132B

**FIGURE 8.16** NEC data-flow processor architecture. (Copyright © 1986 NEC Electronics, Inc.)

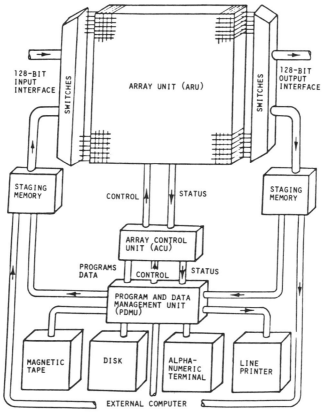

**FIGURE 8.17** Massively parallel processor (MPP) (from [Batcher80] Copyright © 1980 IEEE)
(a) Block diagram of the massively parallel processor (MPP)

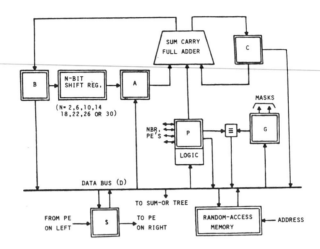

TABLE I
SPEED OF TYPICAL OPERATIONS

| Operations | Execution Speed* |
|---|---|
| Addition of Arrays | |
| 8-bit integers (9-bit sum) | 6553 |
| 12-bit integers (13-bit sum) | 4428 |
| 32-bit floating-point numbers | 430 |
| Multiplication of Arrays (Element-by-Element) | |
| 8-bit integers (16-bit product) | 1861 |
| 12-bit integers (24-bit product) | 910 |
| 32-bit floating-point numbers | 216 |
| Multiplication of Array by Scalar | |
| 8-bit integers (16-bit product) | 2340 |
| 12-bit integers (24-bit product) | 1260 |
| 32-bit floating-point numbers | 373 |

*Million Operations per Second

FIGURE 8.17  Continued
(b)  One processing element
(c)  Speed of typical operations

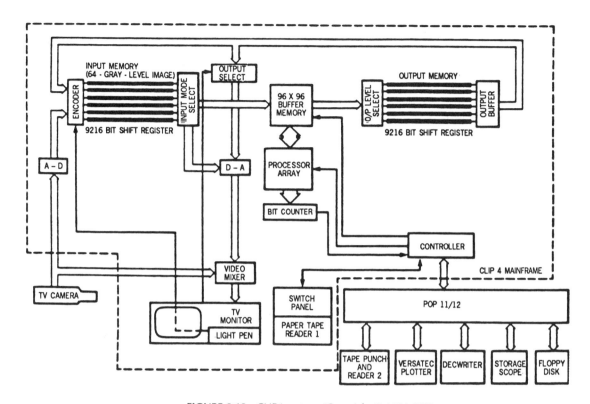

**FIGURE 8.18** CLIP4 system. (Copyright © 1981 IEEE)

networks of relatively simple neuron-like units that form neural networks. There appear to be numerous potential applications of neural networks, although few concrete examples of practical networks are currently available. Pattern recognition, including character recognition and image processing applications and direct and parallel implementation of relaxation algorithms, is an example of one potential application.

The brain is composed of approximately 20 billion nerve cells termed *neurons*. Although each of these elements is relatively simple in design (and may easily and efficiently be replicated in silicon); it is believed the brain's computational power is derived from the interconnection, hierarchical organization, firing characteristics, and sheer number of these elements.

Neural or connectionist computing relates to image description in another way. If a semantic net is a symbolic network, then neural nets are subsymbolic reasoning mechanisms that may be connected to mimic the structure of the brain's semantic net. In this manner, unification may be implemented directly and in parallel. What is not simple is the mapping of an arbitrary problem to the neural network domain.

NEURAL NETWORK MODEL

The essence of neural networks is the interconnection of a massively parallel array of nonlinear logic elements that have variable interconnections. Specifically, there are five general entities that characterize the design and application of a neural network and make the comparison of alternative approaches straightforward:

1. **The individual neural unit activation (or "firing") characteristic.** Examples are shown in Figure 8.19. This activation characteristic may, for example, be simply a threshold characteristic, thus emulating a relay characteristic. Conversely, the possibility of external (i.e., not the output of other neurons) input to the neural unit, inhibitory input (as in the perceptron (Minsky, 1969)) and weighted and nonlinear combinations of input are also possible. Minsky's perceptron and other types of threshold logic were early attempts to apply neural-like networks to classification problems in pattern recognition. In a more general sense, neural units may be thought of as programming objects. Feldman and Ballard (1982) describe a number of characterizations of this concept. Although significant performance differences exist, we do not distinguish between continuous and discrete firing characteristics.

2. **The neural unit interconnection strategy or network structure.** This may be as simple as allowing each neural output to be connected to all other neurons (perhaps with varying interconnection strength) or constraining the neural unit interconnection to be localized (similar to the diameter-limited perceptron). Conversely, the neural network interconnection strategy may be quite complex and reflect an *n*-dimensional and/or hierarchical structure. The latter may reflect the organization of biological systems.

3. **The goal or desired behavior of the network.** This is reflected in the choice of a numerical performance index (similar to Hopfield, 1982 & 1984), enumeration of a set of stable network states, or specification of a desired network.

4. **The choice of features used as input to the network as well as interpretation of the output state of the network.** This aspect ranges considerably in neural

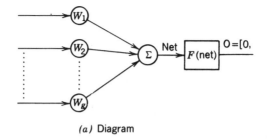

(a) Diagram

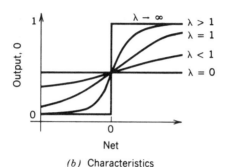

(b) Characteristics

**FIGURE 8.19** Sample neural model
(a) Diagram
(b) Hopfield sigmoid function model

network implementations, from situations where, for example, the states of individual neurons correspond to values of individual pixel intensities in the input image to cases where groups of neurons are used to represent the values of certain features of an object. Carpenter and Grossberg (1987) call the latter selection of "critical features." An example of the former case is shown below in the character recognition example, and the latter is exemplified by the labeling problem.

5. **The training or preprogramming of the network.** This is an optional aspect of network development, since it is not required that networks have a learning capability in all applications. In many cases, however, it is desirable to pre-program the network with information regarding preexisting stable states (e.g., in the character recognition problem). Furthermore, it is often desirable to store new information in the network as new input occurs. This may be done in several ways, including adjustment of the interconnection network. For example, the Hopfield network uses minimization of the performance index (see item 3 above) via modification of the interconnection network (see item 2 above) to store additional states.

The design of a neural net for a specific application involves considering the characteristics above in an interrelated manner. For example, one may not choose the performance index, neural activation characteristic, and network interconnection for a given application independently of each other. These design parameters are interrelated, and the choice of the third parameter is often constrained by the choice for the other two.

The connectionist approach is in some ways a generalization of the neural network concept, where the individual unit or "extended neuron" is slightly more complex than the neuron defined above.

### SAMPLE NEURAL NETWORK APPLICATIONS

We illustrate two examples that show the utility and behavior of neural networks for computer vision. The first neural network example is for low-level image data feature extraction, representation and matching and consists principally of using the neural net as an *associative* or *content-addressable memory* (CAM) for character recognition. The second example illustrates an alternative formulation of symbolic constraint satisfaction (specifically, labeling) examined in Chapter 7. These examples involve the use of Hopfield-like networks, defined below.

*The Hopfield Approach to Neural Computing.* Hopfield (1982, 1984) and Hopfield and Tank (1985) have shown a computational paradigm for using a neural net as an associative or content-addressable memory. The following variables are defined:

$o_i$: the output state of the $i^{th}$ neuron

$u_i$: the activation threshold of the $i^{th}$ neuron

$w_{ij}$: the interconnection weight, that is, the strength of the connection between the output of neuron $j$ and one input to neuron $i$. Thus, $\Sigma\, w_{ij}\, o_i$ is the total input to the $i^{th}$ neuron. $w_{ij} \in R$.

In the Hopfield network, every neuron is allowed to be connected to all other neurons, although the value of $w_{ij}$ may vary (it may also be 0 to indicate no connection). To avoid false reinforcement of a neuron state, the constraint $T_{ii} = 0$ is also employed. The $w_{ij}$ values, therefore, play a fundamental role in the structure of the network. In general, the $w_{ij}$ values indicate a network with significant interconnection.

In simplest form, Hopfield neurons have the firing characteristic:

$$o_i = \begin{cases} 1 \text{ if } \sum_{j \neq i} w_{ij}\, o_i > u_i \\[2em] 0 \text{ otherwise} \end{cases} \tag{8-7}$$

Commonly, $u_i = 0$. Thus, the neuron activation characteristic is nonlinear. Neurons may also have input from other sources as well as a continuous range of activation values; however, we ignore detailed examination of these characteristics in our examples.

Thus, viewing the state of an $n$-neuron Hopfield network at time (or iteration) $t_k$ as an $n \times 1$ vector, $\underline{v}(t_k)$, we note that the state of the system at time (or iteration) $t_{k+1}$ may be described by the nonlinear logical operation:

$$[W]\, \underline{v}(t_k) \; **> \; \underline{v}(t_{k+1}) \tag{8-8}$$

where the $**>$ operator indicates the element by element state characteristic of Eq. 8-7 to determine $\underline{v}(t_{k+1})$. $[W]$ consists of the $w_{ij}$ interconnection weights. Note that the matrix-like formulation above uses matrix multiplication for the formation of the LHS; the $**>$ does not imply equality or assignment, however. It is merely a convenient notational shorthand and allows an interpretation of stable network states in a manner analogous to a linear algebra formulation. It is important to note that the basis of the computation is a network-wide nonlinear characteristic of interconnected elements.

For the case of $u_i = 0$, stable (stored) states correspond to minima of the following energy function:

$$E = -(1/2) \sum_{i \neq j} \sum w_{ij} \, o_i \, o_j \qquad (8\text{-}9)$$

This leads to the rule for determination of $w_{ij}$ from Eq. 8-9 and 8-7 and a set of desired stable states $\underline{v}^s$, where $s = 1, 2, \ldots, n$ as

$$w_{ij} = \sum_s (2o_i^s - 1)(2o_j^s - 1) \qquad (8\text{-}10)$$

(and the previous constraint $w_{ii} = 0$). The reader should verify the consistency of Eq. 8-7, Eq. 8-9, and Eq. 8-10 for achieving a minimum in $E$.

The following comments can be made on the Hopfield formulation:

1. The determination of stable states in the formulation of Eq. 8-8 parallels that of the stable states of the unforced discrete linear time invariant system:

$$\underline{x}_{k+1} = A \, \underline{x}_k \qquad (8\text{-}11)$$

We seek, on the basis of $A$, to determine states such that as $k$ approaches infinity:

$$\underline{x}_{k+1} = \underline{x}_k \qquad (8\text{-}12)$$

It is well known that these states are given by the eigenvectors of $A$ that correspond to unity eigenvalues.

2. When employing the network in certain constraint satisfaction problems, the energy of a state can be interpreted (Hinton and Anderson, 1981) as the extent to which a combination of hypotheses or instantiations fit the underlying neural-formulated model. Thus, low-energy values indicate a good level of constraint satisfaction.

3. One of the most interesting aspects of the Hopfield network is that stable states other than those prescribed by Eq. 8-10 may arise due to the nonlinear nature of the network. Thus, the user of the network may, in the course of storing a set of desired stable states ($\underline{v}^s$, $s = 1, 2, \ldots, n$), introduce other local minima in $E$.

4. The convergence of the network to a stable state is a function of the Hamming distance between the initial state and the desired stable state. Different stable states that are close in Hamming distance are undesirable, since convergence to an incorrect stable state may result. Hopfield suggest that an $n$-neuron network allows approximately $0.15n$ stable states; other researchers have proposed more conservative bounds.

The reader should note (as we show in the examples below) that alternative activation characteristics, interconnection strength computations, and energy functions are allowable. The Hopfield approach thus serves as a framework for other related neural network design paradigms.

### SAMPLE NETWORK PROCESSING RESULTS

*Character Recognition Example.* As an example of pattern recognition, suppose it is desired to recognize characters in a spatially discretized array of binary intensities. Figure 8.20 illustrates one approach, as follows:

1. Map an $n \times n$ binary intensity array into an $n^2$-neuron network. In other words, interpret the state of an $n^2 \times 1$ neural array as a 2-D binary character. Note that this essentially ignores the 2-D nature of the problem.
2. Store each character to be recognized as a stable state using Eq. 8-10. The state of each neuron in a stable state corresponds to its binary value in a stored character.
3. Given an unknown input character, make the neural representation of this character the initial state of the neural network and hope the network converges to a stored character that is close to the input.

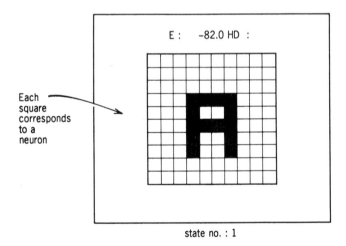

(a) Neural Network Mapping to 2-D
Binary Image (10 x10 Pixels; 100 Neurons)

**FIGURE 8.20** Neural network as CAM for character recognition
(a) Neural network mapping to 2-D binary image (10 × 10 pixels; 100 neurons)
(b) Stored stable states (block versions of uppercase A,C,E,P)

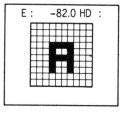

state no. : 1

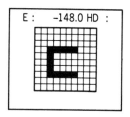

state no. : 2

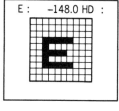

state no. : 3

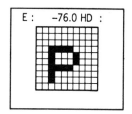

state no. : 4

(b) Stored Stable States
(Block Versions of Uppercase A,C,E,P)

**FIGURE 8.20** *Continued*

We show the performance of a neural-based classification with some simple results, using a prototype neural network simulator. For illustration, we use a $10 \times 10$ character box where each cell in the box represents a neuron state. The underlying neural network therefore comprises a $100 \times 1$ neuron vector, and $w_{ij}$ represents a $100 \times 100$ interconnection matrix. Figure 8.21 shows the network convergence for the case of four stored stable states (which, as shown in part *b* of Figure 8.20, are in some cases close in Hamming distance).

This application of a neural computing approach is a relatively unsophisticated example of neural network capability. Other similar examples are possible (Fukushima and Miyake, 1982). The direct mapping of (binary) pixel intensity to neuron state is conceptually obvious and is somewhat successful in that the network behaves as a content addressable memory (CAM). An alternative neural network implementation, based on a Hamming network (Lippmann, 1987) is possible. In this case the neural network behaves essentially as a binary correlator.

*Symbolic Constraint Satisfaction (Labeling Revisited).* As suggested above, one of the principal utilities of neural networks is in problems involving constraint satisfaction. The mapping of symbolic information into a neural network in a manner that facilitates feature extraction and high-level recognition in the form of

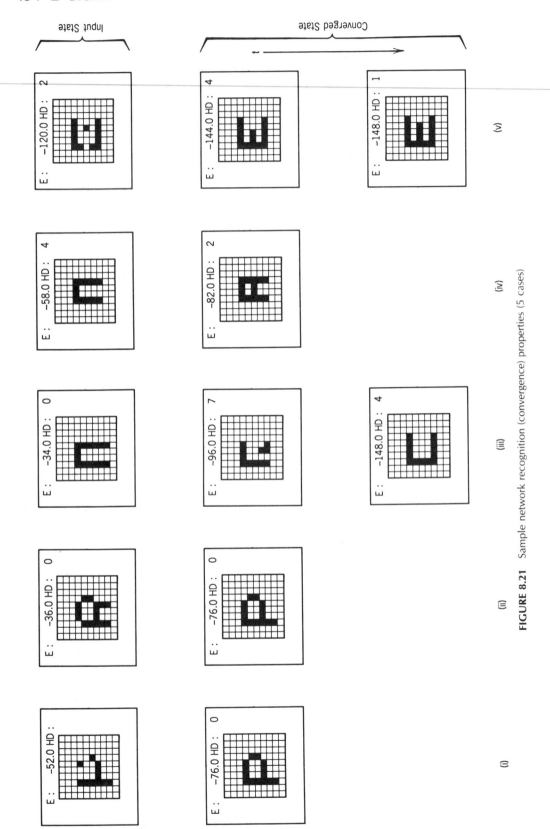

**FIGURE 8.21** Sample network recognition (convergence) properties (5 cases)

unification of observed data, i.e., low-level inputs, with a high-level semantic model recognition is desirable. We explored the use of relaxation for the solution of the labeling problem in Chapter 7. We show a variant of this solution by developing a suitable neural network. This involves choosing a suitable network representation, energy function, and interconnection determination strategy. The details of this example are given in Jamison and Schalkoff (1988).

The interactive activation and competition (IAC) network used for the solution of the image labeling problem is similar to the formulation of the Traveling Salesman problem (Hopfield and Tank, 1985). Each neural unit represents a pairing of an image region and a label. Thus, for the case of $n$ regions and $m$ possible labels, $nm$ neural units are required. Units are therefore conceptually grouped into clusters, where units representing potential labels for one region are grouped together. There are $n$ such clusters, each consisting of $m$ neural units.

The determination of an energy function for the labeling problem is nontrivial and is summarized in Figure 8.22. Jamison and Schalkoff (1988) present a detailed

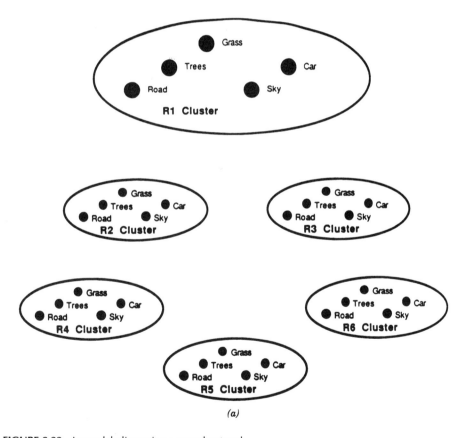

(a)

**FIGURE 8.22**  Image labeling using a neural network
(a)  Cluster interpretation of Hopfield optimization network (inter- and intra-cluster weights not shown)

$$E = \frac{1}{2} \sum_i \sum_j w_{ij} \cdot o_i \cdot o_j - \sum_j I_j \cdot o_j$$

where $w_{ij}$ = the value of the weight connecting unit i and unit j,

$o_i$ = the value of the output of unit i,

$I_i$ = the value of the input bias of unit i.

(i) General energy form

$$E = \frac{A}{2} \sum_i \sum_p \sum_{p=q} o_{ip} \cdot o_{iq}$$

$$+ \frac{B}{2} \left( \sum_i \sum_p o_{ip} - n \right)^2$$

$$+ \frac{C}{2} \sum_i \sum_p o_{ip} \cdot \left[ 1 - \min \left\{ 2^{(k-1)} \prod_k (r_k(i) c_k(p) + (1 - r_k(i))(1 - c_k(p))) \forall \text{unary } k, 1 \right\} \right]$$

$$+ \frac{D}{2} \sum_i \sum_{j=i} \sum_p \sum_q o_{ip} \cdot o_{jq} \cdot \left[ 1 - \min \left\{ 2^{(k-1)} \prod_k (r_k(i,p) c_k(j,q) + (1 - r_k(i,p))(1 - c_k(j,q))) \forall \text{binary } k, 1 \right\} \right]$$

where A, B, C, and D are positive numbers, and

$o_{xy}$ = output value of the unit representing the assignment of label x to object y.

(ii) Energy function for labeling formulation ($r_k$ and $c_k$ represent unary and binary constraints, see [Jamison and Schalkoff, 1988]).

$$w(\ell_{ip}, \ell_{jq}) = - A \delta(i,j)(1 - \delta(p,q))$$

$$- B$$

$$- D(1 - \delta(i,j)) \left[ 1 - \min \left\{ 2^{(k-1)} \prod_k (r_k(i,j) c_k(p,q) + (1 - r_k(i,j))(1 - c_k(p,q))) \forall \text{binary } k, 1 \right\} \right]$$

(iii) Interconnection weights

$$I(\ell_{ip}) = Bn - C \left[ 1 - \min \left\{ 2^{(k-1)} \prod_k (r_k(i) c_k(p) + (1 - r_k(i))(1 - c_k(p))) \forall \text{unary } k, 1 \right\} \right].$$

(iv) Neuron bias term

**FIGURE 8.22(b)**  Derivation of energy function, interconnection and bias in Hopfield net for labeling

study. Briefly, this function must constrain the neural solution so that

1. Only one neuron per cluster is activated (i.e., each region has only one label).
2. Each cluster has one activated neuron (i.e., all regions are labeled).
3. Each labeling satisfies the binary and unary constraints formulated (i.e., "adjacent to," "moving," and "highest").

From this energy function (which is considerably more elaborate than Eq. 8-9), the unit interconnection weights, $w_{ij}$, may be determined.

Sample network results and convergence properties are shown in Figures 8.23 and 8.24.

# ■ TYPICAL IMAGE PROCESSING SYSTEM COMPONENTS

### MAJOR SYSTEM COMPONENTS

Basic components of a digital image processing system are:

1. A means of acquiring images from varied sources (i.e., the sensor).
2. A means of converting the image data into computer-manipulable form.
3. A means of processing the acquired data (through either a host CPU and/or peripheral processors.
4. Software for the processors (and perhaps a software development environment).
5. A means to display processed imagery.
6. Other specialized devices such as an image hardcopy unit.

These components are shown in Figure 8.25.

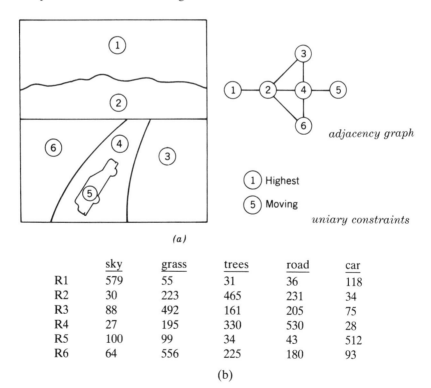

(a)

| | sky | grass | trees | road | car |
|---|---|---|---|---|---|
| R1 | 579 | 55 | 31 | 36 | 118 |
| R2 | 30 | 223 | 465 | 231 | 34 |
| R3 | 88 | 492 | 161 | 205 | 75 |
| R4 | 27 | 195 | 330 | 530 | 28 |
| R5 | 100 | 99 | 34 | 43 | 512 |
| R6 | 64 | 556 | 225 | 180 | 93 |

(b)

**FIGURE 8.23** Sample neural network input and response
(a) Input image and constraints
(b) Matrix representation of unit output values during network convergence (normalized [0..1000])

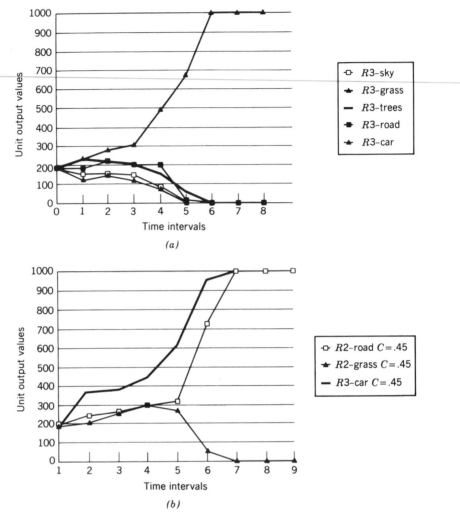

**FIGURE 8.24** Sample labelling convergence properties for the neural network used with input of Figure 8.23(a)
(a) "Competition" between labels for R3
(b) Correct solution progression C = .45

## COMMERCIALLY AVAILABLE IMAGE PROCESSING SYSTEMS

The MPP is an example of a parallel machine that has received considerable attention for image processing and computer vision research applications. As a practical (and economic) matter, devices such as the MPP are currently only in the realm of governmental agencies and large research institutions. In this section, we consider aspects of practically available systems. We distinguish between *system-level products* and *board-level products*. Figure 8.29 shows a sample taxonomy of available systems.

### SYSTEM-LEVEL PRODUCTS

These systems, made by vendors such as Gould Imaging or Vicom, represent the high-end of the commercial market. One common aspect of these systems is that

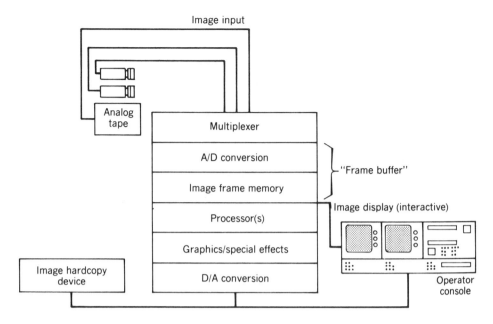

**FIGURE 8.25** Typical "dedicated" image processing system

the hardware and software are designed for (close to) real-time operation necessitated by applications such as robotics. This processing capability is achieved via specialized parallel or pipelined processors and multiple bus architectures. Processing of high-resolution and time-varying imagery is facilitated by providing large amounts of reconfigurable image memory, which may be "tiled" for specific image configurations. Multiple simultaneous input sources and color image acquisition and processing capability (e.g., red, green, blue (RGB) input and dedicated memories for image RGB components) are typical. Many of these systems use external host computers (e.g., VAX or Sun workstations are common choices). Costs of basic systems are in the approximately $75–100,000 range (excluding the computer). Figure 8.26 shows an example. Note the use of several dedicated hardware processors and the use of a multiple bus architecture.

BOARD-LEVEL PRODUCTS

These products, typified by the Data Translation boards shown in Figure 8.27, are relatively inexpensive, entry-level products (approximately $1500 without computer) for microcomputer-based processing of images. Typically, image input and display are limited to a single frame of 512 × 512 or 256 × 256 pixels. Image input and display formats are typically restricted to RS-170 monochrome images. The amount of dedicated ancillary processing hardware is minimal, although lookup tables and some arithmetic and logical functions may be provided.

We note that the processing of image data on personal computers (in particular, the IBM PC/AT or compatibles) is rapidly expanding due to the increasing computing power of PCs and the availability and economic attractiveness of the aforementioned image acquisition and display hardware. For an overview, see "Image Processing with Personal Computers" (1985). Figure 8.28 illustrates a typical setup.

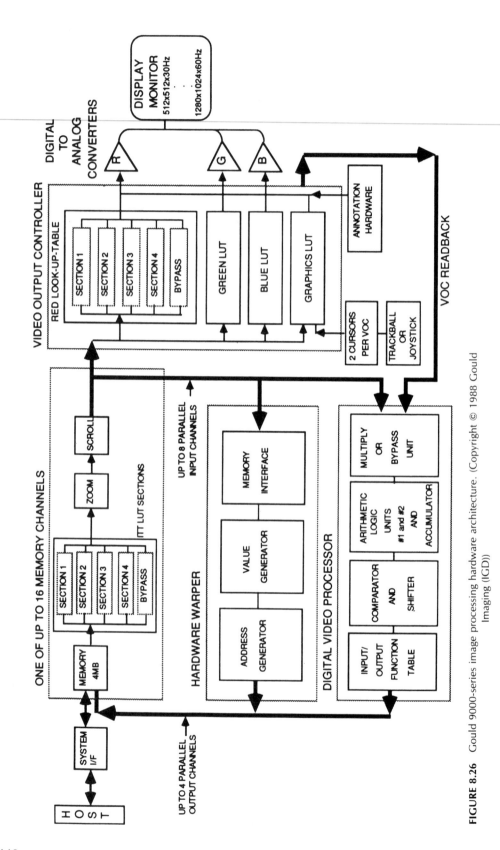

**FIGURE 8.26** Gould 9000-series image processing hardware architecture. (Copyright © 1988 Gould Imaging (IGD))

440

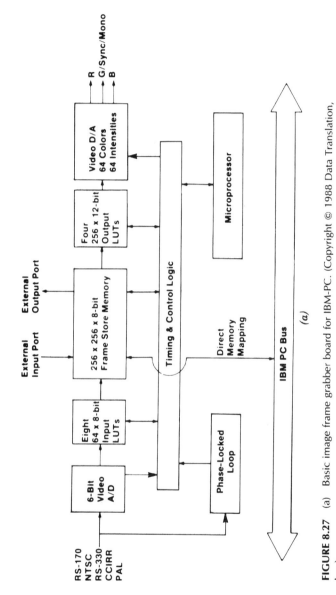

**FIGURE 8.27** (a) Basic image frame grabber board for IBM-PC. (Copyright © 1988 Data Translation, Inc.)

(b) Image processor and frame grabber board for micro VAX systems. (Copyright © 1988 Data Translation, Inc.)

441

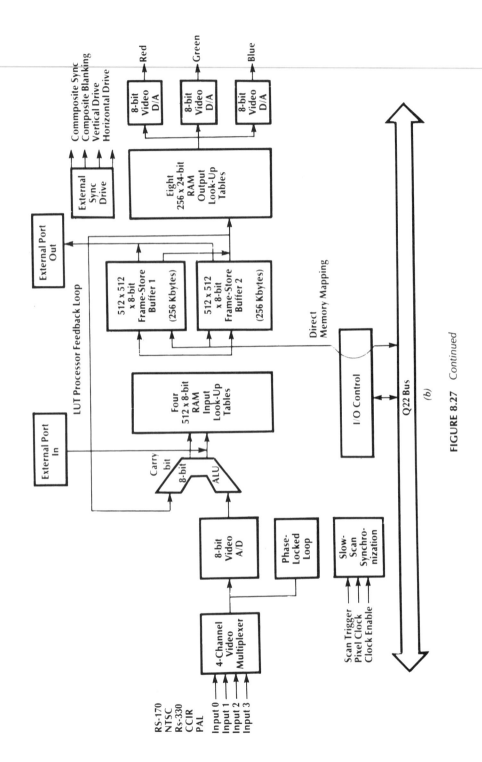

**FIGURE 8.27** *Continued*

442

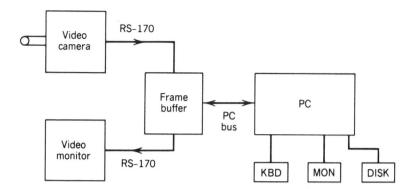

**FIGURE 8.28** Typical low-cost PC-based image processing system

| Vendor | System configuration | System characteristics | Approx. cost |
|---|---|---|---|
| 1. *System-level products* | | | |
| Gould Imaging | IP 8500 w/ host (e.g. Vax) computer | up to 2k × 2k images dedicated processing hardware large software library | $50–100k (excl. computer) |
| Vicom | Digital Image Processor VME-512 w/ host (e.g. Sun) computer | up to 2k × 2k images integral processor dual bus, pipelined processor, software library | $50–100k (excl. computer) |
| 2. *Board-level products* | | | |
| *a. Higher capability* | DT 2851 Frame Grabber DT 2859 Coprocessor | 512 × 512 pixels some dedicated proc. | $5k (excl. computer & |
| Data Translation | with host μVax II computer | hardware, software (VMS) available | software) |
| *b. PC-based* | DT 2803 Frame Grabber with host IBM PC/AT or | 256 × 256 pixels LUT's software (DOS) | $1.5k (excl. computer & |
| Data Translation | clone | available | software) |

**FIGURE 8.29** Sample taxonomy of available image processing systems

## ■ REFERENCES

Adam, J. A. "Counting the Weapons," *IEEE Spectrum*, July 1986, Vol. 23, No. 7, pp. 46–56.

Barbe, D. F. "Imaging Devices Using the Charge Coupled Concept," *Proc. IEEE*, Vol. 36, Jan. 1975, pp. 38–67.

Batcher, K. E. "Design of a Massively Parallel Processor," *IEEE Trans. Computers*, Vol. C-29, No. 9, Sept. 1980, pp. 836–840.

Buss, D. and Melen, R. *Charge Coupled Devices: Technology and Applications.* New York: IEEE Press, 1977.

Dennis, J. B. "Dataflow Supercomputers," *IEEE Computer*, Vol. 13, No. 11, Nov. 1980, pp. 48–56.

Duff, M. J. B. and Levialdi, S. (eds.) *Languages and Architectures for Image Processing*. New York: Academic Press, 1981.

Feldman, J. A. and Ballard, D. H. "Connectionist Models and Their Properties," *Cognitive Science*, Vol. 6, 1982, pp. 205–254.

Flynn, M. J. "Some Computer Organizations and Their Effectiveness," *IEEE Trans. on Computers*, Vol. C-21, No. 9, Sept. 1972, pp. 948–960.

Halstead, R. H. "Parallel Symbolic Computing," *IEEE Computer*, Vol. 19, No. 8, Aug. 1986, pp. 35–43.

Hinton, G. E. and Anderson, J. A. (eds.), *Parallel Models of Associative Memory*, Hillside, N.J.: Lawrence Erlbaum & Associates, 1981.

Hoffman, W. C. "The Neuron as a Lie Group Germ and a Lie Product," *Quart. Appl. Math.*, Vol. 25, 1968, pp. 423–440.

Hopfield, J. J., "Neural Networks and Physical Systems with Emergent Collective Computational Abilities," *Proc. Natl. Acad. Sci.*, Vol. 79 (Biophysics), April 1982, pp. 2554–2558.

Hopfield, J. J., "Neurons with Graded Response Have Collective Computational Properties Like Those of Two-state Neurons," *Proc. Natl. Acad. Sci.*, Vol. 81 (Biophysics), May 1984, pp. 2554–2558.

Hopfield, J. J. and Tank, D. W. "Neural Computation of Decisions in Optimization Problems," *Biological Cybernetics*, Vol. 52, 1985, pp. 141–152.

Hwang, K. and Briggs, F. A. *Computer Architecture and Parallel Processing*. New York: McGraw-Hill, 1984.

Jamison, T. A. and Schalkoff, R. J. "Image Labelling Via a Neural Network Approach and a Comparison With Existing Alternatives," *Image and Vision Computing*, Vol. 6, No. 4, Nov. 1988, pp. 203–214.

Levine, M. D. *Vision in Man and Machine*. New York: McGraw-Hill, 1985.

Lippmann, R. P. "An Introduction to Computing with Neural Nets," *IEEE ASSP Magazine*, April 1987, pp. 4–22.

Maggiollo-Schettini, A. "Comparing Some High-Level Languages for Image Processing," in *Languages and Architectures for Image Processing* (Duff & Levialdi, eds.), 1981, Chapter 12, pp. 157–164.

Minsky, M. and Papert, S. *Perceptrons—An Introduction to Computational Geometry*. Cambridge, MA: MIT Press, 1969.

NEC Electronics, Inc., *1987 Microcomputer Products Data Book*, Vol. 2, August 1986.

Schalkoff, R. J. *Artificial Intelligence: An Engineering Approach*, New York: McGraw-Hill, to be published

"Video Programs and Technology," *IEEE Spectrum*, Vol. 23, No. 2, February 1986.

Yalamanchili, S. and Aggarwal, J. K. "Analysis of a Model for Parallel Image Processing," *Pattern Recognition*, Vol. 18, No. 1, 1985, pp. 1–16.

# ■ BIBLIOGRAPHY

Baer, J. L. *Computer Systems Architecture*. Rockville, MD: Computer Science Press, 1980.

Batcher, K. E. "Bit-Serial Parallel Processing Systems," *IEEE Trans. Computers*, Vol. 31, No. 5, May 1982, pp. 377–384.

Carpenter, G. A. and Grossberg, S. "A Massively Parallel Architecture for a Self-Organizing Neural Pattern Recognition Machine," *Comp. Vision, Graphics and Image Processing*, Vol. 37, 1987, pp. 54–115.

Clarke, K. A. and Ip, H. H. S. "A Parallel Implementation of Geometric Transformations," *Pattern Recognition Letters*, Vol. 1, October 1982, pp. 51–53.

Danielsson, P. E. and Levialdi, S. "Computer Architectures for Pictorial Information Systems," *IEEE Computer*, Nov. 1981, pp. 53–67.

Deutsch. *Theory and Design of Television Receivers*. New York: McGraw-Hill, 1951.

Feldman, J. A. "Connectionist Models and Parallelism in High-Level Vision," *Computer Vision, Graphics, and Image Processing*, Vol. 31, 1985, pp. 178–200.

Fountain, T. J. "CLIP4: A Progress Report," in Languages and Architectures for Image Processing (Duff and Levialdi, eds.), 1981, pp. 283–293.

Fukushima, K. and Miyake, S. "Neocognition: A New Algorithm for Pattern Recognition Tolerant of Deformations and Shifts in Position," *Pattern Recognition*, Vol. 15, No. 6, 1982, pp. 455–469.

Hockney, R. W. and Jesshope, C. *Parallel Computers 2: Architecture, Programming and Algorithms* (2nd ed.), Adam Hilger, Ltd. (distributed by Taylor and Francis, Philadelphia, PA), 1988.

IEEE Computer Society, *Proc. of the 1985 IEEE Computer Society Workshop on Computer Architecture for Pattern Analysis and Image Database Management*, Miami Beach, FL, November 1985.

"Image Processing with Personal Computers," *Electronic Imaging*, Vol. 4, No. 3, March 1985, pp. 44–51.

NCR Corporation. Data Sheet for NCR45CG72, Geometric Arithmetic Parallel Processor, Dayton, Ohio, 1984.

Pecht, J. "Speeding-Up Successive Minkowski Operations with Bit-Plane Computers," *Pattern Recognition Letters*, Vol. 3, No. 2, March 1985, pp. 113–117.

Reeves, A. P. "The Local Median and Other Window Operations on SIMD Computers," *Computer Graphics and Image Processing*," 19, pp. 165–178 (1982).

Roizen, J. "Dubrovnik Impasse Puts High-Definition TV on Hold," *IEEE Spectrum*, Vol. 23, No. 9, Sept. 1986, pp. 32–37.

Rummelhart, D. E. and McClelland, J. L. *Parallel Distributed Processing—Explorations in the Microstructure of Cognition, Volume 1: Foundations*. Cambridge, MA: MIT Press, 1986.

Rummelhart, D. E., Smolensky, P., McClelland, J. L. and Hinton, G. E. "Schemata and Sequential Thought Processes in PDP Models," *Parallel Distributed Processing*, Vol. 2, pp. 7–57.

Schalkoff, R. J. "A Parallel Decomposition and Architecture for Implementing Geometric Image Transforms," in *Proc. of the 1985 IEEE Computer Society Workshop on Computer Architecture for Pattern Analysis and Image Database Management*, Miami Beach, FL, November 1985, pp. 292–298.

Shapiro, E. "Concurrent Prolog: A progress report" *IEEE Computer*, Vol. 19, No. 8, Aug. 1986, pp. 44–58.

Sequin, C. H. and Thomsett, M. F. *Charge Transfer Devices*. New York: Academic Press, 1970.

Taylor, R. and Wilson, P. "Process Oriented Language Meets Demands of Distributed Processing," *Electronics*, Nov. 30, 1982, pp. 89–95.

Tung, Y. W. and Moldovan, D. I. "Detection of AND-Parallelism in Logic Programming," in *Proc. 1986 International Conf. on Parallel Processing*, University Park, PA, August 1986, pp. 984–991.

Wah, B. W. and Li, G. J. (eds.) *Computer for Artificial Intelligence Applications*. Washington, DC: IEEE Computer Society Press, May 1986.

# ■ PROBLEMS

1. Two discrete sensors, each with an interpixel spacing of p, are used in a stereo vision system. Their relative orientation differs only by a translation of d units, and may be assumed to be of the form of Chapter 2, Figure 2.6. Assume that the interpixel spacing reflects the overall sensor system resolution.

   a. Compute, as a function of p, d f and $z_o$, the minimum discernible surface variation ($\Delta z_o$) with this sensor resolution.

   b. For the case of p = 18μm, f = 100mm, d = 1m and $z_o$ = 4m, what is $\Delta z_o$?

2. A CCD imaging sensor is composed of sampling elements of dimension $\Delta x$ by $\Delta x$ and periodicity p/2 (assuming 2:1 interlace) as shown in following figure.

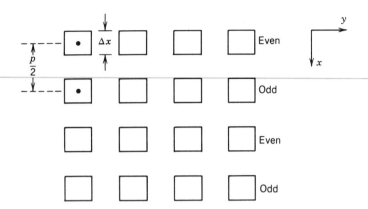

a. Considering only the x direction, compute the MTF of this sensor, as a function of $\Delta x$ and p.

b. Repeat a for the case where the line spacing is p, not p/2 (no interlacing). Plot the sensor MTF response as a function of normalized spatial frequency ($f/f_{max}$ where $f_{max} = 1/p$) for the cases $\Delta x = p$, $\Delta x = p/2$ and $\Delta x = p/4$.

c. Consider the system response to a horizontal "stripe" incident on the sensor array of width $w_s$ in the x direction as shown below.

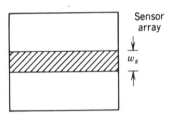

d. Assume 2:1 interlace and $\Delta x = p/2$. Describe quantitatively the sensor output in the frequency domain as $w_s$ is varied from $\Delta x/4$ to $\Delta x$. On the basis of this analysis, determine the minimum image dimension for reasonable imaging.

e. An ideal lensing system, modeled as a pinhole camera with focal length, $f$, is now coupled with the above sensor. For a magnification ratio of 1000, relate the results of part d to minimum object dimensions in 3-D.

3. (Data from this problem were extracted from Landgrebe (1981), referenced in Ch. 6).

a. The Landsat-3 satellite operates in four bands (two visible; 2 near infrared) at a near-circular orbit of 920 km (570 mi). Intensity resolution in each of the four bands is 6 bits. Nominal resolution of the sensor is 2400 × 3240 pixels; the optics are adjusted to image an extent of the Earth's surface 185 km (100 miles) wide. What is the minimum feature dimensions?

b. A normal magnetic tape provides storage of digitally encoded data at a density of 1600 bits per inch (bpi) and is approximately 2400 feet long. Ignoring the spacing due to blocking of the data, how many Landsat images from part (a) above occupy one tape?

**4.** a. Using Figure 8.6 derive the relationship between discernible scene dimension and sensor focal length for a fixed interpixel spacing. Relate this to the system magnification ratio.

b. Derive the relationship between TFOV and sensor focal length (assume fixed-extent sensor).

c. On the basis of a and b relate TFOV and discernible scene dimension. Is the result as expected?

**5.** Consider the parallel implementation possibilities for the sample region split-and-merge algorithm. (You may wish to employ modifications suggested in Problem 30 of Chapter 6.)

**6.** The purpose of this problem is to consider the interconnection relationship between an $m \times m$ systolic array and an $n$-cube of processors. An $n \times n$ systolic array, as shown in Figure 8.8i consists of $n^2$ processing elements, each with four nearest connected neighbors. Similarly, an $n$-cube as shown in the Figure consists of $2^n$ processing elements, each connected to $n$ nearest neighbors, as shown in Figure 8.8g.

a. For the case of n = 2, draw both the systolic array and the $n$ cube network. Compare the interprocessor connection capability.

b. Repeat (a) for the case of n = 3. (Pay attention to the relative number of processors.)

c. Repeat (a) for the case of n = 4. (Draw two 3-cubes and their interconnections for visualization.) If the systolic array had communications wrap-around, how would the two structures differ?

d. Repeat part a for n = 5.

e. Comment on fabrication concerns as a function of $n$.

**7.** a. Using any reasonable set of assumptions regarding an SISD architecture, calculate an approximate speedup for the IP8650 implementation example.

b. For an n × n image, how is the speedup related to $n$?

**8.** Determine a decomposition and write a program (using the IP8650 instruction set) to implement Roberts' operator on an n × n image.

**9.** a. Write a program using the IP8650 instruction set to calculate a histogram of an n × n image. Comment each instruction.

b. What is the speedup (vis-à-vis a serial processor) in this implementation?

**10.** Develop the code for the algorithm given by Eq. 8-30 in OCCAM for

a. A single pixel result.

b. The result of an n × n image.

You may rewrite the equations, if necessary.

**11.** Draw a data flow graph and suggest a dedicated parallel implementation for the separable LOG operator of Chapter 4.

**12.** The purpose of this problem is to implement the labeling problem of Chapter 7, using the IP8650 systolic array. You may choose either the label-discarding rule or the probabilistic formulation.

a. How is the problem decomposed for mapping into the IP8650 array?

b. Show the commented program in IP8650 instructions. How is convergence detected?

13. Using a pyramidal processor interconnection, as shown in Figure 8.8$k$ suggest a method for implementation of a multiresolution matching (correlation) algorithm.

  a. Is the resulting architecture SIMD or MIMD?

  b. What operations are required of each processor? Do they depend on the level?

  c. What data is passed via the communication lines?

14. An interesting and useful conceptual tool for study of the systolic array involves viewing the array image data as matrices and the SIMD instructions as operations on these matrices. In fact, many of these operations may be viewed as matrix operations. The input image is denoted $[f]$.

  a. Show a matrix formulation for N, S, E, and W shifts of the data in the form:

$$[f_{out}] = P[f]Q$$

  b. Extend (a), using signal matrix addition operations, to show extraction of image horizontal and vertical spatial gradients.

  c. Repeat (b) for computation of a $3 \times 3$ neighborhood average.

  d. Is the representation of geometric transforms possible with this approach? *Hint*: consider dilation (magnification) and rotation.

15. In this problem, consider possible algorithm classes that involve the Cartesian product of

$$\{DP, \overline{DP}\} \text{ and } \{AP, \overline{AP}\}$$

Given an $n \times n$ image memory available or accessible in parallel, cite (with explanation) cases of algorithm decompositions that involve

  a. (DP,AP)

  b. (DP,$\overline{AP}$)

  c. ($\overline{DP}$,AP)

  d. ($\overline{DP}$,$\overline{AP}$)

16. a. Show (in detail) that a normalized correlation surface for two binary images may be computed using an implementation consisting of counters and the logical exclusive OR function, or the logical function $AB + \overline{A}\overline{B}$.

  b. Compare the technique of part (a) above with simply integrating the difference image over the window area.

# 9

# THE FUTURE (EPILOG)

The previous eight chapters have presented an overview of an emerging and maturing field. Additional information on any topic covered in this book is available from any of the sources listed in the chapter references and from other monographs and technical papers and reports. The reader should now be more comfortable with the myriad of interrelated topics and terminology shown in Figure 6, Chapter 1.

The reader should be left with the following overall impressions regarding the field of digital image processing and computer vision:

1. An enormous amount of work has been done (much of which is not covered in this book).

2. A great deal more work needs to be done.

3. The problems are challenging and multidisciplinary. Solutions will require the combined efforts of computer engineers and scientists, mathematicians, cognitive scientists, and optical specialists.

4. The problems are real. Computer vision problems are easy to describe to the layman.

5. Much future research will concern the problems of modeling and representation. New, more comprehensive models spawn the development of new and more robust solution algorithms. As shown in this text, the study of image processing and computer vision can be made quantitative.

6. Future approaches will likely encompass more AI applications. This does not imply that all low-level processing problems are solved. For example, generally applicable algorithms for optical flow computation are still elusive.

7. More and more applications for image processing and computer vision are being recognized. Examples are in the industrial, military, and medical sectors.

Throughout the presentation, numerous theoretical and practical tools were shown to be useful for specific image processing and computer vision tasks. Geometric models, estimation theory, and transforms, are just a few examples. In addition, many of the computer vision tasks were shown to be related. Some depended on the results of others for input (e.g., line detection provided features to a classification algorithm), while others shared a common need (e.g., correspondence information for stereo vision and motion analysis). Other tasks, when considered in a unified way (such as motion and structure determination), yield potentially synergistic solutions. Finally, Chapter 8 indicated that theoretical solutions alone were insufficient to enable practical achievement of even low-level image processing capabilities with real-time constraints.

One of the most significant practical problems faced by computer vision system developers is the need to develop and implement robust algorithms. The HVS adapts well to changes in viewing parameters, and it is desirable to emulate this behavior in autonomous systems.

In any scientific area, new results are generated in both the experimental and theoretical areas. Certainly this is true of image processing and computer vision. This book serves as evidence of progress on both fronts. However, as in most emerging disciplines, results are ad hoc, sporadic, application-specific, and often nonrepeatable. An observer surveying image processing and computer vision 20 years ago would probably have posed the same lament, but such an observer would probably acknowledge considerable success over the two decades. In another two decades, those currently involved in image processing and computer vision research are likely to be surprised at the amount of progress.

We hope that it is a technology we will use wisely. This, then, is our major challenge for the future.

# CONCEPTS FROM GEOMETRY

## ■ GEOMETRIC PRIMITIVES IN N-DIMENSIONS

Geometry in 2-D and 3-D is fundamental to image processing and computer vision. We review a few simple concepts.

### LINES (2-D AND 3-D)

2-D LINES

A line (in 2-D or 3-D) may be determined by two points. In 2-D the so-called slope-intercept form is popular, where, in the $x$-$y$ plane,

$$y = m\,x + b \tag{A.1-1}$$

Notice this representation fails for vertical (infinite slope) lines. Thus, we derive an alternate representation based on the perpendicular distance of the line from the origin, denoted $\rho$, and the angle of the normal, denoted $\theta$. This is often referred to as the normal form of the line and given as:

$$x \cos \theta + y \sin \theta = \rho \tag{A.1-2}$$

This relationship is shown in Figure A.1-1.

Another useful and popular representation is the ratio form where

$$\frac{x - x_o}{a} = \frac{y - y_o}{b} \tag{A.1-3}$$

Rewriting the normal form for any two points $(x1, y1)$ and $(x2, y2)$ on a 2-D line

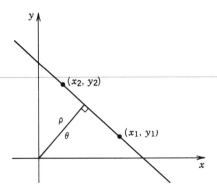

**FIGURE A.1.1** Normal parameterization of a line

yields the set of equations:

$$x1 \cos \theta + y1 \sin \theta = \rho \tag{A.1-4}$$
$$x2 \cos \theta + y2 \sin \theta = \rho$$

Subtracting the second from the first yields

$$(x1 - x2) \cos \theta - (y1 - y2) \sin \theta = 0 \tag{A.1-5}$$

which may be rewritten as

$$(x1 - x2)/(y1 - y2) = \tan \theta \tag{A.1-6}$$

The latter equation is easily verified via Eq. A.1-1.

### 3-D LINES

Given two points in 3-D space represented by $3 \times 1$ vectors, $\underline{x}_1$ and $\underline{x}_2$, the parametric representation for the line determined by these points is

$$\underline{x} = \underline{x}_1 + t (\underline{x}_2 - \underline{x}_1) \tag{A.1-7}$$

where $\underline{x}$ is any point on the line and $t$ is a free parameter. Varying $t$ through the range $[-\infty, +\infty]$ generates all points on this line.

Another convenient form used in Chapter 2 is the 3-D ratio representation, where a line containing the point $(x_o, y_o, z_o)$ may be described by the equation.

$$\frac{x - x_o}{a} = \frac{y - y_o}{b} = \frac{z - z_o}{c} \tag{A.1-8}$$

The parameters $a, b, c$ in Eq. A.1-8 are the *direction numbers* of the 3-D line.

### PLANES

A 3-D plane may be simply described in terms of all points in 3-D space $(x_o, y_o, z_o)$ that satisfy

$$a x_o + b y_o + c z_o + d = 0 \tag{A.1-9}$$

where $a, b, c,$ and $d$ are the plane parameters.

A more convenient form for this plane is achieved using homogeneous coordinates (Chapter 2) as

$$\langle \underline{\hat{x}}, \underline{\rho} \rangle = 0 \tag{A.1-10}$$

where $\langle \ \rangle$ denotes the inner product of two vectors and $\underline{\rho}$ is the parameter vector that determines the plane; that is,

$$\underline{\rho} = \begin{bmatrix} a \\ b \\ c \\ d \end{bmatrix} \tag{A.1-11}$$

Three noncolinear points determine a plane. Given these three points, $\underline{x}_1$, $\underline{x}_2$, $\underline{x}_3$, we may find the plane by forming (normalizing $d = 1$)

$$\begin{bmatrix} \hat{\underline{x}}_1^T \\ \hat{\underline{x}}_2^T \\ \hat{\underline{x}}_3^T \\ 0\ 0\ 0\ 1 \end{bmatrix} \underline{\rho} = \begin{bmatrix} 0 \\ 0 \\ 0 \\ 1 \end{bmatrix} \tag{A.1-12}$$

Defining the matrix on the left side of Eq. A.1-12 to be $M$, we may find $\underline{\rho}$ as

$$\underline{\rho} = M^{-1} \begin{bmatrix} 0 \\ 0 \\ 0 \\ 1 \end{bmatrix} \tag{A.1-13}$$

That is, $\underline{\rho}$ equals the last column of this inverse.

This procedure (the reader should verify this) fails for planes that pass through the origin. A more general procedure, given $\underline{x}_1$, $\underline{x}_2$, and $\underline{x}_3$, is to form

$$\begin{vmatrix} x_o & y_o & z_o & 1 \\ & \hat{\underline{x}}_1^T & & \\ & \hat{\underline{x}}_2^T & & \\ & \hat{\underline{x}}_3^T & & \end{vmatrix} = 0 \tag{A.1-14}$$

and equate the resulting coefficients with $a$, $b$, $c$, and $d$ in Eq. A.1-9.

### DIRECTION COSINES

The convenient representation of relative 3-D coordinate system orientations is often facilitated (c.f. Chapter 5) by the use of *direction cosines*. Let $\underline{x}_1 = (x_1, y_1, z_1)^T$ and $\underline{x}_2 = (x_2, y_2, z_2)^T$ by any two points that determine a line. Furthermore, let d equal the distance between $\underline{x}_1$ and $\underline{x}_2$. The *direction angles* $\alpha$, $\beta$, $\gamma$ that this line (or any line parallel to this line) makes with the $x$, $y$, and $z$ coordinate axes, respectively, are used to form the *direction cosines*

$$\cos \alpha = \frac{x_2 - x_1}{d}$$

$$\cos \beta = \frac{y_2 - y_1}{d} \tag{A.1-15}$$

$$\cos \gamma = \frac{z_2 - z_1}{d}$$

It is easy to show the direction cosines satisfy

$$\cos^2 \alpha + \cos^2 \beta + \cos^2 \gamma = 1 \qquad (A.1\text{-}16)$$

In addition, the direction cosines are related to the direction numbers, $a$, $b$, $c$, of a line in the ratio form of Eq. A.1-8 by

$$a:b:c = \cos \alpha : \cos \beta : \cos \gamma \qquad (A.1\text{-}17)$$

## ■ AFFINE TRANSFORM SUMMARY

The 2-D affine transform is used to model small image function perturbations. Basically, the 2-D affine transform operates on the arguments of a 2-D function as follows:

For an image function of the form $f(\underline{x})$, where

$$\underline{x} = \begin{bmatrix} x_1 \\ x_2 \end{bmatrix} \qquad (A.1\text{-}18)$$

the general affine transformed version of this function is denoted by

$$f'(\underline{x}) = f(\underline{x}') \qquad (A.1\text{-}19)$$

where

$$\underline{x}' = A\underline{x} + \underline{b} \qquad (A.1\text{-}20)$$

It should be noted that both $A$ and $\underline{b}$ may be functions of time. Thus, the affine transform, with respect to the indices of $f(\underline{x})$, represents a linear transformation of the plane onto itself.

Expanding Eq. A.1-20:

$$\begin{bmatrix} x_1' \\ x_2' \end{bmatrix} = \begin{bmatrix} a & b \\ c & d \end{bmatrix} \begin{bmatrix} x_1 \\ x_2 \end{bmatrix} + \begin{bmatrix} b_1 \\ b_2 \end{bmatrix} \qquad (A.1\text{-}21)$$

In Eq. A.1-20, $A$ is denoted the homogeneous affine transform matrix, and $\underline{b}$ is the translation vector. Two well-known versions of the homogeneous affine transform ($\underline{b} = 0$) are:

$$A = \begin{bmatrix} \alpha & 0 \\ 0 & \alpha \end{bmatrix} \qquad \text{(magnification or dilation)} \qquad (A.1\text{-}22)$$

$$A = \begin{bmatrix} \cos \theta & -\sin \theta \\ \sin \theta & \cos \theta \end{bmatrix} \qquad \begin{array}{l} \text{(rotation about the} \\ \text{origin through an} \\ \text{angle, } \theta) \end{array} \qquad (A.1\text{-}23)$$

Another important case is where $A = I$, and

$$\underline{b} = \begin{bmatrix} \Delta x_1 \\ \Delta x_2 \end{bmatrix} \qquad \text{(translation)} \qquad (A.1\text{-}24)$$

One important affine transform representation is a rotation through an angle $\theta$ about a point, $(h,k)$, where $(h,k) \neq (0,0)$. This rotation may be represented as

$$\begin{bmatrix} x_1' & -h \\ x_2' & -k \end{bmatrix} = \begin{bmatrix} \cos \theta & -\sin \theta \\ \sin \theta & \cos \theta \end{bmatrix} \begin{bmatrix} x_1 & -h \\ x_2 & -k \end{bmatrix} \qquad (A.1\text{-}25)$$

which may easily be simplified to

$$\begin{bmatrix} x_1' \\ x_2' \end{bmatrix} = \begin{bmatrix} \cos\theta & -\sin\theta \\ \sin\theta & \cos\theta \end{bmatrix} \begin{bmatrix} x_1 \\ x_2 \end{bmatrix}$$

$$- \begin{bmatrix} (\cos\theta - 1) & -\sin\theta \\ \sin\theta & (\cos\theta - 1) \end{bmatrix} \begin{bmatrix} h \\ k \end{bmatrix} \tag{A.1-26}$$

This expression represents an equivalent rotation about the origin (first term) and translation (second term). The translational term is often of importance. Two additional points should be noted:

1.  Combined affine transforms, such as a rotation followed by translation, then another rotation, and so on, may also be represented by a resultant affine transform of the form in Eq. A.1-20. However, the order in which these transforms occur is significant because the result of a rotation followed by a translation is not necessarily the same as if the transform were instead the translation first, then the rotation.

2.  Since the affine transform operates on the image function arguments by transforming the coordinate axes, viewing the image function in the original coordinates, $A$ and $\underline{b}$ actually affect the image function in the opposite manner. For example, if

$$A = \begin{bmatrix} .9 & 0 \\ 0 & .9 \end{bmatrix} \quad ; \quad \underline{b} = \underline{0} \tag{A.1-27}$$

we would actually see the image function magnified by a factor of $1/0.9$ in both directions. Likewise, if $A$ represents a rotation of $\theta$ on the coordinate system, the image function is actually rotated by $-\theta$.

## ■ REPRESENTATION IN HOMOGENEOUS COORDINATES

A single affine transform may be represented in homogeneous coordinates as the $4 \times 4$ matrix

$$\hat{A} = \begin{bmatrix} A & \underline{b} \\ 0 \quad 0 & 1 \end{bmatrix} \tag{A.1-28}$$

where, in homogeneous coordinates,

$$\underline{\hat{x}}' = \begin{bmatrix} \underline{x}' \\ 1 \end{bmatrix} \quad \text{and} \quad \underline{\hat{x}} = \begin{bmatrix} \underline{x} \\ 1 \end{bmatrix} \tag{A.1-29}$$

Composite affine transforms may then be represented by the multiplication (in correct order) of these matrices. For example, representing the composite of affine transforms 1 followed by 2 (with physical parameters $A_i$ and $\underline{b}_i$, respectively) we arrive at

$$\underline{\hat{x}}' = \hat{A}_c \underline{\hat{x}} \tag{A.1-30}$$

where the $4 \times 4$ matrix

$$\hat{A}_c = \left[ \begin{array}{cc|c} A_2 & & \underline{b}_2 \\ \hline 0 & 0 & 1 \end{array} \right] \left[ \begin{array}{cc|c} A_1 & & \underline{b}_1 \\ \hline 0 & 0 & 1 \end{array} \right]$$

$$= \left[ \begin{array}{c|c} A_2 A_1 & A_2 \underline{b}_1 + \underline{b}_2 \\ \hline 0 \quad 0 & 1 \end{array} \right]$$

which, when converted to physical coordinates, yields the correct result.

# CONCEPTS FROM LINEAR ALGEBRA

This appendix presents a review of a number of topics from linear algebra and estimation theory that will prove useful in developing image models and corresponding processing algorithms. The differentiation of matrices and vectors is useful in Chapter 4 (Edge Detection) and Chapter 5 (Dynamic Image Models). The least-squares estimation techniques are a fundamental part of the stereo vision and surface mapping discussion in Chapter 2.

## ■ DIFFERENTIATION OF MATRICES AND VECTORS

Let $f(\underline{x})$ be a scalar-valued function of $n$ variables $x_i$, written as an $n \times 1$ vector $\underline{x}$. (Note: $n = 2$ includes the image function.) The derivative of $f(\underline{x})$ with respect to $\underline{x}$ is an $n \times 1$ vector defined as

$$\frac{\mathrm{d}f(\underline{x})}{\mathrm{d}\underline{x}} = \begin{bmatrix} \dfrac{\partial f(\underline{x})}{\partial x_1} \\[2ex] \dfrac{\partial f(\underline{x})}{\partial x_2} \\[2ex] \dfrac{\partial f(\underline{x})}{\partial x_n} \end{bmatrix} \qquad (\text{A.2-1})$$

This quantity is often referred to as the gradient vector of $f$, denoted as $\nabla_x f$ or grad$_x f$. It defines the direction of maximum increase of the function.

The differentiation of a vector function (i.e., $f(\underline{x})$ where $\underline{f}$ is $m \times 1$ and $\underline{x}$ is $n \times 1$) results in a $m \times n$ matrix of the form:

$$\frac{d\underline{f}(\underline{x})}{d\underline{x}} = \begin{bmatrix} \dfrac{\partial f_1}{\partial x_1} & \cdots & \dfrac{\partial f_1}{\partial x_n} \\ & & \\ & \vdots & \\ & & \\ \dfrac{\partial f_m}{\partial x_1} & & \dfrac{\partial f_m}{\partial x_n} \end{bmatrix} \tag{A.2-2}$$

where the $ij^{\text{th}}$ element of this matrix is given by

$$\frac{\partial f_i}{\partial x_j}$$

This matrix is also referred to as the Jacobian of $\underline{f}(\underline{x})$, denoted $J_x$. The differentiation of a matrix with respect to a vector requires a 3-D array and generally employs tensor notation.

Examples of properties using the above definitions may be easily derived and are summarized below.

(i) $\dfrac{d}{d\underline{x}}(A\underline{x}) = A$

(ii) $\dfrac{d}{d\underline{x}}(\underline{y}^T A \underline{x}) = A^T \underline{y}$ $\qquad$ (A.2-3)

(iii) $\dfrac{d}{d\underline{x}}(\underline{x}^T A \underline{x}) = (A + A^T)\underline{x}$

## ■ STEEPEST (ASCENT) DESCENT PROCEDURE

Because, as mentioned, grad$_x \underline{f}$ defines the direction of maximum increase in the function, we may maximize (or minimize) a scalar function $f(\underline{x})$ by recursively calculating grad$_x f$ and adjusting $\underline{x}$ until we reach a minimum (or maximum). This algorithm for minimization of a function, termed steepest descent, is

(a) chosen initial guess, $\underline{x}^0$

(b) compute grad$_x f$, i.e., $\dfrac{df(\underline{x}^0)}{d\underline{x}}$

(c) adjust $\underline{x}^0$ to get $\underline{x}^1$ based on moving in a direction *opposite* to the gradient, i.e.,

$$\underline{x}^1 = \underline{x}^0 - K\frac{df(\underline{x}^0)}{d\underline{x}}$$

(d) stop when $\underline{x}^{n+1} - \underline{x}^n$ is sufficiently small.

# ■ TAYLOR SERIES EXPANSIONS (MULTIDIMENSIONAL)

The Taylor series expansions for a scalar function of a vector variable, $f(\underline{x})$, about point $\underline{x}_0$, is written using the results of the previous section as

$$f(\underline{x}) = f(\underline{x}_0) + \frac{df(\underline{x}_0)^T}{d\underline{x}}(\underline{x} - \underline{x}_0) + 1/2\,(\underline{x} - \underline{x}_0)^T \left[\frac{d^2f(\underline{x}_0)}{d\underline{x}^2}\right](\underline{x} - \underline{x})$$

$$+ \text{ higher order terms.} \quad \text{(A.2-4)}$$

Similarly, a vector function expansion is

$$\underline{f}(\underline{x}) = f(\underline{x}_0) + \frac{d\underline{f}(\underline{x}_0)}{d\underline{x}}(\underline{x} - \underline{x}_0) + \text{ higher order terms.} \quad \text{(A.2-5)}$$

# ■ LEAST SQUARES TECHNIQUES (DETERMINISTIC)

## BASIC CONCEPT

Suppose we are given an overdetermined linear equation of the form

$$\underline{b} = A\underline{x} \quad \text{(A.2-6)}$$

where $\underline{b}$ is $m \times 1$, $\underline{x}$ is $n \times 1$, and $A$ is an $m \times n$ matrix of rank $n$. Clearly, there is no way to exactly satisfy this equation for arbitrary $\underline{b}$. We define an $m \times 1$ error function vector corresponding to some approximate solution, $\bar{\underline{x}}$:

$$\underline{e} = \underline{b} - A\bar{\underline{x}} \quad \text{(A.2-7)}$$

and then determine a procedure to minimize some function of this error. Often, in unweighted least squares, this function, denoted $J$, is chosen to be

$$J = \underline{e}^T\underline{e} \quad \text{(A.2-8)}$$

To find the minimum of this function, we set

$$\frac{dJ}{d\underline{x}} = \underline{0} \quad \text{(A.2-9)}$$

Applying the results of A.2-1 yields the so-called normal equations; that is,

$$A^TA\bar{\underline{x}} = A^T\underline{b} \quad \text{(A.2-10)}$$

from which $\bar{\underline{x}}$ may be determined. Note that in theory $A^TA$ may be inverted to yield $\bar{\underline{x}}$, but in practice this is avoided as described below.

## THE MODERN APPROACH

The modern approach proceeds from a geometrical view of vector-matrix relationships in $m$- and $n$-dimensional spaces. For example,

$$A\underline{x} = \underline{b}$$

may be thought of as a way to map the $n$-dimensional vector $\underline{x}$ into the $m$-dimensional vector $\underline{b}$. The problem concerns inverting this mapping.

In the overdetermined case, $\underline{b}$ does not lie in the column space of $A$, denoted as the range of $A$, or $R(A)$. Thus, we desire a solution, $\bar{x}$, such that the orthogonal distance between $A\bar{x}$ and $\underline{b}$ is minimum. As in the previous approach, we characterize this as the length of the error vector $\underline{e}$, where

$$\underline{e} = \underline{b} - A\bar{x} \tag{A.2-11}$$

The geometrical proof says that the length of $\underline{e}$ is minimal when $\underline{e}$ lies in a vector space orthogonal to $R(A)$. This space is known as the null space of $A^T$, denoted $N(A^T)$. Any vector, $\underline{y}$, in this space is characterized by

$$A^T\underline{y} = \underline{0} \tag{A.2-12}$$

Therefore, the modern or geometrical approach stipulates $\underline{e}$ must satisfy

$$A^T\underline{e} = \underline{0} \tag{A.2-13}$$

from which the so-called normal equations, identical to the previous solutions, arise.

The geometrical solution also characterizes the solution as finding the *projection* of $\underline{b}$ onto $R(A)$ (call this $\underline{b}^P$) and then finding the vector $\bar{x}$ that exactly satisfies

$$A\bar{x} = \underline{b}^P$$

This approach also yields the normal equations.

Once the normal equations have been formed, if $(A^TA)$ is invertible, we may form the solution for $\bar{x}$ as

$$\bar{x} = (A^TA)^{-1}A^T\underline{b}$$

The quantity $(A^TA)^{-1}A^T$ is known as the pseudoinverse of $A$.

# ■ PRACTICAL CONCERNS REGARDING LEAST SQUARES SOLUTIONS

## *Q − R DECOMPOSITION*

Although, in theory, the quantity $(A^TA)^{-1}$ exists, significant numerical difficulties may exist in computing this inverse in cases where $A^TA$ is nearly singular. In addition, the process of forming $A^TA$, for large $A$, is computationally expensive. The numerical errors incurred in forming $A^TA$ and in forming its inverse lead to alternate approaches.

One solution is to avoid forming the normal equations explicitly, but still to follow the geometrical approach. This solution is known as $Q − R$ decomposition. $Q − R$ (or generally orthogonalization) methods are based on decomposition of the $m \times n$ matrix $A$ (with rank $m$) into

$$A = QR \tag{A.2-14}$$

where $Q$ is $m \times m$ and satisfies

$$Q^TQ = D \tag{A.2-15}$$

$D$ is a diagonal matrix with non-zero diagonal elements. $R$ is an upper triangular $n \times n$ matrix with diagonal entries $r_{kk} = 1$. (Notice, therefore, $R^{-1}$ exists.) Given

Eq. A.2-6 and Eq. A.2-14, we may reformulate the least-squares solution as

$$R^T Q^T(\underline{b} - A\underline{x}) = 0 \tag{A.2-16}$$

Since

$$Q^T A = Q^T QR = DR \tag{A.2-17}$$

the preceding equation may be rewritten as

$$R^T(Q^T\underline{b} - DR\underline{x}) = 0 \tag{A.2-18}$$

Thus, we arrive at

$$DR\underline{x} = Q^T\underline{b}$$

or

$$R\underline{x} = D^{-1}Q^T\underline{b} \tag{A.2-19}$$

Thus, if this equation were formulated, we could solve for $\underline{x}$ via back substitution. The problem of computing $Q$, $R$, and the above quantities is addressed via a modified Gram-Schmidt procedure as shown in Dahlquist, (1974).

# ■ COMPLEX MATRICES

Given a matrix, $F$, whose elements are complex variables, that is,

$$F = [\propto_{ij} + j\,\beta_{ij}] \tag{A.2-20}$$

the *conjugate* of $F$, denoted $F^*$, is given by

$$F^* = [\propto_{ij} - j\beta_{ij}] \tag{A.2-21}$$

If $(F^*)^T = F$, the matrix is said to be *Hermitian* (which is the same as symmetric for real matrices). A complex matrix is said to be *Unitary* if $F^{-1} = (F^*)^T$, which compares with $F^{-1} = F^T$ in the case of real orthogonal matrices.

(COMPLEX) VECTOR INNER PRODUCT

If $\underline{x}$ and $\underline{y}$ are complex vectors, the complex vector inner product is given by

$$\langle \underline{x}, \underline{y} \rangle = (\underline{x}^*)^T \underline{y}$$

Note that if $\langle \underline{x}, \underline{y} \rangle = 0$ the vectors are said to be orthogonal.

# ■ SOLVING SYSTEMS OF EQUATIONS WITH A PRIORI UNKNOWN SOLUTION CLASSES (HOUGH TRANSFORMS)

In a number of image processing and computer vision applications, the following problem arises:

Given $p$ equations in $n$ variables $(x_1, x_2, \ldots x_n)$, each of the form:

$$f^i(\underline{x}) = 0 \qquad i = 1, 2, \ldots p \tag{A.2-22}$$

where $\underline{x}$ is an $n \times 1$ vector. Each of the $p$ equations corresponds to one of $j$ (unknown a priori) solution classes. The problem is to determine

    (a)   the number of solution classes (i.e., $j$), and

    (b)   the solution $\underline{x}^k$, $k = 1, 2, \ldots j$ for each class.

Typically, $j \ll p$. Notice, also, that it is not essential that $f^i$ be linear in $\underline{x}$, nor that the set of equations in Eq. A.2-22 be linearly independent.

The solutions to this apparently unpromising problem employ the concept of *clustering of possible solutions* and attributing large clusters in the solution space to the likely solutions.

Applications for the preceding formulation include the following:

    (a)   Line and curve detection. For example, given a number of points in the image plane, it is desired to determine (i) the number of line segments these points describe, and (ii) the parameters of these line segments. This is typically referred to as an application of the "Hough transform," although the concept is more generally applicable (see Chapter 6).

    (b)   Motion parameter determination. In this case, spatial and temporal derivatives of the intensities of a set of pixels are used to constrain a parametric description of the motion(s). The observed motion may be common to all points or consist of the motion of several independently moving groups of pixels, perhaps reflecting the corresponding motion of several objects in the scene (see Chapter 5).

Note that a common characteristic of each of these problems is that a single equation represents an underdetermined case, therefore the obvious solution approach of simply solving each equation independently is not possible. In addition, the equally obvious approach of partitioning the set of $p$ equations into all possible subsets and exhaustively calculating the solutions to each of these (where possible) is not practical, because of the approximately $c^p/c!$ possible partitions of these $p$ equations into $c$ nonempty sets.

### A Simple Linear Example

Consider a single linear equation in two variables with given coefficients $a_1$, $a_2$, and $a_3$,

$$a_1 x_1 + a_2 x_2 = a_3 \qquad\qquad \text{(A.2-23)}$$

Clearly, this single equation does not, in general, determine the 2-D solution $\underline{x} = (x_1, x_2)^T$ uniquely, but it does *constrain* this solution to lie in an $N - 1$ dimensional (i.e., 1-D) subspace. Here that subspace is a line, as indicated by Figure A.2-1. A solution to a pair of equations of the form of Eq. A.2-23 may be formed by plotting the $N - 1$ dimensional constraint equation corresponding to each equation. In the linear case there may be no solution, an infinite number of solutions or a unique solution formed as the intersection of the constraint lines, shown in Figure A.2-1 as point $P$.

Arguments for the nonlinear case are similar; the existence or uniqueness of a solution for arbitrary equations is much more difficult to ascertain. One such

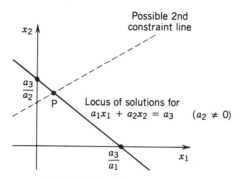

**FIGURE A.2.1** Linear constraints in 2-D

nonlinear case of significant interest is the so-called *point-to-curve transformation* encountered in fitting image points to line segments (Chapter 6). This approach relies on the equation of a line in normal form as

$$(\cos \theta) \, x + (\sin \theta) \, y - p = 0 \qquad \text{(A.2-24)}$$

where $(x, y)$ represents a point on the line. Chapter 6 discusses this application in more detail.

### PRACTICAL RAMIFICATIONS (IMPLEMENTATION)

The digital implementation of the clustering approach requires discretization of the solution space into appropriately sized "cells," followed by exhaustive enumeration of the $n-1$ dimensional solution subspace corresponding to each of the $p$ equations. The computational complexity and memory requirements for this scheme warrant further investigation. Suppose that each element in $\underline{x}$ (i.e., $x_i$ $i = 1, 2, \ldots n$) is discretized to $v$ levels. The choice of $v$ would be based principally on the desired solution accuracy and the a priori known or assumed range of $x_i$. This discretization results in an $n$-dimensional accumulator array with the number of cells, denoted $N_{\text{cells}}$, given by

$$N_{\text{cells}} = v^n \qquad \text{(A.2-25)}$$

For example, suppose $n = 3$ and each $x_1$ is in the range $[-1, 1]$. If the desired solution accuracy for $x_i$ is on the order of 0.01, then each $x_i$ requires approximately.

$$\frac{2}{0.01} = 200 \text{ cells,}$$

and the entire array consists of

$$(200)^3 = 8 \times 10^6 \text{ cells.}$$

Even for this low-dimensional problem this represents a sizable memory array. In addition, the computational requirements necessary to form the resulting array are significant. To reduce this practical burden, several approaches may be taken. For example, a coarse (or reduced dimension) accumulator array may be used to get an estimate of the number of distinct solutions ($j$) together with rough parameter estimates corresponding to each of these solution classes. This process could then be repeated on data from each of the $j$ classes using more finely discretized (but reduced range) individual accumulator arrays to obtain refined solution estimates.

# ■ REFERENCES

Strang, G. 1976. *Linear algebra and its applications*. New York: Academic Press.

Eykhoff, P. 1974. *System identification*. New York: Wiley.

Deutsch, R. 1965. *Estimation theory*. Englewood Cliffs, NJ: Prentice-Hall.

Dahlquist, G., Bjorck, A., and Anderson, N. 1974. *Numerical methods*. Englewood Cliffs, NJ: Prentice-Hall.

# MULTIDIMENSIONAL FOURIER TRANSFORMS AND EFFECTS DUE TO AFFINE PERTURBATIONS

The consequences and utility of the 2-D affine transform in image processing are numerous and are illustrated in Appendix 1. In this section, frequency domain effects of affine transformed image functions are examined. This yields a general model with numerous applications, including the following:

1. Tracking and motion estimation (Chapter 5);
2. Reconstruction (Chapter 4); and
3. Matching (Chapter 6).

Recall the Fourier transform of a 3-D function may be written as

$$\mathcal{F}[f(\underline{x},t)] \triangleq F(\underline{u},w) = \int_{X,T} f(\underline{x},t)e^{-j2\pi[\underline{u}^T \mid w]}\begin{bmatrix} \underline{x} \\ t \end{bmatrix} d\underline{x}\,dt \qquad \text{(A.3-1)}$$

where $X$ and $T$ are the regions in 2-D space and 1-D time over which $f(\underline{x},t) \neq 0$. Note that the integral sign represents a 3-fold integral.

Letting

$$f'(\underline{x},t) = f(\underline{x}',t) \qquad \text{(A.3-2)}$$

where

$$\underline{x}' = A(t)\,\underline{x} + \underline{b}(t) \qquad \text{(A.3-3)}$$

it is useful to consider the effects of the affine transform on

$$F'(\underline{u},w) = F[f(\underline{x}',t)] \tag{A.3-4}$$

especially if a functional relationship between $F'(\underline{u},w)$ and $F(\underline{u},w)$ may be established. By definition

$$F'(\underline{u},w) = \int_{X',T'} f'(\underline{x},t)e^{-j2\pi[\underline{u}^T;w]}\begin{bmatrix}\underline{x}\\t\end{bmatrix}d\underline{x}\,dt \tag{A.3-5}$$

A change of variables is made as follows:

$$\begin{bmatrix}\underline{x}'\\t\end{bmatrix}\begin{bmatrix}A(t) & 0\\0 & 1\end{bmatrix}\begin{bmatrix}\underline{x}\\t\end{bmatrix} + \begin{bmatrix}\underline{b}(t)\\0\end{bmatrix} \tag{A.3-6}$$

and

$$d\underline{x}' = D \cdot d\underline{x} \tag{A.3-7}$$

where $D$ is the Jacobian of the transformation in Eq. A.3-3, that is,

$$D = |det\,A(t)| \tag{A.3-8}$$

It is a simple matter to show the inverse transform of Eq. A.3-6, that is,

$$\begin{bmatrix}\underline{x}\\t\end{bmatrix} = \begin{bmatrix}A^{-1}(t) & 0\\0 & 1\end{bmatrix}\begin{bmatrix}\underline{x}'\\t\end{bmatrix} - \begin{bmatrix}A^{-1}(t)\,\underline{b}(t)\\0\end{bmatrix} \tag{A.3-9}$$

Substitution of Eqs. A.3-7 and A.3-9 into Eq. A.3-5 yields

$$F'(\underline{u},w) = \int_{X',T}\frac{e^{j2\pi\underline{u}^T A^{-1}(t)\underline{b}(t)}}{|det\,A(t)|} \cdot [f(\underline{x}',t)e^{-j2\pi\underline{u}^T A^{-1}(t)\underline{x}'}d\underline{x}']e^{-j2\pi wt}dt \tag{A.3-10}$$

Making the substitution

$$\underline{u}_0^T = \underline{u}^T A^{-1}(t) \tag{A.3-11}$$

it is seen that Eq. A.3-10 may be reduced to

$$F'(u,w) = \int_T\frac{e^{j2\pi\underline{u}^T A^{-1}(t)\underline{b}(t)}}{|det\,A(t)|} F[(A^T(t))^{-1}\underline{u}]e^{-j2\pi wt}\,dt \tag{A.3-12}$$

As a final note, several of the well-known 2-D (spatial) transform relations may be derived from Eq. A.3-12 for the case of time-invariant functions $f(\underline{x})$ and $f'(\underline{x})$. In this case,

$$f(\underline{x},t) = f(\underline{x})\delta(t)$$
$$f'(\underline{x},t) = f'(\underline{x})\delta(t) \tag{A.3-13}$$
$$A(t) = A$$

and

$$\underline{b}(t) = \underline{b}$$

so the relation between the transform pairs becomes

$$f(\underline{x}) \Leftrightarrow F(\underline{u}) \tag{A.3-14}$$

$$f'(\underline{x}) = f(A\underline{x} + \underline{b}) \Leftrightarrow F'(\underline{u}) = \frac{1}{|det\,A|}e^{j2\pi u^T A^{-1}\underline{b}}\,F[[A^T]^{-1}\underline{u}]$$

Equation A.3-14 may be used to show a variety of effects of the affine transform on the Fourier transform of the image function. Some special cases are as follows:

(1) $A = I$ ; $\underline{b} = \begin{bmatrix} b_1 \\ b_2 \end{bmatrix}$

in which case $F'(\underline{u})$ only differs from $F(\underline{u})$ in phase; and

(2) $\underline{b} = \underline{0}$ and

$$A = \begin{bmatrix} \cos\theta & -\sin\theta \\ \sin\theta & \cos\theta \end{bmatrix}$$

in which case

$$[A^T(t)]^{-1} = A(t)$$

since $A$ is orthogonal. Thus, the coordinate axis in Fourier space is rotated through the same angle as in image space.

# PROBABILITY AND RANDOM VECTORS

## ■ PROBABILITY

The *probability* of the outcome of a single *event*, $E$, is a numerical assignment of the likelihood of the occurrence of this event; that is,

$$0 \le P(E) \le 1 \tag{A.4.1-1}$$

Given a set of all outcomes, $E_i$, $i = 1, 2, \ldots n$

$$\sum_i P(E_i) = 1 \tag{A.4.1-2}$$

The probability of the joint occurrence of *independent* events is given by

$$P(ABC) = P(A)P(B)P(C) \tag{A.4.1-3}$$

One of the most significant (and useful) concepts from probability is that of *conditional probability*, where the probability of occurrence of outcome $A$ is conditioned on occurrence of outcome $B$; that is,

$$P(A|B) = \frac{P(AB)}{P(B)} \tag{A.4.1-4}$$

*Bayes theorem* is an extension to Eq. A.4.1-4 that provides a means to convert a priori probabilities to a posteriori probabilities; that is,

$$P(A|B) P(B) = P(B|A) P(A) \tag{A.4.1-5}$$

469

## ■ RANDOM VARIABLES

### (CONTINUOUS CASE)

We define a variable $X$, which takes on values at random, depending on the outcome of an event. A cumulative probability distribution function (cdf) for $X$ is defined as

$$F_X(x) = P(X \le x) \qquad \text{(A.4.2-1)}$$

This concept leads to the *probability density function*

$$p_X(x) = \frac{dF_X(x)}{dx} \qquad \text{(A.4.2-2)}$$

where $p_X(x)$ may be viewed as the probability that the random variable $X$ takes on values in the infinitesimal interval around $x$. Thus, $p_X(x)$ has "histogram-like" characteristics.

From the preceding two equations,

$$\int_{-\infty}^{\infty} p_X(x)\, dx = 1.0 \qquad \text{(A.4.2-3)}$$

Often we need to simultaneously consider more than one random variable. (An example of this is the co-occurrence matrix of grey-levels in Chapter 7.) This leads to joint probability distribution and density functions

$$F_{XY}(x,y) = P(X \le x \text{ AND } Y \le y) \qquad \text{(A.4.2-4)}$$

and

$$p_{XY}(x,y) = \frac{\partial^2 F_{XY}(x,y)}{\partial x \partial y} \qquad \text{(A.4.2-5)}$$

If $X$ and $Y$ are independent random variables,

$$F_{XY}(x,y) = F_X(x)\, F_Y(y) \qquad \text{(A.4.2-6a)}$$

and

$$p_{XY}(x,y) = p_X(x)\, p_Y(y) \qquad \text{(A.4.2-6b)}$$

Note: The superscript $X$ on $F$ and $p$ is often omitted when it is clear

(1) *which* random variable is meant; and
(2) that $X$ is a random variable and $x$ is a value that the random variable may assume.

As in the first section, it is important to characterize the conditional probability density of two random variables. By analogy with Eq. A.4.1-4, this may be shown to yield a relationship for conditional pdf's:

$$P_{X|Y}(x,y) = \frac{p_{XY}(x,y)}{p_Y(y)} \qquad \text{(A.4.2-7)}$$

### THE DISCRETE CASE

Numerous instances exist, however, wherein $X$ is a discrete random variable. Examples are where $X$ is constrained to be an integer, or where $X$ is binary valued. Given that $X$ may assume only one of $m$ discrete values, $x_1, x_2, \ldots x_m$, the probability density function Eq. A.4.2-2 consists of dirac delta functions. Furthermore, integrals of the form of Eq. A.4.2-3 are replaced by sums of the form

$$\sum_x p_X(x) = 1.0 \qquad (A.4.2-8)$$

## ■ STATISTICAL CHARACTERIZATIONS

In order to characterize a random variable, the cdf or pdf would be sufficient. However, these are often neither convenient nor achievable characterizations, and therefore several statistical measures are often employed. The most popular is the measure of *expectation*:

$$E(X) = \int_{-\infty}^{\infty} x p_X(x) \, dx \qquad (A.4.3-1)$$

which is often referred to as the *mean* or first moment of $X$, and

$$E(X^2) = \int_{-\infty}^{\infty} x^2 p_X(x) \, dx \qquad (A.4.3-2)$$

referred to as the second moment of $X$. The latter quantity may be normalized by the mean to yield a measure of the *variance* or *scatter* of $X$; that is,

$$\text{Var}(X) = E\left[(X - E(X))^2\right]$$
$$= \int_{-\infty}^{\infty} [x - E[X]]^2 \, p_X(x) \, dx \qquad (A.4.3-3)$$
$$= E[X^2] - (E[X])^2$$

Note that expectation is a linear operator. As noted in the previous section, summation-based analogies for these operators exist for the discrete case. The *covariance* of two scalar random variables $X$ and $Y$ is given by

$$E\left[(X - E(X))(Y - E(Y))\right]$$
$$= \int_{-\infty}^{\infty} \int_{-\infty}^{\infty} (x - E(X))(y - E(Y) \, p_{XY}(x,y) \, dxdy \qquad (A.4.3-4)$$
$$= E[XY] - E[X] E[Y]$$

where the quantity $E[XY]$ represents the *correlation* of $X$ and $Y$. If $X = Y$ in the above formulation, $E[XY]$ is the *mean squared value* of $X$.

## ■ EXTENSION TO VECTOR RANDOM VARIABLES

Vector random variables find application in numerous image modeling situations. A vector random variable, denoted $X$, is a vector whose components, $X_i$, are themselves random variables; that is,

$$\underset{n \times 1}{\underline{X}} = \begin{bmatrix} X_1 \\ X_2 \\ \cdot \\ \cdot \\ \cdot \\ \cdot \\ X_n \end{bmatrix} \tag{A.4.4-1}$$

Vector random variables give rise to multivariate probability distribution and density functions. The cumulative distribution function of the vector random variable $\underline{X}$ (also referred to herein as a *random vector*) is a *scalar* function defined by

$$F_{\underline{X}}(\underline{x}) = P(X_1 \leq x_1 \text{ AND } X_2 \leq x_2 \ldots \text{ AND } X_n \leq x_n) \tag{A.4.4-2}$$

Therefore, $F_{\underline{X}}(\underline{x})$ is a monotonically nondecreasing function of any component of $\underline{x}$.

A scalar function $p_{\underline{X}}(\underline{x})$, which satisfies

$$F_{\underline{X}}(\underline{x}) = \int_{-\infty}^{x_1} \int_{-\infty}^{x_2} \ldots \int_{-\infty}^{x_n} p_{\underline{X}} (\xi_1, \xi_2, \ldots \xi_n) \, d\xi_1 \, d\xi_2 \ldots d\xi_n \tag{A.4.4-3a}$$

or

$$F_{\underline{X}}(\underline{x}) = \int_{-\infty}^{x} p_{\underline{X}} (\underline{\xi}) \, d\underline{\xi} \tag{A.4.4-3b}$$

is called the probability density function of $\underline{X}$. The fundamental theorem of calculus yields

$$p_{\underline{X}}(\underline{x}) = \frac{\partial^n}{\partial x_1 \, \partial x_2 \ldots \partial x_n} F_{\underline{X}} (\underline{x}) \tag{A.4.4-4}$$

Conditional probabilities and corresponding distributions and densities may be developed for random vectors. The vectors need not have the same dimension. For example, we develop the conditional pdf

$$p_{\underline{X}|\underline{Y}}(\underline{x}|\underline{y}) = \frac{p_{\underline{X}\underline{Y}}(\underline{x},\underline{y})}{p_Y (\underline{y})} \tag{A.4.4-5}$$

Equation A.4.4-5 may be used to develop a Bayesian formulation analogous to Eq. A.4.1-5.

The expectation of a random vector is defined in a manner similar to that of its scalar counterpart; that is,

$$E(\underline{X}) = \int_{-\infty}^{\infty} \underline{x} \, p_X \, (\underline{x}) \, d\underline{x}$$

$$= \begin{bmatrix} E(X_1) \\ E(X_2) \\ \cdot \\ \cdot \\ \cdot \\ \cdot \\ \cdot \\ E(X_n) \end{bmatrix} \tag{A.4.4-6}$$

$$\overset{\triangle}{=} \underline{m}_{\underline{X}}$$

The *covariance matrix* of $X$ is defined as

$$\sum_{\underline{x}} \overset{\triangle}{=} E \{(\underline{X} - \underline{m}_{\underline{X}}) (\underline{X} - \underline{m}_{\underline{X}})^T\}$$
$$= E \{\underline{X} \, \underline{X}^T\} - \underline{m}_{\underline{X}} \underline{m}_{\underline{X}}^T \tag{A.4.4-7}$$

Finally we note that a multitude of estimators for the mean and covariance of a random vector exist. Given $v$ sample vectors, $\underline{x}_k$, $k = 1, 2, \ldots v$, two unbiased estimators are given by

$$\underline{m}_{\underline{X}} = \frac{1}{v} \sum_{k=1}^{v} \underline{x}_k \tag{A.4.4-8}$$

and

$$\sum_{\underline{x}} = \frac{1}{v-1} \sum_{k=1}^{v} (\underline{x}_k - \underline{m}_{\underline{X}}) (\underline{x}_k - \underline{m}_{\underline{X}})^T \tag{A.4.4-9}$$

## ■ THE GAUSSIAN PROBABILITY DENSITY FUNCTION

With the properties of pdf's defined on page 470 and the corresponding statistical characterizations on pages 471 and 472, we introduce perhaps the most popular multivariate pdf, due to its suitability and mathematical tractability. The multivariate Gaussian, or normal, pdf for a $d$x1 vector $\underline{x}$, is given by

$$p(\underline{x}) = \frac{\exp \left[ -\frac{1}{2} (\underline{x} - \underline{m})^T \sum^{-1} (\underline{x} - \underline{m}) \right]}{(2\pi)^{d/2} |\Sigma|^{1/2}} \tag{A.4.5-1}$$

where the $d$x1 mean vector, $\underline{m}$, and the $d \times d$ covariance matrix, $\Sigma$, uniquely determine the pdf. The previous section indicated how to obtain estimates of these quantities. The contours of constant density in $\mathbb{R}^d$ are, in general, hyperellipsoids along which the quantity $\| \underline{x} - \underline{m} \|_{\Sigma^{-1}}^2$ is constant.

# DISCRETE MATHEMATICS REVIEW

In this appendix, concepts from discrete mathematics such as relations, graphical structures, and logic are summarized. This forms a rigorous basis for the approaches of Chapter 7.

## ■ RELATIONS

Representation and manipulation of relations among entities is fundamental to image understanding. The descriptive terms "color of," "above," and "next to" denote relations between certain objects.

*Definition.* If $A$ and $B$ are sets, a *relation* from $A$ to $B$ is a subset of $A \times B$. Here $A \times B$ denotes the Cartesian product of the sets $A$ and $B$. A relation may be enumerated as a set of ordered pairs—for example, a relation $R2$, based on symbolic entities, might be

$$R2 = \{ \text{ (floor, foundation), (rug, floor), (chair, rug)}$$
$$\text{(person, chair) }\}$$

where we might view the sets as composed of entities that lie on one another.

The relation $R3$, where

$$R3 = \{ \text{ (car, wheels) (car, driver) (driver, license)}$$
$$\text{(tire, tread) (car, engine) }\}$$

demonstrates the relation "has."

# ■ GRAPH REPRESENTATIONS OF RELATIONS

If

$$A = \{a,b,c,d \ldots\}$$

and

$$B = \{x,y,z, \ldots\}$$

since a relation from $A$ to $B$, denoted $R$, satisfies $R \leq A \times B$, we may depict $R$ graphically, using an arrow to show each element of $R$. When $R \subset A \times A$, a *directed graph* or digraph is a convenient tool to represent the relationship between elements of one set. Suppose

$$A = \{a,b,c,d\}$$

Then

$$A \times A = \{(a,a), (a,b), (a,c), (a,d), (b,a), (b,b), \ldots\}$$

Assume for this example that

$$R = \{ (a,b), (b,c), (b,d), (b,a), (c,c), (d,a) \}$$

This relationship is shown in Figure A.5-1, where the elements of $A$ are nodes in the graph and the elemental relationships are indicated by arrows. The use of arrows indicates a direction to the relationship.

**FIGURE A.5.1**   Digraph for R = {(a,b), (b,c), (b,d), (b,a), (c,c), (d,a)}

Two graphs may be isomorphic, as a consequence of the arbitrary choice of nodes to represent elements of $A$. The structure of the graphs resulting from any choice of nodes (or vertices) will be the same, however. The significance of iso-morphism of graph structures becomes important when we attempt to assign labels to (a priori unknown) entities with observed (known) relations through a consistent matching or constraint satisfaction process.

Relations involving symbolic quantities extracted from image data are of significant interest. For example, suppose we have been given a processed image with several extracted regions, as shown in Figure A.5-2a. Regions are given symbol labels that are elements of the set

$$L = \{a,b,c,d\}$$

A relationship between these labels (a subset of $L \times L$) which connotes "con-tained inside of" or "enclosed within" is shown in Figure A.5-2b.

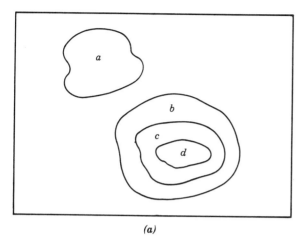
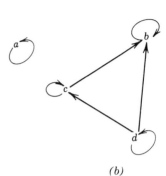

**FIGURE A.5.2** Example of a relation using processed image data
(a)  Image regions
(b)  Relation "contained in" from part (a) shown as digraph

# ■ RELATION PROPERTIES

Three properties of a relation $R$ are important:

1. reflexive: $R$ is reflexive if, for all $a \in A$, $(a,a) \in R$.
2. symmetric: $R$ is symmetric if, for all $(a,b) \in R$, $(b,a)$ is also $\in R$.
3. transitive: $R$ is transitive if, for all $(a,b) \in R$ and $(b,c) \in R$, $(a,c) \in R$.

### A NOTE ON SYMBOLS

The symbol $\in$ represents "is an element of," which, in the case of a single element, may also be interpreted as "contained in." More generally, the symbol "$\subset$" is used to denote "contained in," or "is a subset of."

# ■ TERNARY (AND HIGHER ORDER) RELATIONS AND CONSTRAINTS

The binary relations considered above form an important structure for studying constraint satisfaction problems. Whereas binary relations describe relationships between objects on a pairwise basis, the reader may wonder about relations (or perhaps constraints) among triples of objects, quadruples of objects, and so on. Fortunately, ternary, quarternary (and higher order) relations may be shown to be defined via straightforward extension of the set-based derivation for the binary case, and may be cast in terms of ordered $n$-tuples, which in turn may be viewed as ordered pairs (each pair consisting of an $(n - 1)$-tuple and a single element), and therefore may be studied within the framework of binary relations.

# ■ SEMANTIC NETS

The use of graphical constructs to quantify both numerical and symbolic relations among a set of entities is fundamental to many image knowledge representation approaches.

A semantic network, or simply semantic net, is a digraph used to describe relations (including properties) of objects, concepts, situations, or actions.

The overall semantic net is usually a large and highly interconnected entity, which causes major difficulty in the *matching* of observed features or entities and their properties to the structure indicated by the semantic net. This is considered in Chapter 7.

## ■ LOGIC FOR RULE BASED REASONING

### *IMPLICATION*

The implication construct is a formalization of the concept of IF-THEN reasoning. IF *a*, THEN *b* is written as

$$a \rightarrow b$$

Implication (i.e., $a \rightarrow b$) is logically equivalent to $\neg a \cup b$, where $\neg$ denotes logical negation and $\cup$ denotes the logical OR operator.

### *MODUS PONENS (MP)*

The logical implication construct, together with a method to derive new information, forms the mathematical basis of rule-based inference. Modus Ponens is shown below.

MP AND IMPLICATION

| | |
|---|---|
| $a \rightarrow b$ | true |
| $a$ | true |
| $b$ | true |

FORWARD CHAINING

Given a rule base consisting of the following set of assertions or rules, in IF-THEN or implication form (each of which we assume to be TRUE):

$$p^1 \rightarrow p^2$$
$$p^2 \rightarrow p^3$$
$$p^3 \rightarrow q^3$$

a paradigm known as forward chaining allows logical inference (specifically MP) in the following sequence:

1. $((p^1 \rightarrow p^2)$ AND $p^1$ being TRUE$) \rightarrow (p^2$ is TRUE$)$
2. (Similar to step 1): $((p^2 \rightarrow p^3)$ AND $p^2$ being TRUE$) \rightarrow (p^3$ is TRUE$)$
3. (Similar to steps 1 and 2): $((p^3 \rightarrow q^3)$ AND $p^3$ being TRUE$) \rightarrow (q^3$ is TRUE$)$

## ■ REFERENCES

Johnsonbaugh, R. 1986. *Discrete mathematics*. New York: Macmillan.

Liu, C. L. 1977. *Elements of discrete mathematics*. New York: McGraw-Hill.

# LISP/PROLOG LANGUAGE SYNTAX

## ■ INTRODUCTION

In this appendix we consider the syntax of languages used for AI applications, in particular the image processing applications shown in Chapter 7.

The need for symbolic representation and manipulation spawned by image analysis application has led to the popularity of several languages, notably PROLOG (PROgramming in LOGic) and LISP (LISt Processing). Programming in the PROLOG and LISP languages is fundamentally different from programming in an imperative language such as FORTRAN or Pascal. In LISP, the programmer does not emphasize the flow of program control, but rather concentrates on the application of functions to data, and the values returned from these applications. In PROLOG, the programmer does not concentrate on the specification of a program execution sequence, but rather attempts to specify the problem (or situation) through development of a database consisting of known facts and rules.

## ■ PROLOG

The underlying concept of PROLOG is quite simple: PROLOG implements a subset of the first-order logic restricted to Horn clauses. The basis for applications implemented in PROLOG is a set of statements containing rules and facts. PROLOG's main utility is in searching this database with the objective of satisfying one or more goals through a process that involves instantiating variables with values or "binding." When one or more consistent solutions are found, the PROLOG system returns these bindings.

## FACTS AND RULES

A PROLOG statement has the syntax

has(roof, house).

The entities "has," "roof," and "house" are PROLOG atoms. The above PROLOG clause form allows definition of the attributes of a situation by a set of fact statements. Another basic PROLOG construct is the goal statement. For example, we might query the PROLOG system with:

?-has(What, door).

indicating we are interested in having the system search the database and indicate what binding on object What satisfies this relationship. The PROLOG system then attempts to match the above statement with one in the database, by finding a substitution for the variable What which yields a statement which otherwise matches. This process is known as unification and typically involves search. If the process is successful, the system responds with the binding or substitution of the variable What to some object (i.e., a constant) in the database. Note that all variables in PROLOG begin with a capital letter.

The most significant construct in PROLOG is the rule. This is typified by the following example:

has($X$, door) :– is_house ($X$)

The symbol :– may be replaced by the word "IF," yielding a more apparent interpretation of the syntax. Rules are seldom as simple as the previous example. PROLOG restricts rules to the form

$p$ :– $q, r, s$

where $q, r$, and $s$ are predicates that may contain constants, variables, and functors (with their associated terms).

The statements that form the database in PROLOG are appropriately termed *clauses*. They consist of rules and facts.

The most important conceptual characteristic of PROLOG is the operation of the built-in mechanism which, given a database of facts and rules, and a goal, employs repeated variable instantiation and depth-first search in order to return consistent bindings of the variables. This process is referred to as the unification mechanism. The rules for unification in PROLOG are as follows:

i. The unifier proceeds from left to right in a rule.
ii. Predicates are tested in the order in which they appear in the database.
iii. When a subgoal matches the left side of a rule, the right side of the rule becomes a new set of subgoals to unify.
iv. A goal is satisfied when a matching fact (a grounded predicate) is found in the database.

v. When a goal fails, variables previously bound in an attempt to satisfy that goal become unbound, and the unification mechanism backtracks to attempt further unification.

The unification procedure in PROLOG implements *depth-first search*. Backtracking in the search process is inhibited via the ! or "cut" operator.

# ■ LISP

A simple example of LISP is shown in Chapter 7, which involves the development of a rule-based image analysis system. The basic idea of the LISP programming language is actually quite simple: The language enables the manipulation of (symbolic and numeric) entities that comprise *lists*. The syntax of LISP is more sophisticated than PROLOG, and numerous dialects exist. LISP has no built-in unification mechanism. The design and application of LISP functions is therefore fundamental to an understanding of the language.

## *LISP SYNTAX*

Elements of the LISP syntax may be subdivided into classes of function types, including:

1. Those that define functions and apply functions to arguments (DEFUN, APPLY, MAP);
2. Those for program control (COND, IF, DO);
3. Those for assignment (SET, SETQ, SETF);
4. Those which are predicates, and related to 2. (EQUAL, MEMBER, T);
5. Those useful for I/O and their returned values versus "side effects" (READ, PRINT);
6. Those which provide arithmetic (SUM or +, MINUS or −) capabilities;
7. Those for error handling, debugging, and tracing (CATCH, TRACE).
8. Those for manipulation of data structures, including list manipulation (APPEND, CAR, CDR) and property management.

A list is a collection of atoms, enclosed by parentheses. The first element of the list (which may itself be a list) is denoted the CAR of the list; the remainder of the list is denoted the CDR.

Symbolic-expressions or *s-expressions* consist of atoms or lists and are the basic data object manipulated by LISP. Function definitions, for example, have list structure and therefore are s-expressions. The quote operator inhibits expression evaluation.

A *function*, as the classical definition indicates, is an entity that takes in arguments (perhaps following evaluation, if these are variable names) and returns a value. A value may not be as simple as an atom; it may be a list. A function is defined in LISP using a built-in function, DEFUN, and we note the entire function definition is itself a list. This is one significant aspect of LISP: programs and data are both lists and therefore indistinguishable.

### PROPERTIES

Because the encoding of 1-place relational information (i.e., properties) of variables is important, LISP provides a built-in mechanism to achieve this through property lists. This type of "manipulable" representation is easily achieved in LISP, via the PROPerty or ASSOCiation list constructs.

The flow of control in the application of functions is achieved with several LISP constructs (functions, either directly or indirectly), perhaps the most notable of which are the IF and COND constructs.

# ■ REFERENCES

Clocksin, W. F., and Mellish, C. S., *Programming in Prolog*, Springer-Verlag, N.Y., 1984.

Brooks, R. A., *Programming in Common LISP*, Wiley, N.Y., 1985.

# INDEX

Printed and bound in Singapore
by Chong Moh Offset Printing Pte Ltd